MECHANISMS in RADIOBIOLOGY

Volume I

General Principles

MECHANISMS in RADIOBIOLOGY

MAURICE ERRERA

Université Libre de Bruxelles
Faculté des Sciences
Bruxelles, Belgium

ARNE FORSSBERG

Radiobiologiska Institutionen
Karolinska Institutet
Stockholm, Sweden

VOLUME I

General Principles

1961

 ACADEMIC PRESS, NEW YORK AND LONDON

ACADEMIC PRESS INC.
111 FIFTH AVENUE
NEW YORK 3, N. Y.

United Kingdom Edition
Published by
ACADEMIC PRESS INC. (LONDON) LTD.
17 OLD QUEEN STREET, LONDON S.W. 1

Library of Congress Catalog Card Number 59-13825

PRINTED IN THE UNITED STATES OF AMERICA

574.19 ER 78
V. 1, C. 1

CONTRIBUTORS TO VOLUME I

TIKVAH ALPER, *Medical Research Council, Experimental Radiopathology Research Unit, Hammersmith Hospital, London, England*

ÅKE GUSTAFSSON, *Genetics Department, Forest Research Institute, Stockholm, Sweden*

EDWIN J. HART, *Argonne National Laboratory, Argonne, Illinois*

F. HUTCHINSON, *Biophysics Department, The Josiah Willard Gibbs Research Laboratories, Yale University, New Haven, Connecticut*

M. G. ORD, *Department of Biochemistry, University of Oxford, Oxford, England*

ROBERT L. PLATZMAN, *Argonne National Laboratory, Argonne, Illinois**

E. POLLARD, *Biophysics Department, The Josiah Willard Gibbs Research Laboratories, Yale University, New Haven, Connecticut***

L. A. STOCKEN, *Department of Biochemistry, University of Oxford, Oxford, England*

THEODORE N. TAHMISIAN, *Division of Biological and Medical Research, Argonne National Laboratory, Argonne, Illinois*

SHELDON WOLFF, *Biology Division, Oak Ridge National Laboratory, Oak Ridge, Tennessee*

* Present address: Laboratoire de Chimie Physique, Paris, France.
** Present address: Whitmore Laboratory, University Park, Pennsylvania.

CONTRIBUTORS TO VOLUME II

CARL-JOHAN CLEMEDSON, *Department of Hygiene, University of Göteborg, Göteborg, Sweden*

LORENTZ ELDJARN, *Norsk Hydro's Institute for Cancer Research, The Norwegian Radium Hospital, Oslo, Norway**

MILAN HAŠEK, *Czechoslovak Academy of Sciences, Institute of Biology, Department of Experimental Biology and Genetics, Prague, Czechoslovakia*

ALENA LENGEROVÁ, *Czechoslovak Academy of Sciences, Institute of Biology, Department of Experimental Biology and Genetics, Prague, Czechoslovakia*

ARNE NELSON, *Medical Department, The Research Institute of National Defense, Stockholm, Sweden*

ALEXANDER PIHL, *Norsk Hydro's Institute for Cancer Research, The Norwegian Radium Hospital, Oslo, Norway*

ROBERTS RUGH, *Department of Radiology, College of Physicians and Surgeons, Columbia University, New York, New York*

D. W. VAN BEKKUM, *Medical Biological Laboratory of the National Defense Research Council T. N. O., Rijswijk (Z. H.), The Netherlands***

---

* Present address: University Clinical Laboratory, Department of Biochemistry, Rikshospitalet, Oslo, Norway
** Present address: Radiobiological Institute of the National Health Research Council T. N. O., Rijswijk (Z. H.), The Netherlands

PREFACE

Active research in radiobiology has been carried on since the beginning of this century. Many fundamental aspects were envisaged by pathologists and physicists in these early days, chiefly in connection with the therapeutic use of X-rays in medicine and the resulting need to study the biological action of these rays. The discovery of H. G. Muller that mutations could be induced by radiation opened a new field for exact, quantitative work. Shortly after the Second World War D. E. Lea made the first, and very successful attempt, to coordinate radiobiological knowledge into a comprehensive picture.

Since then we have witnessed a tremendous expansion of research work in radiation physics, chemistry, and biology, which has been further stimulated by the rapid development of atomic energy. Radiochemical reactions and the mechanism of energy transfer are now far better understood. Precise methods of irradiating biological units with α-particles, neutrons, etc., have afforded more definite notions of the effects on various cell structures, of the mechanism of gene action, cell division, and differentiation.

The development of radiobiology has run parallel with the advancement of biology in general and a wealth of data has thus accumulated, far more than one man can possibly cover. This is why it was felt that a comprehensive treatise, written by experienced scientists, might result in a useful handbook for the student as well as an informative book of reference for the advanced research worker.

Volume I deals with physical and chemical aspects of radiation effects as well as biochemical changes produced *in vivo* and *in vitro*. The treatment of cytological effects has particularly emphasized cellular damage as it appears under the electron microscope. Radiation effects on free living cells and radiation genetics have been treated chiefly from the point of view of principles and mechanisms of action. In Volume II radiation effects on embryonic and adult organisms are discussed, chiefly in mammals. Special chapters are devoted to immunological processes in irradiated organisms, to the mechanisms of action of protective and sensitizing agents, as well as to the experimental possibilities of enhancing the recovery of irradiated mammals.

The editors are of course aware of the difficulty of covering the whole field of radiobiology and related disciplines. Also, science has made rapid headway between the stage of planning of this book and the final stage of preface writing. Paramagnetic resonance measurements have been developed as an important tool for determinations of free radicals during the past few years. Some topics, such as bacterial genetics and lysogeny have not been included since there are many review articles available. Other, more practical aspects, such as problems related to internal radiation sources have been superficially treated because of their very specialized nature.

The editors wish to acknowledge the pleasant cooperation of all the authors and the Academic Press during the preparation of this book.

Bruxelles and Stockholm
April, 1961

M. ERRERA
A. FORSSBERG

ABBREVIATIONS

ACTH — Adrenocorticotropic hormone

ADP — Adenosine diphosphate

AET — Aminoethylisothiuronium bromide hydrobromide

AMP — Adenosine monophosphate

ATP — Adenosine triphosphate

BAL — British antilewisite = 2,3-dimercapto-1-propanol

CSH — Cysteine

CSSH — Cystine

DNA — Deoxyribonucleic acid

DNase — Deoxyribonuclease

DOCA — Deoxycorticosterone acetate

DOPA — 3 - (3,4 - Dihydroxyphenyl)alanine

DPN⁺ — Diphosphopyridine nucleotide

DPNH — Diphosphopyridine nucleotide (reduced)

EDTA — Ethylenediamine tetra-acetate

EEG — Electroencephalogram

ERG — Electroretinogram

G.I. — Gastrointestinal tract

GSH — Glutathione (reduced)

GSSH — Glutathione (oxidized)

ICRP — International Commission for Radiological Protection

IQ — Intelligence quotient

LD_{50} — Dose lethal to 50% of animals

$LD_{50(30)}$ — Dose lethal to 50% of animals during the 30 days following irradiation

MEG — S-mercaptoethylguanidine hydrobromide

MLD — Mid-lethal dose

p.i. — Postirradiation

PVP — Polyvinyl pyrrolidone

RBE — Relative biological efficiency

RNA — Ribonucleic acid

RNase (pH6) — Ribonuclease (pH optimum = 6)

RNase (pH8) — Ribonuclease (pH optimum = 8)

STH — Somatotropic hormone

TEM — Triethylene melamine = 2,4,6 - tris(1 - aziridinyl) - s - triazine

TPN⁺ — Triphosphopyridine nucleotide (oxidized)

TPNH — Triphosphopyridine nucleotide (reduced)

UNITS

ev — Electron volt. The energy of each quantum of electromagnetic radiation is given in ev by $12{,}400/\lambda$, where λ is the wavelength in angstroms.

rad — Unit of absorbed energy equal to an energy absorption of 100 ergs per gram of irradiated material at the point of interest. It is applicable to any ionizing radiation provided the energy deposited is measured or calculated in the material actually irradiated.

r — Roentgen, the unit of exposure dose to X- or γ-rays. One r is an exposure dose of X- or γ-radiation such that the associated corpuscular emissions per 0.001293 gm of air produces in air, ions carrying one electrostatic unit of electricity of either sign.
Produces 2.1×10^9 ion pairs in 1 cc of air.
Absorption of 83 ergs per gram of air or 93 ergs per gram of water.

rep — Roentgen equivalent physical. One rep liberates the same energy in water or tissues as one r of X-rays. (This unit has now generally been replaced by the rad.)

c — Curie, the quantity of radioactive nuclide in which the number of disintegrations per second is 3.7×10^{10}.

n — Neutron unit, the amount of neutron radiations which produces the same discharge of the 100-r Victoreen dosimeter as does one r of X-rays. (The n has now been generally replaced by the rad.)

LET — Linear energy transfer, the linear rate of loss of energy (locally absorbed) by an ionizing particle traversing a material medium. LET can be expressed in kiloelectron volts per micron.

RBE — Relative biological effectiveness is used to compare the effectiveness of absorbed dose of radiation delivered in different ways. *Example:* one rad of α-radiation produces a particular biological response in the same degree as 10 rads of γ-radiation. The RBE depends on many factors which should always be made clear. For X-rays and β-rays, RBE ≈ 1; for α-rays, RBE ≈ 10.

rem — Unit of RBE. The dose in rem equals the dose in rads multiplied by RBE.

The definitions of units have been taken from: Report of the United Nations Scientific Committee on the Effects of Atomic Radiation, General Assembly, Official Records of the 13th Session, Suppl. No. 7 (A/3838), New York, 1958; Z. M. Bacq and P. Alexander, "Fundamentals of Radiobiology," Academic Press, New York, 1955.

CONTENTS OF VOLUME I

CONTENTS OF VOLUME II, MECHANISMS IN RADIOBIOLOGY

Multicellular Organisms

Physical Principles of Radiation Action

F. Hutchinson and E. Pollard*

*Biophysics Department, The Josiah Willard Gibbs Research
Laboratories, Yale University, New Haven, Connecticut*

Contents

I. Introduction

It is now over sixty years since the discovery of the two major sources of ionizing radiation: X-rays by Roentgen in 1895, and the radioactivity of uranium by Becquerel in 1896. That a precise theory of the biological action of radiation does not yet exist is a result of the complexity of living process and form and also of the complex character of the ionizing radiations themselves.

* *Present address:* Whitmore Laboratory, University Park, Pennsylvania.

Speaking for the moment broadly, there are five major types of radiation of importance: fast electrons, fast positive ions, electromagnetic radiation of high energy, ultraviolet light (electromagnetic radiation of the atomic energy range), and neutrons. Almost all five classes of radiation are quite closely linked by interactions, and the result is a seemingly complex physical system in which the relatively simple aspects are hidden.

From the radiobiological point of view radiation is actually seen as rather simpler than the physicists' view. Many important processes are not of great interest in biological action. Hence in this chapter we have attempted to stress those features of radiation action which are of the greatest value to biologists, rather than trying to give a short summary of all that radiation entails. Many other summarized accounts exist (1–10), each having its own specialized objective.

The physical processes of radiobiology fall into three broad areas of interest. The first is the nature of the interaction between X-rays and γ-rays and matter, including the process of transfer from energy as electromagnetic radiation to energy as fast electrons and the continued transfer from fast electrons to electrons in atoms. The second is the nature of absorption and action of ultraviolet light, involving quite detailed transitions between molecular energy levels and, as yet, unexplained consequences of absorption. The third is the interaction between neutrons and nuclei with the resulting production of recoil nuclei, products of nuclear reactions and of electromagnetic radiation. With the advent of space travel there may develop a fourth area: that of the action of very energetic, multiply ionized, primary cosmic-ray particles, whose intensity in space is not yet known and whose biological action still remains to be determined.

The processes of X-ray and γ-ray absorption have been under continuous study for the whole of the present century. In his first communication Roentgen described careful work on the transparency of different materials, pointing out that the density was the major (but not the only) factor in determining the penetrability of X-rays. The early work was complicated by the varying hardness of the tubes and by a lack of a good quantitative measure of intensity. Nevertheless, by 1902 tables of absorption coefficients were appearing, and the exponential absorption relation, already familiar from the absorption of light, was being used. It is not in place here to give the long story, intimately related to the development of modern knowledge of the atom, of the elucidation of the character of X-rays, as being both continuous radiation and characteristic radiation; of photoelectric absorption, Compton scattering, and pair formation; and further of the nature of the energy loss by a secondary electron produced in one of those processes. Instead, a short description of the phenomena involved is given in the next paragraphs. Some of the processes described are elaborated on later, others are left for more specialized texts.

Energetic electromagnetic radiation can originate in two major ways. The first is as a transition between two energy levels in either the atom itself or its nucleus. The former are designated *characteristic X-rays*, the latter *γ-rays*. The second is by the deceleration of electrons, usually in a target (though acceleration in a betatron or synchrotron merely by circular motion also produces radiation). The radiation is not homogeneous in wavelength but consists of a statistically distributed aggregate of photons with a maximum energy equal to that of the causative electrons. This radiation is the *continuous* radiation, or *bremsstrahlung*. All the classes of radiation differ only in frequency. Gamma rays have frequencies up to 10^{22} cycles per second, X-rays from a 250-kev X-ray tube have frequencies around 5×10^{19} cycles per second. In an X-ray tube the radiation is produced by electrons which have gained energy in an electric field, being abruptly stopped in a target. This excites characteristic X-rays, by disrupting the atoms of the target, and also produces continuous radiation. Gamma rays are produced by the decay of radioactive elements which are left excited by the primary particle emission of radioactivity. Gamma rays, like characteristic X-rays, are of discrete frequencies.

When such high-frequency electromagnetic radiation in its turn encounters matter, it interacts with the atomic substructure of the absorber. Since the laws of quantum physics involve probabilities only, there is necessarily a strong element of chance in the nature of each encounter between atom and radiation. This is expressed in the exponential nature of absorption and can be written mathematically as follows: Let n be the number of absorbing elements (electrons or atoms, depending on the method of absorption) per unit volume, S be a parameter describing the absorption process on each element, and x be the thickness traversed. Then if N photons are incident on a unit area and $-dN$ are removed from the beam, the fraction absorbed, $-dN/N$, is equal to the fractional area of atomic absorption exposed. In an increment of thickness dx and unit area, this is $nS\,dx$, so that

$$- \frac{dN}{N} = nS\,dx$$

or, if N_0 is the number of photons at the start of a thickness x, and N is the number which emerge,

$$\ln \frac{N}{N_0} = -nSx \tag{1}$$

or

$$\frac{N}{N_0} = e^{-nSx}$$

The parameter S is called the "cross section," and equation 1 is a useful method of describing a great variety of absorption processes. It is more usually encountered in the form

$$\frac{N}{N_0} = e^{-\mu x} \tag{2}$$

where μ is the *linear absorption coefficient*. Various forms of the above equation are used. These are excellently described by Johns and Laughlin (2).

For X-rays the cross section measured by equation 1 is a composite of at least two and possibly three processes. These are *photoelectric absorption*, *Compton scattering*, and *pair formation*. In Section IV.A a brief description of these processes is given. They are independent of one another, which means that we can write

$$S = S_{\text{photo}} + S_{\text{compt}} + S_{\text{pair}}$$

where S_{photo}, S_{compt}, and S_{pair} refer to the cross sections for the three processes. All three methods of interaction yield the result that photon energy is transferred to electron energy. The interest in the process of interaction with matter is thus not simply contained in these three effects. What the fast electrons do is of great, indeed paramount, importance.

The fast secondary electrons interact with atoms in their path via the electric fields they produce. In more ordinary terms, they undergo collisions. As will be shown later, the energy releases occur more frequently if the electrons are of low energy, and this has the important result that the absorption process becomes more effective as the electron slows down. Each collision, on the average, reduces the electron energy by only a small amount, so that many are needed before the electron is stopped. Such a process leads to a more or less definite *range*, or thickness traversed, for each electron. Thus the over-all process we have described is one of transfer of energy, following an exponential absorption law, to electrons which have a finite range. We need to elaborate considerably on the whole phenomenon later in the chapter.

The discovery of the neutron by Chadwick in 1932 and the rapid consequent development of nuclear physics has brought a completely different agent into the field of radiobiology. Neutrons interact exclusively with atomic nuclei, and, since the physical area of the nucleus of the atom is so minute, the absorption of neutrons is relatively weak. It is, however, random in character, so that the exponential absorption relation holds again. The cross section, however, depends on the interaction by nuclear forces between neutron and nucleus. Such forces are very large, but very limited in distance, so that the cross section of many nuclei for neutron scattering is very nearly the cross section of the nucleus itself. The collisions involved are of two kinds, those in which energy and momentum are conserved and the neutron and nucleus merely recoil from each other, and those in which nuclear reactions of various degrees of elaboration take place, resulting in the emission of charged particles and γ-rays. In either event, the predominant effect is the transfer of neutron energy to fast particles, electrons, ejected nuclear fragments, or knock-on nuclei. Such nuclei produce very intense ionization of the matter they traverse. Once again the over-all process has been the transfer of energy from the incident radiation to fast charged particles traveling through the target.

In the unknown complexities of interstellar space, ionized atoms of all kinds are formed and accelerated. These form the *primary cosmic radiation*, which probably reflects in the distribution of ionized atoms the relative abundance of elements in the universe. Such radiation contains protons, carbon nuclei, oxygen nuclei, and iron nuclei, to name only a few, at energies reaching up beyond 10^{15} ev, about a millionfold higher than man's best achievement so far. Such particles ionize densely themselves, and also produce in matter a most complex cascade transition which results in a grand mixture of particles and radiation known as a "shower." Thus the problems of space travel may well present to radiobiologists the very greatest challenge of all classes of radiation. Attention is beginning to be focused on this new problem.

1. Fast Charged Particles

A. RATE OF ENERGY LOSS

This term refers to all the ways in which a fast charged particle moving through matter loses energy. A closely similar term, the linear energy transfer, or LET, refers to that part of the energy which is transmitted directly to the atoms of the stopping material (11) and neglects the radiation losses which become particularly important at relativistic energies.

. THE ELEMENTARY THEORY

A simple theory of the nonrelativistic energy transfer can be obtained by considering an incident particle of mass M, charge Z, energy E, and velocity V, moving in a cloud of electrons, whose binding to atoms will for the moment be neglected. From the classical Rutherford scattering equation (9) it can then be calculated that for nz electrons per unit volume, where n is the number of atoms per unit volume and z is the number of electrons per atom, the number of recoil electrons per unit path length having an energy lying between w and $w + dw$ is given by

$$\frac{2\pi Z^2 e^4}{m V^2} nz \frac{dw}{w^2} \tag{3}$$

where e and m are the charge and the mass of an electron.

For this process, the rate of energy loss, $-dE/dx$, is then given by

$$-\frac{dE}{dx} \sim \frac{2\pi Z^2 e^4}{mV^2} \int_{w_{min}}^{w_{max}} \frac{w\,dw}{w^2} = \frac{2\pi Z^2 e^4}{mV^2} \ln \frac{w_{max}}{w_{min}} \tag{4}$$

where w_{min} and w_{max} are the minimum and maximum energy transfers possible. Since the electrons are actually bound in atoms, the minimum energy transfer will be of the order of magnitude of the mean ionization potential of the electrons in the stopping material, I. For incident heavy particles, such as protons, w_{max} is the maximum energy which can be transferred and still conserve momentum. An observer on the incident heavy particle would see an electron coming in with a velocity V, and, for a head-on collision, going out again with a velocity V in the other direction, for a net change in electron velocity of $2V$. Since the velocity of a heavy particle will change very little in a collision with an electron, the actual change of electron velocity will be the same $2V$, leading to an energy transfer of $2mV^2$, and for heavy particles

$$-\frac{dE}{dx} \sim \frac{2\pi e^4 Z^2}{mV^2} \ln \frac{2mV^2}{I} \tag{5}$$

For electrons, all the energy in the incident electron may be transferred to an atomic electron, but, because of the indistinguishability of electrons, the faster electron coming out of the collision will be identified as the incident one, and w_{max} will be $E/2 = \frac{1}{4}mV^2$, leading to the approximate equation for electrons:

$$-\frac{dE}{dx} \sim \frac{2\pi e^4 Z^2}{mV^2} \ln \frac{mV^2}{4I} \tag{6}$$

Although of the right order of magnitude, this estimate does not take properly into account the large number of energy transfers comparable to the binding energy of the atomic electrons. The mechanism of these transfers may be discussed by considering the electric field produced by the charged particle at some atom to one side of the particle track. This field is time-dependent, rising from zero to a maximum value when the particle is at its distance of closest approach, and dropping to zero again. If the particle is traveling fast enough, the Fourier components of this electric pulse will contain appreciable intensities in the frequency range in which the atom absorbs electromagnetic radiation. The process significantly increases the total rate of energy dissipation. The point of view was first used by Fermi (12) and elaborated somewhat by Gaunt (13).

Detailed calculations have been carried out by Bethe (14) and by Bloch (15). With relativistic corrections added, the rate of energy loss can be written (6)

$$-\frac{dE}{dx} = \frac{4\pi e^4 Z^2}{mV^2} nB \tag{7}$$

where B is called the stopping number and has different forms for different incident particles.

For heavy particles:

$$B = z\left[\ln\frac{2mV^2}{I} - \ln(1 - \beta^2) - \beta^2\right] \tag{7a}$$

For electrons:

$$B = z\left\{\ln\frac{mV^2}{2I}\sqrt{\frac{e}{2}} + \frac{1}{2}\left[\ln 4\frac{1 - \sqrt{1 - \beta^2}}{\beta^2(1 - \beta^2)^{3/2}}\right.\right.$$
$$\left.\left. - (2\sqrt{1 - \beta^2} - 1 + \beta^2)\ln 2 - \beta^2 + \frac{1}{8}(1 - \sqrt{1 - \beta^2})^2\right]\right\}$$
$$= \frac{z}{2}\left[\ln\frac{mV^2E}{2I^2(1 - \beta^2)} - (2\sqrt{1 - \beta^2} - 1 + \beta^2)\ln 2\right.$$
$$\left. + 1 - \beta^2 + \frac{1}{8}(1 - \sqrt{1 - \beta^2})^2\right] \tag{7b}$$

where

$$\beta \equiv \frac{V}{c}$$

The first form of equation 7b is convenient because the quantity in the square brackets goes to zero as β^2 vanishes.

The theoretical calculation of I in terms of the various atomic parameters is not too successful, and I is best determined experimentally. In Table I is listed a number of such experimentally determined I values.

In the absence of suitable data the value of I for an element may be estimated from the relation given by Bloch (15):

$$I = 13.5 z \text{ ev} \tag{7c}$$

where z is the atomic number of the element (see also ref. 16a).

Many years ago Bragg (17) propounded the law which now bears his name, that the stopping power of an element is independent of its state of chemical combination. Thus, the stopping in water is equal to the stopping in a mixture of 2 parts of hydrogen to 1 part of oxygen. In Table I it will be noticed that for the light elements there are measurable differences in the I values for the same element in different chemical combinations. Thus

TABLE I

EXPERIMENTAL VALUES OF I

Element	Chemical state	I (ev)	Ref.
H	Saturated compounds	15.5	(16)
	Unsaturated compounds	13.0	(16)
C	Saturated compounds	69.3	(16)
	Unsaturated compounds	67.2	(16)
N	Molecular	76.3	(16)
	Amines	89.4	(16)
	In rings	68.8	(16)
O	—O—	88.5	(16)
	=O	79.8	(16)
	Molecular	88.3	(16)
Al	Metal	163	(16a)
Cu	Metal	378	(16a)
Au	Metal	1136	(16a)

the Bragg law is not strictly true. Only ln I occurs in equations 7, however, and for a 1-Mev proton a 10 % change in I changes the stopping number by less than 3 %, with an even less effect for swifter particles. In general, most of the experimental data on the stopping by light elements combined in various chemical forms are consistent with the Bragg law to within 1 or 2 % (10, 18, 19). As might be expected, the deviations from the Bragg law are much larger at low energies (10).

2. LOW-ENERGY EFFECTS

An important correction is the reduction of the effective mean square charge of a heavy positively charged particle caused by the capture of electrons into stable orbits about the incident ion. There are no reliable theoretical calculations either of the effective mean square charge, or of the contribution to the energy loss caused by the processes of electron capture and loss as the ion passes through matter. Theoretical estimates of the mean square charge in gases have been made by a number of investigators (20–23).

Allison and Warshaw (10) have an extensive compilation of the data on capture and loss cross sections in various gases. It is clear that for singly charged particles slower than a 50-kev proton, and doubly charged particles slower than a 1-Mev α-particle, the capture and loss phenomenon exerts a marked effect on the rate of energy loss.

It is possible that in condensed media, which are the chief concern of the radiobiologist, the mean square charge of a charged particle might be considerably larger than in a gaseous medium. Bohr and Lindhard (24) have interpreted range data on fission fragments in media of different density in the light of the following picture. A moving ion nearly always captures an electron into a highly excited orbit. If the time before the ion collides with the next atom is large compared to the time it takes the electron to radiate and move to a lower-lying state, as is usually the case in a gas, then the electron is less likely to be removed in the succeeding collision. In liquids and solids, on the other hand, the next collision is almost certain to occur with the electron in the same state in which it was captured, with the consequent almost certain loss of the electron. There is even some evidence that this process may operate with protons of energy of 5 to 50 kev in biological material (25).

If the velocity of the incident particle is sufficiently low, the maximum energy which it can transfer to an atomic electron will be comparable to or even less than the binding energy of the atomic electron, and the stopping power of any such atomic electron will be sharply reduced. In biological material this will be particularly true for the K-electrons. Walske (26) has calculated a correction, C_K, to be substracted from the stopping number, B, the magnitude of which may be inferred from Table II. Other ways of making this correction have been considered by Lindhard and Scharff (27) and by Neufeld (28).

3. NUMERICAL VALUES FOR THE RATE OF ENERGY LOSS

The numerical values may be calculated from equations 7 with the I values given in Table I and the correction for K-shell binding, to an accuracy of perhaps 1 to 4%. The calculations are more accurate for high energies and for stopping media of low atomic weight. In Table II are given rates of energy loss for electrons and for heavy ions in water, calculated in this way. More extensive tables are given by Lea (1) and by Nelms (29). Since the rate at which energy is dissipated is determined mainly by the electron density, it is customary to determine the energy lost per unit mass, such as million electron volts per gram. A convenient unit for visualizing the processes taking place in tissue is the energy loss in electron volts per 100 A, which is numerically equal to the rate of energy loss in million electron volts per gram, multiplied by the density of the tissue as compared to water.

These calculations do not allow for electron capture and loss by heavy charged particles, which can be allowed for with accuracy only by experiment. In Fig. 1 such data are given for protons and α-particles in air, together with a theoretical curve for electrons. All the processes involved, including electron capture and loss, depend only on the velocity and charge of a particle. Thus, for example, the stopping of a deuteron of energy E_d

TABLE II

CALCULATED RATES OF ENERGY LOSS IN WATER

Heavy particles, mass M atomic units, charge Z electron charges
(For particles other than singly charged particles, multiply tabulated values by Z^2.)

E/M (Mev/amu)	$\ln \dfrac{2mv^2}{I}$	K correction	Relativistic correction	Total
0.3	623.7	14	0.000	638.0
1.0	282.7	−6.8	0.000	276.0
3.0	123.3	−2.2	0.000	121.1
10	46.56	−0.27	0.002	46.29
30	18.43	−0.032	0.006	18.41
100	6.49	−0.002	0.015	6.50

Electrons

Energy (Mev)	$\ln \sqrt{e/2}\,\dfrac{mv^2}{2I}$	K correction	Relativistic correction	Polarization correction	Radiation	Total
0.01	23.8	−0.088	0.007	—	—	23.7
0.1	4.20	−0.001	0.098	—	—	4.30
1.0	1.63	−0.000	0.301	−0.026	0.006	1.91
2.0	1.52	—	0.43	−0.069	0.023	1.90
5.0	1.48	—	0.64	−0.144	0.078	2.06
10.0	1.47	—	0.81	−0.243	0.196	2.24
20.0	1.47	—	0.94	−0.350	0.475	2.54
50.0	1.47	—	1.17	−0.499	1.390	3.53
100.0	1.47	—	1.33	−0.606	2.814	5.00

is equal to that of a proton of energy $(M_p/M_d)E_d$, where M_p and M_d are the masses of the proton and deuteron.

The ratio of the stopping number, B (as defined in equations 7), for a given substance to the stopping number for air is sometimes referred to as the stopping power relative to air. If the experimental stopping powers for air are multiplied by this ratio, a rate of energy loss for the substance can be obtained which allows for all the various corrections, including electron capture and loss, under the assumption that these corrections are the same in air and in the substance in question. This is not strictly accurate for capture and loss, which does depend on the mean atomic number of the medium, but the approximation is probably not too bad. In Table III are given calculated stopping powers relative to air for several elements, for water, and for nucleoprotein. The very slow variation with energy is quite apparent.

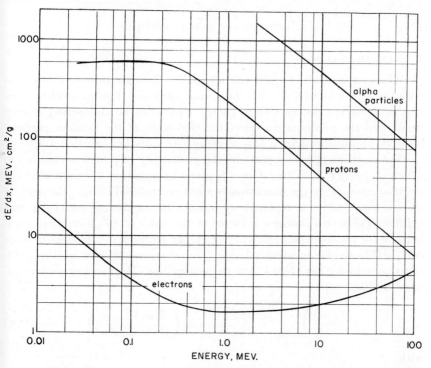

Fig. 1. Rate of energy loss for charged particles in air. The proton and α-particle data are experimental values given by Bethe and Ashkin (6). The electron data are calculated figures given by Nelms (29).

TABLE III

STOPPING POWER FOR VARIOUS MATERIALS RELATIVE TO AIR FOR HEAVY IONS

(The relative stopping power depends on the velocity, or the ratio E/M. Here E is given in million electron volts, M in atomic mass units. The figures were calculated from the I values given in Table I, with corrections made for K-shell binding, but not for electron capture and loss.)

Material	E/M				
	0.75	1.5	4	10	∞
H—relative stopping power/atom	0.216	0.205	0.189	0.180	0.138
C—relative stopping power/atom	0.853	0.856	0.853	0.846	0.826
N—relative stopping power/atom	0.967	0.968	0.968	0.963	0.964
O—relative stopping power/atom	1.103	1.089	1.085	1.085	1.101
P—relative stopping power/atom	1.55	1.70	1.74	1.80	2.07
S—relative stopping power/atom	1.61	1.78	1.86	1.92	2.20
Water—relative stopping power/gm	1.218	1.199	1.175	1.160	1.072
Nucleoprotein[a]—relative stopping power/gm	1.161	1.150	1.133	1.119	1.11

[a] Composition of nucleoprotein was that assumed by Lea (1): H—7% by weight, C—49%, N—16%, O—25%, P—1%, ash (as sulfur)—2%.

4. NUCLEAR COLLISIONS

When an incident charged particle passes through matter, it interacts with the nuclei as well as with the atomic electrons. For an incident electron or positron, the maximum energy which can be transferred is very small, and the predominant effect is a deflection of the incident particle, possibly accompanied by a loss of energy as radiation (Section I.A.6).

For an incident heavy particle, the probability of a nuclear collision in which an energy, w, is transferred is given by equation 3, except that the electron mass, m, in the denominator must be replaced by m_n, the mass of the nucleus, and nz is replaced by just n, the number of nuclei per unit volume. These two changes, a factor of the order of 10^4, more than compensate for the increased efficiency of energy transfer to a nucleus of mass comparable to the incident particle, and characteristically nuclear collisions account for less than 1 % of the energy loss. The loss has been calculated by Bohr (30):

$$-\frac{dE}{dx}\bigg)_{\text{nuclear}} = \frac{4\pi e^4 Z^2 z^2}{m_n V^2}\, n \ln\left(\frac{M m_n V^2}{M + m_n}\frac{a}{Z z e^2}\right) \tag{8}$$

with

$$a = \frac{h^2}{4\pi^2 m e^2}\,(Z^{2/3} + z^{2/3})^{3/2}$$

where h is Planck's constant, and a represents a characteristic distance at which the interaction is limited by screening effects of the surrounding electrons. Snyder and Neufeld (31) have calculated the effects of nuclear collisions for nuclei from hydrogen to oxygen passing through wet tissue. For sufficiently heavy particles at very low energies the energy transfer to electrons is sharply reduced because of the low velocity of the ion, and nuclear collisions finally become the predominate process. In Table IV is

TABLE IV

ESTIMATED ENERGY AT WHICH NUCLEAR AND ELECTRONIC LOSSES ARE
APPROXIMATELY EQUAL FOR HEAVY IONS PASSING THROUGH
WET TISSUE (31)

Incident ion	Energy (Mev)
H^1	0.0015
He^4	0.013
C^{12}	0.094
N^{14}	0.13
O^{16}	0.18

given their estimate of the energy of various ions for which the nuclear
and electronic losses are equal.

5. DENSITY EFFECT

For particles whose velocities are well under the velocity of light, the
stopping power of a substance seems to be reasonably independent of
whether the material is in gaseous or condensed form. The stopping power
for polyethylene has been measured experimentally for 5-Mev α-particles
to be the same within a few per cent as that for gaseous ethylene having
the same atomic composition, $(CH)_n$ (32), and that for polystyrene is
equal to the stopping power for acetylene (33).

The one substance for which there has been a real question on the
possibility of anomalous stopping power has unfortunately been the substance of most interest to biologists, water. Michl (34), Philipp (35), and
Appleyard (36) all reported a stopping power for liquid water about 10
to 15 % lower than that predicted by Bragg's law and that found experimentally for water vapor. Later measurements, however, by de Carvalho and
Yagoda (37), Thompson (16), and Ellis et al. (38) have given results in
excellent agreement with the vapor phase data and Bragg's law, so that

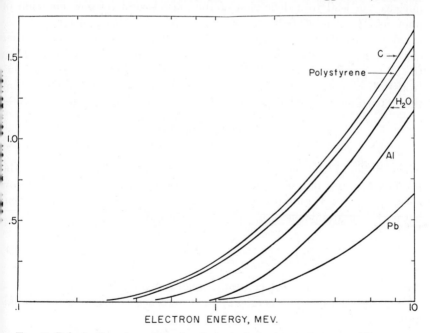

FIG. 2. Polarization corrections for electrons in various substances. The corrections plotted are to be *subtracted* from the stopping number, B, as given in equation 7b.
Data from ref. 29.

it must be concluded that there are errors in the earlier data, and no real anomaly exists.

A true density effect does exist under some conditions, as was first pointed out by Fermi (39). The energy transferred to an atom at a distance from the incident particle track may be visualized as being carried there by the transient electric field produced by the particle at the atom. The presence of matter in the intervening space will weaken the electric field at the distant atom by polarization effects and thus reduce the energy lost by the particle. A complete discussion of this effect is given by Sternheimer (40). The faster the incident particle, the larger is the fraction of energy in the high-frequency components of the electric field at the distant atom, and the greater are the polarization effects on the energy loss. In Fig. 2 are given some calculated polarization corrections, showing the rise in the magnitude of the correction with increasing velocity.

Sternheimer (41) has also demonstrated the existence of a polarization effect at low energies.

6. RADIATION LOSSES

A collision between an incident fast charged particle and an atomic nucleus can lead to a deflection of the particle and possible emission of photons. The details of this process are reviewed by Rossi (9).

With incident fast electrons, radiative collisions can take place either close to the atomic nucleus or at distances comparable to or larger than the atomic radius. In the latter case the screening effect of the atomic electrons will play an important role. It may be shown from the theory that the importance of screening is determined by the value of the parameter

$$\gamma = \frac{100}{z^{1/3}} \frac{mc^2}{U} \frac{W}{U - W}$$

where W here is the energy of the emitted photon, and $U = E + mc^2$, the total energy, rest plus kinetic, of the incident electron. For sufficiently low energies, E, $\gamma \gg 1$, radiation will take place only in close collisions, screening effects of atomic electrons may be neglected, and

$$-\frac{dE}{dx}\bigg)_{\text{radiation}} = \frac{4\alpha e^4}{mc^2} z^2 n \frac{U}{mc^2} \ln\left(\frac{2U}{mc^2} - \frac{1}{3}\right) \tag{9}$$

Here α is the fine structure constant, equal to $2\pi e^2/hc = 1/137$.

For sufficiently high energies, $\gamma \approx 0$, screened collisions will predominate, and

$$-\frac{dE}{dx}\bigg)_{\text{radiation}} = \frac{4\alpha e^4}{mc^2} z^2 n \frac{E}{mc^2} \left(\ln \frac{183}{z^{1/3}} + \frac{1}{18}\right) \tag{10}$$

In considering radiation losses it is convenient to measure distances in units of a length called the radiation length, X_0, which is defined as

$$\frac{1}{X_0} = \frac{4\alpha e^4}{mc^2} z^2 n \frac{1}{mc^2} \ln \frac{183}{z^{1/3}} \qquad (11)$$

Distances in a stopping material expressed in these units are given by $t = X/X_0$. The previous equation for radiation losses by very fast particles then becomes

$$-\frac{1}{U}\frac{dU}{dt} = 1 + \frac{1}{18 \ln 183 z^{-1/3}} \qquad (12)$$

or almost independent of z. This equation also shows that physically the radiation length is the distance in which radiation losses reduce the total energy of the incident electron to $1/e$ of its initial value.

It can be shown that the rate of energy loss, with the radiation length as a unit, is not critically dependent on z, even at lower energies. In Fig. 3 are plotted the radiation losses in air and in lead.

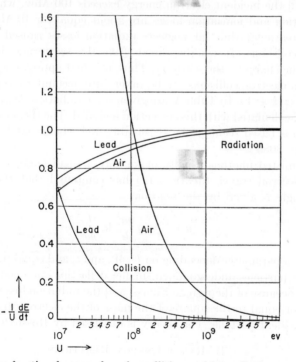

FIG. 3. The fractional energy loss, by collision and by radiation, per radiation length of air or lead. Reprinted from ref. 9 by courtesy of B. Rossi and Prentice-Hall.

TABLE V

RADIATION LENGTH, X_0, IN VARIOUS SUBSTANCES (9)

Substance	X_0 (gm/cm²)
Carbon	44.6
Nitrogen	39.4
Oxygen	35.3
Aluminum	24.4
Argon	19.7
Iron	13.9
Copper	12.9
Lead	5.83
Air	37.7
Water	37.1

Figure 3 also shows the collision losses plotted in the same units. It is apparent that in materials of low atomic number, such as are met within living systems, the radiation losses do not become equal to the ionization losses until the incident electron energy exceeds 100 Mev, whereas in lead the radiation and ionization losses are about equal for 10-Mev electrons.

The treatment thus far neglects radiation losses caused by electron-electron collisions. It can be shown that the scattering depends basically on the charge of the scatterer. Thus, to a first approximation the effect of electron-electron collisions can be taken into account by replacing z^2 by $z^2 + z = z(z + 1)$. In Table V are given some radiation lengths in various materials, calculated with this correction included. The theory on which this discussion is based seems to be reasonably well confirmed by experiment (ref. 9, pp. 308ff).

The emitted photons usually make only a small angle with the direction of electron travel. Stearns (42) has computed that the root-mean-square angle is given by the relation

$$(\bar{\theta^2})^{1/2} = q \frac{mc^2}{U} \ln \frac{U}{mc^2} \tag{13}$$

where q is a parameter depending on U, W, and z, and equal to 0.65 ± 0.15.

Heavy particles undergo much smaller deflections in a collision than do electrons because of their greater mass, and the radiation losses are reduced by a factor equal to the square of the mass of the electron divided by that for the incident particle. The theory is discussed by Rossi (9).

B. RANGE-ENERGY RELATIONS

The range of a charged particle is usually taken to be the thickness of material which can be penetrated by a particle of given energy. Although defined as a distance, it is frequently expressed as a mass per unit area, such as grams per square centimeter, since only the number of atoms encountered, and not the spacing along the track, is important.

1. HEAVY PARTICLES

For heavy charged particles the range, R, may be calculated by integration of the expression for the rate of energy loss (equation 7).

$$R = \int_E^0 \frac{1}{dE/dx}\, dE \qquad (14)$$

In general this must be done numerically.

From equation 7 and the various corrections to it (such as that for the binding of K-electrons), it can readily be seen that the stopping in a given medium depends only on the velocity of the particle, or the ratio E/M. Thus it is possible to write

$$R = \frac{M}{Z^2}\, h\left(\frac{E}{M}\right) \qquad (15)$$

where $h(E/M)$ is a function of E/M (or velocity) characteristic of the stopping material. From this relation it is clear that the range of a deuteron, for example, is twice the range of a proton of the same E/M, or half the energy.

The dependence on E/M for particles of the same charge is exact. The dependence on Z, however, fails at low energies because of electron capture and loss, which depends on Z as well as on the stopping material. The correction is small for $Z \leq 3$ and is usually taken into account by an additive term. The experimental ranges for α-particles in air are 0.20 cm longer (6) than those calculated from proton data based on equation 15.

The variation of the range with different stopping materials is complicated. To a surprising accuracy, especially in media of low atomic number, the range is determined by the number of electrons per unit volume; this may be expressed, in materials in which the mass of hydrogen is not too large a fraction of the whole, simply by giving the range as the mass per unit area. A more exact comparison of the ranges of a given particle in two different materials may be made by correcting for the mean stopping power of one material relative to another (see Table III). The slow variation of the relative stopping power with particle energy makes a relatively accurate estimate possible.

In Fig. 4 are given experimental curves for protons and for α-particles in air. A number of other range-energy curves have been published for slow α-particles in air (43) and for heavy particles in hydrogen (6), in metals (6, 44, 44a) and in organic materials (45, 45a).

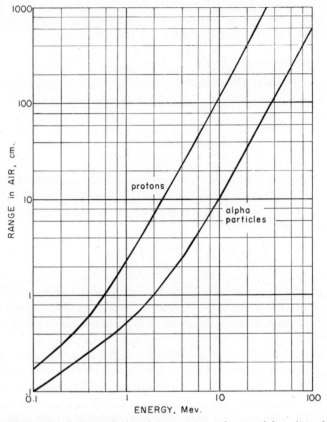

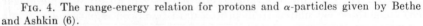

FIG. 4. The range-energy relation for protons and α-particles given by Bethe and Ashkin (6).

2. STRAGGLING AND SCATTERING

The concept of range is useful in considering the penetration of heavy ions into matter because the particles travel in almost straight lines for a distance which is almost the same for similar ions of the same energy. In each of its encounters with the atomic electrons of the stopping medium, the heavy ion loses only a small fraction of its energy, because of the restrictions imposed by the conservation of momentum. For the same reason, the deflection in angle in a single encounter is also small.

Although each of the individual energy losses is small, there is a statistical fluctuation in the energy transferred in the individual encounters which gives rise to a distribution in the energy of individual particles at a fixed depth in an absorber, a distribution which gives rise to a variation in the

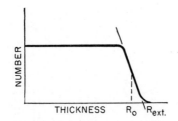

FIG. 5. The range-number curve for heavy charged particles. R_0 is the mean range, and $R_{ext.}$ the "extrapolated range."

depth to which individual particles penetrate. These fluctuations in energy and range are referred to as straggling.

For monoenergetic particles the number as a function of depth in the absorber is given by a curve similar to Fig. 5. A theory of the straggling valid for the case of small fractional energy losses per collision has been given by Livingston and Bethe (46). They find for the mean square fluctuation in range from the mean range, R_0,

$$\overline{(R - R_0)^2} = \int_0^E \frac{4\pi e^4 Z^2 n z'}{(dE/dx)^3} \left(1 + \sum_n \frac{k_n I_n z_n}{mV^2 z'} \ln \frac{2mV^2}{I_n}\right) \qquad (16)$$

Here z_n is the number of electrons in the shell having an ionization potential equal to I_n, k_n is a constant having a value of the order of $\frac{2}{3}$ for light elements, and z' is the number of electrons for which the ionization potential, I_n, is less than $2mV^2$. The summation extends only over the terms for which $I_n < 2mV^2$.

In Fig. 6 is plotted the straggling for protons in air, expressed as a percentage of the total range. From equations 16, 15, and 7 it may be seen that the *fractional* fluctuation in range, $\sqrt{\overline{(R - R_0)^2}}/R_0$, is a function only of the velocity, or E/M. The per cent straggling in range for any heavy particle is equal to that for the proton of the same E/M. The straggling depends on the charge only through the effect of electron capture and loss. As can be seen from equation 16, the dependence of straggling on the material is complex, but for light elements the variation is small, and Fig. 6 can be used for tissue, protein, etc.

More comprehensive theories of straggling which take into account large changes of energy on a single encounter in nuclear collisions, by radiation, and by electron scattering of incident electrons, have been developed by Landau and by Symon and are discussed by Rossi (9).

Scattering refers to the sum of all the angular deflections sustained by the ion. Cloud chamber photographs show only just measurable deviations from a straight line for all heavy ions, except for very slow ones, or a rare

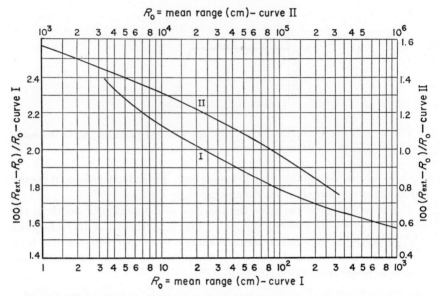

FIG. 6. Straggling of protons in air, expressed as per cent difference between extrapolated range, $R_{ext.}$, and mean range, R_0. Reprinted from ref. 6 with permission of H. A. Bethe and John Wiley & Sons.

particle now and then which makes a direct hit on a nucleus. These nuclear interactions occur so infrequently that they are probably not important in radiobiology, with the important exception of neutron irradiation.

The theory of multiple small-angle scattering is intricate but has been well worked out by Molière (46a) and by Snyder and Scott (47). A full discussion is given by Bethe and Ashkin (6). The scattering not only deflects the heavy ions but also decreases slightly the maximum distance the heavy ions can penetrate, since the particles must travel a somewhat longer path than if they had gone in a straight line.

3. ELECTRON RANGES.

Electrons differ from heavy ions in that the deflection in a single collision may be large. This leads to scattering to such an extent that the range of an electron in the same sense as used for heavy particles is simply not applicable, and the observed straggling is of the same order as the total path length. Indeed, a fair percentage of an incident beam will scatter back from an absorber because of multiple collisions within the material. The straggling is also increased because of the greater statistical fluctuation in the energy loss per collision, but the straggling because of scattering is so severe that this loss fluctuation is usually of significance only in considering straggling in thin foils.

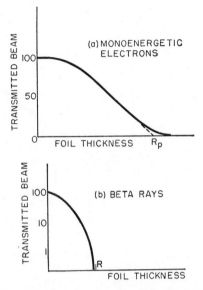

FIG. 7. Range-number curve for electrons in solids. R_p is the "practical range"

If a beam of monoenergetic electrons is incident on a foil, the transmitted beam decreases with increasing foil thickness in a manner shown by the solid line in Fig. 7a. The most reproducible part of the curve seems to be the point where the steep linear portion extrapolates to the axis and is usually referred to as the practical range, R_p. The tail at longer ranges is not in general repeatable. On the other hand, if a beam from a radioactive β-emitter is used, the transmission curve is as shown in Fig. 7b, and the range is taken as the asymptote to the measured curve. Katz and Penfold (48) have reviewed the data in the literature and show that both ranges in aluminum are given quite accurately by the same range-energy curve, as shown in Fig. 8. The solid line is given by the relation

$$R(\text{mg/cm}^2) = 412E^{1.265-0.0954 \ln E} \qquad (17)$$

(with E in million electron volts) and fits the data quite accurately from 20 kev to 2.5 Mev. Above this energy the data are better fitted by the dashed line, a plot of the equation

$$R(\text{mg/cm}^2) = 530E - 106 \qquad (18)$$

These range-energy relations are reasonably accurate for materials of low atomic weight other than aluminum when the range is expressed in milligrams per square centimeter. A more precise value can be obtained by using appropriate ratios of stopping powers as in Table III.

Below 20 kev, practical ranges have been measured in aluminum by

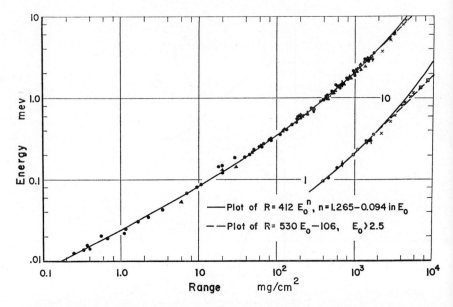

FIG. 8. Range-energy relation for electrons in aluminum, as given by Katz and Penfold (48). The experimental points are both for monoenergetic electrons and for β-rays. Above 2.5 Mev, the linear relation is a better fit to the experimental data. Reproduced by courtesy of L. Katz and the American Physical Society.

TABLE VI

RANGES MEASURED ALONG THE TRACK FOR ELECTRONS IN WATER
(Calculated by D. E. Lea, ref. 1, p. 24. See also the tables of Nelms, ref. 29.)

Electron energy (kev)	Range (μ)
0.1	0.0031
0.3	0.01005
0.5	0.01963
1.0	0.05544
2.0	0.1595
5.0	0.7468
10	2.517
20	8.473
30	17.33
50	42.70
70	76.64
100	141.2
150	278.1
300	832.0
480	1651

Schonland (49) and by Young (50), in protein by Davis (51), and in composite foils of aluminum and plastics by Lane and Zaffarano (52). The data are only in fair agreement but can be fitted within perhaps 25 % down to 0.6 kev by an expression proposed by Cole (53).

$$R(\text{mg/cm}^2) = 0.0045(E + 0.07)^{1.75} \tag{19}$$

Here E is in kiloelectron volts.

For some purposes, the range along the particle track is of interest. This corresponds to the heavy-particle range previously discussed. The numerical values in Table VI have been calculated by Lea (ref. 1, p. 24) for water, and they appear to be in good agreement with data from cloud chamber experiments, in which the range along the track was measured directly from photographs (54, 55). It should be noticed that these ranges along the track are appreciably larger than the experimental ranges deduced from the penetration of absorbers.

C. DISTRIBUTION OF THE ENERGY RELEASE IN THE TRACK

1. THE TRACK OF AN IONIZING PARTICLE

A fast charged particle loses its energy in making specific interactions, excitations and ionizations, with the atoms of the stopping medium.

Bloch (15) has shown that the energy loss by a nonrelativistic particle to the medium beyond a radius b from the track is given by

$$\frac{4\pi e^4 Z^2}{mV^2} nz \sum_i f_i \xi_i K_0(\xi_i) K_1(\xi_i)$$

$$\xi_i \equiv \frac{2\pi\nu_i}{V} b \tag{20}$$

For $\xi_i \gg 1$, this becomes

$$\frac{4\pi e^4 Z^2}{mV^2} nz \sum_i f_i \ln \frac{1.123V}{2\pi\nu_i b} \tag{20a}$$

Here $K_0(\xi_i)$ and $K_1(\xi_i)$ are modified Bessel functions (56), and f_i is the oscillator strength for the effective oscillators in the medium having a resonant frequency ν_i. The only restriction is that b is large enough so that the electric field of the particle at any oscillator beyond b is reasonably constant over the physical extent of the oscillator. A minimum distance here might be $b = 3A$. For water, with the f_i and ν_i values given by Halpern and Hall (57), the energy lost directly to the medium beyond $3A$ lies between 10 and 18 % for electrons of energy 1 to 50 Kev and for protons and α-particles having energies between 1 and 20 Mev. Thus it is clear that the primary interactions are located close to the track of the particle.

It is usually assumed that the primary events are distributed at random along the track. This would be expected from the mechanisms involved, and there appears to be no reason to doubt it, although the authors are not aware of any experimental proof.

2. DISTRIBUTION IN ENERGY OF THE PRIMARY INTERACTION

The amount of energy transferred per event varies from very small values up to the maximum energy which can be transferred to an electron in a direct collision. A qualitative notion of the distribution in energy of these energy transfers can be obtained from experiments in which strictly monoenergetic electron beams are passed through foils so thin that only one primary event takes place on the average. The transmitted beam is then analyzed with an electrostatic or magnetic spectrometer of sufficient resolution to measure energy losses as low as a few electron volts (58). In Fig. 9 is shown the energy losses in collodion for a 5-kv electron beam (59). It shows clearly a peak at about 25 ev, a peak observed with many materials (58). A most significant point is the small number of excitations, or energy losses below 10 ev, produced directly by the primary particle. This feature is also found for many substances (58). It should be pointed out that this is contrary to the calculations of Bethe (14), who computes that excitations in atomic hydrogen are three times as numerous as ionizations. It would, however, seem difficult to explain away the experimental evidence that primary excitations are rare.

The discrepancy between the thin foil data and Bethe's calculations is probably explained by a recent paper of Fano (59a). He shows that in calculating probabilities of transitions it is not legitimate to neglect the interac-

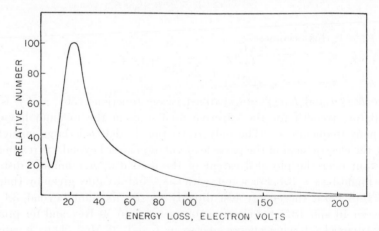

FIG. 9. A plot of the loss of energy suffered by 5-kev electrons in passing through a very thin (~100-A) collodion film. After Ruthemann (59).

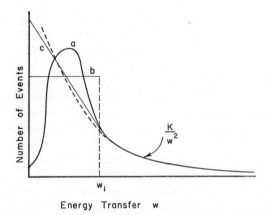

Energy Transfer w

FIG. 10. A plot of φ, the probability of an energy transfer, w, from an incident charged particle, as a function of w. Curve a represents the assumed form of the function, becoming equal to K/w^2 at sufficiently high energies (equation 3). Curves b and c indicate two extreme assumptions made to obtain a function which can be integrated in equation 21.

tions between neighboring atoms when the electron density exceeds a certain critical value. The effect of such interactions is to displace particularly the low energy transitions of the order of 5 ev to higher energies. The theory as yet is not able to make a quantitative estimate of the effect, but qualitatively it appears adequate to explain the difficulty.

As the energy transfer becomes high enough, it would be expected that the effects of electronic binding would become unimportant, and the distribution in energy of the primary events would be given by equation 3. There does not seem to be any reasonable experimental evidence as to the limiting energy at which this equation is valid, but the lower limit of 100 ev first introduced by Lea (1) has been widely used. The distribution in energy of the primary interactions is therefore probably given by a curve of the general shape of curve a in Fig. 10.

3. MEAN ENERGY PER PRIMARY IONIZATION

The energy necessary to ionize most organic molecules, at least in the gaseous phase, is in the range of 8–12 ev (60). Thus each interaction transferring more energy than this will give rise to a primary ionization. The number of such primary ionizations occurring in a condensed (liquid or solid) phase is desired. From the preceding section it is apparent that there is good reason to believe that the course of events will be different in condensed and in gaseous phases. However, because only data in gases is as yet available, the discussion in this section will be concerned directly with gases only.

Pollard and Forro (61) and Slater (62) have reviewed the data for the mean energy per primary ionization for electrons of energy of the order of a million electron volts. They concluded that for the gases air, neon, nitrogen, and oxygen this mean energy is 110 ± 10 ev. For argon, the mean is about 83 ev, and for hydrogen, about 60 ev (63). For helium, the experimental data give about 60 ev (63), but impurities in the helium give rise to high percentage of spurious ionizations (see Section II.C.5), and the data are consistent with an actual mean energy per primary ion pair of 114 ev (64).

For electrons in the range of 5 to 30 kev Sommermeyer and Dresel (65) used an ingenious apparatus in which the primary positive ions formed by a beam of electrons passing through a gas at low pressure were measured. The gas pressure was so low that the chance of a secondary electron from a primary ionization creating another positive ion in the sensitive volume was remote. With more accurate figures for the rate of energy loss, their results show that for N_2, O_2, CO_2, and SO_2 about 90 ± 10 ev is expended per primary ionization, with no detectable change with electron energy. For A the energy is about 83 ev per primary ionization.

For five compounds containing hydrogen—H_2, H_2O, NH_3, C_2H_2, and C_2H_4—their data give about 75 ev per primary ionization. It is difficult to see how the presence of hydrogen atoms in a molecule can so alter the energy needed to create a primary ion, since for nonhydrogenous materials very drastic changes in electron configurations do not produce notable changes in this energy. Molecules containing hydrogen are extremely likely to decompose after ionization, a frequent effect being the splitting off of one or more hydrogen atoms (66). It is quite possible that some reactions connected with such decompositions are increasing the number of positive ions formed near the electron beam, giving an apparent decrease in the energy expended per primary ion.

Since the maximum energy which can be transferred to an atomic electron increases with increasing energy of the incident particle, it would be expected that the mean energy per primary ion will increase also. To calculate this increase, one needs to know the probability, φ, of an energy transfer, w, as a function of w. Then the mean energy per primary ionization, $\bar{w}$, is

$$\bar{w} = \frac{\int_0^{w_{max}} \varphi w \, dw}{\int_0^{w_{max}} \varphi \, dw} \qquad (21)$$

Since the exact form (Fig. 10, curve a) is not known, the variation in $\bar{w}$ has been computed by using both a constant value of φ below some critical energy, $\bar{w}_1$ (Fig. 10, curve b), and a linear relation (curve c). The constants are so chosen that the total energy loss, given by $\int_0^{w_{max}} \varphi w \, dw$, is equal to that given by the Bethe-Bloch equation. For both curve shapes this calculation gives approximately

$$\bar{w} = Y \frac{-dE/dx}{-dE/dx + \kappa \left[\ln \left(Y/I \right) + 0.5 \right]} \quad \text{(heavy particles)}$$

$$= Y \frac{-dE/dx}{-dE/dx + \kappa \left[\ln \left(Y/I \right) + 1.7 \right]} \quad \text{(electrons)} \quad (22)$$

$$\kappa = \frac{4\pi e^4 Z^2}{mV^2} nz$$

Here Y is the maximum value for $\bar{w}$ with very high-energy radiation. It is seen that the mean energy per primary ionization is not particularly dependent on the low-energy distribution.

Bethe (14) has given a theory for the probability of primary ionization which gives a relation of the same form as equation 22, with the expression in the square brackets equal to 3.04 for heavy particles in atomic hydrogen. This leads to a very rapid variation in $\bar{w}$ with energy. From equation 22, with $I = 70$ ev for water, and $Y = 120$ ev, the values listed in Table VII are obtained.

We conclude that this rough theory gives only a slow change in $\bar{w}$ with energy, and, because of the rapid variation in the rate of energy loss with energy, considerable accuracy would be needed to show this. The somewhat lower values of $\bar{w}$ found by Sommermeyer and Dresel (65) for 10-kev electrons suggest a lower $\bar{w}$ than for 1-Mev electrons, although the accuracy of the data is not good enough to establish this point. The figures in Table VII also indicate that the mean energy per primary ionization for energetic electrons is about that for heavy particles of corresponding energy.

TABLE VII

VARIATION IN $\bar{w}$ FOR WATER WITH ENERGY OF INCIDENT PARTICLE,
FROM EQUATION 22

Heavy particles		Electrons	
E/M (Mev/amu)	$\bar{w}$ (ev)	E (kev)	$\bar{w}$ (ev)
1	99	1	71
10	106	10	87
100	109	100	95
		1,000	100
		10,000	105

Considering all the data, and bearing in mind the possible errors in the rare gas data because of impurities, we find that a mean energy per primary ionization of 100 ev seems to be the best value at present for all particles of energy of the order of 1 to 10 Mev. For very-low-energy electrons, it may be as low as 70 ev per primary ionization.

4. DELTA RAYS

Many of the electrons ejected by the incident fast particle will have enough energy to ionize other atoms. These electrons which spray out from the track of the primary are known as δ-rays, and their distribution in energy can be visualized from the distribution in energy of the primary energy loss shown in Fig. 10, if one bears in mind that 10 to 20 ev of the transferred energy has been used in removing the electron from the atom.

Those electrons which have an energy of less than about 100 volts travel only a very short distance. For many simple organic molecules, the cross section for scattering of 10- to 100-volt electrons is of the order of the physical size of the molecule, and the cross section for ionization is perhaps a quarter of the size (8). In other words, such a slow electron is strongly deviated in direction by each atomic encounter and ionizes an atom on each fourth or fifth encounter, with consequent loss of a large fraction of its energy. Lea (1) introduced the concept of treating these ionizations as a unit, which he termed a cluster. The dimensions of a cluster are not well defined but presumably are of the order of a few angstroms only.

The distribution of electrons of energy greater than about 100 volts is presumably given by equation 3.

$$\frac{2\pi e^4 Z^2}{mV^2}\, nz\, \frac{dw}{w^2} \tag{3}$$

which is equal to

$$3210\, \frac{Z^2 M}{E}\, \frac{dw}{w^2} \quad \begin{array}{l} \text{δ-rays per micron in water in the} \\ \text{energy range } w \text{ to } w + dw \end{array}$$

where w is the transferred energy in electron volts, E the incident particle energy in million electron volts, M the incident particle mass in atomic weight units, and Z the charge. Here the contribution from the K-electrons of oxygen have been neglected.

The total energy carried by these δ-rays may be calculated from the integrated form of equation 3, given by equation 5, with $w_{min} = 100$ ev. Comparison with the Bethe-Bloch equation for the total energy lost (equation 7), with $I = 70$ ev for water, shows that almost precisely half the incident particle energy is carried away by these δ-rays of energy of 100 ev or greater.

The upper limit, w_{max}, to the energy of a δ-ray is given by conservation of momentum in the collision, and for incident heavy particles it is

$$w_{max} = 4 \frac{m}{M} E$$

For electrons the upper limit to the δ-rays is half the energy of the incident electron, since—as remarked before—the highest-energy electron emerging from the collision will be considered as the primary.

The δ-rays are projected initially at an angle, θ, to the path of the incident particle given by

$$\cos^2 \theta = \frac{w}{w_{max}} \tag{23}$$

Thus the maximum energy recoil is initially directed down the track. The scattering of electrons is so important, however, that the δ-rays appear to come off in all directions. The maximum distance any δ-ray can ionize from the track would be given by the practical range of the electron having the maximum recoil energy.

Once the energy has dropped below the ionization threshold, the δ-ray will quickly lose most of the rest of its energy by a few collisions in which excitations are produced. The rate of loss of energy by electrons whose energy is less than that needed to excite electronic transitions is very low. These electrons, called subexcitation electrons by Platzman (67), can lose energy only by excitation of oscillation modes of the lattice (68) or, in dipolar materials, to dipolar relaxation (69). For water both processes are of the same order of magnitude, and for electrons with energies of 1 to 5 ev they lead to rates of energy loss of the order of 0.1 ev per 100 A, compared with 100 ev per 100 A for electrons of a few hundred volts of energy and capable of ionizing. For media with relatively fixed dipoles, such as ice, the dipolar relaxation becomes negligible, but the excitation of oscillation is not much changed. With such low energy losses the range of such subexcitation electrons is very large—of the order of $10^3 A$. The distance between the start and the end of the track will be much smaller than this, because of the very large scattering.

Multiple ionization, or the ejection of two or more electrons from the same atom, is a process which occurs with a frequency of the order of 10^{-2} to 10^{-4} relative to single ionization events (70). It can take place either by direct excitation of two different electrons by the incident primary, or by the Auger effect. In the latter effect, when a K-electron is removed by the incident ion, an L-electron drops down into the K-shell. The excess energy, instead of being radiated as characteristic X-rays, is transferred to another L-electron by a radiationless process, resulting in the double ionization of an atom. For all the light elements such an Auger process occurs for about 99% of the K-shell ionizations. Platzman (70) has calculated that for a 3-Mev proton in water 80 K-shell ionizations (and therefore 80 Auger electrons) are produced, out of a total of 10^5 ionizations, and that 4% of the total energy is lost by the primary in these interactions.

5. ENERGY EXPENDED PER ION PAIR

The most significant point about the average energy absorbed per ion pair formed in a gas is its unusual constancy, with respect to both the type of radiation used and the kind of gas molecule. This general constancy is shown by the data in Table VIII for the variation in this energy expenditure in air for different radiations, and in Table IX for the variation with gas molecule for three types of radiation.

The values in the tables are all relatively recent data and vary somewhat from the earlier figures, most especially for the rare gases such as helium. Jesse and Sadauskis (84) showed that the then-accepted energy of about 30 ev per ion pair for helium was actually caused by a small contamination of argon atoms being ionized by energy transferred to them in collision with metastable helium atoms. Thus the measured energy per ion pair is not so constant for different gases today as the earlier measurements indicated, but the variation is still surprisingly small. The constancy with type of radiation is even more striking. Although there appears to be a very small increase of about 1 ev in going from the highest-energy electrons to the lowest, it would be difficult to maintain that the variation was an

TABLE VIII

ENERGY PER ION PAIR IN AIR FOR DIFFERENT RADIATIONS

Radiation	Electron volts per ion pair	Ref.
22-Mev X-rays	32.8 ± 0.6	(71)
17.5-Mev X-rays	33	(72)
P^{32} β-rays (max. energy = 1.7 Mev)	33.5	(73)
Co^{60} γ-rays (1.2 Mev)	33.0 ± 0.3	(74)
2-Mev X-rays	33.9	(75)
S^{35} β-rays (max. energy = 167 kev)	33.6 ± 0.3	(76)
	33.7 ± 0.3	(77)
	34.1	(78)
C^{14} β-rays (max. energy = 155 kev)	34.0	(78)
Ni^{63} β-rays (max. energy = 67 kev)	34.1	(78)
H^3 β-rays (max. energy = 18 kev)	33.9	(78)
Po^{210} α-particles (5.4 Mev)	35.5	(78)
Pu^{239} α-particles (5.24 Mev)	35.0	(79)

TABLE IX

ENERGY PER ION PAIR FOR SEVERAL GASES FOR THREE DIFFERENT RADIATIONS
(Numbers in parentheses are reference numbers.)

Gas	Ionization potential	β-rays (average of several energies) (78)	Po^{210} α-rays (5.4 Mev) (78)	ThC recoils (117 kev) (81)
He	24.58 ev (82)	42.3 ev	42.7 ev	
Ne	21.56 (82)	36.6	36.8	
A	15.76 (82)	26.4	26.4	
Kr	14.00 (82)	24.2	24.1	
Xe	12.13 (82)	22.0	21.9	
H$_2$	15.42 (83)	36.3	36.3	81 ev
Air	—	34.0	35.5	
N$_2$	15.58 (83)	35.0	36.6	
O$_2$	12.08 (60)	30.9	32.5	
CO$_2$	13.79 (60)	32.9	34.5	102
C$_2$H$_4$	10.51 (60)	26.2	28.0	104
C$_2$H$_6$	11.65 (60)	24.8	26.6	
CH$_4$	12.99 (60)	27.3	29.2	111
C$_2$H$_2$	11.41 (60)	25.9	27.5	
H$_2$O	12.59 (60)	30.0 (80)		

actual one, and not a consequence of different techniques in different laboratories. The increase for all gases except the rare gases for α-particles seems quite clear, although it is only a few per cent. Only with the thorium C recoil nuclei, with a velocity equivalent to that of an electron of energy 0.3 ev, is the increase a spectacular one.

It must be emphasized that these data are all for gases only. No really reliable data appear to exist for either liquids or solids, but those bits of evidence that do exist tend to support the concept that the energy per ion pair in a solid or liquid is of the order of 25 to 30 ev. Mohler and Taylor (85) have reported a mean energy per ion pair in liquid carbon disulfide of 24 ev, compared to 26 ev for the vapor phase, but the figure is dependent on certain theoretical assumptions. Sternglass found that his theory for the production of secondary electrons by incident electrons (86) and positive ions (87) gave results in reasonable agreement with experiment if he assumed that an electron is set free in a solid for each 30 ev absorbed from the incident radiation. To support this assumption of 30 ev per ion pair in a liquid or solid it can be argued that condensation of a gas changes the energy levels of the molecules by amounts which are less than the differences in the various gases listed in Table IX. Since most of the gases in the table need of the order of 30 ev per ion pair, this line of reasoning would lead to the same, or perhaps slightly lower, values for condensed media.

6. THE ION CLUSTER

From the preceding sections may be seen the spatial pattern of the energy release from the passage of charged particles—the track, the primary ionizations along it, and an occasional δ-ray branching out, the whole marked out by the ionizations. Another characteristic which may be observed is the ion cluster, which will be defined in rather vague terms as a group of ions "closely" spaced together.

Consider the case of a fast (∼1-Mev) electron passing through matter. The rate of energy loss is of the order of 3 ev per 100 A, and the primary ionizations will be thousands of angstroms apart. From integration of equation 3 [or from a more accurate form (14) which takes into account exchange terms in electron-electron scattering] it may readily be determined that about 40 % of the total energy lost is carried away by events involving the transfer of 100 ev or more, amounting to about 7 % of the total number of collisions. For an over-all figure of 100 ev per primary ionization, this amounts to 60 ev expended per ion cluster formed along the track, the remaining 40 ev of the 100 ev per primary ionization being the kinetic energy of the δ-rays.

If the energy carried away by the δ-rays is considered to form separate ion clusters with the same efficiency, then the over-all energy per cluster will be the same 60 ev. In fact, the slower δ-rays will probably produce more cases of ionizations so close together that the number of recognizable clusters formed will be considerably reduced. Suppose, for example, 40 ev put into δ-rays produces only half as many clusters, or $\frac{1}{2} \times (40/60) = 0.33$ clusters; then the over-all efficiency would be $(60 + 40)/(1 + 0.33) = 75$ ev per ion cluster, which might be regarded as a reasonable estimate for fast electrons and X-rays.

In discussing the distribution in space of energy release, it might be well to mention the distribution of excitations. An average of 30 ev is needed to produce an ionization requiring 10 to 15 ev, which leads to an estimate of 3 to 4 excitations of 5 ev per ion formed. Since there is reason to believe (Section II.C.2) that few excitations are produced by rapidly moving charges, it may be concluded that most of the excitations are produced by very slow electrons and will thus be located very near the ion clusters.

D. DISTRIBUTION OF ENERGY RELEASE IN A CHARGED-PARTICLE BEAM

In a collimated beam of heavy charged particles each ion will in general penetrate in a straight line to its full range. The outstanding characteristics

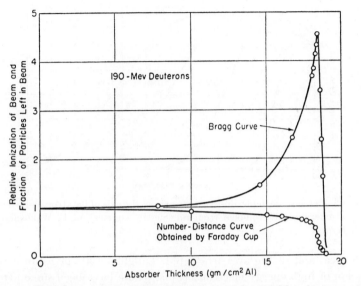

FIG. 11. Bragg curve and number-distance curve for 190-Mev deuterons in aluminum. Reprinted from ref. 87a by courtesy of C. A. Tobias and *American Journal of Roentgenology, Radium Therapy and Nuclear Medicine.*

will be the preservation of the initial collimation and the rapid rise in energy release at the end of the range, the so-called Bragg curve shown in Fig. 11. The rise in ionization, caused by the increasing energy loss with decreasing energy, would be even more spectacular without the range straggling, shown in the lower curve. In the curve pictured, the slow fall-off in numbers over most of the curve is caused by inelastic collisions of the incident deuterons with nuclei. Incident particles of lower energy will not make enough of these inelastic collisions to be noticeable, and the number-distance curve will be as in Fig. 5.

Accounts have been given (88, 89) of the various factors involved in dosimetry of such beams. A point of some importance is the fact that the LET is quite well defined at any place in the beam except right at the Bragg peak.

High-energy electron beams are immensely more complicated because of the scattering of the incident electrons. The general course of the energy release along the axis is shown by the curves in Fig. 12. A moderate rise in dose is followed by a relatively flat maximum, which is then followed by a long, almost linear drop, reaching a small value at about the practical electron range defined in an earlier section. At the same time, the beam cross-sectional area spreads out with increasing depth.

The change in dose with depth and the spreading of the beam are both complicated functions of the beam energy, of the initial intensity distribu-

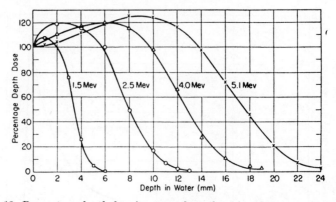

Fig. 12. Percentage depth dose in water along the axis of betatron electron beams for several energies. Reproduced from ref. 89a by courtesy of F. Wachsmann and *Strahlentherapie*.

tion in area, and of the area irradiated. Laughlin (90) gives an extended discussion of high-energy electron beams. There have been some attempts to calculate dosage distributions in these beams (91).

III. Radiation Dosimetry

In this section dosimetry refers to a measure of the amounts of radiation delivered, without reference to other characteristics of the radiation which might profoundly affect the biological response, such as the mean spacing between primary events, or the linear energy transfer (LET).

Any effect produced by ionizing radiation which can be measured quantitatively may be used as the basis for a method of dosimetry. The discussion which follows is centered on those methods which seem to be of most importance to radiobiologists. For an extensive discussion of dosimetry the reader is referred to the book "Radiation Dosimetry" (2).

A. Ionization Methods

1. THE ROENTGEN

The most obvious unit to use in measuring ionizing radiation is the ionization produced. Only the ionization produced in gases can be measured (except in certain special cases), and the most commonly used unit, the roentgen, is based on the ionization produced in air. As adopted by the Congress of Radiology in Chicago, 1937, "The roentgen shall be the quantity of X- or gamma-radiation such that the associated corpuscular emission per 0.001293 gm of air produces, in air, ions carrying 1 esu of quantity of electricity of either sign."

The intensity of an X-ray or γ-ray beam may be measured by a "free-air ionization chamber" (2, 92, 93), in which the ionization produced in a small, well-defined volume of air is measured as an electrical current. The arrangement is such that there are no electrodes, or any matter except air, near the volume from which the ionization is collected, so that no corrections are needed for scattered electrons. Free-air chambers are regularly used as primary standards but are not practical for use in routine measurements.

2. THE BRAGG-GRAY CHAMBER

In ordinary dose determination, the ionization produced in a small "thimble" chamber, or Bragg-Gray cavity, is used. The principle is as follows (2, 94, 95):

Assume a very small gas-filled cavity within a homogeneous medium. By "very small" is meant a cavity so small that its presence does not appreciably affect the spectrum of the electrons released in the cavity walls by the ionizing radiation. In traversing the cavity these electrons will release in the gas an amount of energy per unit mass equal to $J_g W_g$, where J_g is the number of ions per unit mass of gas, and W_g is the energy needed to produce an ion. The energy release per unit mass in the walls, E_w , will be this energy multiplied by the ratio of the mean stopping powers per unit mass, $\bar{s}_w$ and $\bar{s}_g$, for electrons in the wall material and in the gas, or

$$E_w = J_g W_g \, \frac{\bar{s}_w}{\bar{s}_g} \qquad (24)$$

Thus the ionization measurement gives a measurement of the energy released in the wall material by the incident radiation

In the case that the wall material is "air-equivalent" so that its radiation absorption is the same function of photon energy as that of air, such a chamber may be used to measure radiation in roentgens. If the gas in the chamber is air, then the complications introduced by the relative stopping powers in equation 24 are removed. A well-known example of this kind of chamber is the Victoreen chamber, but many variants of this general design have been used.

In practice, the construction of chambers which adhere strictly to the principles given above is not always practicable—for example, chambers are frequently made larger than would conform to the discussion given above, to give more ions to measure. Furthermore, it is not clear that it is possible to make a cavity which will have *no* effect on the electron spectrum (96). For these reasons, it is usual to check such cavities experimentally against free-air chambers.

The walls of a cavity chamber must be thicker than the range of the highest-energy electron released, so that the spectrum at the cavity is the equilibrium distribution. A common practical case here is the necessity of adding a 3-mm plastic cap to the Victoreen chamber designed for 200-kv X-rays, so that measurements may be made at 2 Mev. On the other hand, too thick a wall will attenuate the X-rays passing through it, giving too low a reading. This is a serious difficulty in the dosimetry of X-rays below 100 kv.

B. Energy Absorption

It is to be noted that in fact the thimble chamber method really gives a measurement of energy absorption. From many points of view it would seem that, if the energy absorbed in a medium appears to be the most fundamental measure of radiation effect, it would be simplest to use a unit based on this, rather than one depending on a related effect (ionization) in an arbitrary substance (air). Furthermore, a unit based on energy absorption would be applicable to types of radiation, such as neutrons, for which the roentgen cannot be used.

1. THE RAD

In 1953, the International Commission on Radiological Units recommended the adoption of a unit of absorbed dose, the rad, defined as the absorption of an amount of energy equal to 100 ergs/gm. For comparison, the energy absorbed in a gram of air by 1 roentgen (r) may be calculated from the definition given above and the latest value of 34 ev per ion pair in air (Table VIII). This gives 87.5 ergs/gm of air, or 0.875 rad.

2. CALORIMETRY

From the very way in which the rad is defined, the most obvious method of measurement to use would be calorimetry, in which the temperature rise caused by the energy absorption is determined. One hundred rads corresponds to the absorption of 2.4×10^{-4} cal/gm. Even for water, which has an unusually high specific heat corresponding to a 1°C temperature rise for the absorption of 1 cal/gm, this is a temperature rise of 2.4×10^{-4} °C, a rise which can be readily measured with accuracy under suitable conditions.

Several devices for the calorimetric measurement of radiation have been built (Chapter 9 of ref. 2). In general, these consist of a block in which the beam energy is absorbed, the block being insulated by a surrounding vacuum chamber, which in turn is enclosed by a thermostated water bath. The temperature rise of the block under irradiation is measured by suitable devices such as a thermistor or resistance thermometer and is calibrated in absolute terms by an electrical heating coil fed with measured amounts of power.

The calorimetric measurement of energy locally absorbed at some particular point in a radiation field has been accomplished (97), but the techniques need considerable development before the method can be generally useful.

C. A COMPARISON OF RADIATION UNITS

1. THE ROENTGEN AND THE RAD

It is important to recognize the difference between the roentgen, measuring the amount of radiation delivered, and the rad, which specifies the energy absorbed by the target material. As an example, consider the doses in rads delivered to various tissues after exposure to 1 r of X-rays, as shown in Table X. The variation is seen to be quite considerable, especially for bone at low photon energies.

It should also be emphasized that the roentgen is a unit applicable only to X-rays and γ-rays. Actually, because of limitations on the design of free-air chambers, it is well defined only for photons below 3 Mev in energy. The rad, however, is equally applicable to any type of radiation.

2. OTHER UNITS

A unit which might well be mentioned at this time is the rep, or roentgen-equivalent-physical. The intent behind the introduction of the rep was to have a unit which would measure dose in terms of energy absorbed, and at the same time would be numerically equal to the roentgen in specifying tissue doses delivered by X- or γ-rays. Unfortunately, at various times it has been defined in various ways in terms of energy absorption in air, in water, and in tissue, and in ways that are not necessarily compatible with each other. The rad as now defined supersedes the rep, which is now only of historical interest because of the large amount of work in the literature in which it has been employed.

The rem, or roentgen-equivalent-man, is a unit which is fairly widely used despite the fact that it has not been officially defined. Generally speaking, a dose of 1 rem from a given radiation is considered to be that dose which will produce the same effect in man as 1 r of 250-kv X-rays. It compensates for the different biological effectiveness of radiations with greatly different effective LET's and is used when it is necessary to add the doses received from two such radiations.

For irradiations with charged particles or with neutrons it is sometimes convenient to give dosages in terms of the flux, in particles per square centimeter, for example. In this case, a complete specification of the dosage requires the energy of the particles used.

TABLE X

ABSORBED DOSE PER ROENTGEN BY BIOLOGICAL MATERIALS
(Based on 34.0 ev per ion pair in air, calculated from Table VI, p. 88, ref. 2.)

Photon energy (Mev)	Energy absorption (ergs/gm/r)		
	Water (muscle)	Fat	Bone
0.010	90.5	46.3	495.8
0.015	89.6	47.6	495.8
0.020	88.0	48.5	494.8
0.030	87.6	51.1	467.6
0.040	88.4	57.7	419.4
0.050	89.6	67.0	347.3
0.060	91.9	76.4	277.2
0.080	94.1	89.2	178.9
0.100	95.2	95.4	132.8
0.150	97.0	99.7	98.8
0.20	97.4	100.7	91.8
0.30	97.4	101.3	88.4
0.40	97.5	101.3	87.6
0.50	97.5	101.3	87.3
0.60	97.5	101.3	87.3
0.80	97.5	101.3	87.3
1.00	97.5	101.3	87.3
1.50	97.5	101.3	87.3
2.0	97.5	101.0	87.3
3	97.3	100.2	88.4
4	96.7	98.8	89.6
5	96.1	97.5	91.0
6	95.6	96.4	92.2
8	95.0	94.5	94.6
10	94.3	92.3	96.7
15	93.1	87.9	100.6
20	92.2	85.4	104.0
30	90.8	81.8	107.7
40	89.6	79.6	109.8
50	88.8	78.2	111.9
60	88.1	77.2	113.0
80	87.4	75.9	114.0
100	87.0	74.8	115.1

3. THE GRAM-RAD

A completely different type of unit is one in which the total or integral dose absorbed by the irradiated organism is given, instead of the dose at a given point. The unit is the gram-rad, and the integral dose in gram-rads is simply the dose expressed in rads to each individual gram of material, summed over the total mass. It is thus equal to the total energy, in units of 100 ergs, absorbed by the irradiated body.

Mayneord (98) originally defined the gram-roentgen as the amount of energy absorbed in a gram of air irradiated with 1 r, an amount of energy then considered to be equal to 83 ergs/gm. The unit has been used ambiguously by many—by some as defined above, by some as though it were a gram-rep (which would be an energy absorption of 93 ergs/gm of tissue), and by others as the product of the number of grams exposed multiplied by the exposure in roentgens. To avoid such confusion, only the gram-rad should be used.

D. OTHER METHODS OF MEASURING DOSE

1. THE CHEMICAL DOSIMETER

The good understanding of certain radiochemical reactions occurring in dilute solution has made their use for dosimetry very attractive. In addition to their good reproducibility, solutions have practical advantages in measuring dosages in irradiation vessels. A number of reactions are suitable (see Chapter II for a detailed discussion), but one is used far more than any other. This is the aerated ferrous sulfate solution in 0.8 N sulfuric acid, in which the over-all action is the conversion of Fe^{++} to Fe^{+++} (99). Weiss et al. (99) give the following prescription for the solution: 2 gm of $FeSO_4 \cdot 7H_2O$ or $Fe(NH_4)_2(SO_4)_2 \cdot 6H_2O$; 0.3 gm of NaCl; 110 ml of concentrated (95 to 98%) H_2SO_4 (analytical reagent-grade); and sufficient distilled water to make 5 liters of solution. The yield for sparsely ionizing radiation is 15.45 atoms of Fe^{+++} formed per 100 ev absorbed, or 16.0 μM per 1000 rads. The amount of Fe^{+++} formed can be determined by measuring the optical density, OD, of the solution at 305 mμ. The molar extinction coefficient, ϵ, of Fe^{+++} is 2174 at 23.7°C, with a temperature coefficient of $+0.7\%$ per degree centigrade. The dose delivered can be calculated from the equation

$$\text{Rads} = \frac{10^9(OD_{\text{sample}} - OD_{\text{blank}})}{16.0\epsilon} \qquad (25)$$

The dosimeter is useful over a total dosage range of 4000 to 40,000 rads. The lower limit is set by the necessity of forming enough Fe^{+++} for accurate reading of the optical density. The upper limit is set by the depletion of the dissolved oxygen in the solution, with a consequent change in the over-all yield of the reaction. The readings are surprisingly independent of the presence of impurities. Since the solution is a dilute one, the radiant energy is absorbed in the water, so that the variation in absorbed dose with the energy of the radiation will be the same as in biological systems. The response is independent of dose rate up to rates of 10^{10} rads/sec (100) but is, unfortunately, dependent on the LET of the radiation, which complicates the use for radiations other than electrons and X- or γ-radiation of energy above about 50 kv. (100a).

2. MISCELLANEOUS METHODS

Many other methods of dosimetry are in use (see ref. 2). For irradiations with charged particles, the total charge delivered is commonly used. Geiger-Mueller and scintillation counters are used, particularly to measure very low levels. Photographic methods are the oldest of all forms, since X-rays were discovered by Roentgen and radioactivity by Becquerel with photographic plates as detectors. They are still in use, and the measurement of heavy-particle fluxes by using special emulsions in which the tracks of the particles can be counted individually is only one recent development in this field.

Irradiation has measurable effects on properties of semiconductors, such as conductivity. It seems highly likely that within the near future devices employing semiconductors will be in use for long-lived, rugged, and compact radiation-measuring instruments.

For very-high-energy radiation, the induction of radioactivity in the target is sometimes a most convenient method of dosimetry. Both the total dosage and the distribution of the dosage in various parts of the target may be determined by counting or by radioautography.

IV. X-Rays and Gamma Rays

A. FUNDAMENTAL INTERACTIONS BETWEEN PHOTONS AND MATTER

The ways in which photons can interact with matter are most usually described in terms of a parameter called the cross section, which refers to the probability per atom that an incident photon interacts. The probability that a photon is absorbed in a thin layer of atoms is given by the product of the cross section multiplied by the number of atoms per unit area in the layer. The unit for specifying such a cross section is that of area per atom; for the processes to be discussed in this section a natural unit to use is 10^{-24} cm^2 per atom, a unit which occurs so often in nuclear physics that it has received a special name, the barn.

1. PHOTOELECTRIC EFFECT

In this process the incident photon is absorbed completely in an inter-action with one of the electronic shells in the absorbing atom, the end result being the emission of an electron having an energy equal to that of the photon minus the binding energy of the electron in the atom. For photons having an energy less than the binding energy of a given electronic shell, no photoelectric effect can take place. The effect in a given shell is maximum for a photon just able to eject the electron and drops off very rapidly with increasing energy above this critical level. The decrease with increasing energy is so rapid that in general most of the absorption is by the most tightly bound electrons which can take part, usually those in the innermost or K-shell.

No simple expression for the magnitude of the photoelectric effect is available. Theoretical expressions are available for the low-energy region and for energies above 2 Mev. In the intervening region there are several numerical calculations. The reader is referred to the reviews of Grodstein (101) and of Davisson and Evans (102) for details and for extensive tables. The calculated values are in quite satisfactory agreement with experiment.

Davisson and Evans (102) report that the photoelectric cross section varies roughly as Z to a power lying between 4 and 5. They also report that the cross section decreases as the inverse cube of the photon energy in the region 50 to 300 kev, but only as the inverse first power of the energy above 1 Mev.

When a K-electron is ejected from an atom of low atomic weight, such as is met with in biological material, the excitation energy of the atom is usually dissipated by the emission of an additional, or Auger, electron in an internal radiationless transfer of the energy to an outer-shell electron (103). In a heavy material such as lead this excitation energy appears as an emitted photon whose energy is characteristic of the emitting atom and is called for this reason a characteristic X-ray.

2. COMPTON EFFECT

In the classical Compton effect, the process is the collision between an incident photon and an electron whose binding energy is small enough to be neglected. In such an encounter the ordinary laws of conservation of energy and momentum apply, and the end result is an electron scattered at some angle, and the photon scattered at another. The energy of the scattered photon is given by the difference between the energy of the inci-dent photon and the energy of the scattered electron. Because the energy of the scattered photon is less than that of the incident, its wavelength is increased, an increase which is given by

$$\Delta\lambda = \frac{h}{mc}(1 - \cos\varphi) \qquad (26)$$

where φ is the angle between the direction of the incident and of the scattered photon, and h is Planck's constant.

The cross section, dS_t, for the number of photons scattered at angle φ into solid angle $d\Omega$ per atomic electron is given by the Klein-Nishina equation (102):

$$dS_t = \frac{e^4}{2m^2c^4}\left[\frac{1}{1 + \alpha(1 - \cos\varphi)}\right]^2\left[1 + \cos^2\varphi + \frac{\alpha^2(1 - \cos\varphi)^2}{1 + \alpha(1 - \cos\varphi)}\right]d\Omega \quad (27)$$

where $\alpha = h\nu/mc^2$, the incident photon energy in units of the electron rest energy.

In considering the Compton effect we must distinguish between three cross sections. The first, S_t, is obtained by the integration of equation 27 over all angles and represents the total probability of scattering a photon out of a collimated beam. The second, S_a, represents the fraction of the incident energy which is absorbed by the scattering medium—that is, the fraction of the incident energy transferred to the recoil electrons. The third cross section, S_s, refers to the fraction of the incident energy which is scattered in the form of photons and is obviously equal to the difference of the first two cross sections.

When the energy transferred to the atomic electron becomes low enough, the assumption that the target electrons are free is no longer valid, and the influence of the electron-binding energies must be taken into account. The over-all effect is a decrease in the amount of inelastic (or incoherent) scattering from that predicted by the Klein-Nishina formula and the introduction of coherently scattered radiation of the same energy as the incident photon (101). The total probability of a photon's being scattered rises somewhat above that predicted by the Klein-Nishina law. The coherent scattering is obviously least important at high photon energies and for light elements in which the electron-binding energies are small. For oxygen, the heaviest element present in large quantities in tissue, the coherent scattering is 3% of the Compton scattering at 100 kev, rising to 50% at 10 kev.

The theory of the Compton effect, with the exception of the coherent scattering at low energies, has been exhaustively checked by experiment. Complete tables are available, giving numerical values for various properties of the scattered photons and of the recoil electrons (101, 102, 104).

3. PAIR PRODUCTION

The energy associated with an electron at rest is equal to mc^2, an energy of 0.511 Mev. A photon having an energy greater than twice this amount,

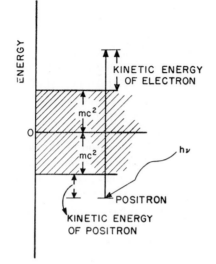

FIG. 13. A schematic diagram of the process of pair production by a high energy photon of energy $h\nu$, according to the Dirac formalism.

or 1.02 Mev, can interact with a strong electric field and convert part of that energy into mass, with both an electron and a positron appearing so so that charge is conserved. The photon energy in excess of 1.02 Mev appears as kinetic energy of the particles produced.

In the Dirac theory of the electron, it is considered that an electron can exist in either positive or negative energy states (Fig. 13). The negative energy states are normally completely filled, and, since the electrons in these states cannot ordinarily exchange energy with their surroundings, they cannot be observed. A photon of sufficient energy, however, can lift an electron into a positive energy state as shown, leaving a positively charged "hole" behind. It may be shown that this hole will have all the observed properties of a positron.

The probability is small that an electron in a positive energy state (i.e., an observable electron) will make a transition to a low-lying negative energy level corresponding to a positron of considerable kinetic energy. Thus the positron normally continues to exist until it has been slowed down by the processes already described for charged particles, and occupies an energy level close to the top of the negative energy band. For these levels the transition probabilities are quite large, and a slow electron in the vicinity of the "hole" or positron will promptly make the downward transition, getting rid of its excess energy by radiation. Two photons, each of energy 0.511 Mev, are ordinarily emitted in opposite directions to conserve momentum. These photons are sometimes referred to as annihilation radiation.

Pair production most frequently takes place in the intense electric field surrounding a nucleus. The theory leads to quite complicated expressions for the cross section for the process. It does show that the cross section varies approximately as z^2, or square of the charge on the nucleus, and is a monotonically increasing function of the energy of the incident photon. The various theoretical expressions are discussed in refs. 101 and 102, which also give extensive tables of the cross sections and show the generally good agreement of the theory with experiment.

Pair production may also take place in the field surrounding an electron. In this case an appreciable fraction of the energy involved is transmitted to the target electron, to conserve momentum in the process. Thus three charged particles, two electrons and a positron, are set in motion. This is sometimes referred to as triplet formation. Because of the energy given to the electron, the process has a threshold of twice that of pair production, or 2.04 Mev. It is most important in low-atomic-weight materials such as water because of the smaller pair production in the field of the low-z nuclei.

4. NUCLEAR PHOTODISINTEGRATION

This process consists in the absorption of a photon by a nucleus, followed by some kind of nuclear reaction, usually the emission of a neutron or proton. Photodisintegration has a threshold of the order of 15 to 20 Mev for most light elements. The cross section rises to a maximum, then drops off again with increasing photon energy, the total width of the peak being the order of 5 to 8 Mev. In Tables XI and XII some data are given on the magnitude of these cross sections, compared with the cross sections for the other processes. It is seen that in general even at the maximum of the photoeffect peak the process absorbs only a few per cent of the flux.

5. THE TOTAL ABSORPTION COEFFICIENT

This is obtained by summing the cross sections for all the four processes discussed. For practical computations a useful form is the linear absorption coefficient, μ, which is obtained by summing the cross sections for all the elementary processes, and multiplying by the number of atoms per unit

TABLE XI

PHOTONEUTRON CROSS SECTION FOR CARBON AS A FUNCTION OF ENERGY (101)

Photon energy (Mev)	21	22	23	24	25	26
Photoneutron cross section (barns)	0.002	0.009	0.013	0.009	0.005	0.003
Total cross section (barns)		0.303	0.300	0.297	0.294	0.292	0.289

TABLE XII

PHOTODISINTEGRATION CROSS SECTIONS

(From Chapter 2 of ref. 2)

Nucleus	Reaction	Threshold energy (Mev)	Energy of peak cross section (Mev)	Peak cross section (barns)	Pair and Compton cross section at peak (barns)
C^{12}	(γ, n)	18.6	22.9	0.013	0.307
	(γ, p)	16.0	21.5	0.034	
N^{14}	(γ, n)	16.5	24.2	0.0028	0.379
O^{16}	(γ, n)	15.6	24.2	0.011	0.461
Cu^{63}	(γ, n)	10.9	18.1	0.10	3.56
Pb (natural)	(γ, n)	7.9	13.7	0.81	18.8

TABLE XIII

X-RAY MASS ABSORPTION COEFFICIENTS FOR VARIOUS ELEMENTS

(Taken from the extensive compilation of Grodstein, ref. 101)

Energy (Mev)	Mass absorption coefficient (cm²/gm)							
	H	C	N	O	Al	Ca	Cu	Pb
0.01	0.385	2.28	3.80	5.93	26.8	96.9	225.0	84.6
0.03	0.357	0.252	0.301	0.371	1.13	4.16	11.1	23.5
0.05	0.335	0.185	0.194	0.208	0.360	0.998	2.56	5.73
0.10	0.295	0.152	0.154	0.156	0.169	0.257	0.461	5.47
0.30	0.212	0.107	0.107	0.107	0.104	0.112	0.112	0.377
0.50	0.173	0.087	0.0869	0.0870	0.0844	0.0885	0.0834	0.152
1.0	0.126	0.0636	0.0636	0.0636	0.0614	0.0637	0.0589	0.0704
2.0	0.0876	0.0444	0.0445	0.0445	0.0432	0.0451	0.0418	0.0463
5.0	0.0502	0.0270	0.0273	0.0276	0.0282	0.0316	0.0316	0.0426
10	0.0321	0.0194	0.0200	0.0206	0.0229	0.0280	0.0305	0.0489
20	0.0209	0.0154	0.0163	0.0173	0.0212	0.0285	0.0334	0.0611
50	0.0133	0.0138	0.0152	0.0165	0.0225	0.0326	0.0404	0.0805
100	0.0109	0.0141	0.0158	0.0175	0.0247	0.0366	0.0460	0.0939

volume. About as helpful, and employed almost exclusively for the purposes of tabulation, is the mass absorption coefficient, μ/ρ, where ρ is the density. A feature of the mass absorption coefficient is that it is roughly the same for all light materials for photons from about 30 kev to 30 Mev. The reason is that for this energy range the absorption process is mainly the Compton effect, which depends only on the number of electrons per gram, which is approximately constant for all materials except hydrogen.

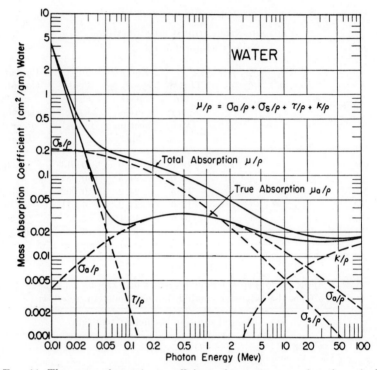

FIG. 14. The mass absorption coefficients for water as a function of photon energy: σ_s and σ_a are the coefficients for Compton scattering and for Compton absorption, i.e., the energy transferred to the electron; τ is the coefficient for photoelectric absorption; and K is the coefficient for pair production. Reprinted from ref. 2 by courtesy of H. E. Johns.

In Table XIII are listed some absorption coefficients for a number of substances. In Fig. 14 is shown the absorption coefficient for water as a function of energy, with the contributions from the various processes indicated separately. A distinction is made between the total absorption coefficient, which includes all the processes which remove a photon from the beam, and the "true" absorption coefficient, which is a measure of the energy which is locally absorbed from the beam.

B. Properties of X- and Gamma-Ray Beams

1. photon energy distribution

X-Ray photons produced by the deceleration of electrons in a target have energies between zero and the full energy of a single incident electron. The most energetic photons are the fewest in number, with a monotonic increase to a maximum at very low energies. Superposed on this continuous radiation spectrum or bremsstrahlung are the sharp peaks of characteristic radiation produced by excited inner shells in the atoms of the target material. By proper arrangement of target materials, filters, and voltage it is possible to get a substantial part of the energy into a single characteristic peak, but ordinarily the continuous radiation carries nearly all the energy.

Filtration by absorption of the radiation within the target and in the wall of the X-ray tube modifies the original spectrum into a bell-shaped distribution (see Fig. 15). In addition, it is useful in many cases to add filters of some material having a rapidly rising photoelectric absorption in the photon energy region toward the lower part of the spectrum. This filter selectively absorbs the "softer" or lower-energy photons. In Fig. 15 are given the distributions in energy of some X-ray beams which are commonly used.

X-Ray beams in the energy range of 50 to 500 kv are customarily specified in terms of their absorption in a specified material. The number usually given is the half-value layer (HVL), or the thickness needed to reduce the beam to half the original intensity. An absorption curve for these radiations is not an exponential, because of the "hardening" effect on the heterogeneous beam, but the specification in terms of the thickness needed to reduce

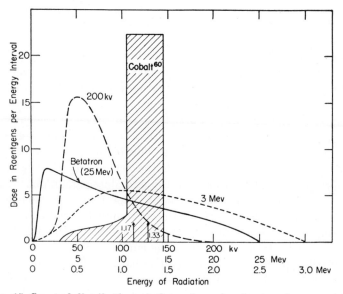

FIG. 15. Spectral distributions at the surface of a phantom for several different kinds of high-energy radiation. The distribution for 200 kv X-rays is derived from the absorption curve in copper by the method due to Greening (105). The 3 Mev and 25 Mev X-ray curves are calculated. The "tail" on the Co⁶⁰ X-ray distribution is from scattered radiation. Reprinted from ref. 2 by courtesy of H. E. Johns.

the beam to half, i.e., the first part of the absorption curve, seems to work reasonably well in practice. Below about 175 kv the HVL is usually given in millimeters of aluminum, and for higher energies in millimeters of copper. It would be far more rational to specify the half-value layer in water, or in a waterlike substance such as Lucite. Not only does this give the absorption in the material of interest, but also the absorption curves are more nearly exponential, because of the very small hardening effect of the Compton effect in water (compare Fig. 14).

As a beam of either heterogeneous X-rays or monochromatic γ-rays passes through matter, the photon energy distribution is continually shifting toward the low-energy side, owing to Compton scattering—and, in the case of million-electron-volt radiation, pair production and consequent annihilation radiation. The resulting spectrum at a given depth may be calculated by Monte Carlo techniques or by analytical methods (106).

2. ELECTRON SPECTRA

The spectrum in energy of the electrons set in motion in a biological material by an X- or γ-ray beam may be readily calculated if the spectral distribution of the photons is known. This is because in general the photon interactions are through the Compton effect, for which the theory is quite reliable.

The direct measurement of the electron spectra in tissue is reasonably simple. A crystal of a scintillating material whose absorption is similar to water, such as anthracene, can be viewed through a Lucite light pipe by a photomultiplier, and the observed pulse heights can be converted directly into electron energies by a simple calibration procedure. Shown in Fig. 16 are electron spectra taken in this manner at various distances from a cobalt-60 source immersed in a water tank (107). The agreement between the observed and the calculated spectra is to be noted. The large number of low-energy electrons is quite striking. This method can also be followed in deducing photon spectra, although the reverse calculation is not so straightforward as that mentioned in the preceding paragraph.

From a radiobiological standpoint an important consequence of the wide variation in electron energies is the concomitant variation in the LET of the electrons which actually do the ionizing. Shown in Fig. 17 are the distributions in LET calculated from the curves in Fig. 15 for the photon energy distribution for several different radiations. The figure shows that the variation in LET for radiations above about 1 Mev is not large and is about the same for all radiations. For the 200-kv radiation, however, a wide variation in LET is shown, with a substantial amount of the energy released by electrons having LET's of an order of magnitude higher than that characteristic of megavoltage radiation. For X-rays of lower energy, of course, the effective LET will be even higher.

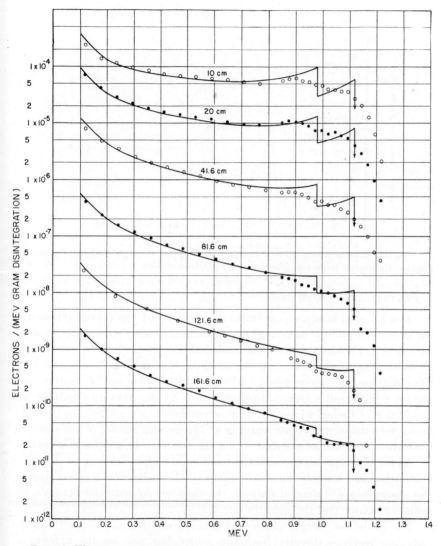

FIG. 16. The measured distribution in energy of electrons set in motion in water by cobalt-60 γ-rays at different distances from the source. The solid lines are calculated curves based on the theory of Spencer and Fano (106). Reprinted from ref. 107 by courtesy of E. Hayward and The American Physical Society.

C. DISTRIBUTION OF THE ENERGY RELEASE IN AN X- OR GAMMA-RAY BEAM

This subject has been extensively developed because of its medical use in the radiotherapy of cancer; for details the reader is referred to more extensive reviews of the subject (108, 109; Chapter 12 of ref. 2).

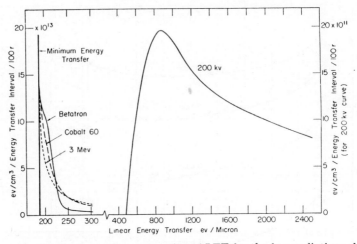

FIG. 17. Energy absorbed as a function of LET for the four radiations shown in Fig. 15. Reprinted from ref. 2 by courtesy of H. E. Johns.

1. CENTRAL-AXIS DEPTH DOSE

As a beam of photons penetrates into a material, the energy released in the irradiated volume in general decreases in a roughly exponential fashion with depth. The decrease is compounded of the interaction of three factors.

With increasing depth into the medium, the distance to the source of the radiation is also increasing, leading to a decreasing flux of photons simply for geometrical reasons. Most sources of X- or γ-rays used for external irradiation of biological materials are essentially point sources, so that this factor introduces a decrease varying as the inverse square of the distance from the source to the point at which the intensity is being determined.

As the beam passes through the medium, a certain fraction of the beam is absorbed in a roughly exponential fashion. For a beam of a given quality, the absorption will depend only on the thickness of material between the radiation source and the point in question.

The radiation energy release at a given point depends not only on the radiation received directly from the source but also on the amount of scattered radiation. This will depend not only on the quality of the radiation but also on the volume of material irradiated. A wide beam will produce more scattered radiation than a narrow one.

Johns *et al.* (110) have shown that the amount of scattered radiation reaching an axial point at a distance s below the surface depends, for practical purposes, only on the quality of the radiation and on the area of the beam at the depth s, but not on the distance of the source from the irradiated material. Figure 18 shows that this is a reasonable result. The dashed

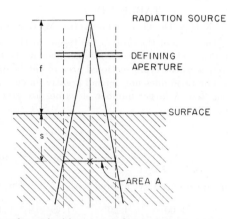

FIG. 18. X-Ray beam incident on a phantom from a source at a distance f from the phantom. The dashed lines show the beam from a source at an infinite distance and having the same cross section, A, at a depth s.

lines indicate the volume that would be irradiated if the source were at infinity. For the same dose of direct radiation received at the center of A the same total number of photons will enter the irradiated material for the source at infinity and for the source at a distance f. For the latter case, the scattered radiation at the center of A will consist of scatter produced by these incident photons, but produced at a somewhat shorter distance than in the case of the distant source. This distance is very little shorter on the average, however, and, furthermore, the increased scatter due to this is compensated by a decreased scatter contribution from the volume below the area, A, where on the average the photons are scattered at a greater distance than for a parallel incident beam.

The decrease in the amount of direct (i.e., unscattered) radiation reaching a specific axial point also depends only on the overlying thickness, s, of tissue. Thus the ratio, $T_A(s)$, of the dose in the tissue to the dose that would be delivered in air at the same point in space depends on the depth, s (affecting both the direct and the scattered radiation), and on the area, A, of the beam at this depth (scattered radiation only). From its initial use in cancer radiotherapy, the ratio $T_A(s)$ is frequently called the tumor-air ratio, the ratio of the dose to the tumor to the dose in air at the same place. Table XIV gives some experimental values of this ratio for different radiations in tissuelike material.

In many cases the dose wanted will be that at given depth, s, in the tissue for a port of a given area, A, on the surface, which is at some standard distance f from the source. From Fig. 18 and the discussion given above,

TABLE XIV
Axial X-Ray Doses in Tissuelike Material

(The figure given is the ratio of the dose in the tissue, at the specified depth, to the dose that would be received "in air" at the same place in the complete absence of material. The area refers to the cross-sectional area of the beam at the depth of the dose measurement. The ratio does not depend greatly on the shape of the area, unless it is greatly elongated. A larger number of values are given in the original reference, ref. 110a.)

Depth (cm)	Area (cm²)				
	0	20	50	100	400
HVL = 1 mm Cu (approx. 200 kv, filtered with 0.5 mm Cu + 1 mm Al)					
0	1.00	1.20	1.29	1.37	1.49
2	0.682	1.08	1.25	1.36	1.58
4	0.472	0.844	1.02	1.18	1.43
6	0.330	0.631	0.799	0.954	1.24
10	0.163	0.341	0.452	0.569	0.838
14	0.079	0.178	0.250	0.325	0.534
20	0.027	0.067	0.099	0.138	0.254
HVL = 3 mm Cu (approx. 250 kv, filtered with 0.66 mm Sn + 0.25 mm Cu + 1 mm Al)					
0	1.00	1.13	1.19	1.24	1.33
2	0.736	1.03	1.15	1.22	1.39
4	0.542	0.828	0.968	1.08	1.29
6	0.404	0.651	0.785	0.905	1.14
10	0.222	0.382	0.480	0.591	0.820
14	0.123	0.220	0.284	0.364	0.552
20	0.051	0.098	0.130	0.171	0.299
Co⁶⁰ γ-radiation					
0.5	1.00	1.012	1.019	1.026	1.047
2	0.904	0.955	0.975	0.993	1.020
4	0.790	0.873	0.905	0.928	0.969
6	0.692	0.788	0.826	0.854	0.909
10	0.532	0.622	0.665	0.700	0.776
14	0.408	0.484	0.525	0.564	0.654
20	0.278	0.336	0.368	0.400	0.500

this dose, $D_A(s)$, will be

$$D_A(s) = D_{air}(f) \left(\frac{f}{f+s}\right)^2 T_{A'}(s) \qquad (28)$$

where $D_{air}(f)$ = air dose at a source-to-skin distance, f.

$A' = A((f+s)/f)^2$, the area of the beam at a depth s when the area is A at the surface.

The dose $D_A(s)$ here depends on the source-to-skin distance, f. Tables for different radiation qualities, beam areas, and source-to-skin distances are available (108).

For X-rays above 1 Mev the dose at the surface of the material is not the highest dose. Instead, the observed dose rises by a factor of the order of 3 to a maximum which is about 4 mm under the surface for 2 Mev, 4 cm for 22 Mev, and deeper for higher energies. The reason is simple enough. For such X-rays the electrons produced by the primary ionizations are ejected mainly in the forward direction. Under the surface of the absorber the number of such electrons will increase up to a depth equal to the range of these electrons, with a consequent increase in energy release. For low-energy X-rays the electron range is so small that the effect is not noticeable. The effect is of considerable practical importance in cancer radiotherapy, since the use of high-energy X-rays can considerably reduce the radiation dose to the skin when underlying tumors are treated.

2. BACKSCATTER

A special case of some interest is the dose at the surface of an absorber, which is higher than the "in-air" dose because of scattered radiation. Numerically, it is given by the "tumor-air" ratio in Table XIV at zero depth. The dependence with photon energy is complicated. For low energies scattered photons are emitted roughly equally in all directions. The scattered radiation is strongly absorbed by the material, and the total volume which can contribute scattered radiation to the surface is small, giving a low backscatter. For higher voltages the absorption of the scattered radiation decreases and a larger volume contributes to the backscattered radiation. The scattered photons are tending more and more in the forward direction, however, and there is a maximum in the backscatter for an X-ray beam generated by 200 kv. Above this voltage the effect of forward scattering becomes more and more pronounced, so that the backscatter is only a few per cent for radiation of the order of 2 Mev, and even less for higher energies.

Naturally, the amount of backscatter also depends on the area of the beam, with a large beam providing a larger volume from which scattering can take place. The backscatter is largest at the center of a field and drops off to roughly half of the maximum at the edge of the field.

Elaborate studies have been made of the backscatter from tissuelike materials and its variation with area, shape of area (round, long, or narrow, etc.), and radiation quality (108, 109; Chapter 12 of ref. 2). For materials of higher atomic number, the backscatter is in general larger than that from the lighter materials.

3. OFF-AXIS DEPTH DOSES

The discussion in the last two sections has been devoted to the dose at the center of an irradiated field. At points off the axis the unabsorbed radiation coming straight from the target is the same, but the scatter radiation is decreased, and the total dose decreases. At the geometrical edge of the beam there is a discontinuity, since the direct radiation from the target disappears, but the scattered radiation drops off smoothly into the region

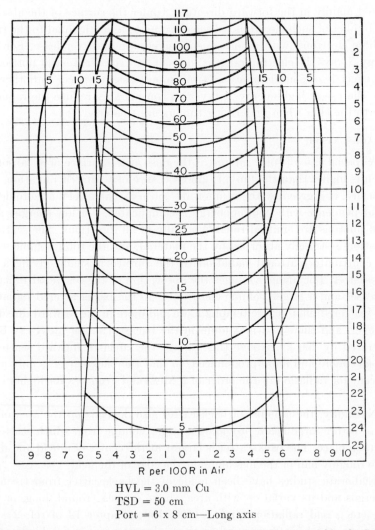

R per 100R in Air

HVL = 3.0 mm Cu
TSD = 50 cm
Port = 6 x 8 cm—Long axis

FIG. 19. An isodose chart showing the doses at various points within the field of an X-ray beam.

beyond the beam, the extent being governed by the quality of the incident X-rays and by the port area.

Merideth and Neary (111) have developed a mathematical method of computing the scattered radiation at any point, using as raw data the axial depth doses as a function of beam area. With such a method the dosage received at any place in a beam of specified quality and area and incident on a tissuelike material located at a given distance from the radiation source may be calculated and plotted on an "isodose chart," as shown in Fig. 19. Alternatively, the dosage distributions with an X-ray beam for given conditions (quality, area, and source-to-surface distance) may be measured experimentally. In general, the theory is in good agreement with experimental measurements.

As the incident radiation energy gets above 1 Mev, the photons tend to be scattered more and more in the forward direction. Thus the scatter radiation tends to be more uniform over the cross section of the beam, and isodose charts show a smaller decrease in dose toward the edge of the beam for 2-Mev X-rays than for 200 kev, for example. At 20 Mev the scatter is so strongly confined in the forward direction that for all practical purposes the isodose charts for this radiation are horizontal lines, extending from one geometrical edge of the beam to the other.

This same forward scattering also decreases the amount of radiation scattered beyond the edge of the beam. Not only does this decrease the dose to structures adjacent to the beam, but it has a tremendous effect on the integral dose received by the irradiated material. For 250-kv X-rays, the doses outside the geometrical edge of the beam (Fig. 19) do not appear excessive, but they extend over such a large volume that the integral dose delivered by the scattered radiation outside the geometrical beam is of the same order of magnitude as the integral dose delivered within the beam. As the voltage increases, this scattered dose decreases sharply.

4. EFFECT OF INHOMOGENEITIES IN THE IRRADIATED MEDIUM

The discussion given above has tacitly presumed a homogeneous material with properties, so far as X-rays are concerned, much like those of water. This is reasonably true for tissues such as muscle, but not for bone on the one hand, or fat and air-filled tissue such as lung, on the other (see Table X). Not only is the energy absorption in bone higher because of its greater density and a larger photoelectric effect in the incorporated calcium, but it throws a "shadow" behind it where the beam has been weakened. Fat absorbs less energy per unit volume and allows more radiation to pass than water. Lung tissue also absorbs less of the incident beam and permits higher doses in underlying tissue. Spiers (112) has considered the corrections which should be made to standard depth-dose tables for these effects.

V. Neutrons

A. INTERACTIONS BETWEEN NEUTRONS AND MATTER

All neutron interactions are with nuclei only, and no interactions occur between neutrons and the electrons in matter. This introduces considerable differences between irradiation with neutrons and with any other kind of radiation.

1. FAST NEUTRONS

The process of energy transfer by fast neutrons is dominated by the area exposed by a nucleus as determined by the nuclear radius. What we know as the nuclear radius is really the confines of the sharply varying nuclear forces, characterized by a nuclear radius $r = 1.5 \times 10^{-13} A^{1/3}$ cm, where A is the total number of particles contained in the nucleus. The neutron itself has the radius of 1.5×10^{-13} cm, and the sum of these two is the total collision radius, R, from which one can derive the collision cross section. Such a cross section then goes into the absorption formula already quoted in an earlier section of this chapter, and the numbers of such collisions can then be estimated in a general way.

We have stressed here the importance of collision because some interaction must take place before any energy can be lost. The larger the nucleus radius, the more chance of collision, but the amount of energy transferred is governed by the necessity of conserving momentum and energy in the encounter, and depends on the ratio of the masses of the nucleus and neutron, m_n and M, respectively. In particular, the *maximum* energy transferred, w_{max}, from a neutron of energy E is

$$w_{max} = \frac{4(m_n/M)E}{(1 + m_n/M)^2} \qquad (29)$$

The equality of mass between the hydrogen nucleus and the neutron permits total transfer of energy in head-on impacts and a larger fraction in all collisions, so that in a hydrogenous medium such as tissue the energy transfer to recoil protons dominates the picture.

The scattering observed is the sum of "potential" scattering caused by the presence of a region of different potential energy in the path of the neutron and of "capture" scattering in which the neutron interacts with the component parts of the nucleus and forms an unstable "compound nucleus," which then decays. In the decay, the most probable result for high neutron energies is the emission of a neutron of the same energy— i.e., the neutron has undergone "capture scattering." A somewhat rarer occurrence, which takes place mainly for incident neutrons of energy above 1 Mev, is the emission of a neutron of lower energy, or "inelastic scattering." Rarest of all at high energies is the capture of a neutron and the emission of a γ-ray or a charged particle.

The cross section for potential scattering is πR^2 at high energies, and that for the sum of all capture processes is $\pi(R + \lambda/2\pi)^2$, where λ is the neutron wavelength.

2. SLOW NEUTRONS

As the neutron energy is reduced, the term $\lambda/2\pi$ for capture reactions becomes greater and greater, until the neutron wavelength finally becomes the dominant factor. The cross-section expression is only an approximate one and in particular does not hold for a neutron whose energy is close to

TABLE XV
THERMAL NEUTRON CROSS SECTIONS

(The cross-sections, in units of barns = 10^{-24} cm², are for elements of isotopic distribution as found in nature. The absorption cross sections are mostly for n, γ reactions, unless stated otherwise. More extensive tables and graphs giving the variation of cross section with energy may be found in the American Institute of Physics Handbook, ref. 113b, and in Brookhaven Report 325, ref. 113c.)

Element	Scattering cross section (barns)	Absorption cross section (barns)
H	38	0.33
He	0.8	0
B	4	755 (n, α)
C	4.8	0.0032
N	10	1.75 (n, p)
		0.13 (n, γ)
O	4.2	0.0002
F	3.9	0.010
Na	4.0	0.50
Mg	3.6	0.063
Al	1.4	0.23
Si	1.7	0.13
P	5	0.19
S	1.1	0.49
Cl	16	0.22 (n, p)
		31.4 (n, γ)
K	1.5	1.97
Ca	9	0.43
Mn	2.3	13.2
Fe	11	2.53
Cu	7.2	3.69
Zn	3.6	1.06
Cd	7	2550.
Pb	11	0.17

an energy level, or "resonance," in the target nucleus. For incident neutrons below a few electron volts, the existence of a nuclear energy level near zero energy gives rise to neutron capture cross sections which vary as the reciprocal of the neutron velocity, the "$1/v$ law."

As the incident neutron energy decreases, the modes of decay of the compound nucleus also change. Inelastic neutron scattering disappears, and the probability increases of neutron capture followed by γ-ray or charged-particle emission.

The potential scattering, yielding elastic scattering only, increases slowly from its high-energy value of πR^2 to $4\pi R^2$ at sufficiently low energies, a change caused by diffraction effects.

A more extended but reasonably simple account of neutron scattering is given by Price et al. (113). A standard advanced treatment is given by Blatt and Weiskopf (113a).

The most important kind of slow neutrons are *thermal* neutrons, or those which are in thermal equilibrum with surrounding atoms and have a mean energy of $\frac{3}{2}kT = \frac{1}{25}$ ev at room temperature. For these neutrons no net energy is transferred to the medium by elastic scattering, and the energy release is entirely from the nuclear capture processes. From Table XV it can be seen that the predominant reactions in tissue will be capture processes in H^1 and N^{14}. The first is a neutron capture reaction releasing a 2.2-Mev γ-ray. In the second reaction the capture of a neutron releases a proton of energy of 0.6 Mev and forms the long-lived radioactive isotope C^{14}.

B. Tissue Doses in a Neutron Beam

Any simple understanding of neutron dosage is greatly complicated by several factors: (1) The drastic changes in the probabilities of the various processes as the incident neutrons are slowed down, changes far greater than any that occur in the scattering of X-rays; (2) the appearance of the released energy in two greatly different forms—as fast heavy particles which dissipate their energy locally at a high LET, and as energetic γ-rays which may travel many centimeters in tissue to release the energy at a low LET; and (3) sensitivity of energy release for slow neutrons to the presence of traces of elements having large slow neutron cross sections. Still a fourth difficulty is the fact that most practical neutron sources (e.g., reactors) produce neutron beams with a substantial contamination of γ-rays.

One useful parameter to consider is the mean free path of the neutron in tissue, or the mean distance traversed before a collision takes place. If tissue is considered to be $(C_5H_{40}O_8N)_n$, Fig. 20 shows the calculated value of the mean free path as a function of neutron energy.

After the first collision, the course of a neutron becomes difficult to visualize in detail as it slows down through elastic and inelastic encounters.

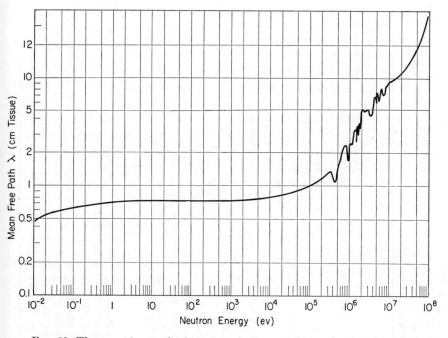

FIG. 20. The mean free path of neutrons in tissue, taken as having the chemical composition $(C_5H_{40}O_8N)_n$. Reprinted from ref. 2 by courtesy of H. H. Rossi.

A striking exception is that of thermal neutrons. Here the scattering mean free path is short compared to the absorption mean free path, and the passage of neutrons through tissue may be likened to a diffusion process, with a superposed absorption. In tissue the slow neutron flux falls off roughly exponentially, with a half-value layer of the order of 2 cm.

The little information available to 1956 on tissue dosage from neutron beams has been summarized by Rossi (Chapter 15 in ref. 2).

VI. Radioactive Sources

A. PROPERTIES OF RADIOACTIVE ISOTOPES

Radioactive nuclei are characterized by a probability that they will undergo an abrupt transition, emitting ionizing radiation and simultaneously transmuting into another element. The probability of this happening to any given radioactive nucleus is constant in time. If, in a certain period of time, half of the radioactive nuclei in a given source have disintegrated, then in the next such period half of those remaining will decay, and so on. The time in which half of the nuclei will disintegrate is a constant for a given isotope and is called the half-life. It is one of the main parameters

TABLE XVI

TABLE OF RADIOISOTOPES

(The data in this table were obtained mainly from the extensive table of isotopes given by Strominger et al., ref. 114, and from the tables in the appendix to "Radiation Dosimetry," ref. 2. Only radiations numbering 0.01 or more per disintegration are listed.)

Isotope	Half-life	Maximum β-ray energies (Mev)[a, b]	γ-ray energies (Mev)[a]	Mean β-ray energy, $\bar{E}_\beta$ (Mev)	Point source γ-ray dose rate, K (r/mc-hr at 1 cm)
H³	12.26 yr	0.0180 [1]		0.0055	
C¹⁴	5568 yr	0.155 [1]		0.049	
Na²⁴	15.0 hr	1.39 [1]	2.76 [1], 1.37 [1]	0.55	18.4
P³²	14.3 days	1.71 [1]		0.69	
S³⁵	87.5 days	0.167 [1]		0.049	
K⁴⁰	1.25 × 10⁹ yr	1.32 [0.9], E.C., 0.0030 X-ray [0.1]	1.46 [0.1]	(0.5 estimated)	0.7
K⁴²	12.5 hr	3.55 [0.8], 2.02 [0.2]	1.53 [0.2]	1.45	1.50
Ca⁴⁵	164 days	0.256 [1]		0.076	
Cr⁵¹	27.8 days	E.C., 0.0049 X-ray [1]	0.323 [0.09]	(0.0049) (X-ray)	0.18
Fe⁵⁵	2.6 yr	E.C., 0.0059 X-ray [1]		(0.0059) (X-ray)	
Fe⁵⁹	45.0 days	0.46 [0.54], 0.27 [0.46]	1.289 [0.43], 1.098 [0.57], 0.191 [0.03]	0.120	6.13
Co⁶⁰	5.2 yr	0.31 [1]	1.333 [1], 1.172 [1]	0.094	12.8
{ Sr⁹⁰	28 yr	0.545 [1]		0.20	
{ Y⁹⁰	64.4 hr	2.26 [1]		0.93	
I¹³¹	8.1 days	0.815 [0.01], 0.608 [0.87], 0.335 [0.09], 0.250 [0.03]	0.722 [0.03], 0.637 [0.09], 0.364 [0.81], 0.284 [0.06], 0.080 [0.06]	0.187	2.18
Cs¹³⁷	27 yr	1.17 [0.08], 0.51 [0.92]	0.662 [0.92]	0.23	3.2
Au¹⁹⁸	2.70 days	0.96 [0.99], 0.29 [0.01]	0.676 [0.01], 0.412 [0.99]	0.32	2.35
Ra and products	1620 yr	Mixed α's and β's	13, with energies between 0.18 and 2.45 Mev		8.4 (with 0.5-mm platinum filter)

[a] Values in brackets indicate number per disintegration.

characterizing a radioactive nucleus. Half-lives vary over one of the widest ranges of any physical parameter known, from greater than 10^{15} years to less than 10^{-9} second, a factor of the order of 10^{30}.

The product nucleus from a radioactive disintegration is frequently stable but in many cases is itself radioactive, undergoing further decay. Many chains are known, and most of the naturally occurring radioisotopes, such as radium-226, are daughters in chains descending from a long-lived parent.

The total number of radioactive nuclei known is very large and is still growing. There are a number of standard references to these isotopes and their properties, of which the compilations of Seaborg and his associates are frequently referred to (114). In Table XVI are listed some of the isotopes most frequently met with in biological work, together with some of their more important properties.

B. RADIATION PROCESSES IN RADIOACTIVE ISOTOPES

1. BETA EMISSION

The most common type of radiation from a radioactive nucleus is β-emission. Radioisotopes with more neutrons than the stable isotopes of the same element (such as C^{14}) in general emit electrons, and those with a neutron deficiency (C^{11}, for example) usually emit positrons. Most isotopes available in quantity are made in a nuclear reactor by irradiation with neutrons. Since this makes only isotopes with neutron excess, negative electron emitters are much more common.

Beta rays from a given radioisotope have a distribution in energy ranging from essentially zero to a maximum energy which is characteristic of the particular isotope. The distribution is bell-shaped, with very few particles with very low or very high energy, and a maximum which is typically about one-third of the maximum energy. The maximum energy is characteristically somewhat less than a million electron volts and in different isotopes varies from about 20 kev to 5 Mev or more. The disintegration of a given nucleus actually involves the loss by the nucleus of an amount of energy equal to the maximum energy of the β-rays, and the energy not accounted for by the β-rays is taken away by neutrinos. These particles are without mass or charge and, unlike electromagnetic radiation, interact very weakly with matter; only recently (115) have they been detected directly. For this reason, only the energy carried by the β-rays is of importance. Some radioisotopes can decay by β-emission in two or more ways, each way having a β-spectrum with its own characteristic maximum energy.

2. GAMMA EMISSION

The product nucleus formed after the emission of a β-ray may be stable (e.g., the nucleus formed by the decay of P^{32}), but more frequently it is left with a surplus of energy which is radiated as electromagnetic radiation, or γ-rays. The energies of the γ-rays emitted are characteristic of the nucleus and are between tens of kilovolts to several million volts. In a single disintegration, the number of γ-rays emitted can vary from none, to one, to as many as four or five in a complicated process. Isotopes such as I^{131} emitting β-rays of two or more energies sometimes yield over a dozen γ-rays of different energies, with different sets of γ-rays emitted for each different mode of beta disintegration.

3. ALPHA EMISSION

With the very heavy elements an instability occurs even for isotopes having the most favorable proportions of neutrons and protons. This instability manifests itself, as in the case of Ra^{226}, by the emission of α-particles, or nuclei of helium. The α-particles emitted all have the same energy characteristic of the radioisotope, which is usually of the order of several million electron volts. Sometimes a γ-ray is also emitted.

4. ELECTRON CAPTURE

Another process is that of electron capture, of which Fe^{55} is an example. Here the nucleus captures one of the orbital electrons, usually one from the K-shell. This will result in the emission of an X-ray characteristic of the atomic number of the nucleus. There may or may not be a γ-ray produced in further nuclear processes.

5. INTERNAL TRANSITION

An internal transition is one in which a rearrangement of the internal constitution of the nucleus results in the emission of a γ-ray without the emission of a particle. In some isotopes the nuclear excitation energy may sometimes be transferred directly to an atomic electron, which is then emitted with the same energy the γ-ray would have had ("internal conversion"). This is the only process which produces radiation without a change in the atomic number, or chemical identity, of the nucleus.

6. THE MILLICURIE

The ordinary unit for measuring the quantity of a radioactive isotope is the millicurie, defined as a source having 3.70×10^7 disintegrations per second. This is approximately the disintegration rate of a milligram of radium, long used as a reference standard. Other widely used units are multiples of this—the curie, one thousand times as big as the millicurie, and the microcurie, smaller by a factor of one thousand.

The millicurie (and the other such units) only measures the quantity of radioactive material present. The dose received by any nearby biological material depends on many factors, such as the type and energy of radiation emitted, as well as the geometrical arrangement of the radioactive source and the material irradiated. The simplest case to consider is that of a point source emitting only γ-rays. If the source is in air (where absorption of the rays will not be important), the intensity will clearly drop off as $1/r^2$, the ordinary inverse square decrease. At some reference distance, say 1 cm, the intensity will be proportional to the source strength in millicuries and will depend on the number and energy of the photons. This last factor can be accounted for in a constant, K, which is a measured characteristic of each radioisotope, and tabulated in Table XVI. Thus the dose rate at a distance of x cm from a γ-source of (mc) millicuries is

$$\frac{r}{hr} = K \frac{mc}{x^2} \tag{30}$$

The relations between source strength in millicuries and dose in rads or roentgens for other cases are discussed below.

C. RADIOACTIVE SOURCES USED FOR EXTERNAL IRRADIATION

The radiations from radioactive isotopes may be used to irradiate biological systems by allowing beams to fall on the material to be treated. This method is widely used with γ-ray emitters such as cobalt-60, to provide inexpensive and trouble-free sources of highly penetrating radiation with a constant dose rate. Any β-rays can usually be absorbed in the walls of the sealed container holding the radioactive material. Such sources may be in the form of one or more small units which are located in shields furnished with ports to form a beam of radiation in much the same way as an X-ray machine. The radioactive material may also be made up in a cylinder or plate, and the sample to be irradiated placed close by. An efficient way to get a high dose over a limited region is to make the source in a hollow cylinder and put the sample inside. The dose rate to be expected from a given arrangement may be calculated from the quantity K tabulated in Table XVI.

Beta- and alpha-particle sources may be used for external irradiation in much the same way. The dose rates are low compared to those obtainable from accelerators, and collimation and dosage measurement problems are sometimes severe. Radioactive sources must usually be sealed in a container to prevent the radioactivity from spreading, and the thin windows needed to pass the α- and β-radiation are frequently a problem.

D. RADIOACTIVE SOURCES USED FOR INTERNAL IRRADIATION

Radioisotopes are unique in that they may be incorporated directly into the material to be irradiated. This may be done deliberately in order, for example, to irradiate selectively that part of the material in which the radioisotope is concentrated. Sometimes the irradiation effects are a side issue, in experiments with tracers, for example.

1. BETA EMITTERS—UNIFORM DISTRIBUTION

For β-emitters, two simple cases are considered. In the first, the radioisotope is assumed to be uniformly distributed throughout a region which is large compared to the range of the maximum-energy β-particle. Under these circumstances, the dose rate in rads may be readily calculated from the average energy, $\bar{E}_\beta$, of the β's (listed in Table XVI) and a knowledge of the average isotope concentration, in microcuries per gram. Using the fact that a microcurie produces 3.7×10^4 disintegrations per second, and converting the mean energy, $\bar{E}_\beta$, to ergs, we readily calculate the dose rate to be

$$\text{rads/hr} = 3.70 \times 10^4 \frac{\text{dis.}}{\text{sec-}\mu\text{c}} \times \left(\frac{\mu\text{c}}{\text{gm}}\right) \times \frac{\bar{E}_\beta \text{ Mev}}{\text{dis.}} \times \frac{1.60 \times 10^{-6} \text{ erg}}{\text{Mev}}$$

$$\times \frac{\text{gm-rad}}{100 \text{ ergs}} \times \frac{3600 \text{ sec}}{\text{hr}} = 2.13\bar{E}_\beta \text{ (Mev)} \left(\frac{\mu\text{c}}{\text{gm}}\right) \tag{31}$$

If the isotope is permanently incorporated into the material, the total dose may be readily calculated by multiplying the dose rate by the exponential decay factor and integrating out to infinite time. This gives

$$\text{rads} = 74.0\bar{E}_\beta(\text{Mev})T_{1/2}(\text{days}) \left(\frac{\mu\text{c}}{\text{gm}}\right) \tag{32}$$

where $T_{1/2}$ is the half-life in days. In many cases, the isotope is turned over by the biological processes involved, and the physical half-life should be replaced by the biological half-life.

These calculations fail at the boundaries of the isotope-containing region, where there is a zone in which the dosage falls off from its maximum value to zero in a distance equal to about twice the β-ray range.

2. BETA RAYS—POINT SOURCE

To handle the case of a nonuniform distribution of a β-ray emitter it is convenient to be able to visualize the distribution of energy release about a point source of β-rays. The dosage produced by a nonuniform distribution may then be obtained by a suitable summation. Loevinger (Chapter 16 of ref. 2) has shown that the dosage at a distance x from a point β-source is given for β-emitters of maximum energy between 0.167 Mev (S^{35}) and 2.24 Mev (Y^{90}) by the expression

$$J(x) = \frac{k}{(\nu x)^2} \left\{ c \left[1 - \frac{\nu x}{c} e^{1-(\nu x/c)} \right] + \nu x e^{1-\nu x} \right\} \tag{33}$$

$$\left[1 - \frac{\nu x}{c} e^{1-(\nu x/c)} \right] \equiv 0, \qquad x \geq \frac{c}{\nu}$$

The parameters k, ν, and c are defined below in the discussion. The energy absorbed at a given distance, x, is proportional to $(\nu x)^2 J(x)$, or to the expression in braces. The term in the brackets equals unity at $r = 0$, and goes to zero at $r = c/\nu$. It can be thought of as representing the dose contribution from the unscattered β-rays from the source. The second term, on the other hand, is zero at the origin, builds up to a maximum, and then drops off at large enough distances as e^{-px}. It can be thought of as the contribution from the scattered β-rays.

From the behavior of the function at large x it is apparent that the parameter ν has the significance of an absorption coefficient. The parameter c can be thought of as a measure of the scattering of the electrons. The experimental data are fitted by the following expressions:

$$\nu = \frac{18.6}{(E_0 - 0.036)^{1.37}} \text{ cm}^2/\text{gm of tissue}$$

$$c = \begin{cases} 2 & 0.17 < E_0 < 0.5 \text{ Mev} \\ 1.5 & 0.5 \ < E_0 < 1.5 \text{ Mev} \\ 1 & 1.5 \ < E_0 < \ 3 \text{ Mev} \end{cases} \qquad (33a)$$

where E_0 is the maximum β-ray energy in million electron volts. The equation for ν is that suitable for the so-called "allowed" β-ray spectra, and for the nonallowed spectra with a different distribution of numbers with energy, such as Sr^{90} and RaE, a slightly modified equation must be used.

The parameter k is determined by the fact that the total energy absorbed must equal the energy released by the source:

$$k = \frac{1.28 \times 10^{-9} \rho^2 \nu^3 \bar{E}_\beta}{3c^2 - (c^2 - 1)e} \qquad (33b)$$

Here ν is in square centimeters per gram; $\bar{E}_\beta$, the average β-ray energy, is in million electron volts per disintegration; ρ, the density, is in grams per cubic centimeter and e is 2.73.

From this function the dosages for many β-ray source distributions have been calculated and tabulated (Chapters 16 and 17 of ref. 2).

Average dosages from internal α-particle emitters can be calculated in much the same way as those for β-particle emitters.

3. GAMMA EMITTERS

The dose rate from a point source of γ-rays has already been discussed. For a medium having a significant absorption, the dose rate at a distance of x cm from a point source of strength (mc) millicuries is approximately

$$\frac{r}{hr} = K \frac{e^{-\mu x}}{x^2} \text{ (mc)} \qquad (34)$$

where K is the constant tabulated in Table XVI, and μ is the absorption coefficient for the energy of the photons emitted. As pointed out before, in many cases the exponential absorption term is sufficiently close to unity that it may be neglected.

For the case of an extended source of a γ-emitter the dose at a particular spot is difficult to calculate because it depends on the relative location of essentially all the radioactivity. If the isotope is uniformly distributed throughout a given region, the intensity at a given point will obviously be proportional to the concentration of radioisotope in microcuries per gram and to the quantity K, the dose rate at 1 cm from a unit source of the radioisotope used. If absorption can be neglected, the remaining factor in the dose rate is a purely geometric one, depending on the size and shape of the area. This geometrical factor has been calculated and tabulated for simple regions such as spheres and cylinders of different sizes (Chapter 17 of ref. 2).

E. RADIOACTIVE SUICIDE

In the case of an internally incorporated radioactive atom, its decay can affect a biological system either by the emitted radiation, by the recoil of the nucleus caused by the emission of the radiation, or by the change in the chemistry of the atom caused by the transmutation. In principle, at least, an equivalent amount of ionizing radiation can be given by an external source. The extent by which the effects of the internal emitter exceed those of the external radiation is a measure of the inactivation produced by the recoil and by the change in chemical identity. These last two processes are usually intertwined to the point where it is hard to disentangle the effect produced by either one. The process involved has received the highly descriptive name of "radioactive suicide." It is useful in studying certain processes, since the effects produced are almost certainly located within the structure in which the radioactive atom is incorporated.

VII. References

1. Lea, D. E., "Actions of Ionizing Radiations on Living Cells," Cambridge Univ. Press, London, 1946.
2. "Radiation Dosimetry" (G. J. Hine and G. J. Brownell, eds.), Academic Press, New York, 1956. For general aspects, Chapter 2, by H. E. Johns and J. S. Laughlin, is particularly useful.
3. Gray, L. H., in "Actions chimiques et biologiques des radiations" (M. Haïssinsky, ed.), Chapter 1, Masson, Paris, 1955.
4. Franck, J., and Platzman, R. L., in "Radiation Biology" (A. Hollaender, ed.), Vol. 1, Part 1, Chapter 3. McGraw-Hill, New York, 1954.
5. Morrison, P., and Platzman, R. L., in "Symposium on Radiobiobogy" (J. J. Nickson, ed.), Chapters 1, 7, and 9. Wiley, New York, 1952.
6. Bethe, H. A., and Ashkin, J., in "Experimental Nuclear Physics" (E. Segrè, ed.) Vol. 1, Chapter 2. Wiley, New York, 1953.

7. Mott, N. F., and Massey, H. S. W., "Theory of Atomic Collisions," 2nd ed. Oxford Univ. Press, London, 1949.
8. Massey, H. S. W., and Burhop, E. H. S., "Electronic and Ionic Impact Phenomena." Oxford Univ. Press, London, 1952.
9. Rossi, B., "High Energy Particles." Prentice-Hall, New York, 1952.
9a. Bohr. N., *Kgl. Danske Videnskab. Selskab. Mat.-fys. Medd.* **18**, No. 8 (1948).
10. Allison, S. K., and Warshaw, S. D., *Revs. Mod. Phys.* **25**, 779 (1953).
11. Zirkle, R. E., and Tobias, C. A., *Arch. Biochem. Biophys.* **47**, 282 (1953).
12. Fermi, E., *Z. Physik* **29**, 315 (1924).
13. Gaunt, J., *Proc. Cambridge Phil. Soc.* **23**, 732 (1927).
14. Bethe, H. A., *Ann. Physik* **5**, 325 (1930); "Handbuch der Physik," 2nd ed., XXIV, p. 273, 1933.
15. Bloch, F., *Ann. Physik* **16**, 285 (1933).
16. Thompson, T. J., *Univ. Calif. Radiation Lab. Rept.* **1910** (1952).
16a. Caldwell, D. O., *Phys. Rev.* **100**, 291 (1955).
17. Kleeman, R. D., *Proc. Roy. Soc.* **A79**, 220 (1907).
18. Gray, L. H., *Proc. Cambridge Phil. Soc.* **40**, 72 (1944).
19. Phelps, J., Huebner, W., and Hutchinson, F., *Phys. Rev.* **95**, 441 (1954).
20. Papineau, A., *Compt. rend.* **242**, 2933 (1956).
21. Gluckstern, R., *Phys. Rev.* **98**, 1817 (1955).
22. Knipp, J., and Teller, E., *Phys. Rev.* **59**, 661 (1941).
23. Nikolaev, V. S., *Zhur. Eksptl. i Teoret. Fiz.* **33**, 417 (1957).
24. Bohr, N., and Lindhard, J., *Kgl. Danske Videnskab. Selskab. Mat-fys. Medd.* **28**, No. 7 (1954).
25. Person, S., and Hutchinson, F., in course of publication.
26. Walske, W. C., *Phys. Rev.* **88**, 1283 (1952).
27. Lindhard, J., and Scharff, M., *Kgl. Danske Videnskab. Selskab. Mat-fys. Medd.* **27**, No. 15 (1953).
28. Neufeld, J., *Proc. Phys. Soc.* (*London*) **66**, 590 (1953).
29. Nelms, A. T., *Natl. Bur. Standards.* (*U.S.*) *Circ.* **577** (1956); *Suppl. to Circ. 577* (1958).
30. Bohr, N., *Phys. Rev.* **59**, 271 (1941).
31. Snyder, W. S., and Neufeld, J., *Radiation Research* **6**, 67 (1957).
32. Wilkinson, D. H., *Proc. Cambridge Phil. Soc.* **44**, 114 (1948).
33. Ellis, R. H., Jr., Rossi, H. H., and Failla, G., *Phys. Rev.* **86**, 562 (1952).
34. Michl, W., *Sitzber. Akad. Wiss. Wien* **123**, 1965 (1914).
35. Phillipp, K. Z., *Z. Physik* **17**, 23 (1923).
36. Appleyard, R. K., *Proc. Cambridge Phil. Soc.* **47**, 443 (1951).
37. de Carvalho, H., and Yagoda, H., *Phys. Rev.* **88**, 273 (1952).
38. Ellis, R. H., Jr., Rossi, H. H., and Failla, G., *Phys. Rev.* **97**, 1043 (1955).
39. Fermi, E., *Phys. Rev.* **56**, 1242 (1939); **57**, 485 (1940).
40. Sternheimer, R. M., *Phys. Rev.* **88**, 851 (1952).
41. Sternheimer, R. M., *Phys. Rev.* **93**, 351 (1954).
42. Stearns, M., *Phys. Rev.* **76**, 836 (1949).
43. Bethe, H. A., *Revs. Mod. Phys.* **22**, 213 (1950).
44. Aron, W. A., Hoffman, B. G., and Williams, F. C., *U.S. Atomic Energy. Comm. Rept.* **AECU-663**, *Univ. Calif., Radiation Lab. Rept.* **121** (1949).
44a. Northcliffe, L. C., *Phys. Rev.* **120**, 1744 (1960).
45. Hirschfelder, J. O., and Magee, J. L., *Phys. Rev.* **73**, 207 (1948).
45a. Schambra, P. E., Rauth, A. M., and Norcthliffe, L. C., *Phys. Rev.* **120**, 1758 (1960).

46. Livingston, M. S., and Bethe, H. A., *Revs. Mod. Phys.* **9,** 245 (1937).
46a. Molière, G., *Z. Naturforsch.* **3a,** 78 (1948).
47. Snyder, H. S., and Scott, W. T., *Phys. Rev.* **76,** 220 (1949).
48. Katz, L., and Penfold, A. S., *Revs. Mod. Phys.* **24,** 28 (1952).
49. Schonland, P. F., *Proc. Roy. Soc.* **A108,** 187 (1925).
50. Young, J. R., *J. Appl. Phys.* **27,** 1 (1956).
51. Davis, M., *Phys. Rev.* **93,** 243 (1954); *Nature* **175,** 427 (1955).
52. Lane, R. O., and Zaffarano, D. J., *Phys. Rev.* **94,** 960 (1954).
53. Cole, A., Ph.D. Thesis, University of Texas, 1957.
54. Alper, T., *Z. Physik* **76,** 172 (1932).
55. Tsien, S. T., Marty, C., and Dreyfus, B., *J. phys. radium* **8,** 269 (1947).
56. Whittaker, E. T., and Watson, G. N., "Modern Analysis," p. 373. Macmillan, New York, 1943.
57. Halpern, O., and Hall, H., *Phys. Rev.* **73,** 477 (1948).
58. Marton, L., Leder, L. B., and Mendlowitz, H., *Advances in Electronics and Electron Phys.* **7,** 183 (1955).
59. Ruthemann, G., *Ann. Physik* **2,** 113 (1948).
59a. Fano, U., *Phys. Rev.* **118,** 451 (1960).
60. Watanabe, K., *J. Chem. Phys.* **26,** 542 (1957).
61. Pollard, E. C., and Forro, F., *Arch. Biochem. Biophys.* **32,** 256 (1951).
62. Slater, M., Ph.D. Thesis, Yale University, 1951.
63. McClure, G. W., *Phys. Rev.* **90,** 796 (1953).
64. Platzman, R. L., private communication.
65. Sommermeyer, K., and Dresel, H., *Z. Physik* **141,** 307 (1955); **144,** 388 (1956).
66. American Petroleum Institute Research Project 44. Carnegie Institute of Technology, 1953–55.
67. Platzman, R. L., in "Symposium on Radiobiology" (J. J. Nickson, ed.), Chapter 9. Wiley, New York, 1952.
68. Fröhlich, H., *Proc. Roy. Soc.* **A160,** 230 (1937).
69. Fröhlich, H., and Platzman, R. L., *Phys. Rev.* **92,** 1152 (1953).
70. Platzman, R. L., in "Symposium on Radiobiology" (J. J. Nickson, ed.), Chapter 7. Wiley New York, 1952.
71. Skarsgard, L. D., Bernier, J. P., Cormack, D. V., and Johns, H. E., *Radiation Research* **7,** 217 (1957).
72. Laughlin, J. S., Beattie, J. W., Henderson, W. J., and Harvey, R. A., *Am. J. Roentgenol. Radium Therapy Nuclear Med.* **70,** 294 (1953).
73. Binks, W., *Acta Radiol. Suppl.* **117,** 85 (1954).
74. Bernier, J. P., Skarsgard, L. D., Cormack, D. V., and Johns, H. E., *Radiation Research* **5,** 613 (1956).
75. Weiss, J., and Bernstein, W., *Phys. Rev.* **98,** 1828 (1955); **103,** 1253 (1956).
76. Gross, W., Wingate, C., and Failla, G., *Radiation Research* **7,** 570 (1957).
77. Bay, Z., Mann, W. B., Seliger, H. H., and Wyckoff, H. O., *Radiation Research* **7,** 558 (1957).
78. Jesse, W. P., and Sadauskis, J., *Phys. Rev.* **107,** 766 (1957).
79. Bortner, T. E., and Hurst, G. S., *Phys. Rev.* **93,** 1236 (1954).
80. Stone, W. G., and Cochran, L. W., *Phys. Rev.* **107,** 702 (1957).
81. Wingate, C., Gross, W., and Failla, G., *Radiation Research* **8,** 411 (1958).
82. "American Institute of Physics Handbook," pp. 7–14. McGraw-Hill, New York, 1957.

83. Herzberg, G., "Spectra of Diatomic Molecules," p. 459. Van Nostrand, New York, 1950.
84. Jesse, W. P., and Sadauskis, J., *Phys. Rev.* **88**, 417 (1952).
85. Mohler, F. L., and Taylor, L. S., *J. Research Natl. Bureau Standards* **13**, 659 (1934).
86. Sternglass, E. J., *Phys. Rev.* **95**, 609(A) (1954).
87. Sternglass, E. J., *Phys. Rev.* **108**, 1 (1957).
87a. Tobias, C. A., Anger, H. O., and Lawrence, J. H., *Am. J. Roentgenol. Radium Therapy Nuclear Med.* **67**, 1 (1952).
88. Birge, A. C., Anger, H. O., and Tobias, C. A., in "Radiation Dosimetry" (G. J. Hine and G. L. Brownell, eds.), Chapter 14. Academic Press, New York, 1956.
89. Pollard, E. C., Guild, W. R., Hutchinson, F., and Setlow, R. B., *Progr. in Biophys. and Biophys. Chem.* **5**, 72 (1955).
89a. Gund, K., and Wachsmann, F., *Strahlentherapie* **77**, 573 (1948).
90. Laughlin, J. S., in "Radiation Dosimetry" (G. J. Hine and G. L. Brownell, eds.), Chapter 13. Academic Press, New York, 1956.
91. Spencer, L. V., *Phys. Rev.* **98**, 1597 (1955).
92. Taylor, L. S., *J. Research Natl. Bureau Standards* **2**, 771 (1929); **3**, 807 (1929); **8**, 9, 325 (1932).
93. Kemp, L. A. W., and Hall, S. M., *Brit. J. Radiol.* **27**, 219 (1954).
94. Bragg, W. H., "Studies in Radioactivity." Macmillan, New York, 1912.
95. Gray, L. H. *Proc. Roy. Soc.* **A156**, 578 (1936); *Brit. J. Radiol.* **10**, 600, 721 (1937).
96. Burch, P. R. J., *Radiation Research* **6**, 79 (1957).
97. Johns, H. E., and Bernier, J. P., Paper presented at the 40th Annual Meeting of the Radiological Society of North America, December, 1954.
98. Mayneord, W. V., *Brit. J. Radiol.* **13**, 235 (1940).
99. Weiss, J., Allen, A. O., and Schwarz, H. A., *Proc. 1st Intern. Conf. Peaceful Uses Atomic Energy, Geneva, 1955* **14**, 179 (1956).
100. Keene, J. P., *Radiation Research* **6**, 424 (1957).
100a. Miller, N., *Radiation Research* **9**, 633 (1958).
101. Grodstein, G. W., *Natl. Bur. Standards (U.S.) Circ.* **583** (1957).
102. Davisson, C. M., and Evans, R. D., *Revs. Mod. Phys.* **24**, 79 (1952).
103. Burhop, E. H. S., "The Auger Effect" Cambridge Univ. Press, London, 1952.
104. Nelms, A. T., *Natl. Bur. Standards (U.S.) Circ.* **542** (1952).
105. Greening, J. R., *Brit. J. Radiol.* **22**, 71 (1951).
106. Spencer, L. V., and Fano, U., *J. Research Natl. Bur. Standards* **46**, 446 (1951).
107. Hayward, E., *Phys. Rev.* **86**, 493 (1952).
108. *Brit. J. Radiol. Suppl.* **5** (1953).
109. Johns, H. E., "The Physics of Radiation Therapy." C. C Thomas, Springfield, Illinois, 1953.
110. Johns, H. E., Bruce, W. R., and Reid, W. B., *Brit. J. Radiol.* **31**, 254 (1958).
110a. Johns, H. E., Morrison, M. T., and Whitmore, G. F., *Am. J. Roentgenol. Radium Therapy Nuclear Med.* **75**, 1105 (1956).
111. Merideth, W. J., and Neary, G. J., *Brit. J. Radiol.* **17**, 151 (1944).
112. Spiers, F. W., *Brit. J. Radiol.* **10**, 52 (1946).
113. Price, B. T., Horton, C. C., and Spinney, K. T., "Radiation Shielding," Chapter 3. Pergamon, London, 1957.

113a. Blatt, J. M., and Weiskopf, V. F., "Theoretical Nuclear Physics." Wiley, New York, 1952.
113b. "American Institute of Physics Handbook," McGraw-Hill, New York, 1957.
113c. Hughes, D. J., and Harvey, J. A., "Neutron Cross-Sections," *Brookhaven Natl. Lab. Rept.* **325** (1955).
114. Strominger, D., Hollander, J. M., and Seaborg, G. T., *Revs. Mod. Phys.* **30,** 585 (1958).
115. Cowan, C. L., Jr., Reines, F., Harrison, F. B., Kruse, H. W., and McGuire, A. D., *Science* **124,** 103 (1956).

CHAPTER 1. PART 2

Target Theory and Radiation Effects on Biological Molecules

F. HUTCHINSON AND E. POLLARD*

Biophysics Department, The Josiah Willard Gibbs Research
Laboratories, Yale University, New Haven, Connecticut

CONTENTS

I. Target Theory

A most important concept in organizing the material of radiobiology is that variously called target theory, hit theory, trefferprinzip, etc. The basis for the concept is simple. An ionization releases a localized amount of energy which is sufficient to disrupt a small surrounding region to a considerable extent. Furthermore, in most cases the energy will be dissipated locally in such a way that the bulk of the immediate damage will be concentrated in the vicinity of the original site. Thus a biological system inactivated by the passage of a single particle or photon may be considered to have a sensitive volume or target, within which the release of sufficient energy causes the loss of function.

The history of the target theory is quite long. It appears to have been first introduced by Dessauer (1) in 1922, followed by Crowther (2) and by Condon and Terrill (3). The most extensive discussions and extensions of the theory have been by Lea (4) and by Timofeeff-Ressovsky and Zimmer (5).

* *Present address:* Whitmore Laboratory, University Park, Pennsylvania.

71

A. Determination of Sensitive Volume

1. the simple theory

Suppose that the material irradiated contains a large number of identical units each capable of some function which can be measured in a quantitative way. These units may be molecules such as enzymes capable of catalyzing a specific reaction, viruses possessing the ability to multiply in the right kind of cell, or even unicellular bacteria or haploid yeasts able to multiply into colonies. If a single structure in each unit must be intact for its future functioning, then the target theory predicts that the decrease in measured function after irradiation will be an exponential function of dose.

To see this, express the dose, D, delivered in terms of the number of inactivating events per unit volume produced randomly through the material. Then if the sensitive volume is V, the average number of such events per target will be VD. The events will, however, be distributed at random, with one event in some targets, two in others, none at all in others, etc. A general statistical result which applies to such random distributions is the Poisson formula, which predicts that, if the average number of random events in a single target is a, then the fraction of targets having exactly n events is

$$\frac{e^{-a}a^n}{n!} \tag{1}$$

We are interested in the number of targets which survive, i.e., have received no hits. Putting $a = VD$ and $n = 0$, we find that the Poisson formula gives the fraction of targets surviving (receiving no hits) as e^{-VD}, or an exponential survival. Independence of dose rate follows from the all-or-nothing nature of the interaction assumed.

A wide variety of biological systems are inactivated by ionizing radiation according to the exponential law, independently of dose rate. This includes essentially all inactivations of biological molecules such as enzymes, antigens, and nucleic acids, of viruses, and of many bacteria and haploid cells such as yeasts. The induction of mutations also follows similar laws.

It should not be concluded, however, that target theory is a necessary consequence of an exponential survival curve. The exponential indicates merely that the inactivation is caused by the passage of a single photon or particle, and independence of dose rate shows that the activated states produced in the irradiated material are sufficiently short-lived so that the chance of those active states produced by one photon or particle interacting with those of another is negligible at attainable dose rates. This might be referred to as a "hit" theory, and the value of V deduced from experiment considered to be merely a parameter describing the radiation inactivation. The term "target theory" would then designate a line of thought in which the physics of the process is taken into account in an interpretation of the experimental values of the parameter. In this connection it might be mentioned that thermal inactivation curves are often exponential, yet no profit has been reaped from a specific target theory of thermal inactivation, at least up to the present.

2. CALCULATION OF TARGET SIZE

It is apparent that, when the dose is such that the surviving activity has been reduced to $0.37 = e^{-1}$, then VD, the average number of inactivating events per target, is equal to 1. Thus, for conceptual purposes, the 37 % survival dose, D_{37}, is that dose for which there has been an average of one inactivating event per target. This is a major reason for the use of the D_{37} to express the inactivation of simple systems. It is clear that the surviving fraction can also be written

$$e^{-D/D_{37}}.$$

The inactivating event is usually considered to be either an ionization or an ion cluster. Excitations probably are not important for the following reasons: (1) In proteins the efficiency of an ionization for inactivation is one or two orders of magnitude higher than the efficiency for excitations (Section II.A); and (2) most excitations are probably in the immediate vicinity of an ion cluster (Section II.C of Part 1).

The simplest assumption is that a single ionization in the sensitive volume will inactivate. The spatial distribution of ionization has been discussed in Section II.C of Part 1, in which it was pointed out that the ionizations typically occurred in clusters, so that for targets larger than a few angstroms the unit of inactivation will actually be the ion cluster.

It is possible that under some conditions only n or more simultaneous ionizations will cause an inactivation. Theories based on this assumption have been developed (6, 6a). However, the discussion here will be limited to the case for a single ionization causing inactivation. If the target is large enough—i.e., large compared to the dimensions of an ion cluster—the cluster will be the effective inactivating event. A dose of D rads will then produce

$$D \text{ (rads)} \times \frac{100 \text{ ergs}}{\text{gm-rad}} \frac{\text{ev}}{1.60 \times 10^{-12} \text{ erg}} \times \frac{\text{ion cluster}}{75 \text{ ev}} \times \rho \frac{\text{gm}}{\text{cm}^3}$$

or $0.83 \times 10^{12} \rho D$ (rads) ion clusters per cubic centimeter. Now, $D_{37}V = 1$, and, expressing the target mass as its effective "molecular weight," $MW = V\rho \times 6.02 \times 10^{23}$, which eliminates the need for the density term, we find

$$D_{37}(\text{rads}) \times MW = 0.72 \times 10^{12} \tag{2a}$$

For a very small target, or one which is smaller than the separation of the ions in a cluster, the individual ions will be the effective events. If for tissue a mean energy is assumed of about 25 ev per ion pair, the same calculation leads to

$$D_{37}(\text{rads}) \times MW = 0.24 \times 10^{12} \qquad (2b)$$

On the other hand, for large enough targets the primary ionization may be the effective event, which gives

$$D_{37}(\text{rads}) \times MW = 0.96 \times 10^{12} \qquad (2c)$$

3. THE "ASSOCIATED VOLUME" CALCULATION

In the simple treatment given above, it has been assumed that the separation of the ion clusters is always large compared to the dimensions of the target. Although this is usually true for most of the ion clusters produced by high-speed electrons (and by the fast electrons produced by high-energy photons), it will not in general be true for the ion clusters produced in the densely ionizing tail of an electron's path. Furthermore, with radiations of higher LET, such as protons or α-particles, the ion clusters will frequently be much closer together on the average than the target dimensions. The effect will be that a certain percentage of the ion clusters are "wasted," in that more than one ion cluster will fall within the target.

To allow for this effect Lea (4) introduced his "associated volume" method. The target is assumed to be a sphere of radius R. For such a target to be inactivated by an ion cluster, the target center must be located within a spherical volume of radius R and centered on the cluster. This volume is said to be the inactivation volume "associated" with such ion cluster for a target of radius R. If an adjacent ion cluster is close enough so that its associated volume overlaps that of the first cluster, then the amount of overlap is a direct measure of the "wastage."

A calculation of the overlap volume must take into account the statistical fluctuations in the cluster separations for a track having a given mean spacing. The fraction $1/F$ of the associated volume which is not overlapped or "wasted," i.e., the actual associated volume, is given by Lea (4) as

$$\frac{1}{F} = \frac{3}{2\xi}\left[1 - \frac{2}{\xi^2}(1 - e^{-\xi}) + \frac{2}{\xi}e^{-\xi}\right] \qquad (3)$$

where $\xi = 2RJ$, and J is the mean number of ion clusters per unit path length. The associated volume corresponding to a length of track producing N primary ionizations is then

$$N\frac{1}{F}\frac{4}{3}\pi R^3 + \Delta \qquad (4)$$

where Δ is an additional term for the volume associated with the δ-rays produced. The δ-ray associated volume is calculated in the same general

TABLE I

Tabulated Values of $1/F$, the Fraction of Ionizations Which Overlap, According to Lea's "Associated Volume" Calculation (4)

ξ	0.0	0.2	0.4	0.6	0.8
<1		$\dfrac{1}{1 + \dfrac{3}{8}\xi + \dfrac{13}{320}\xi^2}$			
0	1.00	0.928	0.865	0.807	0.755
1	0.707	0.644	0.625	0.590	0.557
2	0.527	0.500	0.475	0.452	0.431
3	0.411	0.393	0.376	0.360	0.346
4	0.332				
>4	$\dfrac{1.50}{\xi + 2/\xi}$				

manner as the volume associated with the track, by using relation 3 of Part 1 to calculate the number of δ-rays in different energy ranges, and then computing the associated volume of each δ-ray by a cumulative process.

In Table I are given values of $1/F$ as a function of the variable ξ, which physically is equal to the average number of primary ionizations occurring in the spherical target for a charged particle crossing along a diameter. Quite complete tables for the associated volumes for several kinds of radiations are given by Lea (4).

These associated volumes are the radiation inactivation volumes determined experimentally. Given the type of radiation used and the measured inactivation volume, the size of the target may be determined within the limitations of the theory. Aside from the usual limitations of target theory— the assumption of fixed yields per ionization and of sharp target boundaries —the associated volume calculation is valid only for approximately spherical targets.

In Fig. 1 is given the relationship between the observed 37 % dose, expressed in rads, and the target diameter. For comparison, equation 2, based on the assumption that a spherical molecule will be inactivated by an ion cluster, is also plotted as the dashed line. The discrepancy between equation 2 and the associated volume calculation for γ-rays is easy to understand: for sufficiently large targets two or more ion clusters can occur within the same target, a factor which is taken into account by the associated volume method, and leads to the larger calculated doses.

B. Target Theory for Heavily Ionizing Particles

A different approach for radiation which has the ion clusters closely spaced together is to consider the inactivation to be caused by the passage of the heavily ionizing particle through the target (6–8). With sufficiently

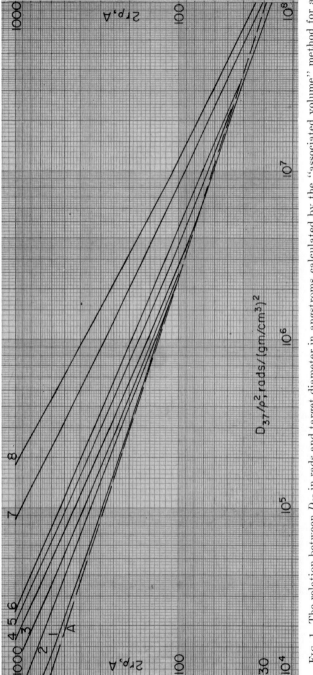

Fig. 1. The relation between D_{37} in rads and target diameter in angstroms calculated by the "associated volume" method for a density ρ gm/cm³. A, relation $D_{37} \times MW = 0.72 \times 10^{12}$ (equation 2); 1, 0.8-Mev γ-rays; 2, 0.15-A X-rays (approximately 200 kv); 3, 1.5-A X-rays (approximately 25-kv continuous radiation); 4, 14-Mve neutrons; 5, 4.1-A X-rays (3-kv photons); 6, 8.3-A X-rays (1.5-kv photons); 7, 6-Mev α-particles; 8, 3-Mev α-particles. Recalculated from D. E. Lea (Fig. 8 on p. 92 of ref. 4).

heavily ionizing particles at least one inactivating event will always take place. The dose will now be measured in incident particles per unit area, and the sensitive volume will be characterized by the cross section it presents to the incident rays.

The relationship between dose and the fraction of targets surviving can be calculated in much the same way as used previously. If the dose is expressed as B particles per unit area, and if the target has a mean cross section S, the average number of tracks crossing a target is SB, and, by equation 1, the fraction of targets which has not been hit is equal to e^{-SB}. Thus an exponential survival curve is again obtained, with the slope of the curve determining the cross section for inactivation.

Combining measurements of target volume V with sparsely ionizing radiation and cross sections S with densely ionizing radiation gives information about the shape of the target. The mean thickness, for example, is equal to V/S.

If the primary ions per unit length of track, J, is low enough so that the average separation becomes comparable to the thickness, t, of the target, there will be a certain chance that a particle will pass through the target without inactivating. The distribution of the ionizations along the track is random, so that the Poisson equation (equation 1) may be used. Since on the average there are Jt ions in the track within the target, the chance that there will be no ionizations within this distance is e^{-Jt}. For a particle characterized by J primary ions per unit track length the cross section observed, S_{obs}, will be given by

$$S_{\text{obs}} = S(1 - e^{-Jt}) \tag{5}$$

The connection between this relation and that for sparsely ionizing radiation can be seen by letting J become very small. In this case, $S_{\text{obs}} = SJt$, and the equation for exponential survival becomes

$$e^{-S_{\text{obs}}B} = e^{-(St)(JB)} = e^{-VD} \tag{6}$$

as it should.

On closer examination it will be found that some of the average values such as S and t for mean dimensions of the target have not been used in a strictly correct way. For example, in equation 5 the value of $(1 - e^{-Jt})$ should be averaged over all the varying thicknesses of the target instead of using the mean thickness, t. The various errors involved in these approximations have been systematically investigated by Ore (9) and shown to be negligible in most cases. Only for very heavy doses to very asymmetric targets will the use of average values produce a significant error.

In the discussion so far the inactivation off the track by δ-rays has been neglected. Unfortunately, no really satisfactory way exists of correcting

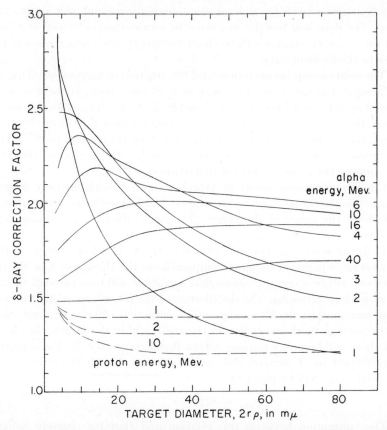

FIG. 2. The factor by which observed cross sections should be divided to get the target cross section. These curves are calculated from the Lea "associated volume" theory (4). The large factors calculated for small targets and low-energy α-particles are very sensitive to the numbers and ranges of low-energy electrons assumed, quantities about which there is considerable uncertainty. The calculated values for targets below 20-mμ diameter for 1- and 2-Mev α-particles are almost certainly much too high.

the observed cross sections for these δ-ray effects. One way is to use Lea's associated volume calculations, comparing the volume associated with the δ-rays to the total associated volume of the track. In Fig. 2 are plotted the factors by which the observed cross sections are to be divided to yield the geometrical cross section of the target. The correction to use depends on the diameter of the target, so that in practice a method of successive approximations must be used.

C. The Zirkle-Tobias Diffusion Model

Nothing has as yet been said about the possibility that the energy released at a given spot might migrate before becoming degraded to the point that it is unlikely to cause a biological effect. Some migration will almost certainly occur, and consequently the boundaries of the target in many cases will not be sharply defined. A particularly important case of this kind will occur in a cell when free radicals are created in the water by the action of the ionizing radiation (see Chapter II). These will diffuse through the water phase until they react with the solid cellular constituents. Zirkle and Tobias (10) have devised a model of this process.

Assume that a radical is created at a distance r from a spherical molecule of radius r_0. As the radical diffuses through the intervening medium there is the possibility that it will react with the various molecules in solution, a possibility specified by an average rate of reaction, a, times the radical concentration. Then it may be shown (11, 12) that the probability that the radical reacts with the specified molecule is

$$\frac{r_0}{r} qe^{-(r-r_0)/\rho} \tag{7}$$

where $\rho \equiv \sqrt{d/a}$.

d = radical diffusion coefficient.

$$q = \frac{1}{1 + k_d/k_c}.$$

Where k_c amd k_d are rate constants for the reaction between the radical between the radical and the molecule, with k_c representing the chemical reaction rate between the surface of the molecule and the radicals already at the molecule's surface, and k_d the rate at which the radicals are transported to the surface by diffusion. When q equals 1, the radicals react as rapidly as they are brought to the surface, and the reaction is diffusion-limited. For very low values of q, the reaction speed is controlled entirely by the rate of chemical reaction at the surface.

Assume now that D units of ionizing radiation are delivered, producing DG radicals per unit volume, where G is the yield for the production of radicals per unit dose. The number of radicals produced in a spherical shell of radius r, thickness dr, and centered on the target molecule, is $4\pi r^2 \, dr \, DG$, and the number of these which will react with the target is obtained by multiplying by expression 7. The total number of radicals inactivating the molecule will then be obtained by integrating over all spherical shells, and multiplying by the probability, p, that a reacting radical can cause enough damage to inactivate. The average number of inactivating radical-molecule collisions is

$$p \int_{r_0}^{\infty} 4\pi r^2 \, dr \, GqD = 4\pi r_0^2 \rho (1 + \rho/r_0) p GqD$$
$$= 4\pi r_0^2 \rho (1 + \rho/r_0) G_m qD \tag{8}$$

Here the yield, G_m—the number of molecules inactivated by unit dose under such conditions that all the radicals react with the specified kind of molecule—has been substituted for pG.

Since the radicals are formed by the radiation at random, the fraction of molecules which will be inactivated by this process will be given by the Poisson formula. With dose expressed in ion clusters per unit volume, and with V the volume for the inactivation by direct effect, the surviving fraction will be

$$\exp - [4\pi r_0^2 \rho (1 + \rho/r_0)G_m q + V]D \qquad (9)$$

The term in brackets has the dimensions and significance of a total inactivation volume. From its definition, ρ has the significance of a mean distance which radicals can diffuse. The first term represents the volume in which the radicals are formed which attack the target, multiplied by factors which represent the efficiency of the attack. The value of q appears experimentally to be the order of 1 (13).

It should be noted that in this formulation the inactivation of a target through the mediation of diffusing radicals is exponential with dose.

D. Nonexponential Survival Curves

Certain nonexponential survival curves may also be profitably interpreted in terms of target theory. In Fig. 3 are shown two common types.

1. SUM OF TWO EXPONENTIALS

Curve b starts out an exponential, which gradually changes over to another slope. A possible interpretation is the presence of targets of two different sizes. The figure shows how the curve is decomposed into the sum of two exponentials, giving the target sizes of both, as well as the initial ratio of the two. Decomposition of such a curve into three or more components is rarely a practical procedure unless some auxiliary information about target sizes or relative concentrations is available.

With experimental curves of this kind, particular care must be used to be sure the "tail" is not the result of nonuniform dose distribution through the sample. Such nonuniformity can be caused by absorption of the beam of radiation, resulting in a lower dose to the deeper parts of the sample, or to variation over the cross section of the beam.

2. MULTIHIT SURVIVAL CURVES

Curve c indicates that several hits must be made on the biological target before the assayable property is lost. Many models have been used to interpret such curves, but only two particularly simple ones will be discussed here.

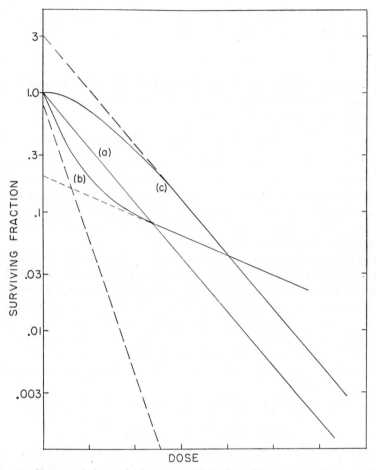

FIG. 3. Characteristic survival curves, with the logarithm of the activity surviving plotted against dose on a linear scale. a, Exponential survival curve. b, Sum of two exponentials. c, Multihit survival curve.

Model 1: Each biological system contains n targets, each of which must be inactivated. We shall call this the "multitarget model."

Model 2: The biological system contains a single target which must sustain n hits before the target is inactivated. We shall call this the "multihit target model."

The properties of the multitarget model (model 1) have been explored in detail (14). With volume V for each target, the probability of a single target's surviving a dose D is e^{-VD}, and the probability of its being knocked out is $1 - e^{-VD}$. The probability of all n targets in a single structure being hit is then

$$(1 - e^{-VD})^n$$

This is the probability that the activity of the unit will be destroyed, and the probability, P, that it survives is then

$$P = 1 - (1 - e^{-VD})^n \qquad (10)$$

For sufficiently large D (or small enough P) this curve becomes an exponential, and, if the natural logarithm of both sides is taken, the equation for the limiting line can be written

$$\ln P = \ln n - VD \qquad (D \text{ large}) \qquad (10a)$$

If this straight-line portion at high dose is extrapolated back to the axis along which $\ln P$ (or $\log P$) is plotted, the intercept will be $\ln n$ (or $\log n$), giving the number of targets involved. This is even true if the irradiated sample contains a distribution of units with varying numbers, n_i, of targets per unit; the intercept measures the true average number of targets per unit. The slope of the line determines V.

For the multihit target (model 2), the survival curve may be calculated directly from the Poisson formula. With a target volume V, a dose D will produce VD hits on the average. The fraction of targets receiving no hits will then be e^{-VD}; the fraction receiving 1 hit, VDe^{-VD}; the fraction receiving 2 hits, $[(VD)^2/2!]e^{-VD}$; and so on, to the fraction receiving $(n - 1)$ hits, which will be $[(VD)^{n-1}/(n - 1)!]e^{-VD}$. Targets receiving more hits will not survive, and so the probability of survival of activity, P, can be written as the sum of those fractions receiving less than n hits, or

$$\begin{aligned} P &= e^{-VD}\left(1 + \frac{VD}{1!} + \frac{(VD)^2}{2!} + \cdots + \frac{(VD)^{n-1}}{(n - 1)!}\right) \\ &= e^{-VD}\sum_{i=0}^{n-1}\frac{(VD)^i}{i!} \end{aligned} \qquad (11)$$

For this model at high doses (low P) the survival curve does not become a true exponential, and no simple extrapolation is possible to determine n. It is still true, however, that low values of n will give a curve which extrapolates back to a low value on the $\ln P$ scale, whereas a large n will give a curve with a final slope which will extrapolate back to a large value on the $\ln P$ axis.

Although the two models give curves which are different in shape, the differences are so small that only with extremely accurate data can a decision usually be made as to which model fits better. An experimental method of distinguishing is to use densely ionizing radiation. In general, the multiplicity of the multihit target will decrease more rapidly with such radiation than for the multitarget model.

II. Direct Effect of Ionizing Radiation on Biological Molecules

A. TARGET THEORY AND IRRADIATION IN DRY STATE

The effect of ionizing radiation on a living cell is exerted first on the molecules of which the cell is composed. The emerging ideas of molecular biology, which suggest that the many functions of the cell, from enzyme action up to the intricate relation between the two forms of nucleic acid and protein synthesis, are due to molecular action encourage the study of radiation action on the important molecules of the cell as providing the probable key to understanding radiobiological action.

There is thus a twofold problem which develops: first, an understanding of the nature of radiation action on molecules of various kinds; and second, the relation of this damage to cell function. The molecular damage occurs in two ways: directly by the release of energy within the structure of the molecule itself, and indirectly by the formation of highly reactive agents from cell constituents, particularly water, which diffuse to critical sites in the cell and there react. This latter "indirect effect" is dealt with more at length in the chapter on radiation chemistry; our main concern here is with the "direct effect" of the radiation on biological molecules.

One method of studying direct action is to observe effects in dry materials, in which the diffusion of reactive chemical species is greatly reduced, if not essentially eliminated. A considerable body of research on this type of material has been reported in the last decade (6), with results which appear to be capable of more simple generalization, in terms of target theory, than was perhaps to be expected. The simple generalization is that in a great majority of cases a remarkable correlation exists between the radiation inactivation volumes and the physicochemical measures of molecular volumes. In other words, the occurrence of an ion cluster within the molecule releases sufficient energy to remove, with a high probability, the biological function. The explanation is probably complex and may lie in the fragility of long-chain nucleic acids, on the one hand, and the migration of an unpaired electron along the covalently bonded structure of a protein, on the other; but the correlation is so impressive and the potentiality of use in a radiobiological theory is so good that it is worth some time to state the case and consider the results.

1. RELATIONSHIP BETWEEN "INACTIVATION" AND TYPE OF ASSAY

The fraction of molecules affected by a given dose depends on the tests applied. If the criterion is the ability to perform a highly specific biological function, then a certain answer may be obtained. A test of something much less specific, such as the solubility of the material after irradiation, will in general produce another result. A check of the sedimentation pattern in the ultracentrifuge would be expected to evoke still a third response.

Unless specifically stated otherwise, in the following discussion we shall be concerned with the ability of the molecule to perform a highly specific biological function, such as an enzyme catalyzing its characteristic reaction, a ribonucleoprotein particle serving as a template, or deoxyribonucleic acid accurately duplicating itself. It is interesting that different specific properties of biological molecules are inactivated at the same rate. The protease and esterase activities of trypsin (15, 16) are inactivated in the same way by radiation, as is the action of xanthine oxidase on aldehydes and on purines (17). The inactivation of the esterase and of the protease activities of chymotrypsin were first reported to be different (18), but later measurements have shown that they are inactivated in the same way (19).

2. RELATION BETWEEN TARGET SIZE AND MOLECULAR WEIGHT

Shown in Fig. 4 is a plot of radiation target size, expressed in terms of the equivalent molecular weight, against physical molecular weight. The 45-degree line drawn is the curve to be expected if the radiation molecular weight is equal to the physical molecular weight. Although many points lie off the line by amounts that are much greater than the experimental errors, the most significant feature of the curve is the strong correlation over several orders of magnitude variation in the size of molecule. Data on a number of irradiated viruses show extremely good agreement between the target volume for inactivation and the nucleic acid content of the virus (20). Because of the protein coating on the virus, these results are not strictly comparable to the data on molecules, but the agreement does reinforce the general argument.

All the radiation molecular weights in Fig. 4 were calculated on the assumption that the inactivating event was the ion cluster. For the smallest molecules, the finite separation of the ions in the cluster will be important, and individual ionizations will be the inactivating events. This undoubtedly explains the tendency of the experimental points to lie above the line for small molecules.

The measurement of the radiation sensitivity of a molecule in the dry state has great possibilities as a method for the determination of approximate molecular weight. The big advantage is that it is possibly the only method in which it is not necessary to purify the compound first. The only requirements are that an assay for the activity of the molecule exists, and that the activity survives drying. In practice, this last condition is much less restrictive than might be supposed. Early approximate molecular weights of several compounds have been determined by this method, including deoxyribonucleic acid (21) and ACTH (22).

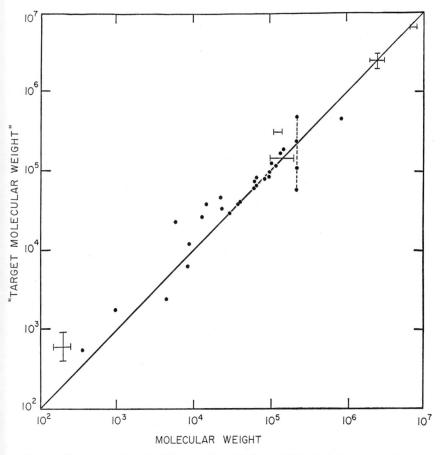

FIG. 4. The apparent radiation target molecular weight plotted against physico-chemical molecular weight for a number of biological molecules. The data are essentially those given in Table II of ref. 8. The meaning of the points connected by a dashed line is explained in the text. Graph courtesy of W. R. Guild.

A number of factors can alter the radiation sensitivity of a given molecule. In Fig. 4 the four points connected by a dashed vertical line represent the effective target sizes of the enzyme catalase for (from the bottom up) −180°C, 20°C, 80°C, and 112°C (23). Other proteins, nucleic acids, and viruses (6, 24) also show an increased radiation sensitivity with increased temperature, indicating that this is probably a general feature of direct action.

The materials in which the molecules are dried also can affect the radiation sensitivity in some cases. Norman and Ginoza have showed that ribonucleic acid from tobacco mosaic virus (25) and catalase (26) have their sensitivity reduced by a factor of 2 by drying down in large concentrations of SH-containing compounds such as glutathione. It has also been shown (27) that a number of other enzymes, including invertase and ribonuclease, may not only be protected but may also have their sensitivity to radiation enhanced by a factor of 2 by drying in certain compounds such as sodium acetate. In general, however, the radiation sensitivity does not depend strongly on the surrounding medium.

Alexander (28) has shown that dry trypsin has an increased sensitivity in the presence of oxygen to sparsely ionizing radiation such as γ-rays, but not to densely ionizing radiation such as α-particles. The radiosensitivity for γ-rays increases with oxygen pressure according to the relationship (29)

$$\frac{2.3 p_{O_2}(\text{cm}) + 1}{p_{O_2}(\text{cm}) + 1}$$

The close parallel between these results and the oxygen effects in cells and tissues (see Chapter 5) is striking.

It is possible that there is a connection between the oxygen effect and the increase in sensitivity with materials such as acetate, since the oxygen effect with acetate present is effectively zero (29).

3. VALIDITY OF TARGET CONCEPT

In applying target theory it is implied that the target volume will be the same for different radiations. Figure 5 shows that this is true for the irradiation of an enzyme with fast electrons (which is equivalent to high-energy X- or γ-rays), deuterons, and α-particles. The experimental points are consistent with the same target size for all three kinds of radiation.

Further evidence for the validity of the target concept as applied to structures of molecular size comes from an experiment on tobacco mosaic virus (31). This virus is long and thin, like a pencil, with a cross section for inactivation by deuterons comparable to the physical size of the virus. Samples of the virus were prepared in which the virus particles were aligned side by side in a known direction. When the samples were irradiated with the virus axis at an angle α with the beam of particles the observed cross section varied as $\sin \alpha$, significantly related to the projected area. As a control, tilting the samples in the other plane, with the particle axis held perpendicular to the beam, always gave the maximum cross section.

This experiment illustrates very clearly the reality of the connection between the radiation target volume and the physical structure of the irradiated material.

4. ROLES OF IONIZATION AND OF EXCITATION

Ionizing radiation produces both excitations and ionizations in matter, and the computation of target sizes from radiation data requires a knowledge of which events should be counted as inactivating ones.

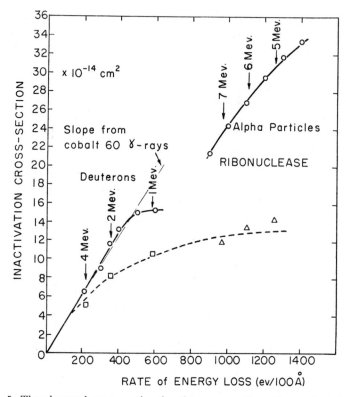

FIG. 5. The observed cross section for the enzyme ribonuclease plotted against the rate of energy loss in accordance with equation 5. The deuteron and α-particle data are from Deering (30): ○, experimental points; □, deuteron points corrected for δ-rays by the factor given in Fig. 2; △, corrected α-particle points; - - - - theoretical curve from equation 5, with $S = 1400$ A², $t = 26$ A. By equation 6, the slope at the origin is determined by the target volume: —— , slope at the origin corresponding to the experimental target volume of 34,000 A³ found by Co⁶⁰ γ-rays (unpublished data of D. K. Ray).

With the near ultraviolet, from about 2000 to 3000 A, it is known that proteins have a quantum yield, or molecules inactivated per photon absorbed, which is only of the order of 10^{-2} (32, 33). With such a low yield, excitation would not be important compared with ionization, which has an effective quantum yield of the order of unity. Setlow (34) has measured the quantum yield for the enzymes trypsin, chymotrypsin, and ribonuclease in the vacuum ultraviolet in the wavelength range 1215 to 2000 A. The yield is essentially constant at roughly 0.01 from 2000 A down almost to 1200 A, when it shoots up abruptly an order of magnitude. Photons of wavelength 1200 A have an energy of 10 ev and apparently are capable of creating some ionization.

These data support earlier results obtained by irradiation of proteins with very low-energy electrons (35). Below about 10 ev, the electrons had very little effect, but there was a very rapid rise in effectiveness with higher energies.

Thus it seems that the ion clusters in a protein will in fact be the inactivating events, with little contribution from excitations. This conclusion is reinforced by the probability that the excitations are located near the ion clusters and increase the energy release in a particular structure without contributing to the inactivation of neighboring molecules (see Section II.C of Part 1).

B. IRRADIATION EFFECTS ON MOLECULES IN CELLS

Within dried cells the radiation sensitivity is the same as the sensitivity in dried extracts for the enzymes invertase, cytochrome oxidase, and succinic dehydrogenase (36), arginine decarboxylase and tyrosine decarboxylase (37), coenzyme A (38), and acetylcholinesterase (39).

In the case of cells in the wet, living state, the molecules are subjected to an additional form of inactivation caused by the diffusion of radiation-produced free radicals through the cell water In this case one visualizes inactivation proceeding both by energy released within the molecule itself (direct action) and from radicals produced in a surrounding shell of liquid (indirect action). The thickness of the shell depends on the distance that the radicals can diffuse, and may be determined with the help of the Zirkle-Tobias model of Section I.C and data on the radiation inactivation of molecules in the cell. For several enzymes in yeast cells such data give a diffusion distance for radicals of the order of 30 A (12), and other data (40, 41) on other cells give distances between 10 and 40 A. Of some interest are the data for acetylcholinesterase in the electric organ of eels, rat brain, and human blood cells (39) and for coenzyme A in beef liver and in beef heart (41). These show the same inactivation in normal tissue as in dried preparations. The obvious implication is that in these tissues the enzyme is located in a region of the cell without much water present even under normal conditions.

The simple picture which has been presented is useful, but more work is needed to put it on a firm footing. The type of complications which arise may be illustrated by the report (42) that the degradation of polysaccharides is *less* efficient in the presence of a small amount of water than in the dry state.

C. OTHER RADIATION EFFECTS ON BIOLOGICAL MOLECULES

1. STRUCTURAL CHANGES

On irradiation of dry proteins the primary structural change appears to be the aggregation of molecules and loss of solubility. This has been reported for hemoglobin (43), bovine serum albumin (44, 45), ovalbumin (46), lysosyme (47), and bovine fibrinogen (48), among others. Some formation of fragments has been reported (45, 48), and new end groups produced by irradiation have been reported in lysosyme (47).

On other biological molecules the primary effect of ionizing radiation appears to be that of degradation. Deoxyribonucleic acid is apparently split into fragments by irradiation, according to light-scattering measurements (49) and changes in viscosity (50). Ribonucleic acid from tobacco mosaic virus has reduced viscosity in solution after irradiation in the virus, indicating a degradation (51). Polysaccharides are also degraded, as measured by viscosity changes (42).

2. SEROLOGICAL CHANGES

The antigenic properties of proteins are reduced by irradiation in the dry state (44, 46). For bovine serum albumin the observed decrease in serological activity is largely due to insolubility (44); when the immunological activity of a monolayer spread on a solid surface was assayed in place on the surface, with no requirement that the material go back into solution, the radiation effect was less than 10 % of that found in an assay where solubility was important (52, 53). Ovalbumin precipitates formed after irradiation in the dry state have been reported to have serological activity (46).

3. PARAMAGNETIC ELECTRON RESONANCE SPECTRA

Gordy and co-workers (54) have reported that X-irradiated proteins give quite simple electron paramagnetic resonance spectra, a fact which points to only a very few types of unpaired electrons formed in the protein. This unexpected result indicates some kind of an energy transfer taking place; some proteins have a spectrum identical to that of irradiated cystine, which indicates the possibility in some cases of energy localized in the S—S bonds known to be responsible for holding a protein together. This transfer of energy to S—S bonds has been demonstrated by a study of S—S bond breakage in the enzyme ribonuclease by irradiation (54a). The existence of electron transfer mechanisms has been demonstrated directly by the observation that a single type of free radical, as measured by electron spin resonance, is produced in irradiated proteins (54b). Irradiation of a mechanical mixture of amino acids produced only a diffuse signal corresponding to a number of different radicals.

D. MECHANISMS OF RADIATION EFFECTS

No satisfactory picture is yet available of the mechanisms by which a molecule is altered by the action of ionizing radiation, though several suggestive experimental findings make it likely that the mechanism is not hopeless of understanding.

1. INFORMATION FROM NONBIOLOGICAL MOLECULES

To understand the structural changes taking place, one possibility is to look at the radiation effects on large synthetic polymers. Although much simpler than macromolecules of biological importance, one would expect that processes taking place in the synthetic materials would also operate in other polymers.

Irradiation effects on synthetic polymers are reviewed in refs. 55 and 56. The basic processes occurring are degradation, or a break in the backbone of the molecule, and crosslinking, in which a covalent bond is formed between two molecules. Frequently accompanying these is the release of gases, such a hydrogen from hydrocarbons, and the formation of double bonds.

The existence of energy transfer within a molecule may be inferred from several experiments. Alexander and Charlesby (57) irradiated a twelve-carbon chain molecule with an aromatic ring connected to various carbons. The addition of the ring provided considerable protection against the formation of cross links, and the effect was most marked when the ring was in the center. This would indicate that the energy can migrate to the ring to be dissipated harmlessly there, and that the migration distance is less than twelve carbon atoms.

It is also well known that when molecules such as octanes or other hydrocarbons are bombarded with electrons in a mass spectrometer, the fragments formed are not those that would be expected on the basis of random breaking of the bonds in the molecule (58). On the contrary, the mass spectrometer patterns indicate that, in general, the weaker bonds, thermodynamically speaking, are far more likely to break, a behavior which again indicates clearly the transfer of energy within a molecule.

2. THEORIES FOR THE INACTIVATION OF BIOLOGICAL MOLECULES

The physical changes which cause the loss of specific biological function have not been identified in any case. According to one point of view, the inactivation is seen as caused by energy transferred to some point of the molecule and there changing the covalent structure (6). Platzman and Franck (59) have pointed out that the sudden appearance of an electric charge at the site of an ionization will produce a "shock" polarization wave in the surrounding structure which would be expected to produce devastating effects in the secondary structure of such molecules as proteins. Morowitz (60) has discussed radiation inactivation as occurring because of the loss of information, as measured by information theory. Probably all these points of view will be included in a successful theory, which should not be long in appearing and represents a challenge to the theoretical mind at present.

III. References

1. Dessauer, F., Z. *Physik* **12,** 38 (1922).
2. Crowther, J. A., *Proc. Roy. Soc.* **B100,** 390 (1926).
3. Condon, E. U., and Terrill, H. M., *J. Cancer Research* **11,** 324 (1927).
4. Lea, D. E., "Actions of Radiations on Living Cells." Cambridge Univ. Press, London, 1946.
5. Timofeeff-Ressovsky, N. W., and Zimmer, K. G., "Das Trefferprinzip in der Biologie." Hirzel, Leipzig, 1947.
6. Pollard, E. C., Guild, W. R., Hutchinson, F., and Setlow, R. B., *Progr. in Biophys. and Biophys. Chem.* **5,** 72 (1955).
6a. Howard-Flanders, P., *Advances in Biol. and Med. Phys.* **6,** 553 (1958).
7. Pollard, E. C., *Am. Scientist* **39,** 99 (1951).
8. Pollard, E. C., *Advances in Biol. and Med. Phys.* **3,** 153 (1953).
9. Ore, A., *Radiation Research* **6,** 27 (1957).
10. Zirkle, R. E., and Tobias, C. A., *Arch. Biochem. Biophys.* **47,** 282 (1953).
11. Wijsman, R. A., *Bull. Math. Biophys.* **14,** 121 (1952).
12. Hutchinson, F., *Radiation Research* **7,** 473 (1957).
13. Hutchinson, F., *Radiation Research* **9,** 13 (1958).
14. Atwood, K. C., and Norman, A., *Proc. Natl. Acad. Sci. U.S.* **35,** 696 (1949).
15. Simons, E. R., Ph.D. Thesis, Yale University, 1953.
16. Augenstine, L., personal communication.
17. Fluke, D. J., *Radiation Research* **5,** 478 (1956).
18. Aronson, D., Mee, L., and Smith, C. L., *in* "Progress in Radiobiology" (J. S. Mitchell, B. E. Holmes, and C. L. Smith, eds.), p. 61, Oliver & Boyd, Edinburgh, 1956.
19. Mee, L., personal communication.
20. Buzzell, A., Trkula, D., and Lauffer, M. A., *Arch. Biochem. Biophys.* **63,** 470 (1956).
21. Fluke, D. J., Drew, R., and Pollard, E. C., *Proc. Natl. Acad. Sci. U.S.* **38,** 180 (1952).
22. Child, R. G., Moyer, A. W., Cox, H. R., and Pollard, E., *Arch. Biochem. Biophys.* **61,** 291 (1956).
23. Setlow, R. B., *Proc. Natl. Acad. Sci. U.S.* **38,** 166 (1952).
24. Pollard, E. C., *Advances in Virus Research* **2,** 109 (1954).
25. Ginoza, W., and Norman, A., *Nature* **179,** 520 (1957).
26. Norman, A., and Ginoza, W., *Radiation Research* **9.** 77 (1958).
27. Braams, R., Hutchinson, F , and Ray, D., *Nature* **182,** 1506 (1958).
28. Alexander, P., *Radiation Research* **6,** 653 (1957).
29. Hutchinson, F., unpublished data.
30. Deering, R. A., *Radiation Research* **5,** 238 (1956).
31. Pollard, E. C., and Whitmore, G., *Science* **122,** 335 (1955).
32. McLaren, A. D. *Advances in Enzymol.* **9,** 76 (1949).
33. Setlow, R. B. *Advances in Biol. and Med. Phys.* **5,** 37 (1957).
34. Setlow, R. B., *in Proc. 1st Natl. Biophys. Conf.,* Yale Univ. Press, 1959; *Radiation Research* **9,** 179 (1958).
35. Hutchinson, F., *Radiation Research* **1,** 43 (1954).
36. Powell, W. F., and Pollard, E., *Radiation Research* **2,** 109 (1955).
37. Pauly, H., and Rajewsky, B., *in* "Progress in Radiobiology" (J. S. Mitchell, B. E. Holmes, and C. L. Smith, eds.), p. 32. Oliver & Boyd, Edinburgh, 1956.
38. Hutchinson, F., Preston, A., and Vogel, B., *Radiation Research* **7,** 465 (1957).

39. Serlin, I., and Cotzias, G. C., *Radiation Research* **6**, 55 (1957).
40. Rajewsky, B., Gerber, G., and Pauly, H., *in* "Advances in Radiobiology" (G. C. Hevesy, A. G. Forssberg, and J. D. Abbatt, eds.), p. 24. Oliver & Boyd, Edinburgh, 1957.
41. Hutchinson, F., and Norcross, C., *Radiation Research* in press.
42. Ehrenberg, L., Jaarma, M., and Zimmer, E. C., *Acta Chem. Scand.* **11**, 950 (1957).
43. Appleyard, R. K., *Arch. Biochem. Biophys.* **35**, 121 (1952); **40**, 111 (1952).
44. McNulty, W. P., and Hutchinson, F., *Arch. Biochem. Biophys.* **50**, 92 (1954).
45. Alexander, P., Fox, M., Stacey, K., and Rosen, D., *Nature* **178**, 846 (1956).
46. Fricke, H., Leone, C. A., and Landmann, W., *Nature* **180**, 1423 (1957).
47. Caputo, A., and Dose, K., *Z. Naturforsch.* **12b**, 172 (1957).
48. Sowinski, R., Oharenko, L., and Koenig, V. L., *Radiation Research* **9**, 229 (1958).
49. Alexander, P., and Stacey, K. A., *in* "Progress in Radiobiology" (J. S. Mitchell, B. E. Holmes, and C. L. Smith, eds.) p. 105. Oliver & Boyd, Edinburgh, 1956.
50. Butler, J. A. V., *Radiation Research Suppl.* **1**, 403 (1959).
51. Lauffer, M. A., Trkula, D., and Buzzell, A., *Nature* **177**, 890 (1956).
52. Hutchinson, F., *Arch. Biochem. Biophys.* **41**, 317 (1952).
53. Hutchinson, F., and Mosburg, E. R., *Arch. Biochem. Biophys.* **51**, 436 (1954).
54. Gordy, W., Ard, W. B., and Shields, H., *Proc. Natl. Acad. Sci. U.S.* **41**, 983 (1955).
54a. Ray, D. K., Hutchinson, F., and Morowitz, H. J., *Nature* **186**, 312 (1960).
54b. Patten, F., and Gordy, W., *Proc. Natl. Acad. Sci. (U. S.)* **46**, 1137 (1960).
55. Bacq, Z. M., and Alexander, P., "Fundamentals of Radiobiology," Chapter 4. Academic Press, New York, 1955.
56. Collinson, E., and Swallow, E. J., *Chem. Revs.* **56**, 471 (1956).
57. Alexander, P., and Charlesby, A., *Nature* **173**, 578 (1954).
58. Wallenstein, M., Wahrhaftig, A. L., Rosenstock, H., and Eyring, H., *in* "Symposium on Radiobiology" (J. J. Nickson, ed.), p. 70. Wiley, New York, 1952.
59. Platzman, R. L., and Franck, J., *in* "Symposium on Information Theory in Biology" (H. P. Yockey, R. L. Platzman, and H. Quastler, eds.), p. 262. Pergamon, New York, 1958.
60. Morowitz, H. J., *in* "Symposium on Information Theory in Biology" (H. P. Yockey, R. L. Platzman, and H. Quastler, eds.), p. 276. Pergamon, New York, 1958.

CHAPTER 2

Radiation Chemistry

EDWIN J. HART AND ROBERT L. PLATZMAN*

Argonne National Laboratory, Argonne, Illinois

CONTENTS

* *Present address:* Laboratoire de Chimie Physique, Paris, France.

I. Introduction

A. Nature of Radiation Chemistry

Radiation chemistry is that branch of chemistry which treats of the chemical action of all varieties of high-energy or "ionizing" radiations, and of the atomic and molecular phenomena that are encompassed in such action. Such radiations include both swiftly moving atomic particles (electrons, protons, α-particles, neutrons, fission fragments, etc.) and penetrating electromagnetic radiations (X-rays and γ-rays).

Activation by these particles or photons, each of which has an initial energy that is invariably very great compared with typical excitation energies of atoms and molecules, is communicated in *every* case along tracks of swiftly moving, electrically charged, atomic particles. Radiation chemistry is, therefore, essentially the study of the chemical changes induced by energetic charged particles. The excited and ionized atoms and molecules that result with different radiations are identical in nature and very similar in number (on an energy basis), and different radiations usually produce similar chemical effects. Quantitative variations, which do occur and are of great importance to investigators in determining the mechanisms, are usually variations in degree rather than in kind, and are in most cases to be ascribed chiefly to differences in spatial proximity of activations, rather than to differences in their character.

In harmony with this view is the basic fact that the chemical effectiveness of ionizing radiations is typically that corresponding to individual acts of molecular excitation and ionization; that is, the number of molecules of the medium which are ultimately transformed is usually of the same order of magnitude as the number of excited or ionized molecules initially produced. (This important general result stands in conspicuous contrast to the greater radiation sensitivity of biological systems, in which the coupled levels of biological organization modify and amplify the initial effects of radiation to such an extent that these effects are very difficult to correlate with observed changes.) The chemical effectiveness of ionizing radiation can, of course, be altered by secondary processes, of which many examples will be discussed below: back reactions may reduce it, or, if the system is thermodynamically unstable, chain reactions may augment it greatly.

B. History of Radiation Chemistry

The name "radiation chemistry" is a new one, coined during the recent war, but the study of chemical effects of ionizing radiations is old. It began with the discovery of chemical transformations occurring during electrical discharges in gases, widely investigated during the nineteenth century, and received marked successive impetus by the introduction of new sources of radiation, of which three are of signal importance: X-ray tubes, discovered in 1895; radioactive substances, discovered during the following year; and nuclear reactors, first achieved in 1942.

That electrical discharges in gases induce chemical changes was known in the eighteenth century. It was involved in the discovery of ozone, and afforded the basis of the important device for producing ozone from oxygen invented by von Siemens in 1857. The early researches were motivated in part by recognition that these reactions can proceed against the thermodynamic potential (as in the case of ozone formation) and therefore offer a means for conversion of electrical energy into chemical free energy; this possibility is no less attractive with contemporary sources of radiation. A review by the noted photochemist Emil Warburg in 1909 (1) lists fifty-five papers—a small sample of those extant—on the subject, including many by renowned scientists, and discusses in detail such reactions as ozone formation, nitrogen oxidation, ammonia decomposition, and carbon dioxide decomposition, reactions that are still of the greatest interest to radiation chemists. That this branch of radiation chemistry never achieved maturity is due to the extreme difficulty of quantitative studies, in particular of the number and character of the initial activations. However, modern developments in the understanding of electrical discharges offer great promise of providing the requisite quantitative basis.

With the availability of X-rays and, especially, of the radiations from radioactive sources, came an emergence of fairly accurate dosimetry, here, as in similar fields, an absolute requisite for building a legitimate science. Pioneering work by Becquerel, the Curies, Bragg, Ramsay, Soddy, and others, during the first decade of the twentieth century, established the foundation of a field of chemistry that quickly became active and widespread, although never truly popular. Early studies often derived from incidental observations made during investigation of radioactivity; among them may be mentioned the self-decomposition of compounds containing radioactive elements (e.g., the intrinsic instability of radium salts: $RaBr_2$ evolves Br_2) and the deterioration of materials used for containment (e.g., coloration and change in mechanical properties of glass, quartz, porcelain, and collodion; decomposition of paraffin and Vaseline). Research on the radiation chemistry of water began about 1900; it was discovered that the evolved gas contains an excess of H_2, owing to retention of H_2O_2 by the solution. Nor were gases neglected: the formation of ozone from oxygen was established, and invoked in explanation of the observed oxidation of many metals when exposed to air during irradiation. Decomposition (chiefly into their elements) of CO, CO_2, NH_3, and HCl, among others, received early attention. The approximate equality of number of ions produced and number of molecules transformed (the analog of the Einstein equivalence law in photochemistry) was demonstrated to obtain in a majority of cases, and instances of departure from equivalence were discussed in terms of secondary reactions. It was noted that the temperature coefficient of most reactions is exceedingly small, proving that activated molecules react on an energy plane greatly in excess of the thermal energy of the milieu, just as in photochemistry. Indeed, the guiding viewpoint was that of the latter, more advanced field; the similarity in nature of the changes caused by light and by ionizing radiation is consistently stressed in the early literature, although the exact character of the primary processes of radiation chemistry defied analysis to anything like the degree of elaboration commonly achieved in photochemistry.

Among the principal schools of research in radiation chemistry during this period, those of Lind, Mund, and Fricke merit special mention. Lind, in the United States, concentrated on gaseous systems; by use of carefully prepared α-particle sources he achieved remarkable accuracy in dosimetry, and his contributions, summarized in his monograph (2), constitute a major foundation of the field. The experiments of Mund (3, 4) in Belgium were similar in scope to those of Lind, particularly in their emphasis on gaseous media and α-particle sources. Fricke, in the United States, in a long series of studies concerned chiefly with aqueous solutions, laid much of the groundwork of contemporary thinking on the radiation chemistry of water and, moreover, made great strides in the difficult task of achieving accurate methods of X-ray dosimetry. He also pioneered in the application of knowledge derived from simple aqueous systems to solutions of complex, biologically important molecules. Other systematic investigations of historical importance were those by Kailan in Austria (β- and γ-rays from radium) and McLennan in Canada (high-speed electrons, *circa* 100 kev).

The modern era of radiation chemistry is dominated by the sources of unprecedented intensity and convenience that have been made available by the development and flourishing of nuclear reactors; included, besides the reactor radiations themselves, are radiations from radioactive sources extracted from reactors, such as spent fuel elements and, especially, concentrated artificially radioactive isotopes, of which Co^{60} and Cs^{137} are of paramount practical importance. At the same time, charged-particle accelerators have evolved to a state in which they provide beams of a variety of particles, energies, and intensities with flexibility and economy. Radiation chemistry is now an important branch of chemistry in its own right, actively pursued in many countries throughout the world, and it commands respect for the information it is providing on chemical kinetics and the properties of free radicals. There is likewise a growing interest on the part of chemical industry in the commercial potentialities of radiation action. The perennial difficulties of dosimetry have now been subjugated in most respects, and investigators are making great strides in such aspects as rigorous exclusion of impurities, identification and assay of minor radiolytic* products, detailed study of kinetics of competitive reactions using mixtures of varying proportions, exploration of radiolyses of complex substances, and interpretation of mechanisms.

C. Literature of Radiation Chemistry

The literature of radiation chemistry is widely dispersed throughout the journals of chemistry, physics, and biology. No single authoritative monograph is currently available. Comprehensive treatments of a number of selected topics may be found in the series of volumes edited by Haissinsky (5–7), and Haissinsky has also provided an excellent introduction to radiation chemistry as part of his book on radiochemistry (8). Concise but detailed summaries of current progress are afforded by a series of annual reviews (9–19). Elementary surveys are included in the books on radiobiology by Lea (20) and Bacq and Alexander (21). For information on chemical reactions occurring in electrical discharges, the monograph by Glockler and Lind (22) should be consulted. The older literature is summarized in the volume by Lind (2); brief discussions can be found in the standard treatises on radioactivity of the last generation (Rutherford, Curie, Kohlrausch, Meyer-von Schweidler).

D. Scope of This Chapter

The present article cannot claim comprehensive coverage of as broad and intricate a field as radiation chemistry has become. It is intended to stand by itself as an introduction to the subject, but its scope has been adapted to the context: some topics are emphasized on the basis of their pertinence, in experimental fact or in concept, to the known and anticipated needs of the radiobiologist. Aqueous systems are therefore the paramount

---

* The term *radiolysis* refers to any chemical changes induced by ionizing radiation, and includes synthesis as well as degradation.

concern; fortunately, their study happens to be the most advanced branch of the field. In Section IV the radiation chemistry of pure water, and of mixtures of water and its various decomposition products, is set forth in detail. Sections V and VI treat aqueous solutions of inorganic and of organic substances. In Section III a very brief survey of the balance of the field is attempted. Preceding these four sections is a review, in Section II, of the diverse properties of transient atomic and molecular species known or believed to exist in irradiated media. An understanding of these properties is indispensable for the interpretation of mechanisms of radiation action. Throughout the entire article the cardinal aim is to present, illustrate, elucidate, and correlate all of the important concepts, and not merely to recite an assemblage of facts.

II. Elementary Processes

A. Temporal Stages of Radiation Action

The absorption in matter of a high-energy particle or photon and any secondary particles that may be generated concomitantly is an exceedingly quick phenomenon, and is essentially completed before any response of the medium has time to develop. It gives rise to a large number of activated molecules, chiefly molecules that are electronically excited or ionized, in a drastically nonuniform spatial arrangement. These activated molecules are called *primary products*, and the period during which they are formed may be termed the *physical stage* of radiation action.

The primary products are extremely unstable and promptly undergo secondary reactions, either spontaneously, or in collisions. This second, or *physicochemical stage* involves some interactions not encountered in other branches of chemistry, as well as many that are familiar from photochemistry. It may comprise a single step, or a complex sequence of them.

Ultimately, the system attains thermal equilibrium, the primary products having been converted to stable molecules (some of which may be reaction products, i.e., molecules different from those originally present) and to chemically reactive species (principally, free atoms and radicals). It thus enters a third, or *chemical stage*, in which these reactive species proceed to react with each other, or with the milieu.

In a biological system there follows a fourth, or *biological stage*, which encompasses the sequential response of the organism to chemical products of irradiation, through a hierarchy of organizational levels.

Although these four stages are by no means sharply demarcated, they provide an enlightening basis for analyzing the complex succession of elementary events that are provoked by absorption of high-energy radiation. It is characteristic that the duration of each stage is very small compared with that of the subsequent one. Actual durations depend very much upon the medium; order-of-magnitude values for a typical aqueous system are: physical stage, 10^{-13} second; physicochemical stage, 10^{-10} second; chemical stage, 10^{-6} second. The biological stage may, of course, extend over many years.

Elucidation of the chemical action of ionizing radiation draws upon knowledge from radiation physics, atomic and molecular physics, and virtually all that contributes to the understanding of mechanisms of chemical reactions. There are three unique factors which are distinctive of ionizing radiation action and set it apart from all other varieties of chemical activation:

1. The brevity of the first stage. Electric charges are separated before the medium can react. In a polar material the ensuing response is therefore violent.

2. The character of the primary products. Very highly excited, and ionized, molecules are formed. These are not produced by absorption of visible or near-ultraviolet light. Although they need not necessarily lead to different entities of the chemical stage (e.g., unique free radicals), they may produce familiar ones in diverse ways.

3. The spatial distribution of primary products. Localization of the latter near particle trajectories has consequences which, with condensed phases, persist throughout the chemical stage and may govern the ultimate chemical action. Such phenomena are called *track effects*.

B. PRIMARY PROCESSES

1. EXCITATION

The primary processes* of radiation chemistry are individual acts of energy transfer to atoms or molecules which lie in the vicinity of the path of a charged atomic particle. Excitation and ionization, the two most important varieties of activation, result from the transient electric force exerted by the particle upon electrons in the neighboring molecules. This impulsive electric field induces quantum transitions in many of the molecules as the particle passes by; the concomitant retardation of the particle is just that discussed in Chapter 1 under the title "stopping power," or LET, and embodied, in the case of swiftly moving particles, for example, in the Bethe formula.

The probability of occurrence of an excitation act which brings the molecule to an excited state, n, is represented by the *effective cross section*, Q_n, defined so that NQ_n is the average number of such events, per unit

---

* The restricted meaning of "primary process" and "primary product" should be noted. These terms are used in various ways, and often loosely, in the literature.

distance traversed by the particle. (Here N is the number of molecules in unit volume of the medium.) Such a cross section depends upon properties of the molecule, and upon properties of the particle (charge and velocity) as well. Scattered data on excitation cross sections for gaseous atoms and molecules are available (23), but they are notoriously difficult to obtain, either by experiment or by theory, and the subject is not in a satisfactory state.

Fortunately, there is an important theoretical simplification at high particle velocities (greater than about 10^9 cm/sec): the cross sections for excitation to the various excited states become approximately proportional to f_n/E_n, where f_n is the product of a universal constant and the absorption coefficient for light of photon energy E_n (f_n is called an *oscillator strength*). For excitation by electrons of kinetic energy T,

$$Q_n = \frac{4\pi a_0^2 R^2}{T} \left(\frac{f_n}{E_n}\right) \ln c_n T, \qquad (T \gg R) \qquad (1)$$

where a_0 is the "Bohr radius of hydrogen" (0.529 A), R is the "Rydberg energy" (13.60 ev), E_n is the excitation energy, and c_n is a constant which depends upon the state n (obviously, c_n has only minor influence upon the magnitude of Q_n). It is this same principle which underlies the derivation of the simple Bethe stopping-power formula. A corollary states that transitions which are optically forbidden, that is, which cannot occur by absorption of light, are likewise absent in excitation by swiftly moving charged particles. Optically forbidden transitions can and do occur with slower particles—for example, with electrons having kinetic energy less than about 100 ev.

The typical dependence of Q_n upon particle energy, T, is illustrated in Fig. 1. The cross section rises from a zero value at the threshold, which is equal to the energy transferred, E_n; attains a maximum value; and then declines monotonically. For optically allowed transitions (like $1^1S \rightarrow 2^1P$ in the figure) this decline is roughly as T^{-1}, as in equation 1; for optically forbidden transitions (like $1^1S \rightarrow 2^3P$ in the figure) it is much steeper. Thus the peak is extremely sharp in the latter case, and such transitions are induced only by slow electrons.

The quantum transitions discussed above are termed electronic excitations because they involve reorganization of the positions and motions of the atomic or molecular electrons. Ionization differs from excitation only in that it includes the outright ejection of one or more electrons.† Study of the various electronic states permitted by the quantum laws is primarily the province of spectroscopy, and a tremendous store of information con-

---

† These are the formal definitions, but the word "excitation"—at least in the English language—is commonly used to signify *any* electronic transition.

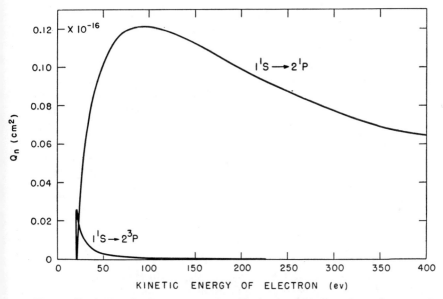

Fig. 1. Typical excitation cross section: Excitation of helium from the ground state (1^1S) to the 2^1P and 2^3P excited states by electrons. (For values of T greater than those in the figure, $Q_{2^1P}(T)$ can be calculated using equation 1 and the constants: $Rf_n/E_n = 0.178$, $c_n = 0.051$ ev^{-1}. If T is greater than about 10 kev, simple relativistic corrections are necessary, but the same two constants determine $Q(T)$. In contrast, there is no known formula for the cross section for the 2^3P excitation, which is an "optically forbidden" transition.)

cerning them is available, the detail and completeness diminishing, however, with increasing complexity of the atom or molecule.

Electronic energy is the only form of internal energy which an atom may acquire. Molecules, however, can exist in states having differing amounts of vibrational energy and of rotational energy. It is possible for charged particles to transfer energy directly to either of these modes, but because heavy particles (of atomic rather than electronic mass) must thereby be set in motion, the corresponding cross sections are several orders of magnitude smaller than for electronic excitation. Moreover, the excitation energies for vibration and for rotation are far smaller than electronic excitation energies. (The latter ordinarily have an order of magnitude of 10 ev; vibrational quanta are smaller by a factor of roughly 100, and rotational quanta still another factor of 100 smaller.) Hence, direct excitation of vibration or rotation is a wholly unimportant type of activation.

Indirect excitation of molecular vibrations is a common by-product of electronic excitation. Since the atomic nuclei move in an average electric field produced by all the molecular electrons, a change in the electronic configuration usually implies a change in the equilibrium configuration of the nuclei. But, in acquiring the excitation energy, the electrons alter their positions very quickly; the heavier nuclei are left in essentially their initial locations and subsequently perform oscillations about their new equilibrium positions. The excited molecule may, indeed, be so strained that it flies apart, or dissociates. Indirect excitation of nuclear motion via the intermediate stage of molecular *potential energy* is obviously a type of activation having important implications for chemical action (cf. Section II.C1.).

The preceding argument, based upon the great disparity in inertia of electron and nucleus, is an example of the application of the Franck-Condon principle. This principle will be invoked repeatedly.

2. IONIZATION

Formally, ionization of a molecule is simply a violent variety of electronic excitation. However, the residual electric charge may alter the behavior of the molecule in many ways, so the distinction between excitation and ionization has important implications in chemical mechanisms.

The probability of ionization acts is again measured by a cross section, Q_i, defined analogously to Q_n and always having the typical dependence upon T of an optically allowed transition (like the upper curve in Fig. 1). Measurement of ionization cross sections in gases is accomplished electrically, and trustworthy data for many atoms and simple molecules are available (23). The product NQ_i gives the average number of ionization acts per unit distance traversed by the charged particle; for very energetic particles this quantity is often called the *specific primary ionization*. For swiftly moving particles, Q_i (like Q_n) is given by a simple asymptotic expression; for incident electrons,

$$Q_i = \frac{4\pi a_0^2 R}{T} M_i^2 \ln c_i T, \qquad (T \gg R) \qquad (2)$$

where M_i^2 is simply an integral of $(f_n R/E_n)$ over all ionized states. Some values of M_i^2 are given in Table I.

In addition to the *total* cross section, Q_i, complete specification of ionization requires knowledge of the nature of the molecular ions which remain, and of the kinetic-energy distribution of ejected electrons. The former is immediately important because the ions are often formed in electronically excited states, and this additional excitation energy, which, in contrast to the ionization energy, is retained by the molecule, may have a decisive influence upon subsequent behavior (cf. Section II.C.1 and Section II.C.4). The latter does not affect chemical action directly, but it determines the spec-

TABLE I

SELECTED VALUES OF THE CONSTANTS IN THE ASYMPTOTIC
FORMULA FOR PRIMARY IONIZATION[a, b]

	H	He	A	H₂	N₂	O₂	C₂H₂	H₂O
M_i^2	0.2834	0.490	4.0	0.711	3.6	3.5	4.8	4
c_i	6.1	0.26	0.20	0.73	0.24	0.36	0.30	0.4

[a] The formula, equation 2, is valid for T greater than about 1 kev. Although simple relativistic corrections are required for T greater than about 10 kev, the same two constants determine the primary ionization, at all relativistic energies.
[b] M_i^2 is dimensionless; c_i is in units of $(ev)^{-1}$.

trum of electrons actually present in an irradiated medium, or *degradation spectrum* (24), and this spectrum, in turn, governs the numbers of various primary products that are produced (cf. Section II.B.4).

In the formation of an ion in its lowest, or *ground* electronic state, a quantity of energy $(I + \epsilon)$ is transferred from the incident particle, but none of this is retained by the molecule. The kinetic energy of the secondary electron, ϵ, is dissipated elsewhere in the medium; an amount equal to the ionization potential, I, is released when the positive and negative charges later recombine.

The spectrum of secondary electrons is represented by a *differential* cross section, Q_ϵ, which is analogous to Q_n and Q_i; indeed, Q_i is the integral of Q_ϵ over all ϵ. For swiftly moving incident particles, Q_ϵ is given by formulas analogous to equations 1 and 2. The spectrum is extremely skew. If $Q_\epsilon = $ constant $\times (I + \epsilon)^{-z}$, the measure of skewness, z, declines with increasing ϵ: for small ϵ, z is in the neighborhood of 3 for most media; for $\epsilon \gg I$, z approaches 2. The spectrum of secondary electrons is discussed more fully by Fano (25). It is illustrated in Fig. 2.

For the ground state of the positive ion, $(I + \epsilon) = E_n$. Hence equation 1, which applies here for each E_n, provided that E_n is not very great compared to I, shows that z is approximately equal to $z' + 1$, where z' is the corresponding measure of skewness for photoionization.

3. OTHER TYPES

Although excitation and ionization are generally the most important primary processes, there are other, less common varieties that can play a role when the irradiated substance has little or even no sensitivity to excitation or ionization of a valence electron. The two most important are direct ejection of an *atom* from its original position when struck by an atomic particle; and Auger disruption, a violent decomposition of a molecule that follows

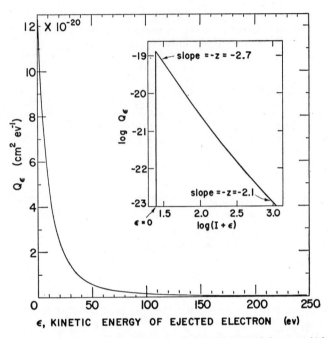

FIG. 2. Typical spectrum of secondary electrons ejected by a swiftly moving charged particle; ionization of helium by 10-kev electrons. (The insert presents the same data on a logarithmic plot, in order to illustrate the gradually diminishing skewness.)

the Auger cascade* resulting from ejection of an *inner* atomic orbital electron (26). Both have application to radiation action in certain chemically inactive solids (cf. Section II.D), to the chemical changes induced by nuclear transformation inside a molecule (Section III.F), and very likely to some cases of ordinary radiolysis as well.

Of the two processes, atom ejection is the better understood. Requiring momentum transfer as well as energy transfer from the colliding particle, it occurs most abundantly with fast neutrons and heavy charged particles, to only a small extent with high-energy electrons and γ-rays, and not at all with electrons or photons having energy less than about 100 kev. It is responsible for most of the physical changes which ionizing radiation causes in solids (so-called "radiation damage") and has been widely investigated (27). Atom ejection by a heavy charged particle occurs in a *nuclear collision*,

---

* The Auger effect, which is in fact a secondary process, although a spontaneous and very quick one, is the reorganization of atomic or molecular electrons following loss of an inner orbital electron which results in the ejection of one additional electron. A discussion of this effect can be found in any textbook on X-rays.

which results from the coulomb force acting upon the particle when it passes through the screened electric field of an atomic nucleus in the molecule. Because momentum is transferred directly to the atom from the incident particle, this process is intrinsically different from that in which an atom is liberated by molecular dissociation, for in the latter only energy was initially transferred, the momentum of the atom deriving from subsequent reorganization within the molecule. The role of atom ejection in chemical transformation is not yet established, possibly because there has been so little study of the most advantageous case, the chemical action of fast neutrons.

Nor have Auger disruptions been disentangled from valence-electron primary processes in the analysis of mechanisms. The total number of disruptions can, in favorable cases (atoms of low atomic number, with fast electrons or γ-rays), attain to roughly 1 % of the number of valence-electron excitations. This would be ample to account for the decomposition of such radiation-resistant substances as aromatic hydrocarbons (cf. Section III). Radiolysis by the ejected electrons also contributes to the chemical result of an Auger cascade. Further discussion can be found in Section III.F.4.

4. MODERATION AND CAPTURE OF ELECTRONS

Electrons, whether primary or secondary, pursue an erratic course through the medium, all the while losing energy in excitation and ionization acts. (It is customary to refer to all electrons that are not primary as "secondary.") This persistent diminution in kinetic energy is called *moderaions*.

The energy distribution of all electrons that may encounter a molecule in an irradiated medium is termed the degradation spectrum. For monoenergetic electrons incident with kinetic energy T_0, for example, this spectrum encompasses all values of T between T_0 and 0. There are two contributions to the component at T: secondary electrons which have been ejected with $\epsilon = T$ by electrons having energy T' greater than T; and electrons which, at any energy $T' > T$, suffer a single energy loss of $T' - T$. The theory of degradation spectra has been developed in detail (28), and extensive tabulations of results are available for various electron radiations in various media. However, the calculations presently available are limited to the high-energy portion of the spectrum $(T \gg I)$.

A typical representation of a *complete* degradation spectrum for monoenergetic incident electrons is given in Fig. 3. For $T \geq T_0/2$, there are no secondary electrons, and the intensity at T is approximately equal to the reciprocal of the stopping power, L, corresponding to T (28). For $T < T_0/2$, the intensity exceeds $1/L$ because of accumulation of secondary electrons, the excess increasing with $1/T$. The precipitous rise in intensity at small T reflects the corresponding skewness of Q_ϵ, but the relationship is

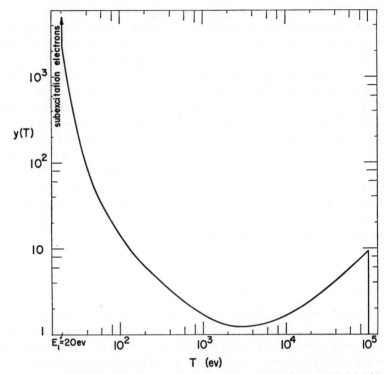

F**ig.** 3. A typical degradation spectrum: monoenergetic electrons (initial kinetic energy 0.1 Mev) in helium. (The function $y(T)$ is proportional to the aggregate distance dx traversed by *all* electrons of kinetic energy T, in losing the energy dT. It is approximately equal to the reciprocal of the stopping power at T, for values of T between 5×10^4 and 10^5 ev. The scale of $y(T)$ is such that one unit on the graph is equal to $1.46 \times 10^{-4} \, P^{-1}$ cm ev^{-1}, when the pressure of the gas is P atm and the temperature is 0°C.)

obviously not a simple one. The total number of primary processes of a given type is determined by the integral over T of the product of a degradation spectrum* like that in Fig. 3 and the appropriate cross section, such as one of those in Fig. 1. The total numbers of excitation and of ionization events are of great importance in theoretical radiation chemistry (cf. Section III.B).

* For other than electron irradiation, more than one degradation spectrum is present. Thus, with γ-rays there are a photon spectrum and a concomitant electron spectrum; with fast neutrons, there are spectra of neutrons, of recoil ions, and of electrons. Obviously, electron spectra are always present. In all cases, the degradation spectrum is that of particles actually present in the medium; it would be observable, in principle, in the interior of a tiny cavity in the medium. Only the spectra of charged particles contribute sensibly to formation of primary products, except in the case of fast neutrons.

The moderation of an electron by excitation and ionization processes ceases when T has dropped below the excitation energy, E_1, of the *lowest* electronically excited state of molecules of the medium. If there were no other means for such electrons, called *subexcitation electrons*, to lose energy, they would accumulate without limit as irradiation proceeded. They do, indeed, accumulate, but to an extent limited by other, more feeble, moderation mechanisms that come into play for $T < E_1$ (30).

Three cases are to be distinguished. In an atomic medium, like a noble gas, subexcitation electrons can be moderated only by transferring kinetic energy to the (comparatively) very heavy atoms. This is a slow process, so that the electrons have a protracted existence. As a consequence, they can encounter and activate impurities, or components of the system present in small concentration, if these have electronically excited states with excitation energy less than E_1. In a molecular but nonpolar medium, like H_2 or N_2, the electrons can excite vibrational or even rotational states, but with probability so small that this case does not differ drastically from that of an atomic medium. However, in a polar medium, like HCl, energy loss to vibration occurs readily, and the subexcitation electrons have a very much shorter life.

Ultimately, free electrons either react with neutral molecules to form negative ions, a process termed *attachment*, or react with positive ions to form neutral species, a very different process called *recombination*. (They may also be removed by an applied electric field, but this case will not be discussed.) The term *electron capture* is usually bestowed indifferently upon both alternatives. Attachment and recombination result in electronic or molecular reorganization; *radiative capture*, in which part or all of the energy released is emitted as light, is noncompetitive and of no importance in radiation chemistry. Electron attachment should be deemed a primary process; recombination is more properly considered to be secondary (Section II.C.5). If a negative ion is formed, it will usually recombine later with a positive ion. Moderation processes are usually (but not always) faster than either attachment or recombination, so that electron energies first fall to the neighborhood of thermal energy (0.04 ev at 20°C) and capture occurs predominantly with thermal electrons. The initial reaction of the thermalized electron has an important bearing on subsequent chemical mechanisms.

Only a minority of chemical substances is able to form stable negative ions; for practical purposes this means essentially only molecules containing a halogen, an oxygen, or, possibly, a sulfur atom. The molecule is usually disrupted by the attachment process, an atomic negative ion being liberated. Examples of *dissociative attachment* occur with molecular halogens, hydrogen halides, water, and molecular oxygen. If the reaction is endothermal, it can occur only with electrons having kinetic energy nearly equal to the sum of the energy deficiency and an increment imposed by the

Franck-Condon principle. The probability of occurrence of this resonance process therefore depends upon its competition with moderation (31). If the "resonance energy" is greater than E_1, attachment cannot compete with moderation and is entirely negligible; if it is smaller than E_1, the two processes are competitive and accurate analysis is required to assess the yield of attachment, which may be substantial; if it is close to zero, attachment can occur with thermal electrons and usually does, for the attachment cross section is then comparatively large. Among the few known stable *molecular* negative ions, O_2^- seems to be highly important; it is formed in collisions of thermalized electrons and O_2 molecules, with comparatively great probability (32). Since oxygen is such a common component of irradiated systems, the participation of O_2^- in chemical mechanisms merits careful attention. In recent years there has been increasing suggestion that it may be an important primary product in irradiated aqueous solutions containing dissolved oxygen (or air).

C. Secondary Processes

1. DISSOCIATION AND INTERNAL CONVERSION

a. Excited Neutral Molecules. If excitation of an atom or molecule is to be effectual chemically, the excitation energy must be retained long enough to permit a chemical response to commence. The competition between chemical utilization of energy, on the one hand, and degradation or removal, on the other, is varied and intricate, and is a principal field of study in photochemistry and radiation chemistry (and also in photobiology and radiobiology).

Emission of excitation energy as light is called fluorescence. This phenomenon is common with atoms, and with complex organic molecules containing systems of conjugated double bonds (dyestuffs, for example); it is less common with small molecules. Diatomic molecules, the simplest case, can be discussed instructively on the basis of potential diagrams (Fig. 4). Here the potential energy of a molecule in a given electronic state is plotted against the separation of the two atoms. Ground states of stable diatomic molecules always have potential curves similar to curve A in Fig. 4. In such a curve, the difference in energy between the horizontal asymptote and the minimum point measures the dissociation energy, or bond energy, of the molecule; the separation corresponding to the minimum point is the equilibrium interatomic distance. Excited states may also be similar (attractive), like C, or they may have the character of curves B and D (repulsive). Attractive excited states usually have smaller dissociation energy, and often have greater equilibrium distance, than the ground state; this may be viewed as a consequence of a weakened chemical bond.

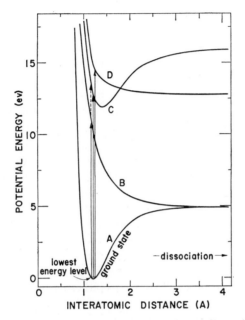

FIG. 4. Some typical potential-energy curves for a diatomic molecule. (Dissociation of a molecule in state A or B forms two atoms in their ground states; dissociation in state C or D produces atoms, at least one of which is excited.)

As already emphasized, the primary process occurs so quickly that all possible excited states have the ground-state equilibrium separation at the moment when they are formed (Franck-Condon principle); this characteristic is indicated by the vertical arrows in Fig. 4. Subsequent behavior of the system corresponds to the frictionless motion of a mass point along hills and valleys corresponding to the potential curves. Therefore, if an excitation process brings the molecule from state A to a state like B or D, dissociation follows immediately, the time required being approximately one-half vibration period, or about 10^{-13} second in most cases. Direct dissociation also occurs from an attractive excited state if its potential curve is so greatly displaced as to intersect the Franck-Condon line above the dissociation limit. If an excited state like C is formed, however, dissociation cannot occur spontaneously. The molecule must emit a photon of light (luminescence), unless there first occurs a collision in which the excitation energy can be transferred elsewhere. However, if the attractive curve C happens to intersect a repulsive one (D), the molecule, oscillating about its equilibrium position in state C, may cross over to D. Such a process, called *predissociation*, leads to the same products as dissociation (from the same repulsive state), but only after a significant delay in time. Predissociation is possible only if excitation brings the molecule to a point on the potential curve not lower than the point of intersection. In Fig. 4 the transition indicated by the solid arrow terminating on curve C does not satisfy this requirement; but the transition indicated by the dotted arrow does satisfy it, and can lead to predissociation.

Each of the two atoms formed in a dissociation event proceeds to undergo chemical reaction upon some later collision. Moreover, because the repulsive curves are usually (but not always) steep, the atoms are often liberated with substantial initial kinetic energy. Although this energy is quickly degraded in subsequent collisions, it can enhance considerably the effectiveness of a prior chemical interaction. Such *epithermal* (or "hot-radical") reactions may be common with dissociation products of small molecules. [The other major source of epithermal atoms and radicals is recoil from a nuclear transformation (cf. Section III.F).] These reactions differ from ordinary (thermal) reactions in a number of ways—for example, their rate is insensitive to changes in temperature. The few studies that have been made thus far (14, 33) have confirmed the potency of atomic kinetic energy, and it is altogether likely that epithermal reactions are more important in radiation chemistry than is generally acknowledged.

Polyatomic molecules can be treated in similar fashion, but impose greater complexity, since the potential energy must be represented by a hypersurface, many coordinates being required to specify the positions of all atomic nuclei. Because the numerous potential surfaces will have abundant intersections, it is possible for an excited state to be transformed spontaneously to a lower excited state, the difference in energy being partitioned among the many possible atomic oscillations; this is yet another secondary process, and is denoted an *internal conversion*. With small molecules, dissociation is the most common consequence of excitation: an atom and a free radical, or two free radicals, are formed. With most large molecules, internal conversion is the most likely consequence, but the violently vibrating molecule may still dissociate if this can occur before the excess energy is removed during collisions with other molecules. However, in contrast to the case of diatomic molecules, the free atoms or radicals thereby liberated usually have very little kinetic energy. Whether or not the molecule dissociates, a substantial portion of the energy released by internal conversion will be retained in the vibrational system and gradually dissipated as heat to the environment, and during this period it will be available for activation of a chemical reaction.

In the case of complex molecules, a highly excited molecule is believed to undergo internal conversion extremely quickly (in 10^{-13} second or less) to the lowest excited state of the same multiplicity* (34). Thus, excited

* An important parameter in the characterization of various excited states of atoms and molecules is the total spin, S, which measures the vector sum of spins

singlets will lead to the lowest excited singlet state, and excited triplets to the lowest triplet. A molecule in the lowest singlet state may emit a photon (but, apparently, cannot undergo internal conversion) in transition to the ground state; for favorable cases the time required is of the order of magnitude of 10^{-9} second (the term *fluorescence* is conventionally restricted to this prompt luminescence). Or it may undergo internal conversion to the still lower, lowest triplet state; such a process is much slower than the internal conversions with unaltered multiplicity described first, and may or may not compete successfully with fluorescence. The energy of a molecule in the lowest triplet state, if not dissipated to the environment during collisions, can also be emitted as a photon, but this process— one of radiation with change of multiplicity—is distinguished by its slowness (delayed luminescence, termed phosphorescence; lifetimes are 10^{-4} second or even longer). Spent interest therefore attaches to molecules in their lowest triplet state, for in them the excitation energy is intact for comparatively protracted periods and therefore potentially available for chemical purposes (35, 36). Lowest excited triplet states of large molecules often lie so low that their excitation energy is in itself insufficient to dissociate a chemical bond in a collision with another molecule, but the energy may still be utilized in more complex processes—in metathetical reactions, for example.

Molecules in their long-lived, lowest triplet state have often been postulated as important intermediates in the physicochemical stage of radiation action, but supporting evidence is usually incomplete. Such activated molecules can be formed in three different ways: (1) direct excitation to a triplet state by a slow electron, followed by internal conversion if this is not the lowest triplet state (as discussed in connection with Fig. 1, such processes are rare, although they may be somewhat more common if the lowest triplet state lies substantially below the lowest singlet, so that a greater portion of the degradation spectrum can be effectual); (2) by internal conversion from the lowest singlet state (the likelihood of this process is enhanced if the molecule contains an atom of high atomic number); and (3) by recombination of an electron and an ion (in the formation of such excited states, triplets are three times as numerous as singlets). The first two of these lead to the lowest triplet state, whereas the last, which is absent if electron-ion recombination is suppressed, initially forms only very highly excited states.

(intrinsic angular momenta) of all orbital electrons; an alternative representation is the *multiplicity*, defined as $2S + 1$. In the vast majority of stable molecules, the individual electron spins (each $\pm\frac{1}{2}$ unit, depending upon orientation) normally are perfectly compensated, so that the ground state has $S = 0$—that is, a multiplicity of one (*singlet*). The most important excited states are either singlet or *triplet* ($S = 1$), the latter having two unbalanced, parallel electron spins. For details of this and, other properties of excited molecules, a book on molecular spectra and structure should be consulted.

It is a characteristic of excitation by swiftly moving charged particles (following from the factor f_n in equation 1) that the states which are produced predominantly are very highly excited, with excitation energies in the range of about 10 to 25 ev. Hence internal conversion is almost always an important *initial* secondary process for excited complex molecules produced by ionizing radiation.

b. *Excited Molecular Ions.* All the principles in the preceding section apply as well if the excited molecule happens also to be an ion. However, excited ions are far more accessible to investigation, for their spontaneous fragmentation can be observed directly in the mass spectrometer; and a great store of information on the dissociation processes is available (37). Apparently, the presence of a single electron vacancy does not modify the character of the process, apart from the consequences of a weakening of one or several bonds in the ion. If, however, two electrons have been ejected in the ionization act, dissociation processes usually occur more promptly (38), a consequence in part of the coulomb repulsion between the positively charged sites.

Since an ionized molecule in its lowest electronic state is usually stable, excitation of the ion (as part of the same primary process that resulted in ejection of an electron) is a requisite for subsequent dissociation. Electronic excitation energy may be quickly degraded to oscillational energy by internal conversion, thereby being added to contributions from the initial internal thermal energy of the molecule and from the acquisition imposed by the Franck-Condon principle as a result of the ionization act. The total vibration energy then fluctuates among the many atomic vibrations and during its varying partition may eventually happen to be sufficiently concentrated in one or another vibrational mode to dissociate the molecule, to rearrange its structure drastically (39), or both.

As is anticipated on the basis of such an analysis, a variety of different modes of dissociation is observed with a given complex molecule (whether neutral or ionized). Moreover, just as expected, experiment shows most fragments to have very little kinetic energy, in contrast to the case of diatomic molecules (discussed above). The fragmentation patterns are in many cases in semiquantitative accord with the simple theory described above (40).

2. ENERGY TRANSFER (35)

The excitation energy of an excited molecule may occasionally be transferred to another molecule before being degraded or emitted as light. Since the latter processes are spontaneous and prompt, intermolecular transfer of excitation energy can occur only under very special circumstances. When it does it may be very important, for it affords a means of canalizing excitation energy in favorable ways, and thereby of augmenting or of diminishing the effectiveness of the absorbed energy.

The most fully understood type of energy transfer is *sensitized fluorescence*.* (It is also called energy transfer via coupled electronic resonators). This may occur when an excited molecule A that exhibits fluorescence collides with a molecule B having an absorption spectrum that overlaps the emission spectrum of A. The energy-transfer process is formally equivalent to emission of a photon by A followed by absorption of the same photon by B. However, the interaction of A and B is strong only while they are separated by a distance smaller than the photon wavelength, and no meaning can be given to a photon having such a brief existence; rather, it is correct to say that the energy is transferred directly. If A and B were both atomic, the energy might be transferred back again subsequently, but with molecules this is not usually the case, because, as was already emphasized, each energy-transfer process is accompanied by dissipation of a portion of the energy to oscillational modes (heat), the possibility of resonance thereby being abrogated.

Sensitized fluorescence has been most thoroughly studied with atomic vapors, and with liquid and solid solutions of aromatic hydrocarbons and of dyes and naturally occurring pigments containing systems of conjugated double bonds (41). An actual collision between the two molecules is not required, for the energy transfer can occur over 20 A or more. Indeed, it may occur between different portions of the same, large molecule. An instructive example of this *intramolecular* energy transfer occurs with certain organic compounds containing rare-earth atoms: light is absorbed in the typical absorption band of an organic group and re-emitted with the line spectrum of the atom (42).

Other means of energy transfer occur in simple crystalline solids (43) (cf. Section III.E.1). It is not known whether they have any direct relevance to liquid systems, or to complex substances such as proteins (44).

Energy-transfer processes are of signal importance in the mechanism of scintillation detectors of ionizing radiation (6-II). Their participation in chemical mechanisms is often invoked, but few instances have been elucidated in any detail (cf. Section III for further discussion, with examples).

3. CHARGE TRANSFER

In a collision between an ion A^+ and a neutral molecule B, an electron may be transferred from B to A^+, in effect shifting the site of ionization.

---

* This term derives from the original discovery of the phenomenon, through observation of light emission from the molecules to which energy had been transferred. In radiation chemistry, greater interest lies in chemical utilization of the transferred energy.

Such a process is occasionally considered to be an instance of energy transfer, but it should be noted that the "energy" of an ion does not become available until a later stage, as a result of recombination.

Charge transfer has been studied thoroughly for the case of atoms (23). The probability of the process is at a maximum when the ionization potentials (I) of A and B are equal, and it tends to be smaller, the greater is $I_A - I_B$; if I_A is smaller than I_B , the process is obviously impossible with atoms having thermal energy. This *resonance* criterion is a clear manifestation of the Franck-Condon principle, for the energy discrepancy $(I_A - I_B)$ must be communicated to A and B as kinetic energy, and it is unlikely that heavy particles will require much momentum during the brief time needed for electron transfer.

Less is known about charge transfer between molecules. With polyatomic molecules the resonance requirement is relaxed by an abundance of molecular energy states, but the collision, enhanced in violence by the polarization force (cf. Section II.C.4 below), is not often a simple one in which an electron is transferred. Rather, the collision complex $(AB)^+$, having many different possibilities for dissociation, commonly decomposes into chemically altered products. This is particularly likely if the ion A^+ was originally excited. Diatomic molecules appear to be intermediate in behavior.

In liquids and solids, there is a possibility for an electron vacancy to be propagated over comparatively great distances (43). The existence of this phenomenon, however, has been established only for certain crystalline solids having a very high regularity in the atomic arrangement (just as for prolonged migration of excitation energy). It is not known whether electron vacancies in less ordered solids and in liquids are so mobile. Such an eventuality, however, would have important implications, for a mobility exceeding atom or radical diffusion would diminish the persistence of track effects into the chemical stage of radiation action.

Charge transfer, like energy transfer, offers a method of concentrating a substantial portion of the radiation effect in a component present only in small amount. It has been exploited particularly by Lind (ref. 2, Chapter 16), who studied the radiolysis of various gaseous substances in the presence of an excess of a chemically inert gas. The behavior was termed *ionic catalysis*. Among the reactions that have been so investigated are the polymerization of C_2H_2, of C_2N_2, of HCN, and of benzene; the oxidation of H_2 and of CO; and the decomposition of CO, of NH_3, of HBr, and of CH_4.

4. BINARY REACTIONS OF ACTIVATED SPECIES

Free atoms, free radicals, and excited molecules which are the primary or secondary products of irradiation behave just as do the same species produced by other means—by absorption of light, for example. The only major peculiarity of this, the chemical stage, is the inhomogeneity of spatial distribution of the activations in the case of liquids or solids (cf. Section II.F below).

Ionized molecules, on the other hand, are not ordinarily produced by other methods of activation. To form them by light absorption would require ultraviolet radiation with wavelength well below 1000 A, a virtually unexplored region. (The photochemical reactions induced in the upper terrestrial atmosphere by solar radiation are a conspicuous exception, and in many respects are more akin to radiation chemistry than to conventional photochemistry.) Great interest is therefore attached to the reactions which ions undergo.

Chemical reactions of molecular ions in binary encounters with neutral molecules are extremely rapid and effective. For example, they are often completed long before dissociation or recombination. Such reactions, commonly called *ion-molecule* reactions, are believed to be important steps in the mechanisms of many reactions induced by ionizing radiation. They may be investigated directly in the mass spectrometer (37, 45, 46). Examples are

$$H_2 + H_2^+ \rightarrow H_3^+ + H, \tag{3}$$

which quickly transforms the ions in irradiated hydrogen [this reaction, the existence of which has been known for a half century, was first studied theoretically by Eyring *et al.* (47), and its predicted rate was verified by experiment much later]; and

$$CH_4^+ + CH_4 \rightarrow CH_5^+ + CH_3, \tag{4}$$

the first step in the ionic component of the mechanism of methane radiolysis. Hydrogen abstraction by the ion is a common process.

The swiftness of ion-molecule reactions stems from the fact that any ion must exert a strong attractive force on any neutral molecule that it encounters, owing to polarization of that molecule. Therefore, all processes that are energetically favorable in the binary collision must proceed with comparatively great probability. Elementary theory shows that the time required for an ion-molecule collision for a system in thermal equilibrium at room temperature is about $10^{-10}/P$ second, where P is the gas pressure in atmospheres. Since experimental cross sections for ion-molecule reactions approximate to theoretical encounter cross sections, it appears that most collisions lead to chemical reaction and not, or at least not often, to stable ion clusters. This fact is plausible because the "collision-complex" molecular ion has a missing electron and therefore often at least one weakened chemical bond, but the excess energy contained in the original ion must also contribute to the effect.

TABLE II

RATES OF SOME TYPICAL PRIMARY AND SECONDARY PROCESSES[a]

	Gas	Liquid or solid	Remarks
Physical stage			
Excitation or ionization by a charged particle	10^{-16} and smaller	10^{-16} and smaller	Must be comparable to or shorter than period of "electronic oscillation" (cf. below).
Absorption of an α-particle	$7 \times 10^{-10} T_0 P^{-1}$	$7 \times 10^{-13} T_0$	T_0 is the kinetic energy in Mev.
Absorption of a high-energy electron	$2 \times 10^{-8} T_0 P^{-1}$	$2 \times 10^{-11} T_0$	T_0 is the kinetic energy in Mev. Valid from about 0.5 to 20 Mev.
Moderation of an electron ($T > E_1$)	$10^{-14} P^{-1}$	10^{-17}	Approximate time per ev lost.
Moderation of a subexcitation electron: dipolar medium	$10^{-10} P^{-1}$	10^{-13} (water)	Approximate time per ev lost.
Moderation of a subexcitation electron: atomic medium	$10^{-8} P^{-1}$	10^{-11}	Approximate time per ev lost.
Auger effect (inner shell)	10^{-15}	10^{-15}	—
Physicochemical stage			
Dissociation: diatomic molecule or ion	10^{-13}	10^{-13}	Predissociation is slower by as much as several orders of magnitude.
Dissociation: polyatomic molecule or ion	10^{-13} and *longer*	10^{-13} and *longer*	The larger the molecule, and the smaller the excess excitation energy, the longer the time.

Process			Remarks
Internal conversion: polyatomic molecule or ion	10^{-13}	10^{-13}	—
Ion-molecule reaction	$10^{-10}P^{-1}$	10^{-13}	—
Charge transfer (positive ion)	$10^{-8}P^{-1}$	10^{-11}	Several orders of magnitude faster in case of resonance.
Moderation of "epithermal" atom	$10^{-8}P^{-1}$	10^{-11}	Approximate time per ev lost.
Fluorescence	10^{-9}	10^{-9}	This is approximate lower limit; numerous cases are slower.
Phosphorescence (triplet state)	10^{-3}	10^{-3}	Applies to molecules containing atoms with $Z < 10$. Presence of heavier atoms shortens lifetime. As Z increases, the distinction between singlet and triplet breaks down.
Chemical stage			
Charge recombination (volume recombination)	$0.03(PI_1)^{-1/2}$ or $2 \times 10^5(PI_2)^{-1/2}$	$10^{-3}I_1^{-1/2}$ or $10^4 I_2^{-1/2}$	I_1 = absorbed-dose rate in rad/sec. I_2 = absorbed-dose rate in ev/gm sec.
Radical-radical reaction: track period	—	10^{-10}	—
Radical-"solute" reaction	$10^{-7}p^{-1}$	$10^{-7}c^{-1}$ (liquid)	For gas, p = partial pressure of "solute," in atm. For liquid, c = millimolar concentration of solute.
Radical-radical reaction: uniform period	$30(PI_1)^{-1/2}$ or $2 \times 10^8(PI_2)^{-1/2}$	$I_1^{-1/2}$ or $10^7 I_2^{-1/2}$	I_1, I_2 defined above.
Characteristic periods of ordinary matter			
Period of "electronic oscillation"	10^{-16} to 10^{-15}	10^{-16} to 10^{-15}	For H_2O: from 6×10^{-17} to 6×10^{-16}
Period of molecular vibration	10^{-14} to 10^{-13}	10^{-14} to 10^{-13}	For H_2O: 0.85, 0.87, and 2.02×10^{-14}
Period of molecular rotation	10^{-12} to 10^{-9}	Often replaced by relaxation time (widely varying)	For H_2O: 1.20, 2.30, and 3.59×10^{-12}. In liquid water, dielectric relaxation time = 10^{-11}; in ice at 0°C, 2×10^{-5}.
Interval between molecular collisions	$10^{-9}P^{-1}$	10^{-12}	—

^{a} The entries are orders of magnitude of the characteristic times required, in seconds. They refer in general to room temperature and a pressure of P atmospheres. When competition in a particular system is to be assessed the rates must often be evaluated carefully, for some of the numbers below are centered on a broad range.

5. RECOMBINATION

If a thermal electron is captured by a molecular positive ion, the energy, I, is finally released and usually dissociates the molecule. Thus, ionization followed by recombination acts like an extreme form of excitation, the effectiveness being delayed for a period during which the ion may have experienced other secondary processes, such as a spontaneous dissociation or an ion-molecule reaction. Hence the rate of recombination is a cardinal factor in determining the pathways of radiation mechanisms. If it is very great, ionization is, in effect, eliminated as a primary process, and its place is taken by excitations of excitation energy approximately equal to I. If it is very small, the positive ions and electrons pursue independent reaction paths which do not coalesce until the chemical stage is well under way. Some typical rates of recombination and its competitive processes are presented in Table II. Quantitative data on recombination rates (48) are sparse and not always trustworthy.

The rate of recombination depends principally upon: (1) the initial spatial disposition of ions and electrons (i.e., the nature and intensity of radiation); and (2) the presence or absence of negative-ion forming substances (or, in condensed phases, of electron-trapping sites). It also depends, but less markedly, upon the nature of the positive ions and the pressure of the gas.

Electron-ion recombination is usually a simple binary reaction, second order in the concentrations of electrons and positive ions. The rate constant (*recombination coefficient*) depends somewhat upon the nature of the ion, but most values for thermal electrons and molecular ions lie in the neighborhood of 10^{-7} to 10^{-6} cm^3/molecule second at normal pressures. The coefficients for true atomic ions are several orders of magnitude smaller. The dominant mechanism for molecular ions is *dissociative recombination*, an analog of dissociative attachment in negative-ion formation. At pressures exceeding about 20 atm, a mechanism of ternary collision competes, the third body carrying off some energy, thereby stabilizing the excited molecule. The latter therefore need not dissociate immediately, although it probably does so eventually. All measurements of recombination coefficients have been limited to atoms and small molecular ions; presumably, complex ions could capture electrons in binary collisions and be stabilized without dissociation.

Recombination of positive and negative ions is also usually second order. There is very little information on the rate constants, which are apparently of the same order of magnitude as for electrons. As would be expected on the basis of the discussion in the preceding section, the collision is likely to be complex. If the ions are molecular, chemical change is almost certain to occur.

Recombination is commonly classified in three categories: (1) volume recombination, in which ion distributions, and therefore the recombination rate, are uniform throughout the irradiated region; (2) initial, or preferential recombination,* in which an electron is recaptured by the same molecule from which it was ejected; and (3) columnar recombination, in which the ions are formed in regions of great local concentration, and recombination occurs, at least in part, at an augmented rate in restricted zones. Recombination can also occur at the vessel walls, but this is ordinarily negligible.

With radiations of small LET, volume recombination prevails, although in gases at high pressure some initial recombination is manifested. With particles of large LET, columnar recombination may be very important, particularly if negative ions are formed.

D. PRIMARY AND SECONDARY PROCESSES IN LIQUID AND SOLID SYSTEMS

For simplicity, most of the above discussion of primary and secondary processes referred to a gas or vapor, that is, to isolated molecules. If the irradiated medium is a condensed phase, with the molecules packed more or less tightly together, numerous features are different; above all, the swiftness of many of the processes may be drastically modified, and the relative importance of competitive reactions thereby altered.

The primary processes themselves may be severely affected. This is probably not so for low-lying excitations of molecular liquids and solids (as distinguished, for example, from such exceptional cases as atomic or ionic crystals), but the much more important excitations of high energy are believed to be shared by small groups of molecules, and thereby to acquire characteristics not possessed by the excitations of isolated molecules. The chemical consequences of such collective excitation are not yet known. Also, some instances may be the altered rate of moderation of slow electrons, owing to energy loss by such electrons to those modes of the medium responsible for dielectric loss. This change in moderation may in turn influence the probability of electron attachment to form negative ions and, through its influence on the time and path length required for thermalization, may affect the rate of recombination.

Some of the secondary processes may be severely modified. Others, like the average lifetime for fluorescence or the time required for dissociation, may be essentially unchanged. One of the most important consequences of the compact structure is the Franck-Rabinowitch effect, or *cage effect*, which is based upon the fact that reactive intermediates are not free to drift away

---

* There is diversity in the literature on the meaning attached to "preferential recombination."

from the site of formation, as they are in a gas, but must instead undergo a very slow diffusion. Fragments from molecular dissociation therefore make many collisions before escaping from one another, and the probability of *initial radical recombination*, with re-formation of the original molecule, is, in general, greatly enhanced, as compared to the same phenomenon in the gaseous phase. The cage effect is well known from photochemical studies, and is no less applicable to dissociation products of excitation by ionizing radiation. Hydrogen atoms ejected from *small* molecules (cf. state B in Fig. 4) retain most of the total amount of kinetic energy released, because of conservation of momentum in the two-body process, and therefore are more likely to escape the "cage."

A second important influence stems from the ease with which vibrational energy can flow out of an activated molecule into neighboring ones. If a particular mode of fragmentation depends upon an unlikely partition of the total vibrational energy produced by internal conversion, it will not compete successfully with the "cooling" effect of the environment. For this reason, results on ion fragmentation obtained from mass-spectrometric investigation are not immediately applicable to condensed phases; in particular, the extent of decomposition is expected to be much smaller.

A third important influence is peculiar to highly polar media (such as water, alcohols, carboxylic acids, and amino acids), and pertains only to secondary processes involving ions. Since the primary products are produced during the brief transit time of charged particles moving past molecules, they are created within an interval which is far shorter than those periods characteristic of the polarization response of the medium (measured by so-called *relaxation times*). The subsequent polarization therefore occurs during the physicochemical stage, and may interfere with various secondary processes. For example, ions produced in an aqueous environment will become hydrated, the energy relationships of their subsequent reactions thereby being drastically transformed.

A fourth influence is the effect of the condensed phase upon the time for electron-ion recombination. In a completely nonpolar medium this would tend to increase the probability of initial recombination, just as higher gas pressures do. However, polar liquids and solids possess diverse propensities for trapping electrons, and recombination may accordingly be partially or even completely prevented.

In addition to electronic excitation and ionization, ionizing radiation produces a rearrangement of the positions of some of the atoms, and in solids this rearrangement may endure and be detectable, particularly in those solids (e.g., metals) in which electronic effects are quickly reversed. Displacement of atoms is a feature of the action of fast neutrons, but it can also occur by direct momentum transfer from charged particles (27), and in some circumstances as a consequence of the Auger cascade (49, 50).

The slowness of diffusion in condensed phases, in addition to causing the cage effect, persists through the physicochemical stage and leads to an initial setting of the chemical stage in which free atoms and radicals are still distributed with pronounced spatial inhomogeneity. (In gases, this is not true, and the distributions are essentially uniform.) Ordinary chemical kinetics is not valid for such a condition, and an elaboration called *diffusion kinetics* is being developed for its treatment (cf. Section II.F).

E. DETECTION OF INTERMEDIATE SPECIES

Interpretation of the mechanism of a reaction of radiation chemistry customarily begins with a postulation concerning the inception of the chemical stage, that is, with certain numbers and kinds of free atoms and radicals (and in addition, for a condensed phase, with an assumption concerning their spatial disposition). With few exceptions, it has not yet been possible explicitly to relate these activated species to their precursors in the earlier stages of radiation action.

The basis for invoking a particular radical may involve information from spectroscopy, from mass spectrometry, from photochemistry, and from thermal-reaction kinetics, as well as some elements of surmise, and it is rarely unequivocal. Consequently, the greatest interest is accorded recent developments which enable unstable intermediate species to be detected, identified, and even assayed. The various methods are still so new that their potentialities and limitations are not fully known, and they have yet to be applied definitively to a system exposed to ionizing radiation.

One method, mass spectrometry, has already been discussed. It is limited to the ionic portion of the reaction, to intermediates formed from the primary ion after at least (but not much more than) a microsecond has passed, and, as already stressed, to gases at low pressure (monomolecular and bimolecular reactions).

A second method, absorption spectrometry, can in principle be utilized for consequences of both excitation and ionization. Because the transient concentrations of the intermediates under conditions of continuous irradiation are far below the sensitivity of the method, it is necessary to augment them. Two means have beeen exploited: build-up of transient concentration by exceedingly great, transient intensity of irradiation; or accumulation by inhibiting reaction of the intermediates, using collection at very low temperature, or in an environment (like a solid, or a viscous liquid) which diminishes their reactivity. The former method has been highly developed by use of strong bursts of light, a technique called *flash photolysis*. Because ultraviolet light transmitted by quartz is employed, ionic intermediates are not produced. Among the radicals already investigated are, in the gaseous phase, OH, CH_3, NH_2, HCO, and HNO (51); and, in the liquid phase, benzyl (52). The method holds great promise for radiation chemistry, and studies using intense, pulsed sources of energetic particles have already been initiated in a number of laboratories. It must be mentioned that the identification of a spectrum with a particular free radical is difficult and demands a skilled spectroscopist; once accomplished, however, the identification is unambiguous.

A third method, electron-spin (paramagnetic) resonance spectroscopy, derives from the capacity of molecules containing one or more unpaired electron spin to absorb microwaves at particular frequencies when they are exposed simultaneously to a magnetic field and a microwave source (53). Since transient species in irradiated materials (ions and free radicals) usually have odd numbers of electrons, the technique affords salutary selectivity and holds great promise in radiation research. It has been applied thus far only to irradiated solids, both inorganic (e.g., H_2SO_4, $HClO_4$, H_3PO_4) (54) and organic (e.g., acids, alcohols, sugars, amino acids, peptides, vitamins, hormones, proteins, nucleic acids) (55). Although comparatively simple to obtain, the resonance spectra which are readily manifested by many irradiated solids are by no means easy to identify; indeed, the nature of the ions or radicals responsible for most spectra thus far reported has yet to be unambiguously established. There are other hazards of the method; for example, a given free radical may, for any of several reasons, fail to record a resonance spectrum (56). It is thus of paramount importance that all measurements of these spectra be accompanied by accurate dosimetry, so as to ascertain whether a major effect of irradiation is being observed, and not merely a conspicuous minor effect.

F. Diffusion Kinetics

As was discussed in Section II. A, the primary products are located initially in the immediate neighborhood of tracks of charged particles (primary and secondary). This condition stands in contrast to the uniform distribution of activated molecules engendered by other agencies, such as heat, light, or sound. The great concentration gradients immediately impel diffusion processes which ultimately must bring the system to spatial uniformity, but, especially in liquids and solids, where diffusion is slow, the inhomogeneities persist throughout the chemical stage and are often a decisive factor in determining the yields of chemical products.

The branch of chemical dynamics designed to account for concurrent outward diffusion and reaction of intermediate species initially located in compact zones is called diffusion kinetics. Although inchoate and inexact, it has already afforded new insight into the behavior of competitive reactions, and has gained wide currency as a vehicle for interpreting details of radiation action, particularly in aqueous systems.

Only very simple schemes have been investigated thus far, most studies having been made on a "one-radical" model, which considers a single reactive species to be present. It is furthermore supposed that this entity, R, is consumed in only two ways: by recombination with another R, to form *molecular product* (R + R → R₂); or by reaction with a solute (R + solute → products). In conventional chemical kinetics, the rate equation would then be

$$\frac{dc}{dt} = -k_M c^2 - k_S cS, \tag{5}$$

where c is the concentration of R, S is the concentration of solute, and k_M and k_S are ordinary chemical rate constants. In diffusion kinetics, however, c depends upon spatial coordinates as well as upon the time, and a diffusion current must therefore be present. The rate of diffusion customarily is presumed to be represented by Fick's law, $\partial c/\partial t = D\nabla^2 c$. (Here, D is the diffusion coefficient; for liquids it is typically of the order of magnitude 10^{-5} cm² sec⁻¹.) Thus the rate equation is

$$\frac{\partial c}{\partial t} = D\,\nabla^2 c - k_M c^2 - k_S cS. \tag{6}$$

The solution of equation 6 depends upon the initial conditions, that is, upon $c(x,y,z)$ at $t = 0$. Since some of the phenomena occurring in the physicochemical stage are poorly understood, it is not yet possible theoretically to deduce a satisfactory description of the nature and spatial distribution of reactants at the onset of the chemical stage in terms of their antecedents.* Certain very simple, model distributions—which have patently severe shortcomings (24)—have therefore been assumed. There are indications, however, that the conclusions may be insensitive to some features of the initial disposition. It remains an important contemporary challenge to divine the salient features of the initial conditions of the chemical stage by application of the theory to experimental results.

Lea (57) was the first clearly to formulate and to attack the problem of chemical diffusion kinetics for tracks of ionizing particles. Considering liquid water, and supposing the reactive entities to be H and OH, he adopted Gaussian, axially symmetrical initial distributions (regardless of the magnitude of LET) for both radicals, the H being located substantially farther away from the axis. He treated only the recombination of unlike radicals to reconstitute water molecules (H + OH → H₂O), and

---

* The initial distribution of primary products is amenable to approximate theoretical analysis (cf. Chapter 1), although the contribution from secondary electrons is very difficult to treat. But that distribution is partially dissipated during the physicochemical stage, by such processes as charge transfer, energy transfer, and epithermal diffusion of electrons and molecular fragments.

calculated the rate of this reaction as compared to the rate of expansion of the column. With such a model, and an infinite medium, all radicals would ultimately recombine, but Lea discovered a pronounced difference in the relative rates between tracks of particles of high and of low LET. With α-particles, for example, reconstitution occurs quickly and is virtually complete after a severalfold expansion of the column, whereas with a high-energy electron it proceeds more slowly and is only one-half complete after a one-hundred-fold expansion. This difference recurs in later elaborations of the model and presages explanation of the dependence upon LET of the yields of secondary products (cf. Section IV).

It is now known that the columnar model does not adequately represent the initial distribution for radiations of low LET (e.g., X-rays and fast electrons). Instead of a continuous track, a great number of small, independent groups of radicals, called *spurs*, is commonly assumed (58). The further postulate of an initial Gaussian distribution of spherical symmetry for each spur leads to the striking result that, even in the absence of solute, a fraction of the radicals escapes recombination. Since such radicals would necessarily react with even a minute concentration of solute, the fraction is identified with the so-called *yield of radicals* (cf. Section IV). In terms of equation 6, the probability of escape of a radical is given by

$$p_R = 1 - \int_0^\infty dt \int_0^\infty (k_M c_1^2/N_0)\ dx\ dy\ dz, \qquad (7)$$

where $c_1(x,y,z,t)$ is the solution for $S = 0$, and N_0 is the initial number of radicals in the spur (or track).

Later studies (59–62) considered the one-radical model in the explicit form of equation 6, and devised approximate numerical solutions (analytic solutions are impossible) for Gaussian initial distributions of either axial or spherical symmetry. By use of an electronic computer, exact numerical solutions have also been obtained (63). Figure 5 depicts the calculated dependence of the fractional radical yield, p_R, from a spur, upon the constants D and k_M (and parameters of the initial distribution). It merits emphasis that, for axial symmetry, p_R calculated from equation 7 is zero; hence the cylindrical track does not provide a simple interpretation of the radical yield, as does the spherical spur. Analysis of this property for particles of high LET must therefore consider finer qualities, such as initial spatial correlations not encompassed in a radial Gaussian distribution, and details of the competition between recombination and reaction with solute.

The one-radical model is not directly applicable to systems of interest,

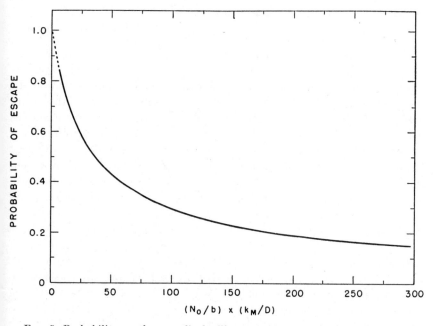

FIG. 5. Probability p_R that a radical will escape from a one-radical, "spherical" Gaussian spur, calculated from equation 6. (The dimensionless abscissa is proportional to the ratio of recombination rate-constant k_M to diffusion constant D; N_0 and b are parameters of the *initial* spatial distribution, $(N_0/\pi^{3/2}b^3)e^{-r^2/b^2}$.

in which at least two different radicals participate in the chemical stage. The two-radical model requires two equations like equation 6, each with its own set of constants D, k_M, k_S, the two equations being coupled together by a common fourth term, $-k_B c_1 c_2$, which represents the back reaction (reconstitution). This pair of equations is much more intractable than equation 6, but its solutions have also been investigated (64, 65). The predicted values of the various radical and molecular yields depend upon the choice of the seven constants and the parameters of the initial distributions, and this complex dependence has been explored in detail (65). However, most applications of diffusion kinetics to the interpretation of experimental results have contrived to use the one-radical model, cognizance being taken of the coupling of the two equations and of the differentiation between the two symmetrical (molecular product) and the unsymmetrical (reconstitution) recombination reactions by means of appended, qualitative reasoning. Since these applications have been directed exclusively to explanation of the radiolysis of liquid water and aqueous solutions, further discussion is now deferred to Section IV.

III. Survey of Radiation Chemistry

A. INTRODUCTION

Some of the classes of chemical action of ionizing radiation are rearrangement, decomposition and synthesis, oxidation and reduction, hydrogenation and dehydrogenation, and polymerization and depolymerization. In the brief space available here, it will be impossible to survey the entire field of radiation chemistry, even cursorily. Instead, a number of examples will be discussed, the selection being designed to illustrate elementary processes treated in Section II as well as to convey a picture of the great variety of radiation action and of the characteristics that have attracted the attention of investigators to particular reactions. Much of the information will be displayed in tables of radiolysis products and their yields. Information on compounds not listed in the tables can occasionally be found in the references for related substances. Most of the data thus far accumulated are for the products which are volatile, a fact which reflects the emphasis of past work as much as the greater difficulties in assay of nonvolatile products. The reported values of the yields are of widely differing trustworthiness. An attempt has been made to suggest their accuracy by curtailing the number of significant figures entered in the tables, but the basis for such an appraisal is far from adequate.

In the following pages, the measure of radiation-chemical yield is defined, and the various factors that determine its magnitude delineated. Then examples are given of reactions in the gaseous, liquid, and solid phases—a division which is common and convenient, although it does hinder the comparison of an individual reaction in the several phases. Water and aqueous solutions are treated in Sections IV to VI.

Among the physical constants to which frequent reference will be made are the ionization potentials and electron affinities of atoms and molecules, and dissociation energies of molecules. A collection of these constants is presented in Table III.

Although plausible and consistent mechanisms can be devised in many cases, it should be avowed at the outset that few if any of them can be maintained as having been fully established. Moreover, probably all radiolyses involve side reactions of greater or lesser complexity.

B. RADIATION-CHEMICAL YIELD

The effectiveness of a particular mode of chemical action of ionizing radiation is conventionally measured in one of two possible ways: by the *ionic* or *ion-pair yield*, M/N_i, or by the *100-ev yield*, G.

The ion-pair yield is defined by

$$\frac{M}{N_i} = \frac{\text{number of molecules produced (or consumed)}}{\text{number of "primary" ion pairs}}, \tag{8}$$

TABLE III

SELECTED VALUES OF IONIZATION POTENTIALS, ELECTRON AFFINITIES,
AND DISSOCIATION ENERGIES

(The primary entries are expressed in electron volts, but values of D in kilocalories
per mole are also presented [in brackets]. The conversion factor
is: 1 ev = 23.063 kcal/mole.)

	I	A	D^a
H	13.60	0.754	
O	13.62	1.47	
Cl	13.02	3.82	
Br	11.85	3.54	
I	10.44	3.23	
He	24.59	0	
Ne	21.56	0	
A	15.76	0	
Kr	14.00	0	
Xe	12.13	0	
H_2	15.43		4.478 [103.3]
N_2	15.58		9.759 [225.1]
O_2	12.08	0.15 (?)	5.081 [117.2]
HO	13.2	2.3 (±0.5)	4.40 [101]
CO	14.01		11.111 [256.3]
NO	9.25	>0	6.489 [149.7]
Cl_2	11.48		2.476 [57.1]
Br_2	10.55		1.972 [45.5]
I_2	9.28		1.542 [35.6]
HCl	12.74		4.431 [102.2]
HBr	11.62		3.755 [86.6]
HI	10.38		3.057 [70.5]
H_2O	12.59		5.16 [119][b]
HO_2	11.5	3 (?)	2.0 [47][b]
CO_2	13.79		5.43 [125][c]
H_2S	10.46		3.9 [90][b]
O_3		?	1.0 [24][c]
NO_2	12.3		3.11 [71.8][c]
NH_3	10.15		4.51 [104][b]
H_2O_2			3.9 [90][b]
H_2O_2			2.3 [52] (into 2OH)
CH_4	12.99		4.38 [101][b]
CH_3Cl	11.28		3.5 [81][d]
CH_3Br	10.53		2.9 [67][d]
CH_3I	9.54		2.3 [53][d]
CH_3OH	10.85		3.9 [90][d]
CH_3OH	10.85		4.3 [100][b]
CH_3NH_2	8.97		3.3 [75][d]
C_2H_6	11.65		3.7 [84][d]
CH_3OCH_3	10.00		3.3 [77][d]
CH_3NO_2			2.5 [57][d]
CH_3SSCH_3			3.2 [73][d]
CH_3SH			3.9 [89][b]

[a] Dissociation energies at 0°K.
[b] For detachment of the first H atom.
[c] For detachment of the first 0 atom.
[d] For detachment of the methyl radical.

the numerator and denominator referring, of course, to the same irradiation. (In accordance with the definition of primary products and processes in Section II, "primary" ions here include all those formed by charged particles, not only those formed by incident particles.) The 100-ev yield is defined by

$$G = 100 \times \frac{\text{number of molecules produced (or consumed)}}{\text{energy absorbed, in ev}}. \quad (9)$$

The relation

$$G = 2306 \times \frac{\text{number of moles produced (or consumed)}}{\text{energy absorbed, in kcal}}$$

is equivalent to equation 9. A given value of G refers to a specific substance which is indicated in following parentheses (a subscript is occasionally used in the literature; thus the yields for a radiolysis

$$A \rightarrow X + Y + Z \cdots$$

are $G(X)$, $G(Y)$, $G(Z) \cdots$, and $G(-A)$, the last referring to the expended reactant. Unless the chemical action conforms quantitatively to a known stoichiometry, all of these G-values are required to specify the radiolysis completely. The relation between the two measures of yield is

$$M/N_i = GW/100, \quad (10)$$

where W is the *mean energy per ion pair* (cf. Chapter 1).

In photochemistry the effectiveness is measured by a quantum efficiency or *quantum yield*, φ, defined as the ratio of number of molecules produced (or consumed) to number of photons absorbed. Since a given irradiation produces N_e excited molecules (and N_i subexcitation electrons) in addition to the N_i ions, the ionic yield manifests the collective contribution of several different φ's:

$$M/N_i = \bar{\varphi}_i + \bar{\varphi}_{se} + (N_e/N_i)\bar{\varphi}_e. \quad (11)$$

In this equation the bars denote averaging over the various primary products; thus, an ion may be produced in one of several different states, each having its own value of φ_i. Various radiolyses differ in the relative importance of the ionic component ($\bar{\varphi}_i$) and the excitation component ($N_e\bar{\varphi}_e/N_i$), but usually both contribute significantly to the consumption of reactant. This is less likely to be the case for formation of specific products, particularly ones of low abundance. The definition of $\bar{\varphi}_{se}$ shows that it can differ from zero only in systems having two or more components.

Interpretation of *absolute* ionic yields, which is an imperative step in the analysis of a mechanism, must proceed from equation 11 and has been retarded by lack of knowledge of N_e/N_i. The difficulty lies in N_e ; N_i can generally be measured directly* (in gases). Although the amount of light emitted by excited molecules is related to N_e, it cannot be used as a quantitative measure, because the efficiency is always smaller than unity even in the most favorable instances ("scintillating" gases, liquids, and solids) and is unknown in magnitude for all cases. This reduction of luminescence reflects the effectiveness of competing processes, both spontaneous ones such as dissociation and internal conversion, and quenching in collisions. However, information on N_e/N_i can be obtained from theory. It will be recalled (Section II.B.4) that N_e and N_i are proportional to average total cross sections for excitation and for ionization, respectively, the averages being weighted over the appropriate degradation spectra. For the noble gases, and all varieties of high-energy radiation, the ratio N_e/N_i is found to be 0.50; it has not been determined accurately for molecular gases, but inference from values of W shows that it must lie in the neighborhood of 1.0 in most cases (66). Frequent statements in the literature that $N_e/N_i = 2$ are incorrect.

Of the two alternate expressions of yield, M/N_i is the one of fundamental import. However, its evaluation from experiment requires determination of N_i, and this quantity has thus far been measured only in the case of gases. For this reason, the yield G was introduced, as a temporary expedient to permit expression of yields in condensed phases—particularly in the important case of liquids. When values of W become available, the G's can be converted to ionic yields by use of equation 10. The magnitude of 100 in the definition of G is of no significance; it was adopted to bring values of G into a convenient range. The use of G for gases is disadvantageous.

Since typical values of φ_i and φ_e are often near unity for major products, so, too, are many ionic yields. And since the compass of W (in gases) is 32 ± 10 ev/ion pair, G often lies between 1 and 10. There are many exceptions, but $M/N_i = 2$ and $G = 6$ to 10 are nevertheless useful "standard" values for appraising the efficiency of radiation action. A radiolysis with a standard yield for consumption of reactant is not very efficient: inasmuch as the energies of chemical bonds lie in the neighborhood of 100 kcal/mole

---

* The numbers N_e and N_i refer to *primary products*, but even the fastest ionization chamber has a response which is slower than most reactions of the physicochemical stage, and it therefore cannot often collect the primary ions themselves. However, no error is introduced, because if electrons are collected, their number is unaltered by elementary processes of the physicochemical stage—recombination excluded, of course; and if ions are collected, their total charge is likewise unaltered, notwithstanding the chemical transformations (such as dissociation or ion-molecule reactions) that they may undergo. An exception is the dissociation of an excited *neutral* molecule into a positive and a negative ion, but this process is rare.

or below (cf. Table III), the G for efficient cleavage of bonds should be 23 or greater. This intrinsic inefficiency stems from the fact that typical ionization potentials, and average electronic excitation energies, are two to four times as great as bond energies. For example, the ionization potential of H_2 is more than three times as great as its dissociation energy, but if recombination of an electron and an H_2^+ ion occurs, only a single molecule will be dissociated.

Yields much smaller than the standard value denote degradation of activation energy to heat prior to chemical effect, or back reaction. Greater yields can arise from secondary reactions, and also from surmounting of the intrinsic inefficiency by chemical reaction of the *primary* products. An important instance of the latter is occurrence of an ion-molecule reaction before recombination. Thus, if primary ion H_2^+ undergoes reaction 3 instead of recombining with an electron, subsequent recombination of the electron with H_3^+ will produce three H atoms, and a total of two H_2 molecules will have been dissociated. Another instance is the occurrence of dissociative attachment prior to electron recombination (cf. the radiolysis of HI, discussed in Section III.C.1). Both of these processes are enabled by the existence of electric charges on the two products of a primary ionization, and it is, in fact, a general property that such charges often tend to cause the contribution to the ionic yield to exceed the excitation contribution (i.e., $\bar{\varphi}_i > (N_e/N_i)\bar{\varphi}_e$). Both of them, if they are possible at all, do indeed usually proceed much faster than recombination.

In the case of condensed media, for which track effects are important, it is feasible to separate the reaction processes of the chemical stage into two consecutive periods: those occurring at the beginning, in restricted regions near particle tracks; and those which take place later, and homogeneously.* Since ordinary chemical kinetics is applicable to the latter period, it is often possible to calculate yields of various molecules and radicals that are present at the end of the tract period, by using observed ultimate yields (G-values) and a hypothesis for the mechanism. Such *inferred* yields will be distinguished by use of the symbol g (cf. Section IV for details).

C. Gaseous Systems

1. Inorganic Reactions (2, 4)

An appropriate first example is the decomposition of hydrogen iodide. The photolysis of HI is a classical and well-understood photochemical reaction. Its mechanism is

---

* The two divisions will be called, respectively, the *track period* and the *uniform period*.

$$\begin{cases} \text{HI} + h\nu \rightarrow \text{H} + \text{I} & \text{(12a)} \\ \text{H} + \text{HI} \rightarrow \text{H}_2 + \text{I} & \text{(12b)} \\ \text{I} + \text{I} \quad \rightarrow \text{I}_2 \, . & \text{(12c)} \end{cases}$$

Reaction 12b occurs instead of $\text{H} + \text{H} \rightarrow \text{H}_2$ or $\text{H} + \text{I} \rightarrow \text{HI}$ because the concentration of HI is vastly greater than that of H or I; indeed, two-body recombination of atoms is impossible because the recombination energy would immediately dissociate the molecule.* The reaction $\text{I} + \text{HI} \rightarrow \text{H} + \text{I}_2$, which is the analog of 12b, does not participate, because it is endothermic (by 35 kcal/mole). The sum of equations 12 is $2\text{HI} + h\nu \rightarrow \text{H}_2 + \text{I}_2$, so that $\varphi = 2$ for consumption of HI, and this is confirmed by experimental data at a variety of wavelengths.

The α-particle radiolysis of HI (67) gives $M(\text{-HI})/N_i \approx 6$; the ionic yield found for X-rays (68) is the same, within experimental error. Inserting $\bar{\varphi}_e = 2$, $\bar{\varphi}_{se} = 0$, $N_e/N_i \approx 1$, and $M/N_i = 6$ into equation 11 gives $\bar{\varphi}_i = 4$. Consumption of four HI molecules for each primary HI^+ ion pair is explained by the mechanism:

$$\begin{cases} \epsilon^- + \text{HI} \rightarrow \text{H} + \text{I}^- & \text{(13a)} \\ \text{HI}^+ + \text{I}^- \rightarrow \text{H} + 2\text{I} & \text{(13b)} \\ 2 \times [\text{H} + \text{HI} \rightarrow \text{H}_2 + \text{I}] & \text{(13c)} = \text{(12b)} \\ 2 \times [\text{I} + \text{I} \rightarrow \text{I}_2]. & \text{(13d)} = \text{(12c)} \end{cases}$$

Reaction 13a is a dissociative attachment which probably proceeds on one of the first few collisions. The fact that this process occurs long before recombination is responsible for an increase of the ionic yield by 2. An alternative to process 13b is the ion-molecule reaction

$$\text{HI}^+ + \text{HI} \rightarrow \text{H}_2\text{I}^+ + \text{I}; \tag{14a}$$

there is no experimental information on this process, but if possible it would replace 13b by the sequence comprised of 14a followed by

$$\text{H}_2\text{I}^+ + \text{I}^- \rightarrow 2\text{H} \text{ (or } \text{H}_2\text{)} + 2\text{I} \text{ (or } \text{I}_2\text{)}. \tag{14b}$$

If the product in reaction 14b were 2H rather than H_2, the yield would be augmented further by 2, giving $M(\text{-HI})/N_i = 8$. The available experimental data suggest, although not conclusively because of their limited accuracy, that this is not the case.

---

* Reaction 12c, and other two-atom recombination processes mentioned subsequently, occur in ternary collisions with a third molecule, the latter absorbing a portion of the recombination energy. In gases at ordinary pressures, such processes are very slow compared to binary reactions like 12b.

The photolysis of hydrogen bromide is analogous to that of hydrogen iodide and follows equations 12, with $\varphi = 2$. In the radiolysis, however, the observed ionic yield is smaller than for HI: $M(\text{-HBr})/N_i$ has been found to be 4.6 for X-rays (69) and about 5 for α-particles* (70), the difference being well within the experimental uncertainty. The elementary processes are analogous to those of HI; the anticipated yields would thus be $\bar{\varphi}_e = 2$ and $\bar{\varphi}_i = 6$, leading to an ionic yield (again supposing that $N_e/N_i = 1$) of 8. Indeed, it was specifically for the case of HBr that this mechanism, the ionic component of which proceeds by reactions 13a, 14a, and 14b, was first devised [by Eyring, et al. in 1936 (73)]. It clearly predicts too great a yield, but the origin of the excess has not yet been identified. A likely possibility is the dissociative attachment (process 13a), which for HBr is endothermal by 0.22 ev (cf. Table III; for HI this reaction evolves 0.17 ev) and is therefore slow. Although it could still proceed by thermal activation, it would have to compete with dissociative attachment to Br_2, a process that is exothermal by 1.57 ev, and even a minute accumulation of reaction product might therefore eliminate reaction 13a and thereby reduce $\bar{\varphi}_i$ (and M/N_i) by 2. The remaining discrepancy cannot be so plausibly explained, particularly in view of the fact that the ion-molecule reaction (14a) for HBr^+ has been found experimentally (74). Two possibilities are: that some of the excited molecules escape dissociation (whence $\bar{\varphi}_e < 2$); or that the recombination of an electron and H_2Br^+ produces H_2 rather than 2H (whence $\bar{\varphi}_i < 4$).

Another familiar photolysis is the decomposition of oxygen to form ozone. This reaction, which is of great importance in the photochemistry of the terrestrial atmosphere (75), is initiated by photodissociation of O_2; each O atom then combines with O_2 (in a three-body collision) to form O_3. Light which dissociates O_2 does indeed give $\varphi(\text{-}O_2) = \frac{3}{2}\varphi(O_3) = 3$, in agreement with the mechanism. Radiolysis would therefore be expected to have an ionic yield, $M(\text{-}O_2)/N_i$, of at least 6, the value which would obtain if each primary excitation yields two O atoms (almost all excitations by ionizing radiation do lead to dissociation) and each primary ionization,

---

* Study of the decomposition of HBr (HI is similar) by either light or ionizing radiation is complicated by the accumulation of reaction products, thereby permitting a back reaction, $H + Br_2 \rightarrow HBr + Br$, which accordingly diminishes the apparent yield. (The competition affords a definitive example of the effect of an epithermal reactant. That process 12b is favored with respect to back reaction by the substantial kinetic energy of H atoms produced by photodissociation has been established by experiments (71) in which the back reaction is found to be enhanced by prior moderation of H atoms through dilution of the system with an inert gas.) The ionic yield of approximately 5, cited above, was obtained from the experimental data (70) by correction for the effect of the back reaction. Other experiments have given a still lower value of 3 (72).

by recombination, also yields two. Since most recombination processes are reactions of O_2^+ and O_2^-, it is possible that more than two atoms would be formed from each ion pair, on the average, so that $M(-O_2)/N_i > 6$. Observed ionic yields are much lower, being about 3 both for α-particles (76) and for fast electrons (77). This deficiency is certainly to be ascribed to decomposition of some of the ozone produced.

Pure hydrogen is the simplest system of which the radiation chemistry can be studied. Two avenues are open to investigation: the conversion of *para*-hydrogen to *ortho*-hydrogen, and isotopic-exchange reactions. The former was first to be measured, and an $M(o\text{-}H_2)/N_i$ of about 1000 was found (78), the great magnitude being ascribed to a chain reaction carried by atomic hydrogen:

$$H + p\text{-}H_2 \rightarrow o\text{-}H_2 + H. \tag{15}$$

Since there is no net change of energy, the chain reaction, once initiated, would run without limit were it not for other processes competing for H atoms. Subsequent analysis (47) proposed the chain-terminating step to be recombination at the vessel walls, the rate being limited by diffusion, and from that rate and the observed ionic yield it was computed that the initial yield of H atoms was approximately $M(H)/N_i = 6$. This value is in accord with the expected efficiencies $\bar{\varphi}_e(H) = 2$ (with $N_e/N_i = 1$) and $\bar{\varphi}_i(H) = 4$, the latter resulting from reaction 3, which gives one H atom, followed by recombination of H_3^+ and an electron to yield three additional H atoms.

More recent investigations have addressed the isotopic exchange $H_2 + T_2 \rightarrow 2HT$ (79) and the corresponding reaction with D_2 (80, 81), and ionic yields as great as 10^4 have been obtained. The mechanism was presumed to be the chain reaction carried by atomic hydrogen (as in equation 15) until discovery of a drastic inhibition by small quantities of Kr or Xe (81). Neither of these substances affects the photochemically induced exchange, which is known to be propagated by H atoms, and it can therefore be inferred that the chain carrier in radiolysis (either para-ortho conversion or exchange) must be an ion. This ion is almost certainly H_3^+, produced by reaction 3 in about 10^{-10} second (at atmospheric pressure) after the primary ionization act. The exchange process is presumably a composite of reactions of the type

$$H_3^+ + D_2 \rightarrow H_2D^+ + HD \tag{16}$$

with various substitutions of H for D (or T); the para-ortho conversion is equivalent. Reaction 16 is expected to proceed at the typical rate of an ion-molecule reaction and therefore to dominate the atomic chain, which must also be operating. In the presence of Kr or Xe, or of certain impurities, H_3^+ is removed and reaction 16 suppressed, but the slower reaction 15 remains. Chain termination, by decomposition of H_3^+, is probably a result of charge transfer, in the case of an impurity with $I < 11$ ev (e.g., Hg), or of an ion-molecule reaction ($H_3^+ + Kr \rightarrow KrH^+ + H_2$), in the case of Kr or Xe. (It cannot be ascribed to charge transfer with Kr or Xe (81) because the reactions are highly endothermal.)

Although the yield of H atoms from H_2 eludes measurement in pure hydrogen because their effects are overwhelmed by those of the ionic chain reaction, the theoretical prediction of $M(H)/N_i = 6$ can be tested by the radiolysis of small amounts of various substances in the presence of a great excess of hydrogen. Thus, in admixtures of I_2 to H_2, the synthesis of HI does indeed proceed at the rate corresponding to the expected yield of H atoms (67). With H_2S in an excess of H_2, the products are H_2 and S, and the yield is $M(-H_2S)/N_i = 2$ (82). Since the mechanism of photolysis is

$$\begin{cases} H_2S + h\nu \rightarrow H + HS \\ H + H_2S \rightarrow H_2 + HS \\ HS + HS \rightarrow H_2S + S, \end{cases} \tag{17}$$

two H atoms are required to consume a single H_2S molecule; hence the inferred yield of H atoms is $M(H)/N_i = 4$, in fair agreement with the theory (83).

Photosynthesis of hydrogen chloride from the elements involves the classic case of a free-radical chain reaction:

$$\begin{cases} H + Cl_2 \rightarrow HCl + Cl \\ Cl + H_2 \rightarrow HCl + H. \end{cases} \tag{18}$$

In the radiation-induced synthesis both H atoms and Cl atoms are secondary products, being the result of primary excitation and ionization of H_2 and Cl_2, and the chain reaction causes ionic yields as great as 10^4 to 10^5 (84, 85). Termination of the chain devolves upon such factors as condition of the vessel walls and nature of impurities, and consequently the measured ionic yield is not a trustworthy basis for deductions concerning primary or physicochemical processes.

Carbon dioxide is extremely resistant to radiation, the ionic yield for decomposition (to $CO + \frac{1}{2}O_2$) being about 10^{-2} or even smaller (77, 86, 87) because of a very effective back reaction. Various secondary processes, not yet fully elucidated, are usually assumed to lead to $CO + O$, and it was formerly thought (83) that the efficient reconstitution of CO_2 is caused by a chain reaction catalyzed by the small quantities of oxygen which are produced in the first stage of irradiation:

$$\begin{cases} O + O_2 \rightarrow O_3 & \text{(19a)} \\ O_3 + CO \rightarrow O_2 + CO_2 \, . & \text{(19b)} \end{cases}$$

However, subsequent studies indicated that reaction 19b has a large activation energy. A mechanism for the back reaction devised recently assumes that part of the primary products yield $C + 2O$, and proposes a sequence of reactions involving two other oxides of carbon, C_2O and C_3O_2, in addition to O, O_2, O_3, C, CO, and CO_2 (88). It is germane that the ratio of CO to O_2 in the gaseous product is slightly less than 2, there being also formed, in small amount, a solid that is presumably a mélange of carbon and various of its oxides. Addition of a small amount of a substance like nitrogen dioxide, which removes free atoms, suppresses the back reaction and promotes rapid decomposition of the CO_2. Thus $M(-CO_2)/N_i$ attains the value of 3 with 1 % admixture of NO_2 (88).

Among other radiolyses may be mentioned the synthesis of H_2O in a mixture of H_2 and O_2, for which $M(H_2O)/N_i = 3$ (89, 90); the decomposition of H_2O vapor (discussed in Section IV because of its pertinence to the radiation chemistry of liquid water); and reactions induced in mixtures of N_2 and O_2. The last are most complex and involve a number of compounds of N, O, and (in the presence of moisture) H. They are of particular interest in connection with the chemical reactions which occur in the atmosphere under the influence of radiations from the sun (75), and their study has also been stimulated by the possible commercial feasibility of radiation-induced fixation of nitrogen (91, 92).

An important characteristic of those radiolyses which result in an increase in free energy (and therefore cannot have ionic yield greatly in excess of the "standard yield") is the fraction of absorbed energy that is stored by virtue of the chemical reaction. This is ordinarily only a few per cent, but in some cases it may reach 10 % (HBr decomposition, O_3 formation from O_2) or more; the greatest value yet attained is 25 %, for CO_2 decomposition with inhibited back reaction.

Many other reactions have been explored (2, 4), but few have been adequately elucidated. Indeed, the detailed study of reaction mechanisms with modern techniques—particularly physical and chemical techniques for investigating individual elementary processes and for identifying transient species—has hardly passed its infancy. Some aspects which demand future attention are avoidance of interference from accumulated products, a common source of error (which arises both from action of radiation on the products, and from reaction of products with transient species); attainment of improved accuracy in ionic yields, few of which are known to within 10 % (dosimetry for gaseous reactions is more difficult than for liquids and solids); and accurate comparison of the action of radiations of different LET, concerning which there is virtually no quantitative information for gases (differences* are expected usually to be smaller than 10%).

A selection of gaseous inorganic reactions and their ionic yields is presented in Table IV.

2. ORGANIC REACTIONS (2, 4, 100)

Study of organic substances in the gas phase is restricted in scope by the requirement of volatility, inasmuch as working at low pressures imposes severe difficulties (for example, in dosimetry), and elevated temperatures always complicate the reactions. Thus far, only some thirty compounds of low molecular weight, mostly aliphatic hydrocarbons, have been investigated. In this section, and also in the later ones dealing with condensed phases, the discussion will be limited to decomposition of initially pure organic substances, thereby omitting all multicomponent systems and such important classes of reaction as oxidation and reduction, for example. Even so, the radiolyses are all complex and yield a variety of products, including ones with greater and with smaller numbers of carbon atoms (cf. Table V). Both C–C and C–H bonds can be broken in primary and secondary processes; the neutral and charged fragments may react with parent or product molecules or with each other, and all mechanisms undoubtedly comprise a number of parallel but not often independent reaction pathways. The gaseous products are accompanied in every case by a solid or liquid mixture of compounds of high molecular weight and more-or-less obscure nature; in the literature this conglomerate is styled the "polymer" product.

Methane is decomposed to hydrogen, ethane, a light-colored liquid "polymer" having approximate composition $(CH_2)_n$, and a number of minor gaseous products. The reaction corresponds roughly to the stoichiometry:

$$2CH_4 \rightarrow \tfrac{3}{2}H_2 + \tfrac{1}{2}C_2H_6 + \text{"}CH_2\text{"}.$$

The ionic yields (Table V) are independent of pressure and of intensity of irradiation over appreciable ranges, and it is a curious (and fortuitous) circumstance that the sum of yields of gaseous products is almost exactly

---

* Such variations are anticipated, even in the absence of track effects, because of small differences between the radiations in the apportionment of absorbed energy among the various primary products. Thus, it is known that W for α-particles exceeds W for β-rays by about 6% for all molecular gases except H_2 (93), probably because of a greater value of N_e/N_i. This means, incidentally, that G_α/G_β is not equal to the corresponding ratio of ionic yields (cf. equation 10); the ionic yield is again more meaningful than the G-value.

equal to that for consumption of reactant, so that only a slight pressure change accompanies radiolysis. Since spontaneous dissociation of CH_4^+ ions in the mass spectrometer follows the pattern:

$$(CH_4^+)_{primary} \rightarrow 47\% \ CH_4^+ + 40\% \ CH_3^+ + 8\% \ CH_2^+ + 4\% \ CH^+ + 1\% \ C^+, \quad (20)$$

the three main reaction pathways are those initiated by CH_4^*, CH_4^+, and CH_3^+.* The last two of these pathways have been examined separately by accomplishing the radiolysis in mixtures of CH_4 with an excess of Kr or of A (113). This discrimination is possible because electron transfer from CH_4 to Kr^+ liberates only 1.01 ev and therefore produces stable CH_4^+, whereas A^+ liberates 2.77 ev, which exceeds the dissociation energy of CH_4^+, and yields $CH_3^+ + H$. (The argument is oversimplified because some of the noble-gas ions are in electronically excited states.) On the basis of these studies a mechanism has been formulated (113) which accounts, at least approximately, for the observed yields. Its chief steps correspond to the two main ionic pathways and are

$$\begin{cases} CH_4^+ + CH_4 \rightarrow CH_5^+ + CH_3 & (21a) = (4) \\ CH_5^+ + \epsilon^- \rightarrow CH_3 + H_2 & (21b) \end{cases}$$

$$\begin{cases} (CH_4^+)^* \rightarrow CH_3^+ + H & (22a) \\ CH_3^+ + CH_4 \rightarrow C_2H_5^+ + H_2 & (22b) \\ H + CH_4 \rightarrow CH_3 + H_2 & (22c) \\ C_2H_5^+ + \epsilon^- \rightarrow C_2H_5 . & (22d) \end{cases}$$

Radiolysis of methane in krypton proceeds predominantly by reactions 21 and is found to have the corresponding $M(H_2)/N_i$ of about 1, whereas in argon reactions 22 obtain, in agreement with the experimental

$$M(H_2)/N_i = 2.$$

In the latter case, it is expected that one of the H_2 molecules is produced as an *ultimate molecule*, that is, directly in molecular form (reaction 22b), and that the other is the result of *hydrogen abstraction* by a free H atom (reaction 22c). Each of these two contributions to the ionic yield of hydrogen was confirmed quantitatively, the direct yield of H_2 by measuring the reaction with added propylene, which removes the H atoms and thus suppresses reaction 22c (such a reagent is termed a *free-radical scavenger*), and the H atoms by measuring the formation of HD with added D_2.

In the radiolysis of pure methane the free methyl and ethyl radicals produced in the sequences 21 and 22 react with each other (and to some extent with other intermediate entities) to form ethane and the other gaseous

---

* A superscript asterisk denotes an electronically excited atom or molecule.

TABLE IV

IONIC YIELDS IN THE RADIOLYSIS OF INORGANIC GASES—A SELECTION

(The ionic yield, $M(x)/N_i$, is denoted by $Y(x)$.)

Reaction	Ionic yield	Radiation	Ref.	Remarks
$HI \rightarrow \frac{1}{2}H_2 + \frac{1}{2}I_2$	$Y(-HI) = 6$	α-rays, X-rays	67, 68	Mechanism among those best understood.
$HBr \rightarrow \frac{1}{2}H_2 + \frac{1}{2}Br_2$	$Y(-HBr) = 5$	X-rays, α-rays	69, 70	Mechanism among those best understood.
$O_2 \rightarrow \frac{2}{3}O_3$	$Y(-O_2) = 3$	α-rays, electrons	76, 77	Yield would be greater if back reaction were completely suppressed.
$p\text{-}H_2 \rightarrow o\text{-}H_2$	$Y(o\text{-}H_2) \sim 10^3$	α-rays	78	Ionic chain reaction; ionic yield limited by impurities or by diffusion of chain carrier to walls.
$H_2 + D_2 \; (\text{or } T_2) \rightarrow 2HD \; (\text{or } HT)$	$Y(HD \text{ or } HT) \sim 10^4$	β-rays, α-rays	79, 81	Ionic chain reaction; ionic yield limited by impurities or by diffusion of chain carrier to walls.
$I_2 + (\text{excess}) \; H_2 \rightarrow 2HI$	$Y(HI) = 6$	α-rays	67	Supports $Y(H) = 6$ in H_2.
$H_2S \; (\text{in excess } H_2) \rightarrow H_2 + S$	$Y(-H_2S) = 2$	α-rays	82	In rough agreement with $Y(H) = 6$ in H_2.
$H_2 + Cl_2 \rightarrow 2HCl$	$Y(HCl) \sim 10^5$	α-rays, X-rays, γ-rays, fission fragments	84, 85	Classical free-atom chain reaction.
$CO_2 \rightarrow CO + \frac{1}{2}O_2$	$Y(-CO_2) = 5 \times 10^{-3}$		86	Very effective and complex back reaction; some "polymer" also formed.
	$Y(CO_2) \sim 10^{-2}$	(α-rays, electrons)	(87, 77)	
$CO_2 \; (+1\% \; NO_2) \rightarrow CO + \frac{1}{2}O_2$	$Y(-CO_2) = 3$	α-rays, γ-rays	88	NO_2 removes free radicals and inhibits back reaction.
$CO \rightarrow \{CO_2 , C, \text{ carbon suboxide "polymer"}\}^a$	$Y(-CO) = 2$	α-rays	87	"Polymer" has composition $(C_2O)_n$ and is formed with yield $Y(-CO$ polymer$) = 1.2$.

Reaction	Yield	Radiation	Ref.	Remarks
$H_2 + \frac{1}{2}O_2 \rightarrow H_2O$	$Y(H_2O) = 3$	β-rays, α-rays	89, 90	No H_2O_2 found in product.
$N_2O \rightarrow \{N_2, NO_2, O_2\}$	$Y(-N_2O) = 4$	Electrons; β-rays γ-rays	94, 95	Proposed as a (gaseous) dosimeter (95).
$HCN \rightarrow \{\text{"polymer"}, N_2, H_2\}$	$Y(-HCN) = 11$	α-rays	96	Almost all product is incorporated in a dark solid "polymer"; gas yields are $Y(N_2) = 0.3$ and $Y(H_2) = 0.1$.
$H_2O \rightarrow H_2 + \frac{1}{2}O_2$	$Y(-H_2O) \sim 10^{-2}$	β-rays, α-rays	97, 98	Very effective back reaction.
$H_2O + (\text{small amount}) \; D_2 \rightarrow$ $HOD + HD$	$Y(-H_2O) = Y(HOD) = 3.3$	β-rays	97	Establishes *radical yield* in water vapor [$Y(-H_2O) = Y(H) = Y(OH)$].
$UF_6 \rightarrow \{F_2, UF_?\}$	$Y(-UF_6) = 0.3$	α-rays	99	As irradiation proceeds, the yield declines because of radiation-induced back-reaction.

[a] Brackets { } in this and subsequent tables indicate that stoichiometry has not been established.

TABLE V

IONIC YIELDS IN RADIOLYSIS OF GASEOUS HYDROCARBONS—A SELECTION

(Some data have been recalculated by using recent values of W.)

Ionic yield, $V = M/N_i$

Substance irradiated	Consumption of reactant	H_2	CH_4	C_2H_6	C_3H_8	$n\text{-}C_4H_{10}$	Higher saturated hydrocarbons	C_2H_4	C_2H_2	Benzene	Reactant → "polymer"	Radiation	Ref.	Remarks
Methane	2.1	1.6	—	0.6	0.04	0.01	0.03	0.01			0.8	Electrons, α-rays, deuterons	101–103	Yields of hydrocarbons with α-rays and with electron irradiation are discordant. The latter are given here.
Ethane	1.7	1.3	0.3	—	0.09	0.2	0.02				1.0	α-rays	102	66% of H_2 and at least 50% of CH_4 are formed as ultimate molecules, i.e., not from H and CH_3 precursors.
Propane	1.7	1.1	0.3	0.2	—	0.2	0.2				0.9	α-rays	102	
n-Butane	1.7	1.3	0.2	0.3	0.2	—	0.1				1.3	α-rays, deuterons	102,103	
2,2-Dimethyl-propane	1.5	1.0	0.4	0.5	0.1		0.4	0.07			0.5	γ-rays	104	
n-Hexane	1.9	0.8	0.1	0.2	0.3	0.3	0.05	0.02	0	0	1.4	α-rays	105	
Ethylene	5	0.5	0.04	0.1		0.2		—	0.9		4	γ-rays, α-rays	106, 96	Yields are independent of pressure.
Propylene	5	0.4	0.3									α-rays	107	
2-Butene	4	0.3	0.3									α-rays	108	

												β-rays; α-rays		Y for consumption of C_2H_2 is unchanged in presence of various inert gases if ionization of added gas is included in N_i (111). Useful as a gaseous dosimeter.
Acetylene	20	0.1								—	1.3	16	β-rays; α-rays	96, 109; 110	
Methyl acetylene	8	0.4	0.1										α-rays	108	
Dimethyl acetylene	6	0.6	0.03										α-rays	108	
Cyclopropane	3												α-rays	107	
Cyclohexane	2.0	0.8	0.1	0.3	0.07	0.07	0	0	0			1.8	α-rays, (electrons)	105, (112)	
Cyclohexene	3.6	0.4	0.06	0.01	0.004	0	0	0.3	0.1		0.02	3.0	α-rays	105, (112)	Y(cyclohexane) = 0.2
Benzene	1.1	0.07	0.002	0.001	0	0	0.004	0.09			—	1.0	α-rays, (electrons)	105, (112)	

products of greater molecular weight, as well as the liquid "polymer." The fact that the ion-molecule reactions 21a and 22b [which have been observed directly (45, 46, 114)] precede† the recombination reactions 21b and 22d governs the character of the radiolysis, explaining, for example, the pressure independence and the constancy of yields of major products at different radiation intensities. Although the foregoing mechanism is in general accord with the principal experimental results, many details remain unexplained; moreover, it makes no allowance for the primary excitation, which unquestionably contributes substantially to the decomposition. Nevertheless, it occupies an important position as an attempt comprehensively and realistically to describe the elementary processes occurring in the radiolysis of the simplest hydrocarbon.

Elucidation of the radiolysis of ethane has not been carried as far. The reactant is consumed with an ionic yield of about 2; hydrogen, methane, butane, and a liquid "polymer" are the principal products. As with methane, there is only slight over-all pressure change during irradiation. Studies using isotopic mixtures and others using free-radical scavengers (ethylene and propylene) have shown (115) that 66% of the H_2 and at least one-half of the CH_4 are formed as ultimate molecules. Thus $M(H_2^u)/N_i = 0.9$, a substantial yield that probably includes contributions both from ion-molecule reactions (analogous to 22b) and from direct formation of molecular hydrogen in dissociation of excited molecules and of excited ions.

Other hydrocarbons undergo still more complex reactions. The ionic yield for consumption of reactant is about 2 for saturated compounds, about 5 when a single double-bond is present, and about 10 when the molecule contains two double-bonds. That unsaturated compounds are consumed more rapidly attests their greater tendency to condense with the various intermediate entities to substances of higher molecular weight, and this is corroborated by the fact that a greater proportion of their product is contained in the liquid or solid "polymer" and a smaller proportion in the gaseous products. The complementary relation between yield for consumption of reactant and fraction of volatile product is, indeed, a general one. Formation of unsaturated from saturated hydrocarbons is meager, although this is certainly ascribable in part to participation of these products in the reaction.‡ Another feature is the considerable synthetic action, a fact no-

---

† The mechanism also presumes that dissociation of primary ions (processes 20) *precedes* the ion-molecule reactions in the range of pressures studied. If this should not be true, sequence 22 would be suppressed, and reaction of $(CH_4^+)^*$ with CH_4, which is not necessarily the same as process 21a, would supervene.

‡ Because many of the data in Table V are obtained from experiments in which the total dose was comparatively great, and the decomposition extensive, the "polymer" undoubtedly includes a substantial contribution from interaction of activated species with reaction products. The yields at smaller total doses therefore are expected often to be considerably different.

ticed early in the development of radiation chemistry. Among higher hydrocarbons the "dimer" (with respect to the carbon skeleton) is usually prominent.

The radiolysis of acetylene, which has been accorded much attention, proceeds with the yield $M(-C_2H_2)/N_i = 20$, for both α-particles (96) and β-rays (109). The only appreciable volatile product is benzene, formed with $M(C_6H_6)/N_i = 1.3$; the balance of the product is found in an insoluble solid "polymer" called cuprene. Photochemical studies suggest that

$$\bar\varphi_e(-C_2H_2) \approx 10,$$

so that $\bar\varphi_i(-C_2H_2)$ must be roughly the same. Investigation of the radiolysis of acetylene in an excess of an inert gas (111) indicates that $C_2H_2^+$ ions produced by charge transfer have the same effect in producing "polymer" as those formed directly. Although the radiation chemistry of acetylene possesses strikingly simple and reproducible kinetics, the yield being insensitive to pressure, temperature, and dose rate, the mechanism is still unknown. Methyl acetylene is also polymerized with ionic yield approximately twice the photochemical quantum yield.

With benzene, the only aromatic compound yet studied in the vapor phase, the rise in radiosensitivity with increasing unsaturation is reversed: benzene is even more resistant than the lower saturated hydrocarbons. This is in harmony with the comparative thermal and photochemical stability of aromatic molecules and, especially, with their common tendency to exhibit fluorescence. Gases, among which acetylene is the only appreciable hydrocarbon product, are evolved only sparsely, and 97 % of the product resides in a liquid "polymer" (105). The ionic yield for condensation (about 1) is only one-half the standard value, which shows that at least three-fourths of the primary products fail to cause chemical action.

Among the few compounds other than hydrocarbons that have been studied may be mentioned CCl_4, which is converted to solid C_2Cl_6 and Cl_2, and vinyl chloride, which undergoes a rapid polymerization (4).

D. Liquid Systems

1. INORGANIC REACTIONS

Few researches on inorganic liquids (other than water) have been essayed. Information upon which comparison of radiation action in liquid and gas phases can be based is particularly scanty, especially because of the circumstance that liquid and gas must usually be investigated at greatly disparate temperatures. G-values for some selected radiolyses of inorganic liquids are collected in Table VI.

Liquid hydrogen bromide is decomposed with a yield of $G(-HBr) = 10$,

TABLE VI

YIELDS IN RADIOLYSIS OF INORGANIC LIQUIDS—A SELECTION

Reaction	Yield	Radiation	Ref.	Remarks
$HBr \rightarrow \frac{1}{2}H_2 + \frac{1}{2}Br_2$	$G(-HBr) = 10$	α-rays	116	
$O_2 \rightarrow \frac{2}{3}O_3$	$G(O_3) = 14$	Electrons	117	
$CO_2 \rightarrow CO + \frac{1}{2}O_2$	$G(-CO_2) = 4$	γ-rays, fission fragments	86	Inhibitor not required for extensive decomposition (yield about one-half as great as for gas with inhibitor).
$N_2O \rightarrow \{N_2, N_2O, O_2\}$	$G(-N_2O) = 12$	γ-rays, fission fragments	86	Yield approximately equal to that in gaseous phase.
$NaOH \rightarrow ?$	$G(H_2) < 4 \times 10^{-4}$	Electrons	118	Extremely resistant to radiation. $G(H_2)$ may be much less than value given, which is an upper limit.
$H_2SO_4 \rightarrow \{SO_2, ?\}$	$G(SO_2) = 1.0$	γ-rays	119	

about one-half of the value for the gas (116). Although there are many ways in which the mechanism may differ in the liquid at the lower temperature, it is likely that at least part of the deficiency stems from back reaction in the α-particle tracks.

Irradiation of liquid oxygen or of liquid mixtures of oxygen and nitrogen produces ozone with $G(O_3) = 12$ to 15; in the mixtures, oxides of nitrogen are also formed, with a total G of about 1.5 (117). The ozone yield is decidedly greater than that attained in the gas and is close to the value expected in the absence of back reaction.

Liquid carbon dioxide is decomposed with $G(-CO_2) = 4$ to 5, even in the absence of inhibitors for the back reaction (86). This yield, about one-half of that attained in the gaseous phase by admixture of NO_2, is reported to be the same for γ-rays and for fission fragments, suggesting that a track effect cannot be responsible for the great difference between the liquid and the gas; rather, it is possible that the reactive species of the chemical stage are altered, perhaps through the agency of the cage effect.

A system with remarkable resistance to radiation is liquid NaOH. Irradiation with high-energy electrons slowly evolves hydrogen, but $G(H_2)$ is smaller than 4×10^{-4}, and possibly much smaller (118).

2. ORGANIC REACTIONS [REFS. 7 (CHAPTER I), 100, 120]

a. General Remarks. During the past decade the radiation chemistry of organic substances has become a major field of study, and it is still developing at an increasing rate. Several hundred different compounds have been investigated, a majority of them in the liquid phase. The experimental results are of varying degrees of completeness. Because of the complexity of the reactions, little is known as yet of mechanisms; indeed, the products, in most cases, are so numerous and diverse that it is rare for their material balance to have been achieved accurately. Discussion here, as in previous sections, will be limited, with a few exceptions, to the action of radiation on pure substances. (A review of radiation-induced oxidation, the most important omission, can be found in refs. 156 and 157. In general, the presence of oxygen enhances the total decomposition, part, but not all, of which is diverted to formation of diverse oxidation products.) Data for some selected radiolyses of liquid organic compounds are presented in Table VII.

Few systematic examinations of the effect of LET, or of the role of dissolved oxygen, have been undertaken. Nor have there been studies of the same substance in both gaseous and liquid phases sufficiently detailed to reveal the nature of the influences of state of aggregation upon elementary processes. (For both cyclohexane and benzene—cf. data in Tables V and VII—there is a marked depression of the yields of lower hydrocarbons, either on an absolute basis or relative to H_2, and also of "polymer," in

TABLE VII

YIELDS IN RADIOLYSIS OF ORGANIC LIQUIDS—A SELECTION.

(Most, but not all, data are for room temperature; cf. references cited.)

Substance irradiated	G-Values									Reactant → "polymer"	Radiation	Ref.	Remarks
	H_2	CH_4	C_2H_6	C_2H_4	C_2H_2	CO	CO_2	H_2O	Other				
n-Pentane	4.2	0.4	0	0	0						Electrons	121	In vapor, $G(H_2)$ is twice $G(CH_4)$ (cf. Table V).
2,2-Dimethyl propane	1.4	3.2									γ-rays	122	
n-Hexane	5.0	0.15	0.3	0.3	0				$G(\text{unsat. prods.}) = 1.5$; $G(\text{"dimer"}) = 2.0$		Electrons	123, 121, 124	$G(H_2)$ decreases with decreasing temperature and reaches about 3 at the melting point (121). Amounts of unsaturated gaseous products decline as radiolysis proceeds.
n-Heptane	4.7	0.2	Trace	Trace	Trace				$G(\text{unsat. prods.}) = 1.5$; $G(\text{"dimer"}) = 2.5$		Electrons, γ-rays	125, 126, 121, 124	
n-Octane	4.8	0.08	0	0	0						Electrons	121, 124	
2,5-Dimethyl hexane	2.7	0.8									Electrons	124	
2,2,4-Trimethyl pentane	2.3	1.0									Electrons	124	
n-Decane	5.2	0.06	0	0	0						Electrons	121, 124	
Cyclohexane	5.3	0.1		0.2	0				$G(\text{cyclohexene}) = 2$	2	Electrons, deuterons, γ-rays, α-rays	127, 112, 128, 124	$G(H_2)$ is independent of LET over a wide range (127), and also independent of temperature (122).
Methyl cyclohexane	4.2	0.2	0								Electrons	124	
Cyclohexene	1.2	0.02		0.1	0.003					12	Electrons	112, 124	Small quantity of benzene ($G \sim 10^{-2}$) also produced. Note smallness of yields of gases.
Cyclooctatetraene	0.02				0.02					0.7	γ-rays	129	

Substance								G values of products	Radiation	Refs	Remarks
Benzene	0.04	0	0	0.02	0		0.9	$G(\text{diphenyl}) = 0.1$; $G(-\text{benzene}) = 0.9$	Electrons, γ-rays	112, 130–132	Gas yields from C_6D_6 are much lower (130): $G(D_2) = 0.01$, and $G(C_2D_2) = 0.01$.
Toluene	0.1	0.008	0	0.002	0.002		0.9	$G(-\text{toluene}) = 0.9$	Electrons	112	
Diphenyl	0.01	10^{-4}	10^{-4}						Electrons	133	
Terphenyls (o, m, or p)	~0.01	~10^{-4}	~10^{-4}	0.002	0.002		0.2	$G(-\text{terphenyl}) = 0.2$	Electrons	133, 134	$T = 400°C$. Very little degradation: e.g., no benzene formed.
Methanol	4.1	1.2	~10^{-2}	0.1		~10^{-3}	1	$G(\text{formaldehyde}) = 2.0$; $G(\text{ethylene glycol}) = 3.1$	γ-rays (α-rays)	135–138	Reported yields are seriously discordant.
Ethanol	4.3	0.6	0	0			1	$G(\text{acetaldehyde}) = 1.7$; $G(\text{glycol}) = 1.0$	γ-rays, α-rays, X-rays	139, 140, 137, 141	Reported yields are seriously discordant. Data for eight higher alcohols are given in ref. 137.
Cyclohexanol	2.8	0	0.6	0.1			~0		γ-rays	139	
Ethyl ether	3.5	0.3	0.6	1.1	0.1	0.1	0.3	$G(C_2H_6) = 0.1$; $G(C_4H_{10}) = 0.1$	α-rays, γ-rays	142, 139	
Isopropyl ether	2.4	0.9	0.1	0.06	0.02	0.07	~0	$G(C_3H_8) = 1.5$; $G(C_3H_6) = 0.6$; $G(\text{acetaldehyde}) = 0.9$; $G(\text{acetone}) \sim 0.8$	α-rays (electrons, γ-rays)	142, 143	
Propionaldehyde	1.3	0.1	1.1	0.3	1.6		0.1(?)		Electrons	144	
Acetone	0.9	2.6	0.5	Trace	0.8			$G(C_3H_8) = 0.4$	γ-rays	145	
Methyl ethyl ketone	1.2	0.9	2.8	0.5	0.8			$G(C_4H_{10}) = 0.2$	γ-rays	145	
Formic acid	2.3			1.2		10	?		γ-rays	146	Yield of CO_2 depends upon radiation intensity, possibly because of a chain reaction.
Acetic acid	0.5	3.4	0.4		0.3	4.2	?	$G(\text{acetone}) \sim 1$	γ-rays, X-rays	139, 147, 148	If water is present succinic acid is formed (cf. Section VI.G.2).
Acetic acid	0.5	1.4	0.8		0.4	4.0	2.1	$G(\text{acetone}) \sim 1$	α-rays	149	
Propionic acid	0.8	0.5	1.1	0.3	0.3	3.9	1.6	$G(n\text{-butane}) = 0.7$	α-rays	149	
Ethyl acetate	0.9	1.1			1.6				γ-rays	139	
Methyl iodide	0.08	0.6	1.1		0.08	0.03		$G(I_2) = 1.3$	X-rays, γ-rays, electrons	150–152	

TABLE VII—*Continued*

Substance irradiated	G-Values									Reactant → "polymer"	Radiation	Ref.	Remarks
	H_2	CH_4	C_2H_6	C_2H_4	C_2H_2	CO	CO_2	H_2O	Other				
Ethyl iodide	0.2	0.007	1.1	2.0	0.1				$G(I_2) = 2.1$		X-rays, γ-rays, electrons	150–152	$G(I_2)$ studied as function of dose, temperature, and other factors (151). $G(I_2) = 1.3$ for α-rays (153). Data for five higher iodides are available (151).
Methylene iodide									$G(I_2) = 1.3$		Electrons	152	
Ethyl bromide									$G(HBr) = 2.0$		X-rays	152	
Ethylene bromide									$\begin{cases} G(HBr) = 18 \\ G(Br_2) = 0.2 \end{cases}$		X-rays, electrons	152	
Bromobenzene									$G(HBr) = 2$		X-rays	152	
Ethylene chloride									$G(HCl) = 4$		X-rays	152	
Carbon tetrachloride									$G(Cl_2) = 3 = G(C_2Cl_6)$		α-rays	154	$G(Cl_2)$ for electrons and to dose rate and to total dose (perhaps because of back reaction of CCl_3 radicals with accumulated Cl_2); values ranging from 1 (155) to 7 (154) have been reported.

radiolysis of the liquids as compared to the vapors. This suggests deactivation of precursors of these products, possibly by removal of oscillational energy as described in Section II.D.) However, the empirical information is already adequate to permit the discerning of many major characteristics of organic radiation chemistry.

The most striking single generalization is the lesser radiation sensitivity of aromatic hydrocarbons and many of their simple derivatives as compared to similar aliphatic or alicyclic compounds. Other important features are:

1. Most nonaromatic organic substances appear to have standard radiosensitivity, that is, G(-reactant) $\sim$ 10 (which does not prove, however, that primary processes are not reversed, because primary products often react with parent molecules).

2. Hydrogen is evolved from all irradiated organic compounds, the amount declining with increasing number of carbon atoms in the early members of a homologous series.

3. Dissociation which breaks C—C bonds is less common than that which breaks C—H bonds, except in highly branched molecules.

4. Chains of carbon atoms tend to diverse fragmentation unless a particularly weak bond is present, in which case rupture of the latter has primacy (examples are C—I, C—Br, C—CH_2NH_2).

5. Stable ring structures such as those in derivatives of benzene or cyclohexane are resistant to ionizing radiation (i.e., G(ring cleavage) $\ll$ standard value).

6. Formation of compounds of high molecular weight (the so-called "polymer" product) augments with increasing unsaturation in the molecule.

These characteristics are also evident in the behavior of gaseous systems (cf. Section III.C.2).

Much current effort is direct toward attainment of more accurate and complete data on yields, toward clarification of the influences of radiation intensity and total dose (reaction products often react rapidly with activated species and can alter the course of a radiolysis even when present in small concentration), and toward elucidation of specific features of a mechanism: especially favored is determination of "radical yields" by means of isotopic or scavenger techniques.

b. Aliphatic and Alicyclic Hydrocarbons. Hydrogen is the most profuse product in the radiolysis of saturated hydrocarbons, $G(H_2)$ usually being only slightly smaller than the standard yield. Thus most of the primary activations, whether excitation or ionization, lead eventually to rupture of two C—H bonds; the fractions occurring by various mechanisms of ultimate-molecule formation and by H-atom production, followed by H-atom

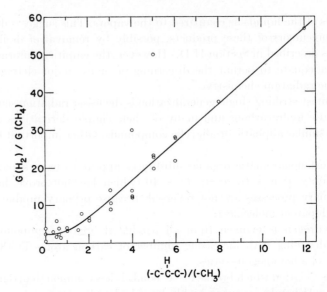

FIG. 6. Relative yields of hydrogen and methane in radiolysis of saturated aliphatic hydrocarbons. (Based upon data from numerous sources, chiefly references cited in Tables V and VII. The abscissa is the ratio of total number of C—H bonds in the molecule, exclusive of those in methyl groups, to the total number of methyl groups.)

abstraction, are known in only few instances, however. Hydrogen formation from alkanes with approximately the standard yield is also observed in the gaseous and solid phases.

Methane is a second general product. Its yield is greater, the greater is the number of methyl groups (Fig. 6); hence it is evolved more copiously in branched-chain than in straight-chain hydrocarbons, and for the latter less copiously, the longer the chain (121, 124, 126). This behavior could stem from decomposition of long-lived activated molecules or ions having great oscillational energy, the chance of this energy being concentrated in a C—CH_3 or C—H bond depending mainly upon the respective numbers of these bonds; or it could arise from dissociation in a repulsive excited state, the chance that this excitation be localized at the respective type of bond again conforming to an intrinsic probability for that event. The latter possibility could, of course, merely reflect the chance of an initial excitation that is more or less localized in the particular bond. In any event, there is no suggestion of energy transfer or other channelling process that diverts excitation to one or another type of bond out of proportion to its abundance. As with hydrogen, the methane yield comprises contributions from ultimate-molecule formation and from H-atom abstraction by methyl radicals.

The gaseous product from saturated hydrocarbons also contains other lower hydrocarbons, predominantly saturated ones. Higher hydrocarbons, which remain in the liquid phase, include both unsaturated and saturated molecules, among which the "dimer" is usually the most abundant. The diversity of products is particularly great in the case of alkanes. Chromatographic analysis of irradiated n-hexane, for example, shows fragments containing all numbers of carbon atoms up to 12 (the limit of the experimental technique), the last being especially prominent (158). The ubiquitous "polymer" is also produced, the more abundantly so, the greater the molecular weight of the parent compound. The behavior appears to be very much the same for gaseous, liquid, and solid phases; however, because of experimental difficulties, data for condensed phases on the yield of "polymer" are regrettably sparse—and so, also, are data on the important yields of all synthetic products (i.e., molecules having greater molecular weight than the parent compound), of which the "polymer" is, of course, composed (cf. Table VII).

Cyclohexane is of particular interest and has been a favorite object of investigation. Hydrogen is evolved with a G of 5, typically that of a saturated hydrocarbon, and G("polymer") is about 2 (112). The hydrogen yield has been demonstrated to be constant over a wide range of LET values (127), in striking contrast to aqueous solutions, for which $G(H_2)$ is highly dependent upon LET. Although few quantitative data are available, it is probable that this insensitivity to LET is frequency for organic substances and reflects the common effectiveness of H-atom abstraction reactions with organic molecules in precluding track effects that result from local accumulation of H atoms. Cyclohexane does not give the diversity of products that is characteristic of saturated aliphatic hydrocarbons; apart from H_2, the chief products are cyclohexene (predominantly) and dicyclohexyl (128), and it is of these that the "polymer" is initially composed. Stability of the ring is thus clearly manifest.

Unsaturated hydrocarbons undergo greater decomposition, but yield smaller quantities of hydrogen and other gases: "polymer" is the major product. Greater degree of unsaturation further elevates the amount of "polymer" and depresses the amount of gas; for instance, "polymer" production is greater from dienes than from olefins. As was discussed for the case of gases, such behavior reflects the ability of these molecules to condense with almost any variety of activated molecule or molecular fragment. For certain classes, like vinyl compounds, the polymerization chains are very long and the values of G correspondingly great.

c. *Aromatic Hydrocarbons.* Aromatic hydrocarbons give very little gaseous product but appreciable "polymer": they are less sensitive to radiation than are other hydrocarbons, although not nearly as much so as the feeble gas evolution alone would suggest. Thus, for benzene, $G(H_2) = 0.04$, and $G(\text{"polymer"}) = 0.9$. The condensed product from benzene has been studied by removing the nonvolatile fraction continuously during irradiation (131). Groups of C_{12} and C_{18} compounds were found to predominate, the former (about 20 % of the total, by weight) consisting chiefly of diphenyl with smaller amounts of its hydrogenated forms, the latter (about 80 %) of hydrogenated terphenyls, and no straight-chain hydrocarbons were detected. Thus "polymerization" occurs by stepwise reaction with parent molecules of activated species having intact C_6 rings, but only about 3 %* of the primary products are able to initiate this reaction. As irradiation proceeds, further condensation occurs, and the proportion of molecules having four or more rings increases.

The resistance of aromatic molecules to radiation stems from the fact that many of their valence electrons are shared by many atoms, whence electronic excitation leads only infrequently to dissociation and usually to light emission or to internal conversion. This radiation resistance has practical value in applications for which decomposition of a compound would preclude its use; for example, terphenyl is employed as a moderator for a nuclear reactor, and aromatic hydrocarbons are the favored luminescent materials in scintillation detectors of high-energy particles. The decomposition which does occur must arise in part, and possibly in large part, from opening and from fragmentation of the ring following an Auger cascade in the carbon atom and from direct atom ejection (cf. Section II.B.3). This points to a marked dependence of the yields (particularly of gases) upon type of radiation and upon LET, a prediction which has not yet been tested by experiment.

Mixtures of a saturated and an aromatic hydrocarbon give smaller yields of *certain* products than would be anticipated on the basis of independent radiation action on the components. This phenomenon, which has been known for a long time (124), is most marked for light gaseous products like H_2 and CH_4. It has been studied in some detail with mixtures of benzene and various nonaromatic hydrocarbons, notably cyclohexane (112, 124, 159, 160). Depression of decomposition by admixture of an aromatic compound is often referred to as "protection," and is believed to result from interference by the aromatic molecule, very early in the physicochemical stage, with the normal consequences of activation of the other component.

---

* This number is the ratio of $G(\text{-benzene})$ to the product of G_{standard} (estimated to be 9) and the average number of benzene residues per molecule of the condensed fraction; it is assumed, in accordance with available experimental evidence, that each of the latter molecules has its origin in a single primary product (excited or ionized benzene). The nature of these effective primary products (e.g., whether excited or ionized molecules), and the nature of the processes whereby the other 97% are deactivated, are unknown.

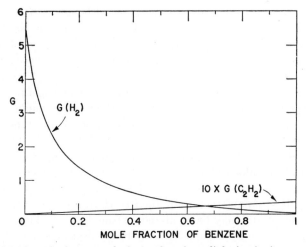

FIG. 7. Yields of hydrogen and of acetylene in radiolysis of mixtures of benzene and cyclohexane. (Based upon data from reference 112).

However, identification of the intermediate state which is attacked has not been achieved. For example, deactivation might occur by charge transfer (aromatic hydrocarbons have lower ionization potentials than aliphatic or alicyclic compounds), or by energy transfer (Section II.C.2), or by both, the resulting activation of the aromatic molecule having normal ineffectiveness (161). It might also result from removal of H atoms by the aromatic compound, thus diverting the decomposition from the volatile to the nonvolatile product, but experiment indicates that this cannot be the sole mechanism (159). Figure 7 depicts the yields of H_2 and of C_2H_2 from mixtures of cyclohexane and benzene. The abundant production of hydrogen from cyclohexane is markedly diminished by small amounts of benzene (10^{-3} M benzene reduces $G(H_2)$ by 10 %); on the other hand, acetylene, which presumably derives from the benzene (cf. Table VII), is formed in approximate proportion to the benzene concentration. The yields of condensed products in such mixtures are unknown. It is evident that the reduction of hydrogen production is substantial but is never complete.*

The same phenomenon is evident in the fact that gas yields from ali-

---

* Other substances also "protect" cyclohexane (160, 162), although perhaps by different mechanisms; thus 10^{-3} M iodine reduces $G(H_2)$ by 20%. And benzene behaves similarly with other substances; for example, the yield of free radicals in chloroform or in carbon tetrachloride (as determined by reaction with scavenger) is greatly reduced by small amounts of benzene (163). It may be noted that interpretation of experiments on mixtures is somewhat ambiguous because of lack of knowledge of both the quantity and the character of the energy imparted to the individual components.

phatic derivatives of aromatic hydrocarbons, although greater than from the parent molecule, are still much smaller than from the corresponding aliphatic hydrocarbon. However, this provides no clue to the nature of the protective process, for any of the possibilities mentioned above would apply as well to an intramolecular event.

d. Alcohols. Irradiated alcohols display a great diversity of products, but hydrogen, glycols, and aldehydes are usually the most abundant ones, with G for consumption of parent molecules being close to the standard value. Secondary and tertiary alcohols give rise to ketones as well. The principal path of radiolysis can be viewed, somewhat schematically, as ensuing from dissociation at the alpha C–H bond, with subsequent dimerization of the radicals to give the glycol, oxidation of the radicals to give the aldehyde (or ketone), and H-atom abstraction by the free H atoms to give H_2. Water is a general product and may be an abundant one, but it is difficult to determine under these conditions and has only rarely been reported (137, 141).

In the case of methanol the stoichiometry (per 100 ev) is given approximately by

$$9.5 \; CH_3OH \rightarrow 4.1 \; H_2 + 3.1 \; (CH_2OH)_2 + 2.0 \; HCHO + 1.2 \; CH_4 + 1.2 \; H_2O + 0.1 \; CO,$$

and shows a standard yield for total decomposition. If this list of products is complete, it is necessary, for material balance, that $G(CH_4) = G(H_2O)$ exactly, regardless of the values of the other yields.

Thorough and detailed analysis of the numerous radiolytic products of many alcohols has been accomplished (137). However, the data of various investigators are extremely discordant, for reasons not yet fully appreciated. Large differences in certain yields for various types of radiation have been recorded in the literature (cf. Table VII); although pointing to interesting track effects, they must be discounted until the experimental basis is made more trustworthy.

e. Carboxylic Acids. The gaseous product from radiolysis of carboxylic acids contains chiefly CO_2 and H_2, with a smaller amount of CO; H_2O is also formed, probably abundantly. Little is known, as yet, about the organic substances that (with H_2O) must comprise the condensed product.

The two principal modes of formic acid decomposition are into hydrogen and carbon dioxide and into water and carbon monoxide. Since $G(CO_2)$ exceeds $G(H_2)$ in formic acid, the chain radiolysis, prevalent in concentrated aqueous solutions (cf. Section VI.G.1), may also occur in pure formic acid. The stoichiometry (per 100 ev) is expressed approximately by

$$19 \; HCOOH \rightarrow 10 \; CO_2 + 2.3 \; H_2 + 1.3 \; CO + (7.7 \; HCHO + 9 \; H_2O).$$

The first three are observed products; the yield of water has not yet been measured, and the formaldehyde is believed to be an unstable intermediate which gives rise to products as yet unidentified.

The γ-ray yields from acetic acid (cf. Table VII) correspond almost exactly to consumption of 4.4 molecules of CH_3COOH (per 100 ev), and, since a standard total yield would be anticipated, it is likely that at least an equal number is consumed in forming condensed products. Succinic acid is probably not among the latter, for, although it is produced in solutions of water in acetic acid, its yield declines with diminishing water content and extrapolates to zero for the pure acid (164). Isotopic studies of methane evolved from deuterated and tritiated acetic acid (147) suggest that much of the methane is formed from methyl radicals as intermediary. The track effect with particles of high LET (Table VII) points to diversion of some of these radicals to ethane (and some also to unidentified organic products).

Cyclohexane carboxylic acid has been studied qualitatively, using α-particles (165). The ratio $G(CO_2)/G(H_2)$ is about 3, as it is for acetic acid with α-particles, and the condensed product consists of cyclohexane and cyclohexene in the ratio of 7 to 1. Although this analysis is manifestly incomplete, it does show again the stability to radiation of the cyclohexane ring.

Solid fatty acids are discussed in Section III.E.2.

f. Halogen Derivatives. Decomposition of organic halides occurs preferentially at the carbon-halogen bond, with abundant production of halogen or hydrogen halide (or both) but of very little hydrogen and with little fragmentation of the hydrocarbon stem. Chlorides give HCl, bromides give both HBr and Br_2, and iodides give chiefly I_2. These general features are in harmony with the comparative strengths of C–H, C–C, C–X, H–X, and X–X bonds, and again argue randomization of activation energy, whether in an excited molecule, an excited ion, or even in the activated complex of an ion-molecule or ion-ion recombination reaction, prior to chemical effect.

Alkyl iodides have received the most extensive study. Their initial dissociation patterns have been examined by means of radiolysis in the presence of radioactive iodine: fragments are identified through analysis of the radioactive iodides formed in the reactions:

$$R + I_2 \rightarrow RI + I. \tag{23}$$

The results (150, 166) prove that most of the alkyl radicals remain intact—in marked contrast, for example, to the behavior of aliphatic hydrocarbons themselves.

Radiolysis of methyl iodide produces chiefly ethane, methane, and iodine, in the approximate stoichiometry (per 100 ev):

$$3.5\ CH_3I \rightarrow 1.25\ I_2 + 1.1\ C_2H_6 + 0.6\ CH_4 + 0.1\ C_2H_4 + 0.05\ H_2 + (0.5\ CH_2I_2?).$$

The yield of methylene iodide has not been determined and is conjectural, although its presence has been reported (150, 166); it is added in order to balance the equation. Moreover, HI is probably also a product: it has been detected (151), although no yields have been recorded, and probably evades analysis because of the swift reactions: $R + HI \rightarrow RH + I$. The yield of 3.5 for consumption of reactant is low because of the back reactions 23, which essentially reverse the primary action. The selectivity of activation in rupturing C–I bonds points to an efficient process and therefore to an initial radical yield of at least the standard value, that is, g(radicals) $\gtrsim 8$. The latter quantity can be inferred from scavenger experiments and is indeed found to be considerably greater than $2G(I_2)$ (151, 152). Clearly, observed products cannot result from homogeneous reactions of R and I during the chemical stage; rather, they must be formed by reaction of primary products with parent molecules during the physicochemical stage. (For example, ethane is not formed by reaction of homogeneously distributed methyl radicals.) From this it can be concluded that only about one in four of the primary products leads to permanent change. This general characteristic is found with all the alkyl iodides studied and finds additional support in the observation that the hydrocarbons having a number of carbon atoms equal to that in the alkyl group predominate (both alkane and alkene are found, the latter in somewhat greater quantity) (150).

Because of reaction 23 the radiolysis product, after it accumulates slightly, partially *stabilizes* the parent substance with respect to further irradiation; this phenomenon is not uncommon and is of great importance in the radiation chemistry of water.

Radiolysis of ethyl iodide is quite similar, and has been studied in detail (151, 167). The iodine yield has been measured as a function of such variables as temperature, dose, concentration of various scavengers, and LET, and the importance of track effects demonstrated.

Less is known about organic bromides and very little about chlorides. It is noteworthy that bromobenzene, for which $G(HBr) = 2$, does not possess the radiation resistance of aromatic hydrocarbons. This vulnerability may be generally true of carbon-halogen bonds in aromatic derivatives. Of pertinence is the fact that, in marked contrast to benzene itself, fluorescence is very weak or absent in the monohalogenated benzenes.

E. Solid Systems

1. INORGANIC REACTIONS

The coloration of ionic crystals by ionizing radiation has been known since the earliest experiments with radioactivity. All types of radiation produce coloring, which varies from one substance to another (thus LiF turns yellow, KCl magenta, KBr blue, and NaCl yellow at first—and black after prolonged irradiation) and is often quite stable at ordinary temperatures.

Electrons liberated in ionization acts and trapped at various sorts of imperfection in the lattice of the crystal are responsible for the absorption of light, and investigation of the absorption spectra due to these *color centers* has been a fertile source of insight into the nature of the crystals (168). The yields of color centers are usually low, with G being in the neighborhood of 1 for the most efficiently formed centers but usually smaller. Many minerals can be colored by irradiation: instances are rock salt, certain fluorites, quartz, and a variety of precious stones. Radiation also colors transparent glasses, the sensitivity and the hue imparted depending upon the composition of the glass.

The coloration of certain naturally occurring micas by α-particles emitted from minute specks of radioactive material embedded within the crystal gives rise to tiny darkened spherical shells concentric about the inclusion. These shells, which are known as *pleochroic halos*, result from irradiation extending over geological ages. The radii of the shells are well-defined because of the maximum in density of ionization (or LET) near the end of the range of an α-particle (Bragg curve), and the various measured ranges can be identified with particles of different energies emitted successively in a radioactive series (169–171). The chemical nature of the alteration is unknown, however. Uranium halos are the most common ones. Pleochroic halos are important in such fields as mineralogy and geochronology, and afford a striking example of the application of radiation chemistry to geology.

Crystals composed of monatomic ions show very little proper chemical change upon irradiation. Part of the absorbed energy is used to eject electrons, chiefly from negative ions; the residual neutral *atom*, which differs from the negative ion in its lack of one electron, is commonly dubbed a "hole." An electron in these crystals is very mobile and has a high probability of encountering a hole and re-forming the negative ion. However, a fraction of the electrons is diverted from recombination by trapping, giving rise to color centers. Holes, too, can be stabilized; thus, electron spin resonance has shown that in alkali halide crystals dihalide ions are formed (e.g., $Cl + Cl^- \rightarrow Cl_2^-$) (172). The other major portion of the radiation energy is imparted as excitation of negative ions. This excitation, because of exact resonance with corresponding states of identical neighboring ions, can be transferred readily from one ion to another. Such a nonlocalized excitation, termed an *exciton*, can migrate over large distances in the crystal, ultimately to be degraded to heat, or, perhaps, to be utilized chemically at the site of an impurity (43). The radiation chemistry of inorganic solids offers unique possibilities for study of the migration of electric charge and of excitation energy, and for the exploitation of this migration for chemical purposes.

The potential chemical change existing in irradiated monatomic ionic crystals can, of course, be brought out by dissolution, or by appropriate chemical treatment, as in the case of irradiated silver halides in photographic emulsions. Thus, when irradiated alkali halide crystals are dissolved in water, H_2 is evolved and halogen and OH^- are found in the solution (173). The H_2 and OH^- are presumably formed by reaction of trapped electrons (color centers) with water:

$$\epsilon^- + H_2O \rightarrow \tfrac{1}{2}H_2 + OH^- \tag{24}$$

and the halogen from trapped holes (e.g., dihalide ions).

With crystals containing polyatomic ions, on the other hand, dissociation may compete with any of the degradative processes enumerated above. Few cases have been examined thus far, but among them extensive decomposition is common. Irradiation of $KClO_4$ gives rise to chlorate, chloride, and oxygen; $KClO_3$ yields chloride, chlorite, some hypochlorite, and oxygen. Oxygen is likewise evolved from nitrates (upon heating or dissolving in water) with concurrent formation of nitrite ion, the latter being demonstrated in the intact crystal by appearance of its characteristic absorption spectrum (174). Color centers also appear, but their yield is characteristically small.

Nitrates have been studied more thoroughly than any other class of inorganic solids (175–177), and it has been demonstrated that the radiolysis is simply

$$NO_3^- \rightarrow NO_2^- + \tfrac{1}{2}O_2 \,,$$

the evolved gas consisting almost exclusively of oxygen. Magnetic measurements show, in fact, that this oxygen exists entirely as molecular oxygen within the irradiated crystal (177). Values of $G(NO_2^-)$ for an extensive series of crystalline nitrates are for the most part in the neighborhood of unity, but they display interesting variations, ranging from about 2 for $Ba(NO_3)_2$ to the unusually low value of 0.02 for $LiNO_3$. The results parallel the quantum yields for the corresponding photolyses (which give the same products) and have been interpreted by the processes:

$$(NO_3^-)^* \text{ or } (NO_3 + \epsilon^-) \rightarrow NO_2^- + O \tag{25a}$$

$$NO_2^- + O \rightarrow NO_3^- \tag{25b}$$

$$O + NO_3^- \rightarrow O_2 + NO_2^-. \tag{25c}$$

The intrinsic yield of oxygen atoms (processes 25a) is presumably about the same for all crystals, but the extent of ultimate decomposition depends upon the competition between the forward reaction (25c) and the back reaction (25b), which is sensitive to details of the chemical nature and structure of the crystal. Indeed, the back reaction is typical of one which would be facilitated by the cage effect. As a crude measure of the probability that an oxygen atom will escape from the "cage," use of a "free volume" of the crystal, defined as the difference between the actual volume and the sum of the (spherical) volumes of all of the ions, has been proposed; and both the photochemical quantum yields (φ) and the values of G are in qualitative accord with this reasonable hypothesis, in that both φ and G for the various nitrates are increasing functions of the free volume (176).

Although the chemical species produced initially can be studied directly in an intact crystal—for example, by light absorption or by electron spin resonance—most studies of inorganic solid-phase radiolyses have depended upon chemical analysis after dissolution. Such work is incomplete because inferences concerning primary radiation products from knowledge of these ultimate chemical products, which are formed while the crystal goes into solution, are rarely cogent.

Yields in the radiolysis of some solid substances are presented in Table VIII.

Research on purely physical changes caused by irradiation of inorganic solids (for example, alteration of the mechanical and electrical properties of metals) has been prolific (27, 188, 189), and many of the results hold great interest for radiation chemistry; however, the subject is beyond the scope of this book. A topic which poses physical and chemical problems simultaneously is the modification of catalytic activity by irradiation. Instances both of elevation and of depression of activity of surfaces have been discovered (190, 191).

2. ORGANIC REACTIONS

In contrast to inorganic crystals, solid organic compounds show no evidence of unique features attributable to the solid phase in their behavior under irradiation. To be sure, typical influences of the condensed state upon secondary processes (e.g., the cage effect and track effects) must be operative in favorable cases. But the experimental results, although most limited in scope, are similar to those of the corresponding liquids, and all the generalizations enumerated in Section III.D.2.a appear to apply to solids as well.

Thus, aromatic substances are highly radioresistant. This was confirmed in several cases for the yield of gas, and with benzoic acid also for the "polymer" product. Further evidence for sparse formation of condensed products, probably similar in nature and in yield to those observed in irradiated benzene, is found in the rate of deterioration of luminescence efficiency of anthracene under protracted irradiation (192). Nonaromatic compounds have approximately standard radiosensitivity, and gas yields are comparable to those of liquids. Hydrogen is the chief gaseous product, provided that radiosensitive groups such as carboxyl are absent.

TABLE VIII
YIELDS OF SOLID-PHASE RADIOLYSES—A SELECTION
(Data are for room temperature unless otherwise noted.)

Reaction	Yield	Radiation	Reference	Remarks
$CO_2 \rightarrow CO + \frac{1}{2}O_2$	$G(-CO_2) = 9$ ($-200°C$)	α-rays	88	Yield approximately equal to that for gas *with* inhibitor.
$NaN_3 \rightarrow Na^+ + \frac{3}{2}N_2 + \epsilon^-$	$G(-N_3^-) = 2$ ($-200°C$)	X-rays	178	Yield rises with increasing T and approaches a limiting value of about 10 above 200°C.
$CsNO_3 \rightarrow CsNO_2 + \frac{1}{2}O_2$	$G(NO_2^-) = 2G(O_2) = 1.7$	γ-rays, X-rays	175, 176	Yields for ten different nitrates are given in these references.
$LiNO_3 \rightarrow LiNO_2 + \frac{1}{2}O_2$	$G(NO_2^-) = 2G(O_2) = 0.02$	γ-rays, X-rays	175, 176	Smallness of yield attributed to strong cage effect.
$KClO_3 \rightarrow \{KCl, KClO_2, KClO, O_2\}$	$\begin{cases} G(-ClO_3^-) = 3 \\ G(O_2) = 3 \end{cases}$	γ-rays, X-rays	177, 179	Value cited for $G(-ClO_3^-)$ obtained from decomposition of chlorate as it accumulates in an irradiated perchlorate crystal (179).
$KClO_4 \rightarrow 0.7\ KClO_3 + 0.3\ KCl + 0.95\ O_2$	$\begin{cases} G(-ClO_4^-) = 5 \\ G(ClO_3^-) = 3.5, G(Cl^-) = 1.5 \end{cases}$	X-rays	179	Yield of Cl^- may depend upon state of division of crystal.
Hexane $\rightarrow$ diverse products	$G(H_2) = 3.1$	Electrons	123	$G(H_2)$ independent of temperature from melting point down to $-200°C$.
Polyethylene $\rightarrow$ modified macromolecules	$\begin{cases} G(\text{crosslink}) = 2 \\ G(\textit{trans}\text{-vinylene}) = 2 \\ G(H_2) = 4 \end{cases}$	γ-rays, mixed γ-rays and neutrons	180–184	Extensive bibliography given in ref. 182
Anthracene $\rightarrow$ {H_2, hydrocarbon gases, "polymer"}	$\begin{cases} G(H_2) = 0.005 \\ G(\text{hydrocarbon gas}) = 0.01 \end{cases}$	Electrons	185	

Reaction	G values	Radiation	Ref.	Remarks
Polystyrene → modified macromolecules	$G(\text{crosslink}) = 0.05$, $G(H_2) = 0.02$	γ-rays	184	
Polymethyl methacrylate → modified macromolecules	$G(\text{scission}) = 2$, $G(H_2) = 0.2$, $G(CH_4) = 0.5$, $G(CO) = 0.4$, $G(CO_2) = 0.3$	γ-rays	184, 186	
Cholesterol → ?	$G(-\text{cholesterol}) = 4$	Electrons, γ-rays	120	
Acetic acid → $\{H_2,\ CH_4,\ C_2H_6,\ CO,\ CO_2,\ H_2O\}$	$G(H_2) = 0.8$, $G(CO) = 0.5$, $G(\text{hydrocarbon gas}) = 1$, $G(CO_2) = 3\ (0°C)$	α-rays	187	Yields of gases are given for a series of six solid fatty acids. $G(\text{benzoic acid} \rightarrow \text{``polymer''}) = 0.3.$
Octanoic acid → $\{H_2,\ CO,\ CO_2,\ H_2O,\ \text{``polymer''}\}$	$G(H_2) = 1$, $G(CO) = 0.5$, $G(CO_2) = 2$	α-rays	187	
Benzoic acid → $\{H_2,\ CO,\ CO_2,\ \text{``polymer''}\}$	$G(H_2) = 0.003$, $G(CO) = 0.003$, $G(CO_2) = 0.3$	γ-rays	120	
$CCl_4 \rightarrow \frac{1}{2}Cl_2 + \frac{1}{2}C_2Cl_6$	$G(Cl_2) = 1\ (-190°C)$	Electrons	154	
$CBr_4 \rightarrow \{Br_2,\ ?\}$	$G(Br_2) = 0.1$	Electrons	154	
$C_6Cl_6 \rightarrow \{Cl_2,\ ?\}$	$G(Cl_2) = 0.02$	Electrons	154	
Methyl iodide → diverse products	$G(I_2) = 0.3\ (-190°C)$	γ-rays	151	
Ethyl iodide → diverse products	$G(I_2) = 0.5\ (-190°C)$	γ-rays	151	$G(I_2) = 1.5$ in a glassy solid at this temperature.
Glycine → diverse products	$G(-\text{glycine}) = 2.8$, $G(CH_3NH_2) = 1.2$, $G(CO_2) = 0.9$, $G(NH_3) = 0.7$, $G(\text{acetic acid}) = 0.5$, $G(\text{dicarboxylic acids}) = 0.6$	Electrons	120	

By far the most active branch of the subject is the study of radiation-induced changes in properties of high polymers. Fostered by the commercial implications of modifying the physical properties (e.g., thermal stability) of familiar macromolecules, and even of creating novel materials, this field has become a coherent science and a major technology within the span of a few years (7-III, 193). Closely related to it is the study of radiation action in polymerizing monomers and in forming copolymers (7-II). Among the many properties altered by ionizing radiation are color, crystallinity, electrical conductivity, electrical-breakdown properties, "melting" behavior and other thermal properties, mechanical and elastic properties, and susceptibility to chemical action.

The basic behavior of polymers again parallels that of related monomers. Chief among the effects of radiation are hydrogen evolution (very little hydrocarbon gas is produced from polymers); degradation, stemming from *scission* (dissociation) of main chains; and *crosslinking*, the formation of covalent bonds between two macromolecules with elimination of a molecule of hydrogen (this is the analog of so-called "polymer" formation from small molecules). Unsaturation is often produced as well. Degradation lowers the viscosity, for example, whereas crosslinking produces a tougher material. The melting behavior, which is of technological importance, is governed by the balance between scission, which tends to lower the melting point, and crosslinking, which tends to raise it. If the latter predominates for a particular macromolecule, prolonged irradiation leads to a state in which the entire material is united by a three-dimensional network of linkages, at which point it becomes virtually infusible and insoluble. In some polymers, such as polyethylene and polystyrene, crosslinking is the dominant effect; in others, for example polyisobutylene, polymethyl methacrylate, and Teflon, scission has the greater radiation-chemical yield.

Polyethylene behaves like a large n-alkane. The evolved gas is 99 % H_2, with $G = 4$; about one-half of this appears to be formed as ultimate molecules (181). Other values of G are 2 for crosslinking and 2 for *trans*-vinylene unsaturation; degradation is slight. If, in contrast, the polymer has alkyl side chains, the yields of both hydrocarbon gas and of scission are increased, the latter having almost the standard value for polyisobutylene, as an example. Aromatic side chains, on the other hand, impose their typical stabilization. Thus, polystyrene acts like an aromatic hydrocarbon; G(scission) is small, and, indeed, $G(H_2)$ is reported to be even smaller than that of (liquid) benzene. With polymethyl methacrylate, scission ($G = 2$) governs the behavior, but there are also appreciable yields of various gases from decomposition of the ester groups.

"Protective" effects of aromatic rings are likewise evident. Thus, 20 % of styrene in a copolymer with isobutylene lowers G(scission) by a factor of 2 (194). In harmony with the behavior of monomeric mixtures (Section III.D.2) this protection is only partial. Polymethyl methacrylate, and doubtless other degrading polymers, can also be partially stabilized against radiation action in this way.

The mechanism of crosslinking, which must obviously be favored by the cage effect, is still obscure, but an insensitivity to radiation intensity, as well as other observations, indicate that it is caused by a single primary activation and does not involve a chain reaction. One common view assumes a reaction sequence starting with dissociation at a C–H bond, followed by H-atom abstraction by this H atom at a neighboring site; if the second H atom is a nearby one in the same molecule, unsaturation results, but if it is part of a different chain, the two polymeric radicals may join to form a crosslink (the cage effect facilitates such a reaction). However, other elementary processes are equally plausible. The presence of air is known to have a marked effect on crosslinking, and also, indeed, on scission and other reaction products, which is to be expected because oxygen reacts readily with any of the radicals or activated species involved.

Solid carboxylic acids decompose very much as the liquids do, CO_2 and H_2 being the chief volatile products. Smaller amounts of CO and H_2O are also formed, and there is a complex solid product which includes the homologous and other hydrocarbons, and often polymerized acids as well (195). The CO_2 appears to originate in unimolecular decarboxylation. Data are available for α-particle radiolysis of an extensive series of straight-chain, saturated fatty acids, with up to 30 carbon atoms (187). The yield of CO_2 declines monotonically with increasing length of the chain, dropping from a G of 3 for acetic acid to one of 0.5 for the C_{22}-acid. In contrast, $G(H_2)$ remains sensibly constant between 1 and 2. This behavior is analogous to that of (liquid) saturated hydrocarbons with respect to their comparative CH_4 and H_2 production: in the long fatty acids the "fraction" of C—COOH bonds decreases with increasing chain length, but the "fraction" of C—H bonds remains constant. From such nonselectivity of attack the same inferences (cf. Section II.D.2.b) can again be drawn. The total decomposition of these and other solid carboxylic acids is 5 to 10 times smaller than the standard yield, which is in harmony with the expected efficacy of the cage effect and ready escape of oscillational energy in solid systems, as explained in Section II.D.

Little is known about the radiolysis of pure, solid amino acids. The several acids that have been studied have nearly the standard yield for decomposition, CO_2 and NH_3 being the most abundant gaseous products (120, 195, 196), but even the few available data are discordant. In no case has complete analysis of the products been reported. To a first approximation, decomposition of glycine by high-energy electrons proceeds stoichiometrically (per 100 ev) as

$$2.8\ NH_3^+CH_2COO^- \rightarrow 1\ NH_2CH_3 + 1\ CO_2 + 0.6\ NH_3$$
$$+ 0.6\ CH_3COOH + 0.6\ (NH_3^+CHCOO^-)_2\ . \tag{26}$$

Although the last of these products has not been identified and is probably more complex than indicated, an equivalent amount of unknown dicarboxylic acid or acids is indeed found. Hydrogen has been recorded only for α-particle irradiation, but it is unlikely to be absent with radiations of low LET. Formation of methyl amine and carbon dioxide as ultimate molecules from the same primary product is the one patent component of the mechanism; the other major products might derive, at least in large part, from loss of an α-hydrogen atom in one molecule and its subsequent reaction with $-NH_3^+$.

Studies of electron-spin resonance in irradiated glycine reveal a spectrum which is remarkably stable, enduring over a year at room temperature and even surviving exposure to a temperature close to the melting point. It has been assigned, after thorough analysis, to the radical zwitterion $NH_3^+\overset{\cdot}{C}HCOO^-$ (197), and has a G of about 0.7 (198). This yield agrees with equation 26 provided that the two radicals composing the dicarboxylic acid are indeed identical and retain their separate identity in the crystal, uniting in the course of treatment for chemical analysis. However, the observed chemical yields and credible mechanisms for them (with the exception of NH_2CH_3 and CO_2) are difficult to reconcile with the presence of only a single radical-species. To be sure, there are indications in the spectrum that another, as yet unidentified species is present, but it is presumably less abundant. Since G(radical) is in fact smaller than $2G$(dicarboxylic acid), there is a suggestion (but not more than that because of uncertainties in all of the data cited) that some of the monocarboxylic-acid radicals have already united in pairs at room temperature, the observed radicals perhaps remaining because of isolation or greater stability. The apparent preponderance of a single radical-species is a curious feature of the electron-spin resonance spectra of many irradiated systems.

The paucity of accurate information on radiolytic yields is particularly unfortunate in view of the current popularity of amino acids, and compounds derived from them, in investigations of the electron-spin resonance spectra engendered by absorption of ionizing radiation. Extensive surveys have been made of the spectra of irradiated amino acids (199), peptides (200), proteins (201), and other molecules of especial biological interest (55, 202). Most amino acids and peptides have characteristic spectra, but the patterns of proteins are far simpler than would be anticipated from the diversity of the spectra of their numerous components. Few data on the absolute yields are offered, although they are indispensable if the spectra are to contribute to elucidation of the radiation chemistry. For a group of seven amino acids irradiated and observed at room temperature, the values of G(radical) lie close to 0.5 (198), but for cystine the G is at least ten times smaller. Molecules differing only slightly in molecular structure may have great differences in the yield of radicals; thus G(radical) for norvaline is orders of magnitude smaller than that for valine. An arresting feature of the spectra is their near identity among certain sulfur-containing amino acids (199). The common pattern is found in molecules containing the C—S—H group (e.g., cysteine) or the C—S—S—C group (e.g., cystine) but not in those containing the C—S—C group (e.g., methionine). It is also observed in a number of peptides and proteins containing such amino acids. This fact has been attributed to migration of an electron vacancy formed anywhere along the protein chain, to the site of a sulfur atom, with eventual trapping there (55). Clearly, such a phenomenon could only be involved in a minor fraction of the elementary reactions leading to decomposition, if the radiolysis yields and radical yields cited above are correct and typical.

F. Chemical Effects of Nuclear Transformations

1. introduction

Nuclear transformation is, on the atomic or molecular scale, a violent event, and in media that are not inert it is almost invariably accompanied by secondary chemical effects. Two kinds of effect can be distinguished in principle, and usually by experiment: (i) chemical action on other molecules by the transformation products; and (ii) decomposition of the molecule that originally contained the transformed nucleus, the latter often being detached with most or all of its orbital electrons and ultimately incorporated into a new molecule. This important subject can be presented only briefly, but detailed reviews are available [8 (Chapter XVII), 14, 203–205]. It is properly classified as a branch of radiation chemistry, for virtually all of its essential phenomena occur also in the action of common ionizing radiations—although some of them do so in such a manner as to be far less accessible to study. The survey here will emphasize the relations to conventional radiation chemistry.

When the nucleus in an atom undergoes either a spontaneous disintegration or an induced reaction, part of the energy released always appears in the form of kinetic energy of the atom or its fragments. If an atomic particle, such as an electron, a proton, or an α-particle, is ejected, it will have kinetic energy comparable to 1 Mev and will therefore be a typical particle of ionizing radiation. However, the remaining nucleus will recoil, and, because of its greater mass, its kinetic energy will usually be smaller than 1 Mev. An atom that emits a γ-ray photon will also recoil. If the incident particle or photon in an induced nuclear reaction has appreciable momentum, this, too, will contribute to the momenta of the products. Calculation of the recoil energy in a given nuclear process is elementary (cf. the reviews cited above). The energies of various recoil atoms span the range from those of ordinary corpuscular ionizing radiations down to those of epithermal atoms. Thus, recoil atoms from α-disintegration have kinetic energies between 0.1 and 0.2 Mev; the C^{14} atom formed in the N^{14} (n,p) reaction induced by a thermal neutron has a kinetic energy of 42 kev; and, at the other end of the scale, N^{14} recoil atoms from the β-disintegration of C^{14} have an average kinetic energy of approximately 2 ev. The more energetic recoil atoms could as well have been included with the familiar ionizing radiations—the point of division being somewhat arbitrary.*

The appellation "hot-atom chemistry," a colloquialism for the study of the chemical behavior of recoil atoms which has, regrettably, gained wide currency, directs attention to the fact that the velocities of recoil atoms are much greater than the thermal velocities of atoms and molecules at ordinary temperatures. Besides being a superlative specimen of confusion of macroscopic and microscopic concepts, the expression "hot atom" is misleading because kinetic energy is not the only kind of activation endued to atoms or molecular fragments by nuclear transformations. Free atoms can be liberated in electronically excited or ionized states; neutral and ionic radicals can possess electronic, vibrational, or rotational excitation. Any of these forms of activation must alter the chemical reactivity.

The mechanisms of nuclear-transformation chemistry can be treated in terms of the same three successive temporal stages useful in the interpretation of ordinary radiation chemistry. The physical stage embraces both immediate effects of nuclear transformation on the original molecule and moderation of the recoil atom with attendant external activation. It is followed by a physicochemical stage, which here includes the final, epithermal behavior of the recoil atom, and thereafter by a chemical stage at the inception of which all fragments have attained thermal energy. The chemical stage can again be subdivided into a track period and a subsequent uniform period.

* The term "recoil atom" in current usage often carries the connotation that the atom has a velocity substantially smaller than that of a typical particle of ionizing radiation, such as a natural α-particle. For example, in the thermal-neutron reaction $B^{10}(n,\alpha)Li^7$ (a reaction useful in radiation chemistry as an internal source of particles of high LET) the initial kinetic energy of the Li atom is 0.84 Mev, that of the α-particle being only 1.47 Mev, and although the former is nominally "the" recoil atom, it is not uncommon to refer to both particles as recoil atoms.

2. RADIOLYSIS

Little is known about radiolysis by recoil atoms—or, indeed, by any atoms having kinetic energy much below 1 Mev. Production and use of such particles involves many experimental difficulties. Recoil atoms from α-decay are perhaps the most easily obtained, and their physical behavior has been studied since the early days of radioactivity. However, only a few fragmentary, qualitative results on their chemical action have been reported, in either the recent (206) or the older literature [2 (Chapter 9)]. It is expected that α-recoils should usually lead to the same products as high-energy charged particles, but with markedly different relative and absolute yields, since only about one-third of their energy is expended in electronic excitation and ionization, the greater part being dissipated by transfer of energy and momentum to atomic nuclei of the medium (the primary process called atom ejection; cf. Section II.B.3). Such nuclear collisions become progressively more dominant as the velocity of the recoil atom declines (207). Indeed, they must also participate simultaneously in the excitation and ionization acts that do occur, leading to concomitant vibrational or rotational excitation or outright ejection of an atom. Alpha recoils should also display extremely pronounced track-effects in condensed phases, for their average LET is ten times that of a natural α-particle.

Recoil atoms having kinetic energies substantially smaller than 100 kev are produced in some induced nuclear reactions. Atoms in this lower range of energies can also be obtained by electrostatic acceleration of ions, and they are common products (often called *canal rays*) in certain types of electrical discharge—particularly arcs. Much information on their physical behavior in gases is available [23 (Chapter VIII)], especially for energies between about 100 ev and 10 kev. The recoil atoms from β-disintegration and from emission of high-energy γ-rays have still lower kinetic energies— usually below a few hundred ev. Although capable of causing ionization (with low yields), these various slow particles are not correctly classified as ionizing radiation; most of their energy is imparted to atomic nuclei of the medium, and very little to electronic systems. Slight attention has been accorded the chemical action of such recoil atoms, and almost no experimental information is available. Theoretical analysis of the absorption in CH_3Br of Br recoil atoms having initial kinetic energies between 100 ev and 3 kev suggests that g for primary production of CH_3 and Br is about 1 (208). Dissociation occurs here entirely by direct momentum-transfer to atomic nuclei and not at all as a result of excitation or ionization.

It is relevant to note at this point that recoil atoms having kinetic energies of 10 to 100 kev are abundant initial products in the absorption of fast neutrons. The radiation chemistry of fast neutrons is still virtually unexplored, but it will assume great importance if fusion reactors are ever realized.

3. RE-ENTRY OF DETACHED ATOMS

Study of recoil atoms has been chiefly concerned, not with the radiolysis they cause, but rather with the factors that determine the nature of the molecules in which they are ultimately bound. These molecules can be identified easily, even if only a comparatively small number of nuclei have been transformed, when the atom produced is radioactive—and in that case, indeed, even if the atom has been unaltered chemically (i.e., only isotopically) by the nuclear transformation. In general, a large proportion of the recoil atoms are found to be re-established in compounds different from the original one. Predicted and then confirmed experimentally by Szilard and Chalmers (209), this effect (210, 211) affords the basis of an invaluable method for concentrating radioactive iostopes, despite the minute quantities usually produced, and it also has useful application in assay of the responsible nuclear reaction. For example, irradiation of ethyl iodide with thermal neutrons transforms the stable isotope I^{127} into the radioactive isotope I^{128} [(n,γ) reaction], and the C—I bond is ruptured as a consequence, I^{128} atoms (but not I^{127}) being liberated. A substantial fraction of this radioactive iodine can be separated as I_2 by adding a trace of free iodine (*carrier*) before irradiation and removing it subsequently (209). Chemical extraction (with or without carrier) is usually the most advantageous technique for gathering the detached atoms, but surface adsorption and ion collection on charged plates have also been used successfully. Most nuclear transformations (all α-disintegrations; almost all induced reactions; some β-disintegrations) impart recoil energy sufficiently great to enable chemical or physical separation of the product.

The fraction of transformed nuclei that are not extracted is called the *retention*. In the example cited 60% of the radioactive iodine appears in the carrier, and the retention is therefore 0.40; for the same nuclear process in methyl iodide it is 0.56. Comparable values of the retention are common. If a Szilard-Chalmers separation is to be successful the product must not undergo isotopic exchange with parent molecules. (In the preceding example thermal iodine-atoms exchange with I_2 but not with C_2H_5I and are quickly incorporated into the carrier, and there is no exchange between I_2 and C_2H_5I.) Of the numerous investigations of the Szilard-Chalmers effect, most have exploited the (n,γ) reaction (radiative neutron capture), which offers decided physical and chemical advantages. Radioactive halogens have been separated from many organohalogen compounds, both aliphatic and aromatic, and from inorganic compounds such as halates and perhalates in aqueous solution. Radioactive isotopes of P, Cr, Mn, Cu, As, Se,

Mo, Sn, Te, and U (among others) have also been separated, generally from irradiated solids or from aqueous solutions (where separation is based upon change in oxidation state).

Two of the factors that may contribute to retention are failure of the original bond to be broken by the nuclear transformation, and reconstitution of the parent molecule by recombination of the *original* fragments. The first is negligible for radiative neutron capture; thus the retention in normal alkyl bromides or iodides containing a small admixture of free halogen is 1 % or even less in the vapor phase. The second can occur only in liquids and solids (cage effect), and then only if the recoil is not so great that the atom escapes from the neighborhood of its residual fragment, a requirement which normally is preclusive. A third factor—the most important one—is formation of a molecule that withstands the separation procedure, by some subsequent reaction of the detached atom. Called isotopic replacement or *re-entry*, such a reaction frequently gives rise to a labelled molecule chemically identical to the original one, but it also can produce diverse new compounds containing the radioactive atom.* Thus, recoil halogen atoms in a variety of organohalogen liquids yield the labeled parent molecule as the main product together with numerous others; with bromine compounds the chief of these is the molecule in which a radioactive bromine atom *replaces a hydrogen atom*. Substances with fewer and with more carbon atoms are also commonly found. In *n*-propyl bromide twenty different products (mostly monobromoalkanes and dibromoalkanes) have been detected (212). Re-entry of recoil atoms has proved valuable as a means of synthesizing isotopically labeled molecules. For example, the (n, γ) reaction provides a variety of labeled molecules in pure gaseous or liquid organohalogen compounds, in solutions of halogens or halogen compounds in liquid hydrocarbons, and in similar gaseous mixtures. Many organic compounds containing radioactive carbon in high specific activity can be prepared by irradiating allied nitrogenous substances with thermal neutrons, thereby inducing the $N^{14}(n,p)C^{14}$ reaction. Tritium labeling can be accomplished in like fashion.

The great sensitivity of radioactive-tracer techniques permits measurement of retention and determination of the final state of chemical binding at very low concentrations of the products, even in the presence of radiolysis by such energetic charged particles as may be involved in the nuclear transformation. It is accordingly possible to compare the retention, and the yields of various specific products, for different nuclear processes—such as (n, γ), (d, p), (γ, n), and $(n, 2n)$ reactions—in which isotopic recoil atoms

---

* The word *re-entry* is used in an extended sense and denotes return of the detached atom to a state of stable chemical binding.

are produced from the same original compound with widely differing initial kinetic energy. On the whole, the yields are found to be the same (213). This result indicates that the ultimate chemical fate of the atom is determined mainly by events near to the very end of its path. Re-entry can occur either during the physicochemical stage, by epithermal reaction of the recoil atom with a normal molecule or with a free radical that it has itself produced, or during the track period of the chemical stage, by reaction of the thermalized recoil atom with such a radical. These two alternatives can in some cases be distinguished by experiment. For example, in C_2H_5Br and in C_2H_5I activated by radiative neutron-capture, use of scavengers which react with diffusing thermalized atoms—but not with atoms during their fleeting epithermal period—shows that 25 % of the recoil atoms that enter organic molecules do so after thermalization, and 75 % do so while they are still epithermal (or directly upon being thermalized) (214). The technique is successful here because thermal Br and I atoms do not react rapidly with the parent molecules. There is no scavenger effect with the analogous chlorides because Cl atoms react so quickly (by abstraction of H) that they are not susceptible to scavenger action; indeed, they scarcely survive to reach thermal velocity. Not only the gross retention, but also the yields of various individual products can be studied in this way; and here again, although the scavengeable fraction varies from one product to another and depends upon the state of aggregation, it does not in general depend upon the character of the nuclear transformation which gives rise to the recoil atom. (This arresting result also includes isomeric transitions, treated in the following section.)

In these cases, and in many others, the uniform period does not contribute to the organic yield. Nor is there any contribution from reaction of thermal atoms with normal molecules. Such a reaction could not lead to compounds of the nature and diversity observed. In particular, the common and truly remarkable product in which a halogen recoil atom has replaced a hydrogen atom cannot be formed from a thermal atom and a parent molecule. Indeed, thermal Cl and Br atoms in hydrocarbons, alkyl halides, and similar media react only by abstracting H atoms, and I atoms are quite unreactive. It is characteristic of epithermal processes, especially with at least moderately complex molecules, that novel products are often formed. As already stressed, electronic excitation and ionization may join kinetic energy in enhancing the reactivity of recoil atoms.

The reactions of re-entry in liquids or solids occur in a localized region which is similar in some respects to the spur produced by ionizing radiation of low LET. This region contains many normal molecules and also some decomposition products, including free radicals, but only a single recoil atom; the unique attribute of the recoil atom spur is that the reactions of that atom alone are relevant. The local decomposition products comprise those produced by the recoil atom during the final stage of its moderation and also—if the initial recoil is so small that the spur is close to the site of the original molecule—radiolysis products of other fragments of the nuclear transformation, particularly electrons (which are often ejected in secondary reorganization of the electron shells).

Elucidation of the behavior of epithermal atoms has been the aim of much experimental and theoretical research in the field; as emphasized in earlier sections, epithermal processes also have prime importance in conventional radiation chemistry, in photochemistry, and even for some ordinary (thermal) chemical reactions. Nuclear-transformation chemistry offers salient advantages for their study, and has contributed greatly to their understanding. However, notwithstanding impressive advances during the past decade, the mechanisms of re-entry remain obscure in many respects.

4. AUGER DISRUPTION

In the nuclear processes treated thus far, initial detachment of the radioactive atom is caused by recoil. However, a retention smaller than unity is often observed—and a Szilard-Chalmers separation is possible—in cases where the kinetic energy of the recoil atom is too small to break even a single chemical bond. This is so, for example, with the emission of comparatively low-energy γ-rays. An important instance is the isomeric transition of metastable nuclei, of which Br^{80} is the one that has been studied the most extensively. The metastable Br^{80}-nucleus (half-life 4.4 hours) decays into "normal" Br^{80} (half-life 18 minutes), and under proper conditions the latter can be separated readily by chemical means. Here, decomposition of the molecule has a different origin. The crucial step is the first one: instead of emitting a γ-ray photon, the excited nucleus undergoes "internal conversion" in an inner electron-shell of the atom, thereby ejecting an electron.[*] This is followed by an Auger cascade and the ejection of many valence electrons from the molecule, which then dissociates in a third step. The same phenomenon has already been discussed as a particular primary process in ordinary radiolysis (Section II.B.3). Obviously, the consequences of a momentary vacancy in an inner electron-shell are independent of the manner in which the vacancy was created. Common ways of ejecting an inner electron are radioactive transformation (orbital-electron capture, internal

---

[*] The nuclear internal-conversion process must not be confused with the entirely different internal conversion in an electronically-excited polyatomic molecule (Section II.C.1). The same terms are used because the processes are formally akin: each is an unreversible, radiationless transition between two states of equal energy, and each competes with a radiative transition to a state of lower energy.

conversion of a γ-ray), photoelectric absorption of an X-ray photon, and (inner-shell) ionization by a swiftly moving charged particle.

Recent experiments using mass spectrometry have verified the theoretical prediction that high positive charges are acquired by atoms following loss of one of their innermost electrons. The ionic charge that is attained increases with the number of electrons in the atom; its mean value is approximately $+4$ for Cl and $+8$ for Xe (215, 216). Isomeric transition in Br^{80} leads to an average ionic charge of about $+10$, but this large value results from two separate Auger-cascades initiated by two successive internal-conversion acts of the radioactive nucleus. An isolated molecule containing Br^{80} is certain to be shattered by the loss of so many electrons. In general, internal conversion in an inner electron shell of any atom will lead to Auger disruption of the molecule, the atom being detached (either as an atomic ion or as part of a molecular ion) and therefore becoming susceptible to Szilard-Chalmers separation. On the other hand, if an excited nucleus emits a γ-ray photon that does not suffer internal conversion, and if also the recoil is sufficiently small, the molecule will not dissociate. A radioactive nucleus that satisfies these conditions is metastable Zn^{69}, and experiment [on $Zn(C_2H_5)_2$] confirms that Zn is not liberated from molecules in consequence of the isomeric transition.

5. CHEMICAL EFFECTS OF BETA-DECAY

Beta-disintegration in a constituent atom disturbs a molecule rather differently than do energetic recoil or Auger disruption—the two causes of dissociation thus far considered. It does so simultaneously in three distinct ways: recoil, "transmutation," and electronic excitation. Recoil from β-disintegration is small (in some cases it suffices to rupture a bond, in others it does not); but the fact that the β-ray energy-distribution is continuous between zero and an upper limit means that there is always an appreciable fraction of molecules that are not dissociated by recoil, although they may be vibrationally or rotationally excited. By "transmutation" is denoted all consequences of the change in chemical nature of the atom (its nuclear charge is increased by one unit in β^--decay, and decreased by one in β^+-decay); this is important precisely because of the marginal character of the disturbance of nuclear and electronic motions. (In α-decay, and in most induced nuclear reactions, there is also a change in atomic number, but it plays no role in the fate of the original molecule because the recoil atom always escapes instantly.) Finally, β-decay perturbs the electronic system of the molecule and can thereby result in excitation or ionization of the product. The differing contributions of these three factors, and their interplay, make the behavior of molecules in β-decay particularly interesting, and also particularly intricate.* In few cases have the factors been disentangled.

The *immediate product* of β^+-decay in a molecule is a molecular negative ion. Since few such ions are stable, and even the stable ones are highly fragile, the immediate product in this case will at once shed the extra electron and revert to a neutral molecule. In contrast, the immediate product of β^--decay, a molecular positive ion, will in general be a physically stable system. Subsequent behavior in both cases depends primarily on the potency of the three factors, and secondarily on environmental influences.

Dissociation arising from electronic excitation of the immediate product is noteworthy because a novel origin of the excitation is involved. Stemming from the sudden change in nuclear charge due to the virtually instantaneous departure of the β-particle from the atom, this excitation is rather different in character from excitation by an energetic particle passing nearby. The orbital electrons are caught in a state of arrangement and motion incompatible with the altered nuclear charge, and in their quick readjustment one or more of them may be promoted in energy so that the immediate product is formed in one or another of its electronically excited or ionized states. The energy for this excitation is subtracted from the energy emitted in the β-disintegration; the correction is, of course, a minute one. Elementary theory shows that the probability of excitation or ionization of a single electron is roughly equal to Z_{eff}^{-2}, where Z_{eff} is the effective nuclear charge acting on the electron. For inner electrons $Z_{\text{eff}} \approx Z$, and there is hence a small but not negligible probability for creation of a vacancy in one of the inner shells. This effect has been observed as an occasional emission of X-rays following β-decay. For valence electrons $Z_{\text{eff}} \approx 1$, and the probability of exciting each outer electron is therefore comparable to unity. (*True ionization* is somewhat less likely; experiments with Kr and Xe (217, 218) give a total probability of 0.1 to 0.2 for ionization in the outermost shell, which in these atoms contains eight electrons.) No reliable quantitative theory for excitation of valence electrons has yet been contrived, but it is known that the predominant excited states lie at significantly smaller excitation energies than do those formed typically by swiftly moving charged particles. Study of the behavior of molecular ions that are the immediate product of β-decay accordingly holds promise of revealing properties of

---

* The β-disintegration of an atom contained in a small biological unit, such as a virus or a single cell, presents a radiobiological analogue. For example, disintegration of a single P^{32} atom (into S^{32}) can often inactivate or otherwise alter the behavior of such a unit. Called *radioactive suicide*, the effect, in some instances at least, is not caused by external action of the β-particle, but rather by one or more of the three kinds of disturbance explained above.

activated molecules not readily accessible through ordinary radiation chemistry.

If the β-decay results in a radioactive nucleus (which is uncommon among the important and convenient species), tracer techniques can be used as discussed previously to measure the yields of various final compounds, and a few such studies have been made. If the daughter atom is not radioactive, other approaches are possible. For example, two radioactive atoms can be incorporated into the molecule; after one of them has disintegrated the other still serves as a label. This technique has been applied to the β^--decay of C^{14} in gaseous ethane (219). Here the immediate product is $CH_3NH_3^+$; if it does not decompose at the C—N bond because of the disturbances previously described, it may achieve stability as CH_3NH_2—perhaps spontaneously or perhaps by losing a proton in a subsequent collision. The experiments show that 47 % of the molecular ions maintain intact C—N bonds during their transformation to methyl amine. Dissociation at the C—N bond of approximately one-half of the immediate product is believed to be caused by β-decay disturbances—partly by recoil and partly by electronic excitation.

A direct and powerful method of investigating the decomposition of the original molecule exploits mass spectrometry without a separate source of ionization; the observed ions are those produced spontaneously in a radioactive gas. Concomitant radiolysis can be reduced to negligible proportions by use of sufficiently low pressure, and the product obviously need not be radioactive. Both intact original molecules, if charged, and charged atomic and molecular dissociation-products can be recorded. The method, a relatively new one, is in fact applicable to any kind of nuclear transformation, although only β-decay has been studied thus far. In this case, if the recoil happens to be small, the results bear directly on the electronic excitations caused by sudden change in nuclear charge. (Transmutation, in contrast to excitation and recoil, gives essentially the same disturbance in every disintegration event.) Observation of the resultant dissociation patterns consequently affords a means of complementing similar studies in conventional mass-spectrometry, where the excitation is produced by external agencies.

The method can be applied to the simplest molecule, molecular hydrogen, by use of either TH or T_2. Tritium (the radioactive isotope H^3) disintegrates into He^3 by β^--emission; in both cases, therefore, the hydrogen molecule is transformed into an isotopic form of HeH^+. This ion, in its ground state, is physically stable, irrespective of the masses of its constituents. All three disturbances contribute to the decomposition caused by tritium decay, although the role of recoil is minor because the β-ray energy —and hence the recoil energy—is exceptionally small. In β-decay of TH,

90 % of the immediate product remains bound, and, curiously, most of the observed rupture yields $He^+ + H$ rather than $He + H^+$ (220, 221). The probability of true ionization (HeH^{++} and its dissociation products) is at most 0.02. Likewise, 95 % of the HeT^+ formed by disintegration of one of the atoms in T_2 remains bound.

The behavior of monotritiated ethane is quite different. No $C_2H_5He^+$ is found, and He^+ is also absent (222). About 80 % of the observed ions are $C_2H_5^+$; the remainder consists chiefly of smaller fragments, in most of which the C—C bond is intact. Here, presumably, the immediate product at once dissociates to $C_2H_5^+ + He$, and one-fifth of the ethyl ions undergo further spontaneous decomposition. The amount of this seconadry decomposition, and its range (C_2H^+ and even C_2^+ are formed), show that many of the ethyl ions are excited, some of them very highly, and therefore prove that an important proportion of the excitation in β-decay is not localized— or at any rate not fixed—in the electrons directly bound to the disintegrating atom. Similar features occur with 1,2-dibromoethane containing a radioactive Br^{82} atom (222): none of the immediate product, $C_2H_4BrKr^+$, survives; most dissociation gives $C_2H_4Br^+ + Kr$; and there is also a substantial production of smaller fragments, which, again, retain the C—C bond. The recoil in β-disintegration of Br^{82} is greater than it is with tritium, but not great enough by itself to account for so high a degree of decomposition.

Although the experiments are too few to permit secure generalization, it seems likely that spontaneous dissociation of the immediate product is the rule, and that preponderant stability in the case of hydrogen is the exception. There are two independent grounds for such a difference. Firstly, hydrogen is unique in having only two valence electrons, and the total probability of its electronic excitation in β-decay is therefore smaller than that for other molecules, which have many more. Secondly, a HeH^+ molecule in an attractive excited state may achieve stability by emitting a photon, but radiation cannot compete successfully with internal conversion in most polyatomic molecules—and internal conversion causes the excitation energy to be retained by the immediate product and ultimately to contribute to its decomposition. To be sure, the disparity between molecular hydrogen and polyatomic molecules in experiments employing H^3 and Br^{82}, both of which decay to noble gases, is favored by the circumstance that a noble-gas atom can be strongly bound to a lone proton, but only weakly, if at all, to a molecular positive ion. The two reasons just adduced, however, apply generally.

IV. Radiation Chemistry of Water

Energy from ionizing radiations or from ultraviolet light absorbed by water in the gaseous, liquid, or solid states forms chemically reactive species. Our treatment of the vapor and solid states shall be b ief because of the limited work carried out in these media but the chemical properties of irradiated liquid water shall be discussed at some length.

A. WATER VAPOR AND ICE

1. WATER VAPOR

Irradiated water vapor displays little or no decomposition. As early as 1913 it was found that water vapor heated to 100–130° during α-particle irradiation decomposed with a total gas yield of only 0.04 molecules per 100 ev (98). However even this yield may be too high because of possible impurities introduced from the wall of the container. Vessels irradiated externally by Co^{60} γ-rays or internally by tritium β-rays require preheating of the reaction vessel at 510° while degassing under high vacua. Under these conditions of pretreatment of the vessel, pure water vapor radiolyzes with an upper limit $G(H_2)$ of 0.02 (97). Ultraviolet light is also reported to decompose water vapor. Hydrogen, oxygen, and hydrogen peroxide are the products (223). Here again, impurity effects may be responsible for the appearance of these products.

While water vapor does not decompose into stable products upon irradiation it does dissociate into free radicals with a yield of 11.7 $\pm$ 0.6 radical pairs/100 ev (97). Deuterium added to H_2O vapor in mole fractions in the range 0.005 to 0.01 is efficiently converted to hydrogen deuteride with a $G(-D_2) = G(HD) = 11.7$. The mechanism postulated is:

$$HOH \rightarrow H + OH$$

$$H + D_2 \rightarrow HD + D$$

$$OH + D_2 \rightarrow HOD + D$$

$$D + D(M) \rightarrow D_2(M)$$

Where M is an effective third body.

The water dissociation yield in water vapor is considerably greater than 3.7, the observable yield in liquid water (see Table XI and Section IV.C.1). The lower yield in liquid water is caused by the cage effect and by recombination within the spur, two effects that are eliminated by the gas phase. Because of these effects gas phase scavengers are much more effective than liquid phase scavengers. Indirect effects in gas phase studies offer considerable untapped potential for the study of reaction mechanisms.

The radical pair yield of 11.7 accords with the one deducible from equations 10 and 11 of Section III.B. Using 28.7 ev/ion pair for W, the mean energy per ion pair produced in water vapor, equation 10 becomes

$$M/N_i = 28.7 \times 11.7/100 = 3.4.$$

Reasonably $\varphi_i = 2$ because

$$H_2O^+ + H_2O \rightarrow H_3O^+ + OH$$

$$H_3O^+ + e^- \rightarrow 2H + OH.$$

Thus 2 water molecules dissociate per ion pair formed. And if we take $\varphi_e = 1$, $\bar{\varphi}_{se} = 0$ and $N_e/N_i = 1$, equation 11 becomes

$$M/N_i = 3.0,$$

a water dissociation yield in good agreement with the observed yield of 3.4.

2. ICE

Comparatively little attention has been paid to the radiation chemistry of ice until it was possible to apply paramagnetic resonance methods to identify the free radical species formed. Sufficient work had been done on the radiolysis of ice to show that it decomposed into hydrogen, hydrogen peroxide, and oxygen (see Table IX). It was further established that chemical reactions took place in ice with dissolved oxygen, ferrous ion, and other materials. But the difficulties of preparing homogeneous ice solutions and of irradiating and analyzing them in the frozen state limited the interest in this area. Besides, in the interpretation of the results there has always been the question of whether the reaction occurred during irradiation or during the melting process. We shall see that postirradiation processes cannot be neglected.

The paramagnetic resonance spectra of H_2O and D_2O irradiated at $-196°$ yield 0.14 radical pairs per 100 ev (224). (See Table IX.) In pure water the hyperfine splittings attributed to the H doublet and the D triplet are a factor of 16 less than those observed in the gas phase, although in irradiated H_2SO_4 or $1:1$ molar $H_2SO_4:D_2O$ the hyperfine splittings are very close to those obtained for gaseous H and D atoms (54). While there may be some question about the assignment of this absorption to the hydrogen atom for irradiated pure water, the evidence for the presence of the hydrogen atom in irradiated acidic ice is positive. The hydrogen atoms in irradiated sulfuric acid are stable indefinitely at $-196°$ but disappear very quickly at $-160°$ by a second order process suggesting radical-radical recombination. Ice irradiated at $-196°$ and examined at $-269°$ revealed a second doublet attributed to the OH radical. This postulate was supported by the γ-ray irradiation of frozen hydrogen peroxide solutions (224). An increase in concentration of peroxide not only increases the separation of these peaks but it also intensifies them.

Continuous annealing of irradiated dilute hydrogen peroxide in H_2O ice shows that the paramagnetic species disappear at temperatures of $-173°$ and higher (224). Most of the paramagnetic species anneal at $-173°$

TABLE IX
Yields in the Radiolysis of Ice

Composition of solution	Irradiation temperature	Radiation	Products	Yields	References	Remarks
Degassed H_2O	-269	γ-rays	H; OH	0.083	224	$\sim10^{-3}$ M radical pairs
Degassed H_2O	-196	γ-rays	H; OH	0.23	224	$\sim10^{-3}$ M radical pairs
Degassed H^3_2O	-196	H^3 β-rays	$H_2 + \frac{1}{2}O_2$	0.27	225	
5:1 moles H_2O: moles H_2SO_4	-196	γ-rays	H	0.04	54	Approximate yields; 2nd order disappearance on warming.
5:1 moles H_2O: moles $HClO_4$	-196	γ-rays	H	0.12	54	Approximate yields; 2nd order disappearance on warming.
Degassed H_2O	-196	γ-rays	H_2	0.098	226	Concentration of products $\sim10^{-3}$ M.
Degassed H_2O	-196	γ-rays	H_2O_2	0.077	226	Concentration of products $\sim10^{-3}$ M.
Degassed H_2O	-196	γ-rays	O_2	0.003	226	Concentration of products $\sim10^{-3}$ M.
O_2 Saturated H_2O	-196	γ-rays	H_2	0.098	226	O_2 shows no effect
O_2 Saturated H_2O	-196	γ-rays	H_2O_2	0.098	226	O_2 shows no effect
O_2 Saturated H_2O	-100	γ-rays	H_2	0.10	226	Initial yields.
O_2 Saturated H_2O	-100	γ-rays	H_2O_2	0.32	226	Initial yields.
O_2 Saturated H_2O	-20	γ-rays	H_2	0.25	226	Initial yields.
O_2 Saturated H_2O	-20	γ-rays	H_2O_2	0.70	226	Initial yields.
Degassed H_2O	-196	α-rays	$H_2 + \frac{1}{2}O_2$	0.14	98	Local destruction of H_2 and H_2O has lowered yields.
Degassed H_2O	-80 or -196	α-rays	H_2	0.7	5	See p. 203 of reference 5
Degassed H_2O	-80 or -196	α-rays	H_2O_2	0.4	5	See p. 203 of reference 5
Degassed H_2O	-80 or -196	α-rays	O_2	0.15	5	See p. 203 of reference 5

and the remainder anneal at $-128°$. It is suggested that the peaks annealing out at $-173°$ are due to free radicals formed in the spur from H_2O^+ while the portion annealing out at $-128°$ is due to OH formation by the reactions

$$H + H_2O_2 \rightarrow OH + H_2O \qquad (27)$$

or

$$\epsilon^- + H_2O_2 \rightarrow OH + OH^-. \qquad (28)$$

Presumably the closely packed hydroxyl groups originating in the spur anneal first and then the radicals generated by equations 27 and 28 react at the higher temperature, possibly with the water decomposition products, hydrogen and hydrogen peroxide. However it must be emphasized that these suggestions are highly speculative and that some paramagnetic species other than hydroxyl radicals may be responsible for this behavior.

Irradiated ice has two thermoluminescence bands (227–229). Ice irradiated to about 10^{18} ev per gm at $-196°$ has a main peak appearing at $-115°$ with a yield of one photon per 10^{10} ev. Emission at this temperature is nearly all in the visible part of the spectrum (229). But with an irradiation of 10^{21} ev per gm the main peak appears at $-155°$ with about 100 times the intensity of the $-115°$ peak. The yield is one photon per 10^{11} ev. The $-115°$ thermoluminescence is attributed to the release and reaction of an electron trapped by an impurity alkali ion (227, 228). The $-155°$ peak may be connected with reactions of the paramagnetic species annealing in the temperature range -140 to $-158°$.

Ice fluoresces during irradiation. Emission from ice irradiated by Co^{60} γ-rays is masked by the Cerenkov radiation (226). But ice irradiated at $-196°$ with 50 kv X-rays emits light with a peak at 3900 A and an unresolved band at 5500 A. With rising temperature of irradiation, the band at 3900 A diminishes in intensity and disappears at $-120°$. The intensity of the 5500 A peak remains nearly constant between -196 and $-120°$.

Ice irradiated at $-196°$ develops an absorption band with a maximum at 2800 A and a shoulder near 2300 A (226). With steady annealing both bands disappear at the same time, suggesting a single species which may be the hydroxyl radical. Two processes occur during annealing: the dominant one reaches a maximum rate at $-152°$; the other disappears completely at $-165°$. The tan color of self-irradiated tritium ice may be from the long wave tail of the 2800 A band (230).

The processes taking place in the temperature range from -150 to $-175°$ appear to be connected with mobility and reaction of free radicals. If the 2800 A absorption band is due to OH radicals, its disappearance correlates with the disappearance of free radicals as deduced from paramagnetic resonance results. Reactions may be of the types:

$$H + OH \rightarrow H_2O$$

$$OH + OH \rightarrow H_2O_2$$

or by the release and reaction of trapped electrons with paramagnetic species. These reactions may also be responsible for the fluorescence. The absence of the 3900 A fluorescence band in ice irradiated at −120° is consistent with the absence of any appreciable concentration of paramagnetic species (224).

Chemical evidence supports the results obtained above. Irradiation at temperatures of −196° and below causes accumulation of hydrogen and hydrogen peroxide as well as trapped radicals (see Table IX). And when the temperature of the irradiated ice is raised, reactions take place. Studies were made on 50 μM hydrogen peroxide saturated with hydrogen, frozen and irradiated at −196° (226). It was found that species formed at −196° reacted with hydrogen peroxide in the narrow temperature range between −183 and −160°. Again this temperature range corresponds to the one at which the free radicals trapped in ice at lower temperatures disappear. Since reaction in this instance is with molecular species distributed uniformly throughout the ice, both reaction and diffusion of radicals are demonstrated.

Reaction of hydrogen and hydrogen peroxide is important in minimizing the decomposition of ice by γ-rays (226). Table IX shows that $G(H_2)$ for ice irradiated at −196° is 0.1 for γ-rays and 0.7 for α-rays. Corresponding yields in liquid water are 0.00 and 1.8. At −196° the free radicals are unable to combine hydrogen and hydrogen peroxide. And since limited free radical concentrations develop during the prolonged irradiation of ice, the free radicals are comparatively ineffective during the warm-up period after irradiation. Ice containing 50 μM hydrogen peroxide and about 700 μM hydrogen shows a $G(-H_2O_2)$ of about 0.2 at −196°. Above this temperature the yield increases continuously to about 4.5 at −5°. A sevenfold increase takes place between −100 and −50°. These results not only show that efficient reactions take place in the solid phase but also demonstrate that $G(H_2)$ and $G(H_2O_2)$ should be very small indeed for γ-ray irradiated ice above −100°.

Ice containing oxygen forms hydrogen peroxide. Some typical yields appear in Table IX. At −196°, oxygen is ineffective in increasing the hydrogen peroxide yields but appreciable yields are obtained at −100 and −20°. Again chemical reactivity is associated with the mobility of the free radicals.

Research on irradiated ice confirms the free radical theory used so successfully in explaining the radiation chemistry of liquid water. It appears that chemical reactions in the solid state parallel those of the liquid state, but even under optimum conditions the yields are a factor of 3 or 4 lower in ice than in the liquid water.

B. GENERAL PRINCIPLES OF THE RADIATION CHEMISTRY OF LIQUID WATER AND AQUEOUS SOLUTIONS

1. OBSERVED PRODUCTS

Stable products resulting from the irradiation of liquid water are hydrogen, hydrogen peroxide, and oxygen. (Ozone, a possible product has not been positively identified.) These compounds are formed in water by either light- or heavy-particle radiations and the yields depend critically on the type of radiation, on experimental conditions prevailing during irradiation, and on the purity of the water. These factors are dealt with in detail below in Sections IV.C, D, and E.

2. HISTORICAL DEVELOPMENT

Mention has already been made of the irradiation of water vapor and ice by α-particles by early workers. The effects of radiations on liquid water and aqueous solutions were also studied in the period from 1900 to 1925 (98, 231–236). As with the vapor and solid states, hydrogen, oxygen, and hydrogen peroxide were found after irradiation, particularly by α-particles. This decomposition of water was regarded as an electrolysis because it was known that an ionized gas conducts an electric current and that an electric current passing through a solution liberates hydrogen and oxygen at the electrodes. It was also shown that the penetrating β- and γ-rays of radium also decompose water and promote chemical reactions (234). Besides decomposing water, the radiations from radium salts reduce ferric sulfate, and liberate halogens from alkali and alkaline earth iodides and bromides (236). These studies were carried out with feeble radiation sources as judged by present-day standards but they were sufficient to establish a new principle for the initiation of chemical reactions.

The next major development in radiation chemistry was the use of the X-ray tube. Although the modern hot filament-anode tube was discovered by Coolidge in 1912, it was not until the mid-twenties that X-rays were applied to chemical studies. And then the principal incentive came through research on the biological effects of X-rays. The X-ray output of tubes developed by 1930 provided radiation sources equivalent to thousands of curies of radium. This solved the problem of adequate radiation sources, but a suitable means of measuring absorbed X-ray energy still needed to be devised.

In 1929, resulting from studies on hemoglobin, the Fricke dosimeter (i.e., aerated ferrous sulfate in 0.8 N sulfuric acid) was devised (237, 238). Hemoglobin, containing only 4 ferrous ions per protein molecule of 68,000 molecular weight was changed on irradiation in aqueous solution to methemoglobin, containing ferric ions with a yield nearly independent of concentration. The striking, highly selective action of the radiation on the oxidation of ferrous ion in the hemoglobin molecule suggested the simpler ferrous sulfate system now widely accepted as a standard of dosimetry for all types of ionizing radiations (see Section V.A.1). Besides providing a dosimeter, studies on this system confirmed the indirect action effect and revealed the importance of oxygen, pH, and impurities on X-ray initiated reactions.

Ionizing radiation proved highly versatile in promoting both oxidation and reduction reactions and the potentials for using radiation in the study of the mechanisms of reactions were realized (239). The activated water hypothesis of Fricke explained the qualitative and the quantitative features of the data obtained up to 1940. According to this theory, two activated water molecules, $(H_2O)'_{act}$ and $(H_2O)''_{act}$, were formed during irradiation. With X-rays of 35 kv effective energy, $G(H_2O)'_{act} = 0.60$ and $G(H_2O)''_{act} = 2.40$. $(H_2O)'_{act}$ leads to the formation of hydrogen peroxide and hydrogen; the reaction was written as (239):

$$(H_2O)'_{act} + H_2O \rightarrow H_2O_2 + H_2 .$$

$(H_2O)''_{act}$ formed with a yield of 2.4 molecules per 100 ev specifically activated oxygen to increase oxidation yields. In terms of the free radical theory its role is more clearly seen if we write

$$(H_2O)''_{act} \rightarrow H + OH.$$

Activation of oxygen is of course effected through reaction of the hydrogen atom with oxygen to form the hydroperoxy radical.

3. THE FREE RADICAL THEORY

The free radical theory of water radiolysis successfully explains the qualitative features of the chemical effects of radiation (9, 239–242). According to this theory, chemical processes begin in irradiated water with the conversion of the initial products (both excited and ionized species) into hydrogen and hydroxyl-free radicals (see Sections II.A and II.B). The electron forms the hydrogen atom,

$$H_2O + \epsilon^-_{aq} = H + OH^-,$$

and the ionized water molecule gives the hydroxyl radical,

$$H_2O^+ + H_2O = OH + H_3O^+.$$

An approximately equal number of hydrogen and hydroxyl free radicals form by excitation of the water molecules in the spur by secondary electrons:

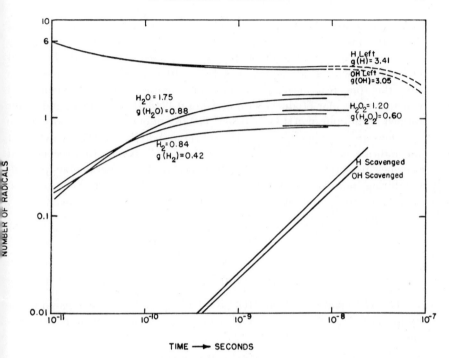

FIG. 8. Time scale for the recombination of hydrogen and hydroxyl free radicals in a γ-ray spur (65). (See Sections II.F and IV.B.3)

$$H_2O + \epsilon^- \rightarrow H_2O^* + \epsilon^-$$

$$H_2O^* \rightarrow H + OH.$$

These free radicals, originating from ionization or excitation, are produced in groups or spurs and pairwise reactions lead to hydrogen and hydrogen peroxide by reactions 29 and 30:

$$H + H = H_2 \tag{29}$$

$$OH + OH = H_2O_2 . \tag{30}$$

In addition, many radicals are lost by recombination of radicals within a solvent cage or spur as well as by the combination of radicals outside the cage or spur by the reaction:

$$H + OH = H_2O. \tag{31}$$

An idea of the time scale for these reactions can be obtained from Fig. 8 which is derived from a numerical solution of the diffusion equations for the two-radical model (65). In this figure the conditions assumed are: 6 water molecules dissociated into free radicals in a spur of 10 A radius, reacting with rate constants of 1.2×10^{-11}, 0.9×10^{-11} and 1.0×10^{-11} cc/molecule second for reactions 29, 30, and 31, respectively, with diffusion constants of 8×10^{-5} for H atoms and 2×10^{-5} cm^2/second for OH radicals. The scavenger, at a concentration of 10^{-3} M, is assumed to react with the H and OH radicals with a rate constant of 1.0×10^{-11} cc/molecule second. Note that the spur reactions are substantially completed in 10^{-9} second and generate molecular products with $g(H_2)$ of 0.42, $g(H_2O_2)$ of 0.60, and water formed in the spur of $g(H_2O)$ of 0.88.* The free radicals remaining after these reactions are complete give us $g(H)$ of 3.41 and $g(OH)$ of 3.05. Reaction of the radicals with 10^{-3} M scavenger is negligible before 10^{-9} second and becomes important only after 3×10^{-8} second. As the parameters prevailing during spur expansion become better known, the contributions of diffusion theory to the radiolysis of water will become more significant.

Oxygen, a secondary product, forms by reactions of the type:

$$OH + H_2O_2 = HO_2 + H_2O$$

$$HO_2 + HO_2 = H_2O_2 + O_2$$

$$HO_2 + OH = H_2O + O_2 .$$

The hydroperoxy radical, HO$_2$, is relatively unreactive compared to the hydroxyl radical and only at high concentrations of peroxide is the reaction

$$HO_2 + H_2O_2 = H_2O + OH + O_2$$

a source of oxygen. We shall deal further with the reactivity of the HO$_2$ radical in Sections IV.E.4 and VI.G.1.

C. Chemical Yields in Irradiated Water

1. The Radiolysis Equation

Regardless of the mechanism of free radical and molecular product formation, the basic radiolysis equation for pure water is

$$(2a + c - e)H_2O = aH_2 + bH_2O_2 + cH + dOH + eHO_2 . \tag{32}$$

The coefficients, $a \ldots e$, if expressed in molecules reacted or formed per 100 ev of absorbed energy, are most helpful in explaining radiation effects. Radiation chemists use the symbol G to designate the chemical yield in molecules/100 ev. In our discussion, capital G's denote experimental yields such as hydrogen peroxide, $G(H_2O_2)$, and ferric ion, $G(Fe^{3+})$; and in order to simplify our symbology, we denote the yield of the radical and molecular products by lower case g's. Thus the molecular yields are $g(H_2)$ and $g(H_2O_2)$ and the radical yields are $g(H)$, $g(OH)$ and $g(HO_2)$. One should remember that these g's are the yields of radicals and products surviving track reac-

---

* See explanation of $g(X)$ in Section C.1.

tions (see Sections III.A and IV.B.3; and Fig. 8). Sometimes it is necessary to specify additional conditions of the irradiations particularly when one or more scavengers are present. For example the yield designated, $G(Fe^{3+})_{O_2, H_2}$, signifies ferric ion formation with oxygen and hydrogen present. Generally however when the solutes are obvious, the subscripts are omitted. The g's depend on solute concentration because free radical scavengers interfere with reactions 29, 30, and 31. However, since radical-molecule rate constants are orders of magnitude smaller than radical-radical rate constants, solute interference becomes appreciable only at concentrations greater than 0.01 M (see Section II.D and Fig. 8).

The application of equation 32 to the radiolysis of aqueous solutions has been made in Table X. Here the product yields of many of the reactions discussed in Sections IV, V, and VI are summarized. This table is useful since free radical or hydrogen peroxide participation in any given reaction can be deduced from the plus or minus sign before the specie of interest. In hydrogen peroxide formation in oxygenated water, hydrogen atoms and molecular hydrogen peroxide increase the yield whereas hydroxyl radicals decrease the yield. Table X contains expressions for the initial yields only, unless qualification appears under "remarks."

2. RADIATION YIELDS IN WATER AND 0.8 N SULFURIC ACID

Typical basic radiation yields appear in Table XI for air-free 0.8 N sulfuric acid and for air-saturated water (243, 244). These g's are derived from studies of the ferrous sulfate and ceric sulfate systems for 0.8 N sulfuric acid.

Free radical yields, $g(H)$ and $g(OH)$, are highest for γ-rays, X-rays, and electrons. As the LET of the particle increases, $g(H)$ and $g(OH)$ decrease whereas $g(H_2)$ and $g(H_2O_2)$ increase (see Fig. 9). Consequently, one uses light particles for maximum free-radical effects per unit of absorbed energy whereas maximum molecular product effects are found with densely ionizing particles.

The observable consumption of water, $g(-H_2O)$, decreases with increasing rate of energy loss of the particle in water. We assume that all water molecules dissociate into hydrogen atoms and hydroxyl radicals, and that recombination reactions 29 and 30 account for hydrogen and hydrogen peroxide formation. Then omitting water reformation reactions, $g(-H_2O)$ becomes:

$$g(-H_2O) = g(H) + 2g(H_2) = g(OH) + 2g(H_2O_2) + 3g(HO_2).$$

The coefficient, 2, arises because two water molecules must dissociate in order to give one molecule of hydrogen or hydrogen peroxide; and the coefficient, 3, arises because three hydroxyl radicals produce one HO_2 radical.

TABLE X

Some Important Radiolyses in Aqueous Solution, and the Relation of Their Yields to the Basic Radiation Yields of Water

Solutes	Yields	Section in which mechanism is treated	Remarks
O_2	$G(H_2O_2) = \tfrac{1}{2}g(H) - \tfrac{1}{2}g(OH) + g(H_2O_2)$	IV.F.2	Decreasing yield as H_2O_2 accumulates; cf. $O_2 + H_2O_2$ below.
$H_2 + O_2$	$G(H_2O_2) = \tfrac{1}{2}g(H) + \tfrac{1}{2}g(OH) + g(H_2O_2)$	IV.F.3	$\tfrac{1}{2}g(OH) = G(H_2O_2)_{H_2,O_2} - G(H_2O_2)_{O_2}$.
H_2O_2	$G(-H_2O_2) = \tfrac{3}{2}g(H) + \tfrac{1}{2}g(OH) - g(H_2O_2)$	IV.F.4	Valid only in dilute solution. Complicated by chain reaction. O_2 accumulates; cf. $O_2 + H_2O_2$ below.
$H_2 + H_2O_2$	$G(-H_2)$ and $G(-H_2O_2) \gg$ basic g-values	IV.F.5	Chain reaction.
$O_2 + H_2O_2$	$G(H_2O_2) = \tfrac{1}{2}g(H)\left[1 - 4\left(1 + \dfrac{k_{42}[O_2]}{k_{27}[H_2O_2]}\right)^{-1}\right] - \tfrac{1}{2}g(OH) + g(H_2O_2)$	IV.F.	Approaches steady state in which $[O_2]/[H_2O_2] = $ constant ~ 2.7.
$Fe^{++} + O_2$	$G(Fe^{3+}) = 3g(H) + g(OH) + 2g(H_2O_2)$	V.A.1	Fricke dosimeter.
$Fe^{++} + Cu^{++}$	$\begin{cases} G(Fe^{3+}) = -g(H) + g(OH) + 2g(H_2O_2) \\ G(O_2) = g(HO_2) \end{cases}$	V.A.2	Measures $g(HO_2)$. Difference in $G(Fe^{3+})$ between this and preceding system gives $g(H)$.
$Fe^{3+} + HCOOH$	$G(Fe^{++}) = g(H) + g(OH)$	V.A.4	Yields increase with increasing concentrations of HCOOH.
$Ce^{4+} + $ air	$G(Ce^{3+}) = g(H) - g(OH) + 2g(H_2O_2)$	V.A.6	Ceric dosimeter.
$Ce^{4+} + Tl^+$	$G(Ce^{3+})_{Tl^+} = g(H) + g(OH) + 2g(H_2O_2)$	V.A.7	Difference in $G(Ce^{3+})$ between this and preceding system gives $g(OH)$.
Tl^{3+}	$G(Tl^+) = \tfrac{1}{2}g(H) - \tfrac{1}{2}g(OH) + g(H_2O_2)$	V.A.9	Note the similarity to the ceric reduction.
Cl^-, Br^-, or I^-	$G(H_2O_2) = \tfrac{1}{2}g(H) + \tfrac{1}{2}g(OH) + g(H_2O_2)$	V.B.2	$g(H_2O_2) < G(H_2O_2)$ when $g(H) > g(OH)$.
$NO_2^- + H_2O_2$	$G(-NO_2^-) - G(-H_2O_2) = g(H_2)$	V.B.3	Measures molecular hydrogen.

System	Equations	Section	Description
$NO_2^- + excess\ H_2O_2$	$G(-NO_2^-) = G(NO_3^-) = \frac{1}{2}g(H) + \frac{1}{2}g(OH)$ $G(-H_2O_2) = \frac{1}{2}g(H) + \frac{1}{2}g(OH) - g(H_2)$ $G(H_2) = g(H_2)$	V.B.3	Measures radical yields.
MnO_4^-	$G(-MnO_4^-) = \frac{1}{3}g(H) + \frac{1}{3}g(OH) + \frac{2}{3}g(H_2O_2)$	V.B.4	MnO_2 is a principal product. Above $10^{-3}\ M$, a chain reaction sets in.
Cr (VI)	$G(Cr^{3+}) = \frac{1}{3}g(H) - \frac{1}{3}g(OH) + \frac{2}{3}g(H_2O_2)$	V.B.4	Similar to permanganate reduction.
$Fe^{3+} + Sn^{++}$	$G(Fe^{++}) = g(H) + g(OH);\ G(H_2) = g(H_2)$ $G(Sn^{4+}) = g(H_2O_2) + g(OH)$		Similar to $Fe^{3+} + HCOOH$, (269).
V [V]	$G(-V[V]) = g(H) + g(OH) + g(HO_2) + g(OH)$		Measures molecular and free radical yields (270).
$AsO_3^{3-} + O_2$	$G(AsV) = \frac{1}{2}g(H) + \frac{1}{2}g(OH)$	V.B.5.	Measures radical yields.
N_2H_4	$G(-N_2H_4) = G(NH_3) = g(H) + g(OH)$		Measures radical yields (271).
NH_2OH	$G(NH_2OH) - G(H_2N_2O_2) = 2g(H) + g(OH) - g(H_2O_2)$ $G(H_2) = g(H) + g(H_2)$		Measures radical yields (272).
$CH_3OH + Fe^{3+}$	$G(Fe^{++}) = g(H) + g(OH)$ $G(HCHO) = g(H) + g(OH) + g(H_2O_2)$ $G(H_2) = g(H) + g(H_2)$	VI.E.2	Measurements of the yields in this system give all 4 basic g-values.
Alcohols	$G(H_2) = g(H_2)$	VI.E.1	Measures g(H).
$HCOOH + O_2$	$G(CO_2) = g(OH)$ $G(-O_2) = \frac{1}{2}g(H) + \frac{1}{2}g(OH)$ $G(H_2O_2) = \frac{1}{2}g(H) + \frac{1}{2}g(OH) + g(H_2O_2)$ $G(H_2) = g(H) + g(H_2)$	VI.G.1	Measurements of the yields in this system give all 4 basic g-values.
Deaerated HCOOH	$G(CO_2) = \frac{1}{2}g(H) + \frac{1}{2}g(OH) + g(H_2O_2)$ $G(H_2) = g(H) + g(H_2)$	VI.G.1	Molecular hydrogen peroxide reacts with formic acid radicals.
Benzene	$G(C_6H_5C_6H_5) + G(C_6H_5OH) = \frac{1}{2}g(OH) + \frac{1}{2}g(H_2O_2) + \frac{1}{2}G(H_2O_2)$	VI.D.3	Measures molecular product and free radical yields.
Benzene + O_2	$G(C_6H_5OH) = g(OH)$ $G(H_2) = g(H_2)$		
Boiling or Bubbling Water	$G(H_2) = g(H_2)$ $G(O_2)_{ss} = \frac{1}{2}g(H_2O_2) - \frac{1}{4}g(H) + \frac{1}{4}g(OH)$	IV.D.3	Under steady-state (ss) irradiation conditions.

TABLE XI

RADIATION YIELDS IN AIR-FREE 0.8 N SULFURIC ACID AND AIR-SATURATED WATER

Radiation	$g(H)$	$g(OH)$	$g(H_2)$	$G(H_2O_2)$	$g(-H_2O)$	
		Air-free 0.8 N sulfuric acid (243)				
Co^{60} γ-rays	3.65	2.95	0.45	0.80	4.55	
Co^{60} γ-rays[a]	3.70	2.92	0.39	0.78	4.48	
18 Mev D^+	2.39	1.75	0.71	1.03	3.81	
8 Mev D^+	1.71	1.45	1.05	1.17	3.80	
32 Mev He^{++}	1.28	1.06	1.14	1.25	3.56	
$B^{10}(n,\alpha)Li^7$	0.23	0.41	1.66	1.57	3.54	
		Air-saturated water (244)				
Co^{60} γ-rays	2.78	2.28	0.42	0.67	3.70	4.76[b]
18 Mev D^+	2.90	2.36	0.40	0.67	3.89	4.42[b]
32 Mev He^{++}	1.55	1.13	0.66	0.87	2.78	4.65[b]
11 Mev He^{++}	1.65	1.07	0.62	0.91	2.57	4.84[b]

[a] Aerated solutions.

[b] $g(-H_2O)_{Total}$.

Clearly, however, we lose some radicals by reaction 31, the water reformation reaction. Now, if we assume that as many radicals disappear by spur reaction 31 as by the sum of reactions 29 and 30, then we have:

$$g(-H_2O)_{tot} = g(-H_2O) + g(H_2) + g(H_2O_2).$$

If this assumption is correct, we predict that $g(-H_2O)_{tot.}$ is independent of the character of the irradiating particles. This is borne out by the data of Table XI.

Free radical yields are higher and molecular product yields are lower in heavy water than in light water (245); $g(-H_2O)$ averages somewhat less than $g(-D_2O)$.

3. EFFECT OF pH ON RADIATION YIELDS

Nearly all radiation-initiated reactions in water are affected by pH. This general effect is caused in part by differences in the reactivities of the undissociated or dissociated free radicals rising from the reactions,

$$OH = O^- + H^+$$

$$HO_2 = O_2^- + H^+$$

$$H = H^+ + \epsilon_{aq}^- ,$$

and in part by differences in reactivity of dissociable solutes with hydrogen atoms and hydroxyl radicals. Another less well understood factor is the

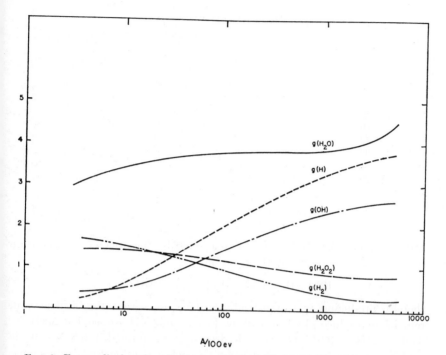

FIG. 9. Free radical and molecular product yields in 0.8 N sulfuric acid as a function of average track distance absorbing 100 ev of energy.

effect of pH on the possible fate of the ionized water molecule, H_2O^+, and the slow electrons. On the whole there is no drastic effect of pH on the total yields, $g(H) + g(\epsilon_{aq})$, and $g(OH) + g(O^-)$. Complete pH studies for any given scavenger system are few. Table XII reports the yields obtained with the 0.01 M formic acid-oxygen system (Section VI.G.1).

Recently evidence has been presented and arguments given to show the participation of water subexcitation electrons in the radiolysis of formic acid (246). (See Section II.B.4 for a discussion of subexcitation electrons and Section VI.G.1 for details on formic acid effects.) If water subexcitation electron action proves general, then any photochemically active solute having an absorption spectrum extending to wavelengths longer than those of water may dissociate in the spur. Consequently, these new radical species must be considered in subsequent radical reactions and in the calculation of free radical yields.

Water subexcitation electrons may increase free radical yields in solutions of the order of 0.01 to 1.0 M in buffers (30). Well-known is the fact that $g(H)$ is higher in acid than in neutral solutions (see Table XII). Sulfuric acid extends the region of high ultraviolet light absorption of water from

TABLE XII

EFFECT OF pH ON Co^{60} γ-RAY YIELDS IN 0.01 M FORMIC ACID[a]

pH	$g(H)$	$g(OH)$	$g(H_2)$	$g(H_2O_2)$	$g(-H_2O)$
0.32	3.59	2.40	0.26	0.86	4.12
1.28	3.52	2.44	0.32	0.86	4.17
2.10	3.47	2.56	0.35	0.80	4.17
2.70	3.02	2.83	0.42	0.51	3.86
3.72	3.29	3.13	0.40	0.48	3.99
4.92	3.13	3.23	0.40	0.35	3.93
6.81	2.98	2.84	0.41	0.48	3.80
11.20	3.05	2.97	0.41	0.45	3.87
11.58	3.10	2.92	0.44	0.53	3.98

[a] From reference 247.

1800 to about 2000 A. Bisulfate ions excited by these water subexcitation electrons may dissociate by the reaction,

$$HSO_4^- \cdot H_2O + \epsilon_{se}^- \rightarrow HSO_4 + H + OH^- + \epsilon^-$$

thereby producing two extra radicals. One notes that the electron still remains to produce a hydrogen atom. From Table XII, we see that $\Delta g(H) = 3.59 - 2.98 = 0.61$, the excess hydrogen atoms formed in 0.8 N sulfuric acid as compared to neutral solution. If each excitation leads to dissociation we have

$$\Delta g(H)/\varphi(H) = 0.61 \text{ excitations/100 ev.}$$

Less is known about the radiation yields in heavily buffered solutions or in strongly alkaline solutions. However excitation of the hydroxyl ion is possible in solutions of the order of 0.01 to 1.0 N since the molar extinction coefficient of this ion rises rapidly below 2000 A.

D. DECOMPOSITION OF WATER

Tables XI and XII report yields for $g(-H_2O)$, the observable water disappearance, in 0.8 N sulfuric acid, in aerated water, and in formic acid–oxygen solutions. $g(-H_2O)$ depends to some extent on the nature of the ionizing particle and on pH. But $g(-H_2O)$ is by no means a measure of the decomposition of pure water represented by $G(H_2)$, $G(H_2O_2)$, and $G(O_2)$. Below we shall see how actual water decomposition depends on LET, on chemical factors, and on physical conditions of the irradiation.

1. LET EFFECTS

Pure air-free water irradiated with γ-rays, X-rays, or electrons shows no continuous decomposition when exposed under static conditions in completely filled cells. On the other hand, heavy particle radiation such as α-rays, or the products of the $B^{10}(n,\alpha)Li^7$ reaction, decompose water continuously when irradiated statically in filled cells.

Recombination of hydrogen and hydrogen peroxide to reform water occurs to an appreciable extent with low LET radiations (242). The net reaction is:

$$H_2 + H_2O_2 \rightarrow 2H_2O. \tag{33}$$

The following free radical reactions explain reaction 33:

$$OH + H_2 \rightarrow H_2O + H \tag{34}$$

$$H + H_2O_2 \rightarrow H_2O + OH. \tag{27}$$

Reactions 27 and 34 are analogous to the gas phase recombination of hydrogen and chlorine (see reaction 18, Section III.C.1).

When the basic free radical yields, $g(H)$ and $g(OH)$, exceed $g(H_2)$ and $g(H_2O_2)$, the water is stable during static irradiation (248). Note in Table XI that the free radical yields exceed molecular product yields for all radiations except the $B^{10}(n,\alpha)Li^7$ recoils, hence only the latter is expected to decompose pure water. But if mixed γ-ray and $B^{10}(n,\alpha)Li^7$ radiations irradiate water, it does not decompose unless the recoil energy absorbed in the water exceeds the absorbed γ-ray energy. Figure 10 illustrates this point. Here hydrogen evolution is shown as a function of boric acid concentration for reactor-irradiated solutions. At a thermal neutron flux of 8.34×10^{13} n/cm^2min and a γ-ray flux of 1.19×10^{18} ev/liter min, a concentration of 0.02 M boric acid is required for continuous water decomposition. The dotted line of Fig. 10 shows the expected rate of decomposition in the absence of the γ-ray flux. From these results, one calculates that 1.3 water molecules must dissociate into free radicals to recombine a total of one molecule of hydrogen and hydrogen peroxide. These complex results have recently been explained by a mechanism consisting of reactions 27, 32, 34, 35, 36, and 42 (249).

2. STABILIZING FACTORS

We have noted how water is stable to static irradiation with γ-rays. Next, chemical stabilization is considered.

Factors increasing the efficacy of the H and OH free radicals will stabilize water. Dissolved hydrogen is excellent. See the bottom curve of Fig. 10 for the effect of 0.0007 M hydrogen. Up to 0.15 M boric acid can be irradiated under these conditions without water decomposition. And in view of the necessary equality of hydrogen and hydroxyl species,

$$g(H) + 2g(H_2) = g(OH) + 2g(H_2O_2) \qquad \text{[if } g(HO_2) \text{ is small]},$$

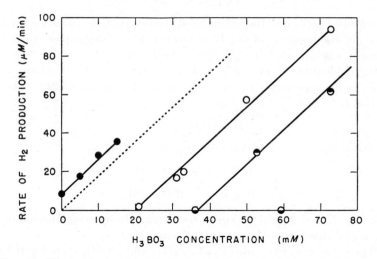

Fig. 10. Effect of boric acid on hydrogen production in air-free solutions exposed to mixed neutron and gamma radiation (248). (Reactor, Argonne National Laboratory CP-3′; neutron flux = 8.34 × 10¹³ n/cm² min, γ-ray energy flux = 1.19 × 10¹⁸ ev/cm³ min.) Key: ○ no additive; ◕ 0.7 mM H₂; ● 0.1 mM KI; ◖ 11.4 mM CdSO₄ .

the hydrogen gas functions catalytically. All hydrogen and hydrogen peroxide generated by the γ-rays and the α- and Li⁷-recoils recombine via reactions 27 and 34. With high initial hydrogen, the oxygen forming reactions,

$$OH + H_2O_2 \rightarrow H_2O + HO_2 \tag{35}$$

$$HO_2 + HO_2 \rightarrow H_2O_2 + O_2 , \tag{36}$$

are suppressed and replaced by the hydrogen and hydrogen peroxide recombining equations 27 and 34.

In reactors, metal ions producing extra γ-rays by the n,γ reaction stabilize water as well. By this means the over-all radical yield relative to the molecular product yield is increased. Cadmium is effective because of the increased γ-ray flux resulting from the Cd¹¹²(n,γ)Cd¹¹³ reaction. The influence of 0.0114 M cadmium sulfate on reactor irradiated boric acid solutions is shown in Fig. 10 (250).

3. DESTABILIZING FACTORS

Free radical poisons cause γ-rays to decompose irradiated water even though it has a high reserve capacity for recombining hydrogen and hydrogen peroxide. Ions having two valence states are particularly effective since they function catalytically by (242):

$$OH + I^- \rightarrow OH^- + I$$

$$I + I \rightarrow I_2$$

$$H + I_2 \rightarrow H^+ + I^- + I.$$

Iodide ion concentration remains unaltered but there is a drastic decrease in the concentration of H and OH free radicals. The net reaction is an iodide ion catalyzed reformation of water according to reaction 31. Water decomposes with a yield, $g(H_2)$, under conditions of efficient free radical poisoning, demonstrating complete suppression of reactions 27 and 34. Under these conditions, we expect the densely ionizing radiations of Table XI to decompose water with high yields and specifically with yields, $g(H_2)$ and $g(H_2O_2)$.

Removing hydrogen from irradiated water is another way to suppress reaction 34 (251). The observed hydrogen yield, $G(H_2)$ closely approximates $g(H_2)$. Above, we saw how added hydrogen stabilized water exposed to mixed γ-ray and B^{10} disintegration ions; therefore we expect water, in which hydrogen is selectively removed, to decompose. Bubbling or boiling irradiated water produces hydrogen and oxygen. The over-all process is simple. After the removal of gaseous hydrogen, hydrogen peroxide decomposes by reactions 35 and 36. The over-all reaction is:

$$H_2O_2 \rightarrow H_2O + \tfrac{1}{2}O_2 .$$

$G(O_2)$ equals $\tfrac{1}{2}g(H_2)$. These relations have been checked for γ-rays and the $B^{10}(n,\alpha)Li^7$ reaction (251).

E. Effect of Water Decomposition Products

Next we discuss the behavior of irradiated water containing hydrogen, oxygen, and hydrogen peroxide.

1. Hydrogen

No apparent reaction takes place in irradiated water containing dissolved hydrogen. However, isotopic changes occur in irradiated light water containing deuterium, hydrogen deuteride, or *para*-hydrogen (252, 253).

The over-all reactions,

$$H_2O + D_2 \rightarrow HDO + HD$$

$$2H_2O + D_2 \rightarrow 2HDO + H_2 ,$$

occur in the water-deuterium system. Up to pH values of 8, $G(HD)$ corresponds to $g(H)$. The mechanism suggested is

$$H + D_2 \rightarrow HD + D \tag{37}$$

$$OH + D_2 \rightarrow HOD + D \tag{38}$$

followed by

$$D + D \rightarrow D_2 . \tag{39}$$

If the latter reaction were slow compared to

$$D + H_2O \rightarrow H + HDO \tag{40}$$

then a chain propagation sequence consisting of reactions 37 and 40 would produce $G(HD)$'s much greater than 3. Therefore reaction 40 must be unimportant compared to 39.

Hydrogen ions have relatively little effect on G(HD). Thus the proposed reaction,

$$H + H^+ \rightleftharpoons H_2^+ \tag{41}$$

is either impossible or is not in rapid equilibrium. Otherwise the reaction,

$$H^+ + D \rightarrow HD^+$$

followed by

$$HD^+ \rightarrow H + D^+$$

would convert deuterium atoms into hydrogen atoms. The absence of a chain reaction in the deuterium system disproves the equilibrium reaction 41 used to explain the oxidation of air-free ferrous sulfate. (See Section V.A.1 for a discussion of this reaction.)

Hydrogen deuteride is changed to hydrogen and deuterium, and *para*-hydrogen is changed to *ortho*-hydrogen when irradiated in aqueous solution. In these cases, a chain radiolysis is observed (252). Chain reactions are expected in these cases since

$$H + HD \rightarrow H_2 + D$$

or

$$D + HD \rightarrow D_2 + H$$

showing that either the hydrogen or deuterium atom reacts with hydrogen deuteride. In the case of *para*-hydrogen

$$H + p\text{-}H_2 \rightarrow o\text{-}H_2 + H.$$

In hydrogen deuteride or *para*-hydrogen, the released atom may continue the chain without the requirement of exchange with the water.

2. OXYGEN

The irradiation of aerated or oxygenated water forms hydrogen and hydrogen peroxide. The chemical properties of the hydroxyl radical remain unchanged but the powerfully reducing hydrogen radical is converted to the relatively inert hydroperoxy radical:

$$H + O_2 \rightarrow HO_2 . \tag{42}$$

Because of the high probability of this conversion, traces of oxygen modify the course of many radiation-induced reactions.

The hydrogen peroxide yield in oxygenated water decreases continuously with dosage until equilibrium is reached (see Fig. 11). Although there may be some uncertainty about the initial yield, $G_0(H_2O_2)$, there is a substantial linear section with $G(H_2O_2) = 1.23$ given by the equation:

$$G(H_2O_2) = \tfrac{1}{2}[g(H) - g(OH)] + g(H_2O_2).$$

Thus, hydrogen atoms in excess of hydroxyl radicals, $g(H) - g(OH)$, are converted into hydrogen peroxide via reactions 36 and 42.

The steady-state peroxide level, $(H_2O_2)_{ss}$, increases nearly linearly with oxygen concentration (254–256). For bubbling oxygen irradiations, $(H_2O_2)_{ss}$ is 0.35 mM for 1.26 mM O_2 (254). In these experiments, hydrogen is continuously swept out of the solution and the steady-state peroxide concentration is determined by the rate constant ratio, $k_{H+O_2}/k_{H+H_2O_2}$ for reactions 42 and 27. This ratio is 1.2–1.5 (254).

In sealed cells, the steady-state peroxide concentration rises rapidly up to 0.003 M initial oxygen and rises more slowly thereafter to a constant value of 2.5 $\times$ 10^{-3} M hydrogen peroxide with 0.03 M oxygen. Under these conditions the steady-state hydrogen concentration passes through a maximum of 0.003 M hydrogen at 0.004 M oxygen concentration, and decreases

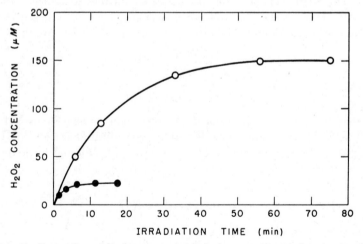

FIG. 11. Formation of hydrogen peroxide in oxygen-saturated water irradiated with γ-rays (254). Oxygen concentration = $\bigcirc$ 0.452 mM, $\bullet$ 0.050 mM, T = 25°, dose rate = 5.53 $\times$ 10^{17} ev/gm. min.

thereafter as the oxygen concentration increases to 0.03 M. This work was carried out with 65 kv X-rays (256).

pH affects both hydrogen peroxide and hydrogen yields. In acid and neutral solutions the initial peroxide yield is high and the general form of the dosage curves is concave downwards. But in alkaline solutions, $G(H_2O_2)$ is lower and dosage curves are linear with the transition from the higher to lower yield occurring at pH 8 to 10 (257, 258). This decrease in yield occurs in the pH range where ionization of the hydroxyl radical is postulated. Hydrogen yields pass through a minimum in the neutral pH range (256, 258).

A mechanism consisting of steps 27, 32, 34–36, and 42 accounts for the general features of the water-oxygen reaction (254). Therefore, in the water-oxygen reaction hydrogen atoms react with oxygen and hydrogen peroxide; hydroxyl radicals react with the radiolysis products, hydrogen and hydrogen peroxide; and hydrogen peroxide is derived from the recombination of hydroxyl radicals in the spur and by the reaction of hydroperoxy radicals formed principally by reaction 42.

Studies with dissolved oxygen enriched in the O^{18} isotope (designated O_2^* below) show a free radical induced reaction with the stoichiometry (258):

$$H_2O + O_2^* = H_2O^* + O_2 .$$

$G(O_2)$, the yield of normal oxygen from solutions of dissolved enriched oxygen, rises sharply in the pH range above 9.0. $G(O_2)$ increases from $\sim$1 to 585. This high yield provides proof of a chain reaction since $g(OH)$ is about 3.0 (Table XII). The following mechanism which is based on the hypothesis of ionization of the hydroxyl radical explains this result:

$$OH \rightleftharpoons O^- + H^+ \tag{43}$$

$$O^- + O_2^* \rightarrow O^{*-} + O_2$$

$$O^{*-} + OH^- \rightarrow O^- + O^*H^-.$$

Note that the successful propagation of the chain involves hydroxyl ions as well as the O^- free radical ion. The hydroxyl radical ionization constant, $K_{43} \cong 10^{-10}$ (258). The chain sequence is strongly inhibited by hydrogen peroxide indicating that the radical ion, O^-, reacts with peroxide as does the hydroxyl radical:

$$O^- + H_2O_2 \rightarrow O_2^- + H_2O.$$

3. HYDROGEN AND OXYGEN TOGETHER

Adding hydrogen and oxygen to water raises the initial peroxide yield and steady state peroxide concentrations. Under initial conditions where

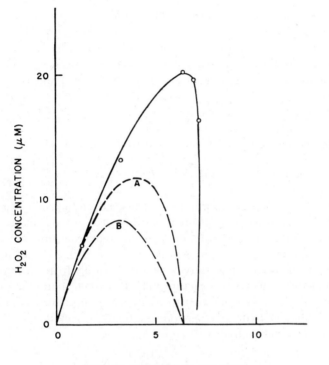

FIG. 12. Hydrogen peroxide formation in γ-ray irradiated water containing 700 μM hydrogen and 25 μM oxygen (259). Solid line, experimental curve. A,B, theoretical curve from integrated equation 45 with $k_{42}/k_{27} = 2, 1$ resp.

hydroxyl radicals react only with hydrogen (reaction 34) instead of with hydrogen peroxide (reaction 35), the initial yield is given by:

$$G(H_2O_2) = \tfrac{1}{2}[g(H) + g(OH)] + g(H_2O_2). \qquad (44)$$

Each free radical now becomes effective in producing hydrogen peroxide. Substituting $g(x)$ for water from Table XI, in equation 44 we find that $G(H_2O_2) = 3.20$ for γ-ray irradiated water. Equation 44 will hold for the initial yields regardless of the type of radiation.

As hydrogen is consumed and hydrogen peroxide forms, $G(H_2O_2)$ decreases and ultimately becomes zero. And, if excess hydrogen is added initially, hydrogen peroxide and hydrogen react according to the over-all reaction 33. Figure 12 shows a typical result (259). After maximum peroxide is formed, the yield of reaction 33 depends on the amount of excess hydrogen. Yields as high as $G(-H_2O_2)$ of 25 have been observed after the oxygen disappears.

The idea that only hydrogen and hydroxyl radicals are active intermediates is inadequate to explain this oxygen-hydrogen reaction (259). If we assume that only hydrogen atoms and hydroxyl radicals are reactive here, and since

$$k_{H+O_2}/k_{H+H_2O_2} = 1.2\text{--}1.5$$

the expected peroxide curve, calculated from equation 45,

$$\frac{d(H_2O_2)}{d(Dose)} = g(H_2O_2) + \frac{1}{2}[g(H) + g(OH)] - \frac{g(H)}{1 + [k_{42}(O_2)/k_{27}(H_2O_2)]}, \quad (45)$$

is given by the dotted lines in Fig. 12 instead of the solid experimental curve (259). In order to explain this difference, one postulates that the hydrogen atom formed by reaction 34 is different from the hydrogen atom generated initially by electron capture in water (249, 259). In pure water the electrons may be quantitatively converted to hydrogen atoms and diffusion kinetics supports this picture (63). But when solutes are added, all electrons need not be converted to hydrogen atoms. For example, in the oxygen–hydrogen–hydrogen peroxide system, we can have electrons reacting with oxygen or hydrogen peroxide,

$$\epsilon^- + O_2 \rightarrow O_2^- \qquad (42')$$

and

$$\epsilon^- + H_2O_2 \rightarrow OH^- + OH, \qquad (28)$$

replacing 42 and 27, respectively. Possibly the final equilibrium hydrogen peroxide concentration in the absence of hydrogen is now determined by $k_{42'}/k_{28}$ instead of by the ratio k_{42}/k_{27} in equation 45. In the hydrogen-oxygen system (where hydrogen atoms from reaction 34 are required to carry the chain), the ratio, $k_{42}/k_{27} \gg 1$. The experimental results support such a hypothesis. (See Sections VI.E.2 and VI.G.1 for additional discussions on electron reactions.)

4. HYDROGEN PEROXIDE

Hydrogen peroxide decomposes in irradiated water by the over-all reaction:

$$H_2O_2 \rightarrow H_2O + \frac{1}{2}O_2 .$$

We have already seen how hydrogen and hydroxyl radicals destroy hydrogen peroxide (reactions 27 and 35) and how the general mechanism of water radiolysis explains peroxide formation in the water-oxygen system (reactions 27, 32, 34, 35, 36, and 42). The behavior of hydrogen peroxide in aqueous solutions is discussed next.

In dilute oxygen-free hydrogen peroxide, both hydrogen and hydroxyl radicals reduce hydrogen peroxide. The expected initial yield is

$$G(-H_2O_2) = \tfrac{3}{2}g(H) + \tfrac{1}{2}g(OH) - g(H_2O_2)$$

in the absence of any radical-radical reactions other than reaction 35. But as soon as oxygen forms, $G(-H_2O_2)$ decreases until an equilibrium between oxygen and hydrogen peroxide is obtained (E.2).

Radiolyses of peroxide solutions in the 10^{-3} to 1.0 M range are complex, probably because of impurity effects. While agreement on absolute yields is unsatisfactory, a number of investigators report chain radiolyses with $G(-H_2O_2)$ increasing as (Intensity)$^{-1/2}$ and $(H_2O_2)^{1/2}$ (260–265). The general mechanism is (263):

$$H_2O = H_2 , H_2O_2 , H, OH \tag{32}$$

$$H + H_2O_2 = H_2O + OH \tag{27}$$

$$OH + H_2O_2 = HO_2 + H_2O \tag{35}$$

$$HO_2 + H_2O_2 = H_2O + O_2 + OH \tag{46}$$

$$2HO_2 + H_2O_2 = 2H_2O_2 + O_2 \tag{47}$$

giving the general equation:

$$G(O_2) = \tfrac{1}{2}[g(H) + g(OH)] + k_{46}\,[(H_2O_2)/k_{47}I_a]^{1/2}.$$

This equation has the required experimental dependences on peroxide concentration and intensity. Reactions 35 and 46 are the chain propagation steps and reaction 47 is the termination step. In solutions greater than one molar, the yield depends on (Intensity)$^{-1/2}(H_2O_2)^{1.0}$.

Rate constants k_{46} and k_{47}, measured by the rotating sector technique, are $k_{46} = 530$ liters mole^{-1} sec^{-1} in 0.1 M H_2O_2 and 1.1 liter mole^{-1} sec^{-1} in >1.0 M H_2O_2; $k_{47} = 2.7 \times 10^{10}$ liters^2 moles^{-2} sec^{-1} in 0.1 M H_2O_2 and 3.1×10^6 liters mole^{-1} sec^{-1} in >1 M H_2O_2 (263, 265). This dependence of rate constants on concentration indicates that the hydroperoxy radical may be partially complexed with H_2O_2 in 0.1 M H_2O_2 and possibly completely complexed in >1.0 M H_2O_2. Perhaps in the concentrated solutions, reactions 46 and 47 become:

$$HO \cdot H_2O_2 + H_2O_2 \rightarrow H_2O + O_2 + OH + H_2O_2 \tag{46'}$$

$$2HO_2 \cdot H_2O_2 \rightarrow 2H_2O + O_2 + 2H_2O_2 . \tag{47'}$$

5. HYDROGEN PEROXIDE PLUS HYDROGEN

When excess hydrogen is present in the hydrogen-oxygen system, the final stages of the irradiation deal with the hydrogen peroxide–hydrogen system (see the descending part of the curve in Fig. 12 and Section VI.E.2).

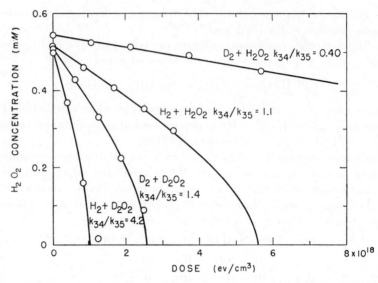

FIG. 13. Isotopic effects in the Co^{60} γ-ray induced recombination of aqueous 0.0007 M hydrogen (or deuterium) and hydrogen (or deuterium) peroxide (248).

The rate of peroxide disappearance increases as the ratio, $(H_2)/(H_2O_2)$, increases (248, 250, 255, 260, 261, 266, 267, 268). And since hydrogen and hydrogen peroxide disappear in equimolar amounts by reaction 33, the ratio, $(H_2)/(H_2O_2)$, increases with time of irradiation if hydrogen is originally present in excess.

$G(-H_2O_2)$ becomes as high as 30 (248, 254, 267). The chain character of this reaction is thereby confirmed. The relative rates of reactions 34 and 35, given by k_{34}/k_{35}, determine the probability of chain propagation. If the hydroxyl radical reacts with hydrogen, the chain propagates; if the hydroxyl radical reacts with hydrogen peroxide, the chain terminates because the comparatively inactive hydroperoxy radical is formed. The ratio of rate constants depends on the isotopic species present, as is shown in Fig. 13. Note that the $H_2 + D_2O_2$ reaction is a factor of about 20 faster than the $D_2 + H_2O_2$ reaction. Relative rate constant data appear in Table XIII. The bubbling hydrogen experiment (254) offers an ideal method for measuring the important ratio, k_{34}/k_{35}, but agreement with the static irradiations is poor.

V. Radiation Chemistry of Aqueous Inorganic Solutions

Hydrogen atoms and hydroxyl radicals are the most reactive of the various products present in irradiated degassed water at the beginning of the chemical stage. In oxygenated solutions, the hydroperoxy radical dis-

TABLE XIII
RELATIVE HYDROXYL RADICAL RATE CONSTANTS

Reactants	k_{34}/k_{35}	Conditions	References
$H_2 + H_2O_2$	0.90	Static	248
$H_2 + H_2O_2$	0.94	Static	267
$H_2 + H_2O_2$	0.25	Bubbling	254
$H_2 + H_2O_2{}^a$	1.00	Static	248
$D_2 + H_2O_2{}^a$	0.40	Static	248
$D_2 + D_2O_2{}^a$	1.4	Static	248
$H_2 + D_2O_2{}^a$	4.2	Static	248

^{a} 0.001 M H_2SO_4 .

places the hydrogen atom because of the reaction $H + O_2 \rightarrow HO_2$, which has a higher rate-constant than do many other hydrogen-atom reactions. Hydrogen peroxide, formed in smaller yields by γ-rays, plays a role secondary to that of the free radicals. This chapter treats principally the chemical reactions of hydrogen, hydroperoxy, and hydrogen free radicals. But the hydrated electron must be considered, too, since recent evidence indicates that it reacts in solutions which contain a molecule or ion that can compete with water for it.

A. REACTIONS OF CATIONS

In general, hydroxyl radicals oxidize either cations or anions, whereas hydrogen atoms reduce them.

In this section we deal chiefly with dilute solutions, for which $g(H)$, $g(OH)$, and $g(H_2O_2)$ of pure water are the yields of the chemically reactive species. At concentrations above 0.1 M, solute ions invade the track and may thereby increase $g(H)$ and $g(OH)$. While hydrogen, H_2 , is usually inert, the magnitude of $G(H_2)$ supplies a very important clue to the mechanism of the reaction.

The potential of oxidation-reduction couples provides a guide as to possible oxidation and reduction reactions. In acid solutions, one has the hydrogen atom and hydroxyl radical couples

$$H(g) = H^+ + \epsilon^- \qquad (E^\circ = 2.10 \text{ volts})$$

and

$$H_2O = OH + H^+ + \epsilon^-. \qquad (E^\circ = -2.8 \text{ volts})$$

Atomic hydrogen is a powerful reducing agent but it is incapable of reducing couples more positive than 2.10 volts. Alkali-metal, alkaline earth, and some of the rare-earth ions therefore cannot be reduced by atomic hydrogen. However, positive ions such as Fe^{3+}, Ce^{4+}, and Cu^{++} are readily reduced, as we shall see. The general reaction is

$$M^{n+} + H \rightarrow M^{(n-1)+} + H^+. \tag{48}$$

Whereas reaction 48 will proceed only with couples electronegative with respect to the hydrogen atom/H^+ couple, an unhydrated electron might reduce ions such as sodium and potassium:

$$Na^+ + \epsilon^- \rightarrow Na.$$

But the sodium atom would then react with water, liberating a hydrogen atom:

$$Na + H_2O \rightarrow Na^+ + OH^- + H.$$

The net reaction is conversion of an electron into a hydrogen atom, so that for practical purposes the hydrogen atom can be considered to be the reactive species. Reactions of the hydrated electron, however, pose problems and differentiation of its reactions from those of atomic hydrogen is difficult (See Section V.A.2.)

Oxidizing agents more powerful than the hydroxyl radical are hyponitrous acid and fluorine, which have $E°$ of -2.85 and -3.06 volts, respectively. Therefore practically any ion not already in its highest oxidation state will be oxidized by hydroxyl radicals. The general reaction is

$$M^{n+} + OH \rightarrow M^{(n+1)+} + OH^-. \tag{49}$$

The extent of reactions 48 and 49 in irradiated water depends in a complex way on the composition of the solution, since hydrogen atoms, hydroperoxy radicals, and hydroxyl radicals also react with hydrogen peroxide. Likewise competing with reactions 48 and 49, thereby diminishing chemical yields, is the radical-recombination reaction $H + OH \rightarrow H_2O$, which takes place outside the spur. This reaction proceeds with a potential of 4.9 volts. Solute concentrations above 10^{-5} M will, in general, utilize these "free" hydrogen atoms and hydroxyl radicals and by this means suppress $H + OH$ recombination.

1. FERROUS ION

Ferrous sulfate in aerated 0.8 N sulfuric acid (the Fricke dosimeter) is oxidized to ferric sulfate by all ionizing radiations. The ferric-ion yield, $G(Fe^{3+})$, depends on the LET of the radiation, and decreases from 15.6 for γ-rays to 3.0 for fission fragments (see Table XIV and Figure 14). These yields are widely exploited for chemical dosimetry of ionizing radiations.

Ferrous sulfate oxidation is typical of many radiation-induced reactions in aqueous solution. The ferric ion yield is practically independent of ferrous-ion concentration from 10^{-4} to 10^{-1} M and of oxygen concentration from $\sim10^{-6}$ to 10^{-3} M. The yield is also independent of dosage rate up to

TABLE XIV

$G(Fe^{3+})$ FOR VARIOUS IONIZING RADIATIONS FOR THE FRICKE DOSIMETER (273)

Radiation	Energy (Mev)	$G(Fe^{3+})$	References
Electrons	2.0	15.45 ± 0.3	274
Co^{60} γ-rays	—	15.6 ± 0.3	275
100-kvp X-rays	—	14.7 ± 0.5	276
60-kvp X-rays	—	13.1	276
8-kvp X-rays	—	13.4 ± 0.6	277
Electrons	0.00569	12.9 ± 0.2	278, 279
Deuterons	21.16	11.3 ± 0.5	280, 281
Deuterons	18.70	11.1 ± 0.4	280, 281
Deuterons	12.0	10.1 ± 0.4	280, 281
Deuterons	6.2	8.5 ± 0.4	280, 281
α-Particles	40	8.7 ± 0.4	281
α-Particles	20	7.05 ± 0.4	281
α-Particles	5.3	5.1 ± 0.1	282
α-Particles	3.4	3.8 ± 0.2	283
Protons	1.99	8.0 ± 0.4	280
Protons	0.98	7.2 ± 0.4	280
$Li^6(n,\alpha)H^3$	4.78^a	5.69 ± 0.12	279, 284
$B^{10}(n,\alpha)Li^7$	2.35^a	4.22 ± 0.08	279, 284
U^{235} fission fragments	162^a	3.0 ± 0.4	285

^{a} Total kinetic energy of separated atoms.

2×10^6 rad/second in 0.001 M ferrous sulfate (air-saturated 0.8 N sulfuric acid). Under these conditions ferrous ion in the irradiated zone is exhausted every 0.03 second and efficient stirring is required to replenish it. But with electron irradiation in short bursts, much higher dose rates can be administered without stirring. With pulses of 1.7×10^{-6} second duration and a total dosage of 13,600 rad, $G(Fe^{3+})$ is reported to be unchanged at an instantaneous dosage rate of $\sim10^{10}$ rad/second in unstirred solution (286). Because of the constancy of $G(Fe^{3+})$ and the excellent analytical behavior of ferrous sulfate, this system, known as the Fricke dosimeter, has gained world-wide usage.

One essential feature of the ferrous sulfate system is shown in Fig. 15 (238). The break in the curve marks the point at which oxygen dissolved in the solution has been consumed. Since ferrous ions continue to be oxidized upon further irradiation, oxidation obviously occurs in deoxygenated as well as in aerated solutions. The over-all reactions have been summarized (287) as follows:

In air-free solutions,

$$Fe^{++} + H^+ \rightarrow Fe^{3+} + \frac{1}{2}H_2 .$$

In oxygenated solutions the following reactions, one dependent on pH and the other independent of pH, account for the observed results,

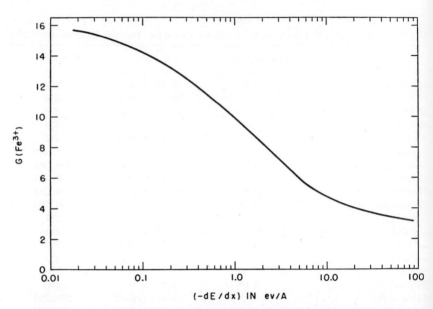

FIG. 14. Ferric ion yields in aerated ferrous sulfate in 0.8 N sulfuric acid as a function of the energy loss $(-dE/dx)$ obtained by dividing the initial energy in ev by the particle range in A. $(-dE/dx)$ for X-rays is obtained from reference 283.

$$Fe^{++} + H^+ + \tfrac{1}{4}O_2 \rightarrow Fe^{3+} + \tfrac{1}{2}H_2O$$

$$Fe^{++} + \tfrac{1}{4}O_2 + \tfrac{1}{2}H_2O \rightarrow Fe^{3+} + OH^-.$$

The mechanism of the aerated ferrous sulfate oxidation is

$$H_2O \rightarrow aH_2 + bH_2O_2 + cH + dOH + eHO_2, \tag{50}$$

$$Fe^{++} + H_2O_2 \rightarrow Fe^{3+} + OH + OH^- \tag{51}$$

$$Fe^{++} + OH \rightarrow Fe^{3+} + OH^- \tag{52}$$

$$H + O_2 \rightarrow HO_2 \tag{42}$$

$$Fe^{++} + HO_2 \rightarrow Fe^{3+} + HO_2^- \tag{53}$$

$$HO_2^- + H^+ \rightarrow H_2O_2. \tag{54}$$

The general radiolysis equation 50 provides the active species for reactions 51, 52, 42, 53, and 54.

Note that each hydroxyl radical produces one ferric ion, each hydrogen peroxide molecule produces two, and each hydrogen atom (or hydroperoxy radical) produces three. Therefore

$$G(Fe^{3+})_{O_2} = 2g(H_2O_2) + 3g(H) + g(OH) + 3g(HO_2) \tag{55}$$

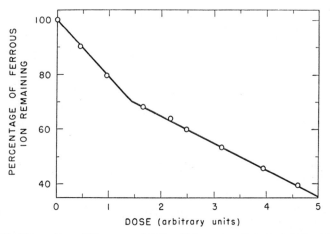

FIG. 15. The action of X-rays on 0.337 mM ferrous sulfate in 0.8 N sulfuric acid initially saturated with air (238). The change in slope occurs when all the oxygen has been consumed, $G(-Fe^{++})$ thereupon assuming a smaller value, as explained in the text.

The decrease of $G(Fe^{3+})_{O_2}$ in Fig. 14 with increasing $(-dE/dx)$ is primarily due to a decrease in $g(H)$. The yield in the absence of oxygen becomes:

$$G(Fe^{3+})_{O_2\text{-free}} = 2g(H_2O_2) + g(H) + g(OH) + 3g(HO_2) \qquad (56)$$

and

$$G(H_2) = g(H_2) + g(H). \qquad (57)$$

(See Table XI for the values of g, which are the basic radiation-yields.)

In oxygen-free solutions, contrary to expectation, hydrogen atoms oxidize ferrous ions, the ferric yield due to hydrogen atoms being independent of pH (288). The reaction can be written as

$$Fe^{++} \cdot H_2O + H \rightarrow Fe^{3+} + H_2 + OH^-. \qquad (58)$$

It may be simply understood on the basis of the polarization of the water molecules in the hydration shell of the ferrous ion induced by the central electric charge. This distortion weakens the H—OH bond sufficiently to permit H-atom abstraction by the free H atom during a collision, the remaining $Fe^{++} \cdot OH$ then dissociating to $Fe^{3+} + OH^-$. (If the H_2O were a normal one the H-abstraction would be endothermal.) An alternative proposal (289),

$$Fe^{++} + H_2^+ \rightarrow Fe^{3+} + H_2 , \qquad (59)$$

is unlikely to be correct because of evidence (cf. Section IV.E.1) that H_2^+ does not form under these conditions, and also because Coulomb repulsion

TABLE XV

EFFECT OF pH ON THE RATE CONSTANT RATIOS INVOLVED IN FERROUS SULFATE OXIDATION (288)

	pH			
	2.70	2.10	1.57	0.4
$\dfrac{k_{H+Fe^{3+}}}{k_{H+Fe^{++}}}$	—	7.2 ± 0.7	1.35 ± 0.1	0.081 ± 0.010
$\dfrac{k_{H+Fe^{3+}}}{k_{H+O_2}}$	0.1	0.007 ± 0.003	—	—
$\dfrac{k_{H+O_2}}{k_{H+Fe^{++}}}$	—	1500 ± 200	—	1200 ± 300
$\dfrac{k_{HO_2+Fe^{3+}}}{k_{HO_2+Fe^{++}}}$	0.3	0.1	—	<0.01
$\dfrac{k_{OH+Fe^{++}}}{k_{OH+H_2}}$	—	5.7 ± 1.0	7.1 ± 1.0	—

would prevent an encounter of Fe^{++} and H_2^+. As ferric ion accumulates in the solution, reactions 53 and 58 compete with 60 and 61:

$$HO_2 + Fe^{3+} \rightarrow H^+ + O_2 + Fe^{++} \qquad (60)$$

$$H + Fe^{3+} \rightarrow H^+ + Fe^{++}. \qquad (61)$$

These back-reactions result in nonlinear dosage curves, particularly pronounced at pH above 2. Applicable rate-constant ratios are given in Table XV (288). Note that the relative rates of 58 and 61 and of 60 and 53 are considerably changed by pH, whereas the relative rates of 42 and 58 are unaffected by pH.

2. FERROUS AND CUPRIC IONS

Cupric sulfate added to ferrous sulfate drastically reduces $G(Fe^{3+})$ for γ-rays from 15.6 to 4.1 in aerated 0.8 N sulfuric acid, and from 13.8 to 0.66 in aerated 0.01 N sulfuric acid (290, 291). A mechanism accounting for these yields consists of reactions 50, 51, 52, and 42 combined with

$$Cu^{++} + H \rightarrow Cu^+ + H^+ \qquad (62)$$

$$Cu^{++} + HO_2 \rightarrow Cu^+ + H^+ + O_2 \qquad (63)$$

$$Cu^+ + Fe^{3+} \rightarrow Cu^{++} + Fe^{++}. \qquad (64)$$

Note that now either the hydrogen or the hydroperoxy radical reduces cupric ion to cuprous ion, a species that reduces ferric ion by reaction 64.

Normally HO_2 oxidizes three Fe^{++} in the absence of Cu^{++} by the sequence of reactions 42, 53, 54, 51, and 52. The yield is given by

$$G(Fe^{3+})_{Cu^{++}} = 2g(H_2O_2) + g(OH) - g(H) - g(HO_2). \qquad (65)$$

A comparison of equations 55 and 65 shows that the yield $G(Fe^{3+})$ is diminished by $4g(H) + 4g(HO_2)$ by the presence of cupric sulfate. This difference affords a means of measuring $g(H)$:

$$g(H) = \frac{1}{4}[G(Fe^{3+}) - G(Fe^{3+})_{Cu^{++}}] - g(HO_2) \qquad (66)$$

The yield, $g(HO_2)$ which can be neglected for γ-rays is discussed below. The Fe^{++}–Cu^{++} system has only limited usefulness since the simple conditions assumed for equations 55 and 56 prevail only over a short pH range. At pH 2, the $g(H)$ of 3.3 obtained by this method compares with 3.47 obtained by the formic acid–O_2 method (Table XII).

Oxygen is a minor product of air-free ferrous sulfate – cupric sulfate irradiations (291). This oxygen is believed to come from the HO_2 formed in a spur reaction between hydrogen peroxide and hydroxyl radical,

$$OH + H_2O_2 \rightarrow HO_2 + H_2O, \qquad (35)$$

oxygen being liberated by reaction 63. The yield $g(HO_2)$, increases from 0.026 for γ-rays to 0.25 for 3.4 Mev α-rays (292). The value for γ-rays is so small as to be negligible. And in ferrous oxidation (in the absence of Cu^{++}) no error is introduced by disregarding $g(HO_2)$—e.g., in equation 55—since three ferrous ions are oxidized by either the products or the reactants of reaction 35. The effect of ferrous sulfate and cupric sulfate on $G(H_2)$, $G(Fe^{3+})_{Cu^{++}}$, and $G(O_2)$ is shown in Fig. 16. Note how $G(Fe^{3+})_{Cu^{++}}$,

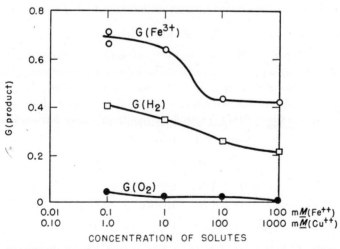

FIG. 16. Effect of concentration of ferrous and cupric sulfates on yields of ferric ion, hydrogen, and oxygen in deaerated acidified (pH > 2) aqueous solutions irradiated with Co^{60} γ-rays (291).

$G(H_2)$, and $G(O_2)$ all decrease with increasing scavenger concentrations. Here reactions 62 and 52 compete with the radical-radical reactions $H + H \rightarrow H_2$ and $OH + OH \rightarrow H_2O_2$. These results emphasize the two-radical character of scavenger action in the ferrous-cupric system.

Because of the similarity in the reactions of atomic hydrogen and free electrons, it is difficult to distinguish experimentally between these two species on the basis of their reaction products. However $G(H_2)$ in Fig. 16 may provide a clue. In water $g(H_2)$ is 0.45, whereas $G(H_2)$ approaches 0.40 at low cupric ion concentrations; the full complement of hydrogen is not found. The difference might arise from direct electron capture by cupric ions

$$\epsilon^- + Cu^{++} \rightarrow Cu^+ \tag{67}$$

although the possible intervention of

$$\epsilon^- + H_2O \rightarrow H + OH^- \tag{68}$$

followed by 62 cannot be positively ruled out. If this yield in reaction 67 is designated by $g(\epsilon)$, we have:

$$g(\epsilon) = 2[g(H_2) - G(H_2)_{Cu^{++}}] = 0.10. \tag{69}$$

Therefore one-ninth of all hydrogen "atoms" forming molecular hydrogen $[2g(H_2)]$, are in fact electrons that can be captured by Cu^{++} in 0.001 M cupric sulfate in the spur. If this speculation is correct, electron capture reactions outside the spur may attain greater proportions and particularly at higher concentrations of Cu^{++}. The possible role of electrons has already been discussed in connection with the hydrogen-oxygen system in Section IV.E.3 and will be considered further in Sections VI.E.2 and VI.G.1.

3. FERROUS ION, OXYGEN, AND ORGANIC COMPOUNDS

Organic compounds increase $G(Fe^{3+})$ in aerated ferrous sulfate solutions by producing oxidizing radicals. Solutions of hydrocarbons (293–296), alcohols (293, 296–298) and acids (299) have been studied. The reaction of a hydroxyl radical with the organic molecule leads to a chain sequence, consisting of reactions 70–74, capable of oxidizing many ferrous ions:

$$OH + RH \rightarrow H_2O + R \tag{70}$$

$$R + O_2 \rightarrow RO_2 \tag{71}$$

$$RO_2 + Fe^{++} \rightarrow RO_2^- + Fe^{3+} \tag{72}$$

$$RO_2^- + H^+ \rightarrow ROOH \tag{73}$$

$$ROOH + Fe^{++} \rightarrow RO^- + Fe^{3+} + OH. \tag{74}$$

For example, $G(Fe^{3+})$ increases from 15.6 in the Fricke dosimeter to 230 in a solution containing 0.0005 M ferrous sulfate, 0.8 N sulfuric acid, and

0.1 M formic acid, and saturated with oxygen (299). Dosage curves are nonlinear because of rising competition of reduction reaction 60 with oxidation reaction 53 as the ferric ion concentration increases.

Carbon dioxide is the principal product from formic acid (299). In the other instances cited, no attempt was made to identify the products. However hydrocarbons, alcohols, and aldehydes are expected to oxidize to alcohols, aldehydes, and acids, respectively. Some hydroxy derivatives of polycarbon alcohols, aldehydes, and acids may also appear.

Chloride ion diminishes the organic chain-oxidation of ferrous sulfate and at sufficiently high concentration restores the original $G(Fe^{3+})$ (297). It is important to remember that the sodium chloride added to the Fricke dosimeter averts organic-impurity effects. The reactions are

$$OH + Cl^- = OH^- + \tfrac{1}{2} Cl_2 \qquad (E° = 1.44 \text{ volt})$$

$$Fe^{++} + \tfrac{1}{2} Cl_2 = Fe^{3+} + Cl^-. \qquad (E° = 0.59 \text{ volt})$$

The chlorine atom, being a much weaker oxidizing agent ($E° = -1.36$ volt) than the hydroxyl radical ($E° = -2.8$ volts), does not readily attack organic molecules in a ferrous sulfate environment.

4. FERRIC ION AND FORMIC ACID

The hydroxyl radical is converted to COOH or HCOO by formic acid

$$OH + HCOOH \rightarrow H_2O + COOH \text{ (or HCOO)} \qquad (75)$$

and this is a *reducing* radical:

$$Fe^{3+} + COOH \text{ (or HCOO)} \rightarrow Fe^{++} + CO_2 + H^+. \qquad (76)$$

At high values of the ratio, $[Fe^{3+}]/[HCOOH]$, all hydrogen atoms reduce ferric ion by reaction 61, whereas at low ratios hydrogen atoms react preferentially with formic acid:

$$H + HCOOH \rightarrow H_2 + COOH \text{ (or HCOO)}. \qquad (77)$$

The yield $G(Fe^{++})$ is independent of the relative concentration of ferric ion and formic acid, since each hydrogen atom leads to the reduction of one ferric ion, whether it be by reactions 77 and 76 or by 61 alone. A striking additional feature of this reaction is that molecular hydrogen peroxide produces no net reduction of ferric ion; the reaction 51, which oxidizes a ferrous ion, is followed by 75 and 76, which reduce a ferric ion. Consequently $G(Fe^{++})$ is given by

$$G(Fe^{++}) = g(H) + g(OH), \qquad (78)$$

and the ferric sulfate – formic acid system measures the sum of the free-radical yields directly (300).

5. FERRIC ION, CUPRIC ION, OXYGEN, AND FORMIC ACID

An experimental shortcoming of the ferric sulfate – formic acid system is the necessity that the solution be deaerated; oxygen interferes with the action as described. However if cupric sulfate is added to the ferric sulfate and formic acid, one obtains a free-radical dosimeter applicable to aerated solutions (301–304). With cupric ion present the additional reactions are 42, 63, and 64. Either hydrogen atom or hydroperoxy radical reduces a ferric ion in this system, and oxygen therefore has no effect on the contribution of $g(H)$ to the yield. Nor does oxygen affect the contribution of $g(OH)$, that is, the reduction of ferric ion according to reaction 76, since the hydroperoxy radical formed by 79

$$COOH \text{ (or } HCOO) + O_2 \rightarrow CO_2 + HO_2 \tag{79}$$

reduces a ferric ion by reactions 63 and 64. Hence equation 78, even in this complex mixture, is again valid.

6. CERIC ION

As expected, hydrogen atoms reduce ceric ions and hydroxyl radicals oxidize cerous ions, the potentials ($E°$) for reactions 81 and 82 being 3.71 and 1.19 volts, respectively. The yield $G(Ce^{3+})$ depends on $2g(H_2O_2)$ and the difference between $g(H)$ and $g(OH)$:

$$G(Ce^{3+}) = 2g(H_2O_2) + g(H) - g(OH). \tag{80}$$

The mechanism is

$$Ce^{4+} + H \rightarrow Ce^{3+} + H^+ \tag{81}$$

$$Ce^{3+} + OH \rightarrow Ce^{4+} + OH^- \tag{82}$$

$$Ce^{4+} + H_2O_2 \rightarrow Ce^{3+} + H^+ + HO_2 \tag{83}$$

$$Ce^{4+} + HO_2 \rightarrow Ce^{3+} + H^+ + O_2. \tag{84}$$

As in the case of the cupric sulfate system, $G(Ce^{3+})$ given by equation 80 is unaffected by oxygen since either a hydrogen atom or a hydroperoxy radical will reduce one ceric ion. Its γ-ray value is 2.39 for dilute ceric sulfate dissolved in 0.8 N sulfuric acid (305).

The yield of OH can be estimated directly in this system by measurement of isotope exchange under irradiation. In a solution containing Ce^{3+} labeled with a radioactive isotope, together with unlabeled Ce^{4+}, reaction 82 is the only one of the preceding four reactions that can lead to labeled Ce^{4+}. The observed rate of exchange induced by 50-kv X-rays, corrected for spontaneous (thermal) exchange, provides a $G(Ce^{3+} \rightarrow Ce^{4+})$ of about 3.2 (306). This is close enough to the value $g(OH) = 2.95$ to be a corroboration of the postulated reaction 82.

7. CERIC AND THALLOUS IONS

Addition of thallous sulfate, which is oxidized by reaction 85, to ceric sulfate precludes the reoxidation of cerous ion by hydroxyl radicals (reaction 82) and therefore increases $G(Ce^{3+})$ (305). Thallous ion removes hydroxyl radical by the reaction

$$Tl^+ + OH \rightarrow Tl^{++} + OH^-, \tag{85}$$

and the transient ion Tl^{++} *reduces ceric* ion by

$$Ce^{4+} + Tl^{++} \rightarrow Ce^{3+} + Tl^{3+}. \tag{86}$$

With γ-rays $G(Ce^{3+})_{Tl^+}$ is 7.85 in 0.8 N sulfuric acid, and since each hydroxyl radical now reduces a ceric ion, $g(OH)$ is given by

$$g(OH) = \tfrac{1}{2}[G(Ce^{3+})_{Tl^+} - G(Ce^{3+})]. \tag{87}$$

From the above data $g(OH)$ is 2.66, a value in satisfactory agreement with $g(OH)$ obtained with other systems. (See Table XI.)

8. CERIC ION AND FORMIC ACID

At constant sulfuric acid concentration, $G(Ce^{3+})$ is increased by addition of formic acid (307–309) just as it is by thallous ion. Formic acid suppresses reaction 82, which oxidizes cerous ion back to ceric ion, and replaces 82 by 75 which creates the reducing COOH (or HCOO)-radical:

$$Ce^{4+} + COOH \text{ (or HCOO)} \rightarrow Ce^{3+} + CO_2 + H^+. \tag{88}$$

However, as the cerous ion concentration increases, competition between reactions 75 and 82 sets in, and $G(Ce^{3+})$ accordingly decreases. At elevated concentrations of sulfuric acid reaction 89 becomes competitive:

$$OH + H_2SO_4 \rightarrow H_2O + HSO_4. \tag{89}$$

The bisulfate radical subsequently oxidizes cerous ion,

$$Ce^{3+} + HSO_4 \rightarrow Ce^{4+} + HSO_4^-, \tag{90}$$

but it does not readily react with formic acid as does the hydroxyl radical. From measurements of the effect of sulfuric acid concentration on $G(Ce^{3+})$, the relative hydroxyl radical rate-constants given by

$$k_{OH+Ce^{3+}}/k_{OH+HCOOH}/k_{OH+H_2SO_4} = 650/380/1 \tag{91}$$

have been obtained (309).

9. THALLIC–THALLOUS ION EXCHANGE

Thallic ions in 0.8 N sulfuric acid are reduced by γ-rays, $G(Tl^+)$ being 1.34. This yield is approximately one-half of $G(Ce^{3+})$. Since two electrons are required for the reduction of Tl^{3+}, it suggests that the mechanism parallels that of ceric-ion reduction given by reactions 80 through 84. For thallic ion reduction a similar mechanism is,

$$Tl^{3+} + H \rightarrow Tl^{++} + H^+ \tag{92}$$

$$Tl^+ + OH \rightarrow Tl^{++} + OH^- \tag{93}$$

$$Tl^{3+} + H_2O_2 \rightarrow Tl^{++} + H^+ + HO_2 \tag{94}$$

$$Tl^{3+} + HO_2 \rightarrow Tl^{++} + H^+ + O_2 \tag{95}$$

followed by disproportionation reaction,

$$Tl^{++} + Tl^{++} \rightarrow Tl^{3+} + Tl^+. \tag{96}$$

Hence

$$G(Tl^+) = g(H_2O_2) + \tfrac{1}{2}[g(H) - g(OH)]. \tag{97}$$

Equation 97, together with the data of Table XI predicts $G(Tl^+) = 1.15$, in fair agreement with experimental data.

Evidence for the unstable-intermediate Tl^{++} of reactions 93 through 96 is provided by the isotopic exchange reaction induced by X-rays (310). This is a chain reaction with G(exchange) reaching values as high as 166. Its rate is independent of $[Tl^+]$ but dependent on $[Tl^{3+}]$ and on intensity. The mechanism,

$$Tl^{++} + {}^*Tl^+ \rightarrow Tl^+ + {}^*Tl^{++} \text{ (rapid)} \tag{98}$$

$${}^*Tl^{++} + Tl^{3+} \rightarrow {}^*Tl^{3+} + Tl^{++} \text{ (slow)}, \tag{99}$$

followed by termination reaction 96 involves only single electron transfers. (Radioactive species are indicated by an asterisk.) Oxidizing ions such as Fe^{3+} and Ce^{4+}, and reducing ions such as Fe^{++} and Ce^{3+}, all suppress this chain reaction by oxidizing or reducing Tl^{++}.

10. AMMONIA

No apparent reaction occurs in oxygen-free solutions. Oxygen oxidizes ammonia to nitrite ion in irradiated aqueous solutions. The $G(NO_2^-)$ increases sharply from a value of zero at pH 4 to one of 0.75 at pH 7, and then more gradually to a maximum of 1.3 at pH 13 (311). Free ammonia is necessary for nitrite formation and the equilibrium

$$NH_3 + H^+ \rightarrow NH_4^+ \tag{100}$$

explains the pH effect. At low ammonia concentration $G(NO_2^-)$ diminishes with dose, which indicates a secondary oxidation to the nitrate (see Section V.B.3). Hydroxylamine, a possible intermediate product, is not found probably because it is too reactive.

Insufficient work has been done to establish a mechanism but suggested steps might include

$$H + O_2 \rightarrow HO_2 \tag{42}$$

$$NH_3 + OH \rightarrow NH_2 + H_2O \tag{101}$$

$$NH_2 + O_2 \rightarrow NH_2O_2 . \tag{102}$$

The HO_2 and NH_2O_2 radicals may then recombine by the three possible recombination reactions

$$2NH_2O_2 \rightarrow NH_2OONH_2 + O_2 \tag{103}$$

$$NH_2O_2 + HO_2 \rightarrow NH_2OOH + O_2 \tag{104}$$

$$2HO_2 \rightarrow H_2O_2 + O_2 . \tag{36}$$

Work has not progressed far enough on this system to warrant further speculation regarding its mechanism. However ammonia oxidation may parallel the nitrite oxidation (Section V.B.3) and be caused by a radiation induced reaction with the peroxides formed in reactions 36, 103, and 104. With hydrogen peroxide the over-all reaction may be

$$NH_3 + 3H_2O_2 \rightarrow HNO_2 + 4H_2O. \tag{105}$$

B. REACTIONS OF ANIONS

Sulfate, phosphate, carbonate, borate, and hydroxide ions are not decomposed by ionizing radiation in dilute aqueous solution. By virtue of this stability the corresponding acids and their alkali salts can act as satisfactory inert buffers over the pH range from 1 to 13. Outside of this pH region, direct action on the acid or base used as a buffer as well as competition of these buffer anions with solute ions for the radiolysis radicals may become appreciable. (See Section V.A.8 for the effect of sulfuric acid on the radiolysis of formic acid-ceric ion solutions.)

Because of the high reducing power of the hydrogen atom and the high oxidizing power of the hydroxyl radical, most anions probably undergo oxidation-reduction reactions such as 106 and 107 during irradiation. In this way the anion can promote the H + OH recombination reaction. For example,

$$A^- + OH \rightarrow A + OH^- \tag{106}$$

$$A + H \rightarrow H^+ + A^-. \tag{107}$$

No effect on the chemistry of the system will be observed, provided that radical **A** reacts with solutes like the hydroxyl radical. Ferrous sulfate oxidation is a case in point. If A^- is the hydrogen-sulfate ion or the chloride ion and **A** is the hydrogen-sulfate radical or the chlorine atom, no effect on the yield of ferrous sulfate oxidation in reaction 52 is observed. However, if **A** is less effective than the hydroxyl radical in a particular reaction, the course of the radiolysis will be changed.

1. SULFATE ION

The sulfuric acid in dilute solutions is unaffected by γ-rays, but SO_2 is produced in concentrated solutions. As the mole fraction of sulfuric acid in the solution increases from 0.2 to 1.0, $G(SO_2)$ rises from 0 to 1.0 (119); below that range little or no SO_2 is liberated. Hydrogen peroxide inhibits the sulfur-dioxide production. The SO_2 is probably formed by direct action of the radiation on H_2SO_4, but the detailed mechanism is unknown.

Hydrogen atoms and hydroxyl radicals react with sulfuric acid in solutions containing no other solutes. Hydrogen atoms generated in a hydrogen discharge tube produce hydrogen sulfide (312). Repeated reaction of hydrogen atoms on sulfuric acid and its reduced intermediates finally gives hydrogen sulfide

$$H_2SO_4 + 8H \rightarrow H_2S + 4H_2O. \tag{108}$$

The first step in this process may be

$$H + HSO_4^- \rightarrow H_2SO_4^- \tag{109}$$

forming a sulfuric acid radical which is much easier to reduce by hydrogen atoms than sulfuric acid.

Hydroxyl radical attack on sulfuric acid leads to hydrogen sulfate radicals (308, 309).

$$OH + HSO_4^- \rightarrow HSO_4 + OH^-. \tag{110}$$

Since hydrogen peroxide is observed in γ-ray irradiated air-free 0.8 N sulfuric acid in yield 0.37, the radicals formed in reactions 109 and 110 may recombine and reform sulfuric acid.

$$H_2SO_4^- + HSO_4 + OH^- \rightarrow 2HSO_4^- + H_2O. \tag{111}$$

By reactions 109–111, hydrogen sulfate ion because of its high concentration protects the molecular hydrogen peroxide from attack by hydrogen atoms and hydroxyl radicals.

2. HALIDE IONS

The stability of pure water under γ-irradiation is contingent upon the efficacy of the hydrogen atom and hydroxyl radical in catalyzing the back reaction, $H_2 + H_2O_2 \rightarrow 2H_2O$. Halide ions (X^-) strongly suppress this reaction and thereby promote the decomposition of water. The postulated reactions

$$OH + X^- \rightarrow OH^- + X \tag{112}$$

$$X + X \rightarrow X_2 \tag{113}$$

$$H + X_2 \rightarrow H^+ + X^- + X, \tag{114}$$

lead to the net reaction

$$H + OH \rightarrow H_2O. \tag{31}$$

Equimolar quantities of H_2 and H_2O_2 form in dilute aqueous air-free iodide or bromide solutions irradiated by γ-rays, with $G(H_2) = G(H_2O_2) = 0.45$ for pH between 2.0 and 3.0. These yields are independent of iodide-ion or bromide-ion concentration from 10^{-7} to 1 M (267, 313). Because of this lack of dependence of $G(H_2)$ on halide-ion concentration, it is presumed that the observed hydrogen yield, $G(H_2)$, is equal to $g(H_2)$, the true molecular yield. Hydrogen in these solutions is protected against the hydroxyl-radical reaction

$$OH + H_2 \rightarrow H_2O + H \tag{34}$$

by reaction 112 even at the lowest halide-ion concentration cited. Free molecular halogen in measureable amounts is not liberated in dilute iodide or bromide solutions, so that an amount of H_2O_2 equal to that of H_2 must be present in order to provide the required oxidation-reduction equivalence. Hydrogen peroxide in excess of the molecular hydrogen disappears by reaction 27 with hydrogen atoms not consumed by reaction 114:

$$H + H_2O_2 \rightarrow H_2O + OH. \tag{27}$$

Since $g(H_2O_2)$ is greater than $g(H_2)$, $g(H)$ must exceed $g(OH)$, and it does so by the necessary amount. From the equation of material balance

$$g(H) + 2g(H_2) = g(OH) + 2g(H_2O_2), \tag{115}$$

and the fact that $G(H_2O_2) = G(H_2) = g(H_2)$ in these solutions, it follows that the hydrogen peroxide yield in halide solutions is

$$G(H_2O_2)_{X^-} = g(H_2O_2) - \tfrac{1}{2}[g(H) - g(OH)]. \tag{116}$$

Since $g(H) > g(OH)$, the experimental hydrogen peroxide yield is always less than the molecular yield, $g(H_2O_2)$.

Bubbling alters the radiation chemistry of irradiated iodide solutions and demonstrates that molecular iodine is, indeed, a transient product of irradiation as postulated in reaction 113. Molecular iodine readily distills from bubbling irradiated 0.001 M iodide solutions. Since iodine is not reported as a product in unbubbled solutions, it is postulated to be present in concentrations much lower than those of hydrogen peroxide. Reaction 114 accounts for the submeasureable amounts of iodine if $k_{H+I_2}/k_{H+H_2O_2} \gg 1$.

In aerated or oxygenated solutions up to 0.01 M in potassium chloride or bromide, hydrogen peroxide and hydrogen are formed with constant yields as long as the concentration of the products does not exceed 10^{-4} M. The hydrogen peroxide yield, $G(H_2O_2)$, here comprises two distinct contributions, namely H_2O_2 from recombination of OH radicals within the track

$$OH + OH \rightarrow H_2O_2 \tag{30}$$

and from H_2O_2 formed outside the track by the reactions 42 and 36. Since each OH reacts with halide ion producing a halogen atom which can react with HO_2,

$$X + HO_2 \rightarrow X^- + H^+ + O_2, \tag{117}$$

only the excess HO_2 corresponding to $g(H) - g(OH)$ can recombine to form hydrogen peroxide. Consequently the hydrogen peroxide yield in oxygenated halide solutions is

$$G(H_2O_2)_{X^-, O_2} = g(H_2O_2) + \tfrac{1}{2}[g(H) - g(OH)]. \tag{44}$$

From these measurements of $G(H_2O_2)$, one may calculate $g(H_2O_2)$ and $[g(H) - g(OH)]$ from equations 116 and 44

$$g(H_2O_2) = \tfrac{1}{2}[G(H_2O_2)_{X^-} + G(H_2O_2)_{X^-, O_2}] \tag{118}$$

and

$$g(H) - g(OH) = 2[G(H_2O_2)_{X^-, O_2} - G(H_2O_2)_{X^-}]. \tag{119}$$

Bromine and iodine are additional products at high halide-ion concentration and appear shortly after the onset of irradiation.

As hydrogen peroxide accumulates, the radiation-induced net reaction,

$$H_2O_2 + 2I^- \rightarrow I_2 + 2OH^-, \tag{120}$$

reduces $G(H_2O_2)$ by liberating iodine. The yields always satisfy

$$G(H_2O_2) + G(I_2) = G(H_2). \tag{121}$$

The yield $G(H_2O_2)$ decreases from 1.30 in aerated bromide-free solutions at pH 2 to 0.69 in 0.01 M potassium bromide solutions (314). A similar decline takes place in potassium chloride solutions, $G(H_2O_2) = 0.36$ being attained at 1 M (315).

Scavenging of hydroxyl radicals in the spurs by halide ions explains the decline in H_2O_2 yield as the halide-ion concentration is increased. Reaction 112 competes with the hydroxyl-radical recombination reaction

$$OH + OH \rightarrow H_2O \tag{30}$$

and $G(H_2O_2)$ accordingly decreases. These scavenging reactions provide an important test for the mechanism of water radiolysis and have wide applications in diffusion kinetics.

3. NITRITE AND NITRATE IONS

Irradiation of deaerated solutions of KNO_2 with γ-rays oxidizes them to KNO_3. Detailed study of this system (316) has shown that the radiolysis is due entirely to a *radiation-induced* oxidation of nitrite ion by hydrogen peroxide that has accumulated in the solution, the stoichiometry being

$$NO_2^- + H_2O_2 \rightarrow NO_3^- + H_2O. \tag{122}$$

In the absence of H_2O_2, the free radicals produced from the solvent have no net effect on nitrite ion; they react with the solute:

$$H + NO_2^- \rightarrow NO + OH^-. \tag{123}$$

$$OH + NO_2^- \rightarrow NO_2 + OH^-, \tag{124}$$

but the products then regenerate the solute in the rapid thermal reaction

$$NO + NO_2 + H_2O \rightarrow 2HNO_2. \tag{125}$$

Thus nitrite ion is yet another substance capable of sensitizing the recombination of H and OH. The initial radiolysis-products in pure nitrite solutions are accordingly simply H_2 and H_2O_2, formed with yields approximately equal to $g(H_2)$.

As hydrogen peroxide accumulates in the solution, however, some of the H is diverted from process 123 by competing reaction 27; this, followed by reaction 124, leads to a production of NO_2 exceeding that of NO and therefore to the observed oxidation, in consequence of the hydrolysis of this excess;

$$2NO_2 + H_2O \rightarrow HNO_3 + HNO_2. \tag{126}$$

The competition has been followed in solutions initially containing both NO_2^- and H_2O_2 in varying proportion, and the $k_{H+NO_2^-}/k_{H+H_2O_2} = 0.47 \pm 0.03$ is thereby established. In contrast, the reaction of OH with H_2O_2 is comparatively slow and is not competitive with reaction 124 in the concentration range studied.

These results can be summarized as a stoichiometric reaction, per 100 ev, of

$$\alpha NO_2^- + (\alpha - \beta) H_2O_2 \rightarrow \alpha NO_3^- + \beta H_2 + (\alpha - 2\beta) H_2O, \tag{127}$$

where $2\alpha = (1 - 2f)[g(H)] + g(OH)$, $\beta = g(H_2)$, and f is the fraction of H atoms that react by 123 rather than by 27. In terms of the concentrations, $f = (1 + [H_2O_2]/0.47[NO_2^-])^{-1}$. If H_2O_2 is absent $f = 1$, $\alpha \approx 0$, and the equation gives

$$2\beta H_2O \rightarrow \beta H_2 + \beta H_2O_2 , \qquad (128)$$

which is simply the aforementioned decomposition of water into molecular products. If this equation is subtracted from the preceding one, an expression is obtained for the G of solute radiolysis alone; it is merely equation 122 with $G = \alpha$. The above definition of α together with the basic g-values gives the yields for nitrite oxidation at any concentrations of NO_2^- or H_2O_2. It may be noted that

$$G(-NO_2^-) - G(H_2O_2) = \beta = g(H_2),$$

irrespective of the relative concentration of NO_2^- and H_2O_2; this and other predictions of the mechanism are fully verified by experiment.

Nitrate is reduced to nitrite by γ-rays in oxygen-free solution. Oxygen, hydrogen peroxide, and hydrogen are other products (317–320). The yields, $G(NO_2^-)$ of 1.24, $G(H_2O_2)$ of 1.60, $G(O_2)$ of 0.07, and $G(H_2)$ of 0.5 are reported for 0.1 M $NaNO_3$ solutions irradiated with 50-kv X-rays (318). At higher nitrate concentrations, $G(H_2)$ and $G(H_2O_2)$ decrease whereas $G(O_2)$ and $G(NO_2^-)$ increase. The increase in nitrite yield and the decrease in hydrogen yield with increasing nitrate concentration indicate that a primary action involves the reducing action of the hydrogen atom:

$$H + NO_3^- \rightarrow NO_2 + OH^-. \qquad (129)$$

This, followed by reaction 126, produces nitrite with an initial yield approximately equal to $\frac{1}{2} g(H)$. It is difficult to establish reliable yields because a rapid oxidation of nitrite back to nitrate occurs.

The hydroxyl radical does not react with nitrate ion but it reoxidizes nitrite or it may produce H_2O_2 and O_2. Hydroxyl radicals generated by Fenton's reaction fail to reduce nitrate ions (319). The yields of hydrogen peroxide and oxygen can most readily be explained by assuming that hydrogen peroxide is formed by recombination of hydroxyl radicals both within and outside the spur and that oxygen originates by reactions 35 and 36. Since the OH and H_2O_2 produced by the radiation must equal the H_2O_2 and O_2 found, we have

$$g(OH) + 2g(H_2O_2) = 2G(H_2O_2) + 4G(O_2) = 3.48 \qquad (130)$$

from the observed $G(H_2O_2)$ and $G(O_2)$.

Since $2g(H_2O_2)$ is about 1.2 in neutral solution $g(OH)$, defined here as hydroxyl radicals forming hydrogen peroxide outside the spur, amounts to 2.3. This yield is close to the accepted $g(OH)$ and therefore it is consistent with the idea that the "inert" hydroxyl radicals recombine in nitrate solutions to form hydrogen peroxide.

There is also a direct action of radiation on nitrate ion in concentrated solutions. The $G(NO_2^-)$ for direct action rises from 0.50 in 0.1 M to 2.55 in 5.0 M sodium nitrate solutions containing 0.8 N sulfuric acid. This effect is shown by irradiating nitrate solutions containing low concentrations (0.0002 M) of Ce^{4+}, which is added to remove H_2O_2 and to reoxidize NO_2^- to NO_3^-. The reactions with Ce^{4+} give equation 80 and the net reaction with nitrite ion is

$$2Ce^{4+} + NO_2^- + H_2O \rightarrow 2Ce^{3+} + 2H^+ + NO_3^-. \tag{131}$$

In this system, a ceric ion analysis is used instead of a nitrite analysis and complexities of nitrite reoxidation by hydrogen peroxide and hydroxyl radicals are avoided.

The direct action yield, $G(NO_2^-)_{da}$ is determined by the excess $G(Ce^{3+})$ found in the presence and absence of sodium nitrate. Since $G(Ce^{3+})$ in the absence of nitrate ion and in dilute nitrate solutions (<0.001 M) is 2.40, the excess ceric yield measures additional nitrite formed

$$G(NO_2^-)_{da} = \tfrac{1}{2}[G(Ce^{3+})_{NO_3^-} - 2.40]. \tag{132}$$

Because nitrate solutions are hydrogen atom scavengers, part of the increase in $G(NO_2^-)$ observed in this system is due to suppression of H_2 formation. Since $G(H_2)$ is only 0.45 as a maximum, any increase in $G(NO_2^-)$ above this amount may be ascribed to direct action of the radiation on the nitrate ion. This direct decomposition proceeds stoichiometrically as

$$NO_3^- \rightarrow NO_2^- + \tfrac{1}{2}O_2 \tag{25}$$

just as in nitrate crystals (Section III.E.1). Nothing definite is known about the mechanism of this direct action, although the photodissociation of nitrate produces nitrite and oxygen.

Concentrated nitrate solutions largely suppress hydrogen formation in the case of mixed neutron and γ-ray irradiation by reaction 25. The $G(H_2)$ for 15.9 M calcium nitrate irradiated in a reactor is 0.025 if only the energy absorbed in the water is used in the calculation of the yield. Here the radiation is a combination of γ-ray and protons from the $N^{14}(n,p)C^{14}$ reaction. This small yield supports the idea that molecular hydrogen, $g(H_2)$, arises by an H atom recombination process rather than through a process giving H_2 in a single step.

4. PERMANGANATE AND CHROMATE IONS

Permanganate ion in 0.8 N sulfuric acid is reduced during γ-irradiation by a mechanism that is complex and not fully understood. This reaction is of interest since the OH radical appears to act as a reducing radical. Manganese dioxide is the principal product; at permanganate concentrations above 5×10^{-4} M, its yield is proportional to dose until 50% of the

MnO_4^- is reduced. The $G(-MnO_4^-)$ varies from 1.8 at 2×10^{-5} M to a value of 8.0 at 0.02 M permanganate. It increases rapidly from the lower limit and is 2.8 at 10^{-3} M permanganate. Above this concentration the yield increases linearly with concentration and is inversely proportional to $(\text{Intensity})^{1/2}$, the latter dependence indicating a chain reaction (321).

The proposed mechanism is

$$MnO_4^- + H \rightarrow MnO_4^{--} + H^+ \tag{133}$$

$$MnO_4^- + H_2O_2 \rightarrow MnO_4^{--} + H^+ + HO_2 \tag{134}$$

$$MnO_4^- + HO_2 \rightarrow MnO_4^{--} + H^+ + O_2 . \tag{135}$$

Oxygen has no effect on this reaction, just as was the case with hydrogen-atom reduction of Cu^{++} and Ce^{++} and Ce^{4+} ions. Indeed, reactions 133 and 135 are quite analogous to 62, 63 and 81, 84. Reduction to manganese dioxide occurs by thermal reaction of the MnO_4^{--} intermediate:

$$2MnO_4^{--} + 2H^+ \rightarrow MnO_4^- + MnO_3^- + H_2O \tag{136}$$

$$MnO_4^{--} + MnO_3^- + 2H^+ \rightarrow MnO_2 + MnO_4^- + H_2O. \tag{137}$$

In 10^{-3} M permanganate (neutral solution), $G(H_2)$ is 0.22, indicating that permanganate ions are excellent hydrogen-atom scavengers.

Explanation of the magnitude of $G(-MnO_4^-)$ requires the participation of hydroxyl radical as a reducing agent instead of in its usual role as an oxidizing agent. At permanganate concentrations above 0.001 M, it is suggested (321) that

$$OH + MnO_4^- \rightarrow MnO_4^{--} + H^+ + O \tag{138}$$

and

$$O + O \rightarrow O_2 . \tag{139}$$

Equations 133 *et seq.* lead at once to

$$G(-MnO_4^-) = \tfrac{1}{3}[g(H) + g(OH) + 2g(H_2O_2)] = 2.73, \tag{140}$$

which is in excellent agreement with the observed $G(-MnO_4^-) = 2.80$ at 0.001 M.

At higher permanganate concentrations the chain reduction is important. It is proposed that hydroxyl radicals are reformed by

$$MnO_4^- + O \rightarrow O_2 + MnO_3^- \tag{141}$$

$$MnO_3^- + H_2O \rightarrow HMnO_3^- + OH. \tag{142}$$

The hydroxyl radicals generated in 142 react according to 138 and continue the chain. Termination may be by oxygen atom recombination reaction 139.

Less is known about the radiolysis of hexavalent chromium ion, which is also reduced (to trivalent chromium) by γ-irradiation. However, the fact that $3G(Cr^{3+}) = 2.55$ is close to $G(Ce^{3+}) = 2.39$ suggests that this reduction parallels that of ceric-ion reduction (322–324). Hence a plausible mechanism is

$$CrO_4^{--} + H \rightarrow CrO_3^- + OH^- \tag{143}$$

$$2CrO_3^- + 2H^+ \rightarrow CrO_2 + H_2O + CrO_3 \tag{144}$$

$$CrO_3^- + CrO_2 \rightarrow CrO_3 + CrO_2^-. \tag{145}$$

Hydrogen peroxide and hydroperoxy radicals reduce Cr(VI) by reactions analogous to 143 and hydroxyl radicals oxidize Cr^{3+} ion (or one of the intermediate species) by a reversal of such a step. Therefore

$$3G(Cr^{3+}) = 2g(H_2O_2) + g(H) - g(OH), \tag{146}$$

which is similar to equation 80 for ceric reduction. Support for this oxidation mechanism is provided by the isotopic exchange between Cr^{3+} and Cr(VI) ions in irradiated mixtures. It is found that G(exchange) is between 2.5 and 3.0, or close to the yield of hydroxyl radicals, $g(OH)$ (324), just as in the case of $Ce^{3+} \rightarrow Ce^{4+}$ exchange (cf. Section V.A.6).

5. ARSENITE, SELENITE, AND PHOSPHITE IONS

These ions fall into the class of substances having a net chemical change equal to $g(H_2)$, the molecular-hydrogen yield. The products are hydrogen and an equivalent amount of the oxidized product. The over-all reactions are:

$$H_3AsO_3 + H_2O \rightarrow H_3AsO_4 + H_2 \tag{147}$$

$$H_2SeO_3 + H_2O \rightarrow H_3SeO_4 + H_2 \tag{148}$$

$$H_3PO_3 + H_2O \rightarrow H_3PO_4 + H_2 . \tag{149}$$

All of these oxidations have yields in deaerated solutions which are independent of solute concentration from 0.001 to 0.1 M, and of pH from 2 to 11 (325). Details of the mechanisms are unknown but the evidence suggests that the reactions parallel nitrite oxidation (cf. Section V.B.3). No net oxidation occurs initially, but it begins when hydrogen peroxide has accumulated in the solution. During the build-up period, the reduction by hydrogen atoms therefore cancels the oxidation by hydroxyl radicals. Accordingly,

$$H + H_3AsO_3 \rightarrow H_2AsO_2 + H_2O \tag{150}$$

$$OH + H_3AsO_3 \rightarrow H_2AsO_3 + H_2O , \tag{151}$$

followed by

$$H_2AsO_3 + H_2AsO_2 + H_2O \rightarrow 2H_3AsO_3 . \tag{152}$$

The detailed mechanism must conform to the fact that no net chemical change occurs for equal numbers of hydrogen and hydroxyl radicals.

Molecular hydrogen peroxide accumulation is prevented by its reaction with hydrogen atoms, reaction 27. The steady-state hydrogen peroxide concentration during irradiation therefore will be determined by the ratio of rate constants, $k_{H+H_2O_2}/k_{H+H_3AsO_3}$, as in the case of nitrite radiolysis. Because excess hydroxyl radicals result from reaction 27, reaction 150 will be suppressed and 151 favored, leading to an excess of H_2AsO_3. Then the disproportionation reaction

$$2H_2AsO_3 + H_2O \rightarrow H_3AsO_3 + H_3AsO_4 . \tag{153}$$

gives arsenic acid. Since the yields of selenate and phosphate are equal to the arsenate yield, it is plausible that the mechanism of oxidation is similar for the three anions.

The introduction of oxygen into arsenite solutions affects yields and pH dependence (326). In aerated solutions at pH of 1.4, the yield of arsenate $G(As(V))$ is 3.2 and $G(H_2O_2)$ is 4.2. Under these conditions

$$G(H_2O_2) = g(H) + g(H_2O_2) \tag{154}$$

$$G(As(V))^* = \tfrac{1}{2}[g(H) + g(OH)]. \tag{155}$$

These yields are explained by the reactions

$$H + O_2 \rightarrow HO_2 \tag{42}$$

$$As(III)^* + HO_2 \rightarrow As(IV) + HO_2^- \tag{156}$$

$$As(III) + OH \rightarrow As(IV) + OH^- \tag{157}$$

$$2As(IV) \rightarrow As(III) + As(V) \tag{158}$$

followed by reaction

$$HO_2^- + H^+ \rightarrow H_2O_2 . \tag{54}$$

The yields at pH 1.4 drop to $G(As(V))$ of 2.5 and $G(H_2O_2)$ of 2.85 at pH 7 but much more drastic changes occur in the pH range from 8 to 13. The yield $G(H_2O_2)$ decreases to zero while $G(As(V))$ increases rapidly at pH 9 reaching a maximum yield of 9 at a pH of 11. A chain reaction is proposed involving the ion, $H_2AsO_3^-$ (pK 9.22) which reacts with hydrogen peroxide

$$H_2AsO_3^- + H_2O_2 \rightarrow H_3AsO_4 + OH^-. \tag{159}$$

This reaction, as with the O_2^{18}–H_2O system shows chain characteristics above pH 9 where ionization of the hydroxyl group is postulated and suggests that the reducing O^- ion may play a role.

*As(III) = H_3AsO_3 and As(V) = H_3AsO_4 .

The remaining systems are less completely studied than the arsenite–arsenate one.

VI. Radiation Chemistry of Aqueous Organic Solutions

The basic radiation-yields—$g(H)$, $g(OH)$, $g(H_2)$ and $g(H_2O_2)$—help in disentangling the complex reactions taking place in irradiated aqueous organic systems. Hydrogen atoms and hydroxyl radicals, being the reactive species, promote many reactions in these media, and a comparison of product yields with $g(H)$ and $g(OH)$ often provides insight into the reaction mechanism.

A. ENERGETICS OF FREE-RADICAL REACTIONS

Hydrogen atoms and hydroxyl radicals usually abstract hydrogen atoms, and in some cases they remove entire radical groups from organic compounds. Rupture of carbon-hydrogen, carbon-oxygen, carbon-nitrogen, carbon-sulfur, and other bonds is common. Table III gives dissociation energies for a number of bonds which may be broken during radiolysis. Of these, disregarding diatomic molecules, the I—I bond in iodine is the weakest and the O—H bond in water is the strongest (except for the C—O bond in carbon dioxide). But H_2 and H_2O are the normal abstraction products of H and OH radicals, and these radicals must therefore be capable of breaking all carbon bonds listed in Table III. Thus we expect reactions of which the prototypes are

$$D + H_2 \rightarrow HD + H \tag{160}$$

$$OH + H_2 \rightarrow H_2O + H \tag{34}$$

$$D + CH_4 \rightarrow HD + CH_3 \tag{161}$$

$$OH + CH_4 \rightarrow H_2O + CH_3 \tag{162}$$

to proceed as written.

Activation energies of these reactions will also be low. Most of the reactions of hydrogen atoms and hydroxyl radicals with organic compounds are exothermic and for this reason they will proceed with activation energies between 4 and 6 kcal/mole. In these exothermic reactions, the activation energy E_a (in kcal/mole) will be roughly equal to $0.055 D_{ab}$ where D_{ab} is the energy of the bond ab (327). Low activation energies therefore prevail for these reactions since bond energies are 100 kcal/mole or smaller. The activation energy of endothermic reactions is obtained by adding the heat of reaction to the activation energy of the reverse exothermic process. Therefore reactions of high endothermicity will be relatively rare in all room-temperature irradiations. Some of the possible reactions for methylamine, together with E_a calculated by the above method, are as shown below (163–168).

Reaction	E_a (kcal/mole)	
$H + CH_3NH_2 \rightarrow CH_3 + NH_3$	4.1	(163)
$H + CH_3NH_2 \rightarrow CH_4 + NH_2$	4.1	(164)
$H + CH_3NH_2 \rightarrow H_2 + CH_2NH_2$	5.6	(165)
$OH + CH_3NH_2 \rightarrow CH_3 + NH_2OH$	4.1	(166)
$OH + CH_3NH_2 \rightarrow CH_3OH + NH_2$	4.1	(167)
$OH + CH_3NH_2 \rightarrow H_2O + CH_2NH_2$	5.6	(168)

Each of the reactions shown will proceed with low activation energy. Note that the rupture of a 101 kcal bond requires only 1.5 kcal more activation energy than the rupture of a 75 kcal bond. Unfortunately, bond energies depend significantly on molecular structure, and without more precise data the course of the reaction cannot be predicted. The many possible reactions of the free radicals with methylamine given in reactions 163 through 168 illustrate the potential complexities of radiolysis.

Hydrogen and hydroxyl radicals react principally with solute molecules as indicated above for hydrogen, methane and methylamine. However, the final products are in large measure determined by the reactions of the less reactive secondary radicals produced in reactions such 163–168. Because radical-radical reactions have low activation energies and hence high rate constants, the product in O_2-free irradiations is often a dimer of the principal radical formed. For example, succinic acid is produced in the radiolysis of aqueous acetic acid. Here we have

$$H + CH_3COOH \rightarrow H_2 + CH_2COOH \tag{169}$$

$$OH + CH_3COOH \rightarrow H_2O + CH_2COOH \tag{170}$$

$$2CH_2COOH \rightarrow COOHCH_2CH_2COOH. \tag{171}$$

The reactions of the acetic acid – water system are treated in detail in Section VI.G.2. The common occurrence of the "dimeric" product in organic radiolyses of gases was abundantly illustrated in Section III.

Oftentimes the organic radical will react with a solute, with a product of solute radiolysis, or with a product of water radiolysis. Reaction with hydrogen peroxide is frequent, and many organic reactions proceed without leaving a perceptible trace of hydrogen peroxide in the irradiated solution. We shall see later how individual organic radicals react with hydrogen peroxide. The general reaction is

$$R + H_2O_2 \rightarrow ROH + OH \quad (E_a = 2.9 \text{ kcal/mole}), \tag{172}$$

and it forms a new hydroxyl radical capable of continuing radical reactions.

Dissolved oxygen changes the course of many organic radiolyses. The complex action of this molecule is by no means fully understood, but its principal role is known to be the capture of a hydrogen atom or of an electron as in reactions 42 and 173.

$$H + O_2 \rightarrow HO_2 \tag{42}$$

$$\epsilon + O_2 \rightarrow O_2^-. \tag{173}$$

Reaction 173 occurs either with a hydrated electron, or with a free electron before it has become hydrated (cf. Section II.B.4) in which case hydration of O_2^- takes place subsequently. The ion O_2^- is an ionic-dissociation product of the hydroperoxy radical. This radical may react with an organic radical to give an organic hydroperoxide,

$$R + HO_2 \rightarrow ROOH, \tag{174}$$

or with another hydroperoxy radical to give hydrogen peroxide,

$$HO_2 + HO_2 \rightarrow H_2O_2 + O_2 . \tag{36}$$

Organic radicals may, of course, react directly with oxygen to form an organic peroxy-radical:

$$R + O_2 \rightarrow ROO. \tag{70}$$

Depending on the nature of the system, oxygen may either promote or inhibit individual radiolytic processes.

B. GENERAL RELATIONS IN AQUEOUS ORGANIC SOLUTIONS

Radiation yields reveal much about reactions occurring in dilute aqueous solutions. Table XVI summarizes the possible relations between basic radiation yields $g(x)$ and product yields $G(x)$ given in Tables XI and XII, and they are applicable to neutral and acid solutions. From a comparison of $G(H_2)$, $G(H_2O_2)$, and $G(-O_2)$ with the expected yields of Table XVI, we learn about hydrogen-atom and hydroxyl-radical reactivity with the solute and about organic-radical reactivity with oxygen. In the following sections we shall consider briefly some specific organic reactions, using the relations in Table XVI to provide clues to steps in the reaction mechanism.

C. THE CARBON OXIDES

1. CARBON MONOXIDE

Dissolved carbon monoxide irradiated with X-rays is in part oxidized to carbon dioxide and in part reduced to formaldehyde. The over-all reactions are

$$CO + H_2O \rightarrow CO_2 + H_2 \tag{175}$$

$$CO + H_2 \rightarrow HCHO. \tag{176}$$

TABLE XVI

GENERAL RELATIONS BETWEEN RADIOLYSIS YIELDS AND BASIC YIELDS IN DILUTE
AQUEOUS ORGANIC SOLUTIONS

A. OXYGEN-FREE SOLUTIONS

$G(H_2) = g(H_2)$; Dehydrogenation of solute does not occur.

$G(H_2) > g(H_2)$; Some dehydrogenation of solute does occur.

$G(H_2) = g(H_2) + g(H)$; Each H removes one H from solute.

$G(H_2O_2) = g(H_2O_2)$; Intermediate free radicals do not react with H_2O_2.

$G(H_2O_2) < g(H_2O_2)$; Some intermediate free radicals react with H_2O_2.

B. SOLUTIONS CONTAINING OXYGEN

$G(H_2) = g(H_2)$; Each H reacts with O_2.

$G(H_2) > g(H_2)$; Some H abstracts H from solute.

$G(H_2O_2) = \frac{1}{2}g(H) + g(H_2O_2)$; HO_2 radicals do not react with solute.

$G(H_2O_2) = \frac{1}{2}[g(H) + g(OH)] + g(H_2O_2)$; HO_2 radicals originate by reactions of the
type: $COOH + O_2 \to CO_2 + HO_2$.

$G(H_2O_2) \gg g(H) + g(OH)$; Oxygen is initiating a chain reaction.

$G(-O_2) = \frac{1}{2}g(H)$; Hydrogen atoms react with O_2; and HO_2 only with HO_2.

$G(-O_2) = \frac{1}{2}[g(H) + g(OH)]$; O_2 reacts with H and with organic radical formed
from OH; the peroxy radicals then liberate O_2.

However the X-ray yields, $G(-CO)$ of 3.5, $G(CO_2)$ of 2.2, $G(H_2)$ of 0.9, and $G(HCHO)$ of 0.27 at pH 3.5, indicate secondary reactions in the reaction mechanism (328). One notes that $G(-CO)$ corresponds to $g(H_2O)$. Each pair of H and OH radicals are necessary to remove one molecule of carbon monoxide. Since each radical may react with CO to give free radical intermediates

$$H + CO \to HCO \tag{177}$$

$$OH + CO \to COOH. \tag{178}$$

These formyl and carboxy radicals in turn may undergo further free radical reactions such as

$$HCO + H \to H_2CO \tag{179}$$

$$COOH + OH \to CO_2 + H_2O \tag{180}$$

to form carbon dioxide and formaldehyde. And since $G(H_2) > g(H_2)$, atomic H reacts with an intermediate to produce H_2. A likely compound is formic acid. This molecule forms carbon dioxide and hydrogen during irradiation (cf. Section VI.G.1). Therefore, in view of the use of H and OH radicals in reactions 179 and 180, the efficiency of H and OH utilization in reactions 177 and 178 is reduced below $g(H) + g(OH)$.

2. CARBON DIOXIDE

The fixation of carbon dioxide occurs to a minor extent in irradiated aqueous solutions. Since the products of carbon dioxide reduction are more reactive than carbon dioxide, a major problem has been to protect the new compounds from reoxidation to carbon dioxide. Successful fixation of carbon dioxide has been carried out with cyclotron beams irradiating CO_2 dissolved in ferrous sulfate solutions and with electron beams irradiating bicarbonate solutions.

In a ferrous-ion reducing environment, formic acid, oxalic acid, formaldehyde, and methanol are produced in low yields from dissolved $C^{14}O_2$ (329). In a typical experiment the solutions—irradiated with 35-Mev helium ions—contain 1.0 M ferrous sulfate (to remove the oxidizing OH and H_2O_2), 0.1 N sulfuric acid, and 0.005 to 0.01 M carbon dioxide. From these results, it appears that atomic hydrogen may react with carbon dioxide as follows:

$$CO_2 + H \rightarrow COOH. \tag{181}$$

Formic and oxalic acids may arise by disproportionation and bimolecular radical-recombination reactions, respectively:

$$COOH + COOH \rightarrow HCOOH + CO_2 \tag{182}$$

$$COOH + COOH \rightarrow (COOH)_2 . \tag{183}$$

Further reduction of this carboxy radical with hydrogen produces formaldehyde, a compound formed by reaction 176 and also in the formic acid radiolysis (see VI.G.1).

Oxalic acid also forms in electron-irradiated solutions of ammonium carbonate, ammonium bicarbonate, sodium bicarbonate, and calcium bicarbonate, but not in sodium carbonate solutions (330). Insufficient work has been done to establish reliable initial oxalic acid yields but they are in the range 0.01 to 0.1. Up to 2 % of the solute is converted to oxalic acid before the yield-dose curves flatten appreciably. The conversion of CO_2 to oxalic acid is pH-dependent because reduction of ammonium carbonate is attributed to an impurity, ammonium carbamate. Since reduction to oxalic acid then is confined to the three bicarbonates studied and not to the carbonate, reduction is favored in the more acid solutions. Oxalic acid results from the formation of COOH by reaction 181 followed by dimerization reaction 183.

That ammonium carbamate produces oxalic acid on irradiation is of interest since the carbon-nitrogen bonds are the weakest ones in this molecule. Ammonia and ammonium ions are unreactive in the absence of oxygen (cf. Section V.A.10), therefore it appears likely that H and OH attack on the carbamate molecule is at the C—N bond. The hydrogen and hydroxyl reactions may both be effective in producing oxalic acid since it is possible to form the same intermediate free radical:

$$H + NH_2COONH_4 \rightarrow NH_3 + COONH_4 \tag{184}$$

$$OH + NH_2COONH_4 \rightarrow NH_2OH + COONH_4 \tag{185}$$

Radical recombination shown in reaction 183 then yields the salt of oxalic acid.

D. HYDROCARBONS

1. SATURATED HYDROCARBONS

Little is known about the reactions of saturated hydrocarbons in irradiated water although extensive work has been carried out on the pure hydrocarbons (cf. Section III.C.2). Hydrogen is formed from methane, showing H atom abstraction, the methane being converted to a water-soluble product—probably methyl alcohol. The following reactions are plausible:

$$CH_4 + H \rightarrow CH_3 + H_2 \tag{186}$$

$$CH_4 + OH \rightarrow CH_3 + H_2O \tag{162}$$

$$CH_3 + OH \rightarrow CH_3OH \tag{187}$$

$$CH_3 + CH_3 \rightarrow CH_3CH_3 \tag{188}$$

$$CH_3 + H_2O_2 \rightarrow CH_3OH + OH. \tag{189}$$

The reactions of methanol are treated in Section VI.E.

In aerated acidified ferrous sulfate solutions, $G(Fe^{3+})$ increases considerably when hydrocarbons are added, as is to be expected when organic free radicals are formed (cf. Section V.A.3). The magnitude of this increase depends on hydrocarbon structure. In the general case:

$$RH + OH \rightarrow R + H_2O \tag{70}$$

$$R + O_2 \rightarrow RO_2 \tag{71}$$

$$Fe^{++} + RO_2 \rightarrow RO_2^- + Fe^{3+} \tag{72}$$

$$Fe^{++} + RO_2H \rightarrow RO^- + Fe^{3+} + OH. \tag{74}$$

The hydroxyl radical formed generates another R radical and continues the chain (see Section V.A.3). In the absence of oxygen, ferric ion is reduced by the organic radicals (294, 331).

$$R + Fe^{3+} + H_2O \rightarrow Fe^{++} + H^+ + ROH. \tag{190}$$

Note that the alcohol is formed by reactions 72, 73, 74 and 190.

2. UNSATURATED HYDROCARBONS

The irradiation of 0.004 M ethylene (water saturated at 760 mm, 15°C) in the absence of oxygen yields hydrogen peroxide, acetaldehyde, n-butyraldehyde, higher molecular weight aldehydes, and an oily polymer (332). At pH 1.2, $G(H_2O_2) = 0.40$, G(total aldehyde) $= 0.24$; the hydrogen and polymer yields are unreported. These data show that $G(H_2O_2) < g(H_2O_2)$

at this pH and that therefore part of the molecular peroxide is used in aldehyde formation. Likely initial reactions of the H and OH radicals are

$$H + CH_2=CH_2 \rightarrow CH_3CH_2 \tag{191}$$

and

$$OH + CH_2=CH_2 \rightarrow CH_2CH_2OH. \tag{192}$$

The new radicals formed in reactions 191 and 192 may then undergo polymerization with ethylene to form polymer and alcohols of four, six, and more carbon atoms.

The free radicals formed in ethylene radiolysis do not react readily with hydrogen peroxide. This reaction, so prominent in formic acid decomposition (Section VI.G.1), is about one-half complete in ethylene-water reaction. It is likely that H_2O_2 is protected from free radical attack by the reactive ethylene. Since $G(H_2O_2) + G(\text{aldehyde})$ is nearly equal to $g(H_2O_2)$, perhaps the aldehydes are formed by a radiation-induced reaction between the alcohols and hydrogen peroxide.

$$RCH_2OH + H_2O_2 \rightarrow RCHO + 2H_2O. \tag{193}$$

In oxygenated ethylene solutions, non-chain reactions produce acetaldehyde, formaldehyde, glycolaldehyde, hydrogen peroxide, and an unidentified organic hydro-peroxide.

The yields, $G(HCHO + CH_3CHO) = 3.0$, $G(CH_2OHCHO) = 2.45$, $G(H_2O_2) = 2.5$, $G(ROOH) = 0.35$, and $G(-O_2) = 6.0$ are found for solutions at pH 1.2 containing 0.003 M C_2H_4 and 0.003 M oxygen. Lowering the relative amount of oxygen reduces aldehyde yields but has relatively little effect on H_2O_2 and ROOH yields.

The yield of 5.8 for oxidized organic molecules shows primary attack on ethylene not only by hydroxyl radicals but also by either hydrogen and/or HO_2 radicals. Thus in addition to reactions 191 and 192 we have

$$HO_2 + CH_2=CH_2 \rightarrow HO_2CH_2CH_2 \tag{194}$$

$$CH_3CH_2 + O_2 \rightarrow CH_3CH_2O_2 \tag{195}$$

$$CH_2CH_2OH + O_2 \rightarrow O_2CH_2CH_2OH \tag{196}$$

and the yield $G(\text{total organic}) \sim g(H) + g(OH)$. Further oxidation of the hydroperoxide in reaction 194 leads to

$$HO_2CH_2CH_2 + O_2 \rightarrow HO_2CH_2CH_2O_2. \tag{197}$$

Since $G(-O_2) = 6$, this last step is unlikely unless oxygen from these peroxy radicals is liberated.

$$RO_2 + RO_2 \rightarrow ROOR + O_2. \tag{198}$$

Little is known about the formation of the aldehydes from these oxy-radicals. Hydrogen peroxide in yield greater than $g(H_2O_2)$ may originate by hydrolysis of intermediate hydroperoxides or by recombination of hydroperoxy radicals by reaction 36.

3. BENZENE

Benzene dissolved in oxygen-free aqueous solution (0.022 M) is converted to phenol and diphenyl. The yields of these compounds do not depend greatly on pH but hydrogen peroxide is present only in the acid solutions (333). The yields obtained in 0.8 N and in neutral solutions, respectively are: $G(C_6H_5OH)$, 0.35, 0.36; $G(C_6H_5C_6H_5)$, 0.96, 1.22; $G(H_2O_2)$, 0.57, 0.00; and $G(H_2)$, 0.39, 0.42.

Since $G(H_2) = g(H_2)$, it is clear that H atoms do not react with benzene to produce H_2. It is assumed that hydrogen atoms react by 199 to form polymer (333).

$$H + C_6H_6 \rightarrow C_6H_7 \rightarrow Polymer. \tag{199}$$

The results accord with the formation of phenyl radicals by OH and their subsequent reactions

$$OH + C_6H_6 \rightarrow C_6H_5 + H_2O \tag{200}$$

$$2C_6H_5 \rightarrow C_6H_5C_6H_5 \tag{201}$$

$$C_6H_5 + OH \rightarrow C_6H_5OH. \tag{202}$$

It has been shown that OH radicals produced by Fenton's reaction react with benzene to form C_6H_5 radicals and that these radicals do not react with hydrogen peroxide. Consequently, any peroxide yields below $g(H_2O_2)$ must be accounted for by reactions with the H, OH, or C_6H_7 radicals. If we assume that the decrease in $G(H_2O_2)$ derives from the reaction of H or the precursor of H, we generate additional OH radicals in a yield of $g(H_2O_2) - G(H_2O_2)$. Taking $g(H_2O_2)$ as 0.8 in 0.8 N sulfuric acid and 0.6 in water, we may calculate $g(OH)$ from the mechanism given by reactions 200, 201, and 202.

$$g(OH) = 2[G(C_6H_5C_6H_5) + G(C_6H_5OH)] - [g(H_2O_2) - G(H_2O_2)]. \tag{203}$$

Calculated $g(OH)$ values are 2.42 for 0.8 N H_2SO_4 and 2.56 for neutral solutions. These values are sufficiently close to $g(OH)$ measured by other methods to support the mechanism proposed.

Oxygen and oxidizing ions prevent diphenyl formation; they produce phenol and an aldehyde instead (333, 334). The yields for aerated 0.022 M benzene obtained in 0.8 N sulfuric acid and neutral solutions, respectively, are: $G(C_6H_5OH)$, 2.64, 2.64; $G(H_2O_2)$, 2.84, 2.88; $G(H_2)$, 0.39, 0.42; $G(-O_2)$,

5.33, 5.33 (333); and G(aldehyde) $\sim$0.2, which is possibly muciondialdehyde (334).

As is expected, $G(H_2) = g(H_2)$ and hydrogen atoms do not react with benzene to form H_2. And except for the high yield, $G(-O_2)$, the phenol yields can be explained by reaction 200 followed by

$$C_6H_5 + O_2 \rightarrow C_6H_5O_2 \tag{204}$$

and

$$C_6H_5O_2 + H_2O \rightarrow C_6H_5OH + HO_2 \tag{205}$$

releasing phenol. In the presence of oxygen, 199 is suppressed; hydrogen atoms form hydroperoxy radicals. Therefore by the above mechanism

$$G(C_6H_5OH) = g(OH) = 2.64. \tag{206}$$

The observed yield, $G(H_2O_2)$, equals 2.84 whereas the expression

$$G(H_2O_2) = \tfrac{1}{2}g(H) \left[1 + \frac{k_{199}(C_6H_6)}{k_{42}(O_2)} \right]^{-1} + \tfrac{1}{2}g(OH) + g(H_2O_2) \tag{207}$$

gives $\sim$3.3 in saturated oxygen solutions. These reactions are complex and the low peroxide yield may be caused by an incomplete removal of HO_2 radicals in reaction 36 or by loss of hydrogen peroxide by its reaction with free radicals (cf. Sections VI.E and G).

Insufficient work has been done to account for the large $G(-O_2)$. It is proposed (333) that the over-all reaction

$$C_6H_5O_2 + C_6H_6 \rightarrow \text{Oxygenated product} + OH \tag{208}$$

takes place and by way of reaction 200 forms another free phenyl radical.

E. ALCOHOLS

1. METHANOL AND ETHANOL

Aldehydes and glycols are produced by the irradiation of aqueous methanol or ethanol. Thus with R as H or CH_3,

$$RCH_2OH \rightarrow RCHO + H_2 \tag{209}$$

$$2RCH_2OH \rightarrow RCHOHCHOHR + H_2. \tag{210}$$

At high alcohol concentrations the aldehyde and glycol are protected from further attack by the radicals. The formaldehyde yield is low in dilute methanol solutions, but it is not known accurately because initial yields are difficult to measure, since a low steady-state formaldehyde concentration develops (328, 335). For ethanol solutions the yields are $G(CH_3CHO) =$

1.9 and $G(CH_3CHOHCHOHCH_3) = 1.6$ (336). It is interesting that the yields in pure ethanol are comparable (cf. Table VII).

Hydrogen atoms extract hydrogen from the alcohols, so that the total hydrogen yield is

$$G(H_2) = g(H) + g(H_2).   \qquad (57)$$

Hydrogen yields for the simple C_1 to C_4 alcohols are 4.2 ± 0.2 and are indeed equal to the sum of atomic-hydrogen and molecular-hydrogen yields. Therefore

$$RCH_2OH + H \rightarrow RCHOH + H_2   \qquad (211)$$

followed by the bimolecular recombination reaction

$$2RCHOH \rightarrow RCHOHCHOHR,   \qquad (212)$$

which gives the substituted glycol. A RCHOH radical also forms as is shown in reaction 211 by hydroxyl radical reaction with RCH_2OH. Note that radical attack occurs on the carbon atom which has the lowest carbon-hydrogen bond energy. Aldehydes may form by reaction of the radical with hydrogen peroxide

$$RCHOH + H_2O_2 \rightarrow RCHO + H_2O + OH   \qquad (213)$$

or by disproportionation

$$2RCHOH \rightarrow RCHO + RCH_2OH.   \qquad (214)$$

We shall see later how analogous organic radical – hydrogen peroxide reactions similar to 213 occur in aqueous formic acid solutions. Apart from the participation of H_2O_2, the mechanism is very similar to that obtaining in the pure alcohols (cf. Section III.D.2.d).

With increasing pH, $G(H_2)$ decreases, approaching the molecular yield $g(H_2)$ at high pH (303) (cf. Fig. 17). This behavior, common for a number of solutes, is comparable to the decline in $G(HD)$ for the deuterium-water reaction (253). In that reaction and in the $CH_3OH–D_2O$ reaction (303), $G(HD)$ is close to zero at pH above 13. In such basic solutions, hydrogen atoms are probably not present in appreciable concentrations, for the equilibrium

$$\epsilon_{aq}^- \rightleftharpoons H + OH^-   \qquad (68)$$

may be shifted far to the left. This would suppress H-abstraction by H atoms in favor of some reaction (not producing H_2) of the hydrated electrons with the alcohols.

Because oxygen reacts with the intermediate free radical, it eliminates glycol formation and raises the aldehyde yield correspondingly (336). For example, in the case of ethanol,

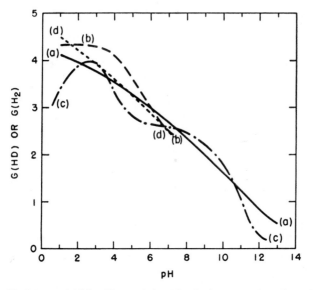

Fɪɢ. 17. Hydrogen yield in dilute methanol solutions as a function of pH (253, 303, 328, 336). (a) 1.0 M methanol $G(HD)$; (b) 3.4 × 10^{-2} M Ethanol $G(H_2)$; (c) D_2 + H_2O $G(HD)$; (d) 10 mM Methanol $G(H_2)$.

$$CH_3CHOH + O_2 \rightarrow CH_3CHOHO_2 \qquad (215)$$

and

$$CH_3CHOHO_2 + HO_2 \rightarrow H_2O_2 + CH_3CHO + O_2 . \qquad (216)$$

Instead of reactions 215 and 216, reaction 36 accompanied by bimolecular termination of the oxy-radical may take place. The yield of hydrogen peroxide is therefore predicted (Table XVI) to be

$$G(H_2O_2) = \tfrac{1}{2}[g(H) + g(OH)] + g(H_2O_2), \qquad (44)$$

and this prediction has been confirmed for ethanol, butanol, and benzyl alcohols (336, 337).

2. METHANOL WITH FERRIC SULFATE

The basic radiation yields can be determined by means of the deaerated methyl alcohol – ferric sulfate – water system (302, 303). The mechanism is

$$H + CH_3OH \rightarrow CH_2OH + H_2 \qquad (217)$$

$$H + Fe^{3+} \rightarrow H^+ + Fe^{++} \qquad (61)$$

$$OH + CH_3OH \rightarrow CH_2OH + H_2O \qquad (218)$$

$$CH_2OH + Fe^{3+} \rightarrow HCHO + Fe^{++} + H^+ \tag{219}$$

$$Fe^{++} + H_2O_2 \rightarrow Fe^{3+} + OH + OH^-. \tag{51}$$

Under conditions where all hydrogen atoms react by 217 the above mechanism leads to

$$G(H_2) = g(H_2) + g(H) \tag{57}$$

$$G(HCHO) = g(H) + g(OH) + g(H_2O_2) \tag{220}$$

$$G(Fe^{++}) = g(H) + g(OH). \tag{78}$$

If the reaction of hydrogen atoms with methanol is suppressed by use of high Fe^{3+}/CH_3OH ratios, $G(H_2)$ approaches $g(H_2)$. Then all of the radical and molecular yields can be obtained. Table XVII presents yields measured in this way for H_2O and for D_2O containing 0.1 N sulfuric acid, with continuous X-radiation averaging 50-kv. The molecular yields are found to be somewhat higher for this radiation than for Co^{60} γ-rays, in accord with expectation.

F. ALDEHYDES

Aldehydes are oxidized to the homologous acids, and at high concentrations they are in part reduced to alcohols. The over-all reactions for formaldehyde are

$$HCHO + H_2O \rightarrow HCOOH + H_2 \tag{221}$$

and

$$2HCHO + H_2O \rightarrow HCOOH + CH_3OH. \tag{222}$$

Equal yields of hydrogen and formic acid are obtained on irradiation of 0.001 M formaldehyde at pH 4. These yields equal 3.1 which indicate

TABLE XVII

BASIC YIELDS[a] IN H_2O AND D_2O[b]

H_2O		D_2O	
$g(H)$	3.29	$g(D)$	3.75
$g(OH)$	2.83	$g(OD)$	2.45
$g(H_2)$	0.64	$g(D_2)$	0.62
$g(H_2O_2)$	0.87	$g(D_2O_2)$	1.27

[a] For X-rays approximately equivalent to 50-kv monochromatic radiation (190-kv radiation filtered by a 0.66 mm Al plate and the glass wall of the irradiation cell) (302, 303).

[b] 0.1 N sulfuric acid.

hydrogen abstraction from HCHO and the formation of one molecule of HCOOH per pair of H and OH radicals.

$$H + HCHO \rightarrow H_2 + CHO \tag{223}$$

and

$$OH + CHO \rightarrow HCOOH \tag{224}$$

$$CHO + H_2O_2 \rightarrow HCOOH + OH. \tag{225}$$

Since $G(H_2) < g(H) + g(H_2)$ some of the H atoms add to the C$=$O group.

$$H + HCHO \rightarrow CH_2OH \tag{226}$$

leading by hydrogen abstraction to methanol, one of the minor products,

$$CH_2OH + HCHO \rightarrow CH_3OH + CHO. \tag{227}$$

Reactions similar to those of formaldehyde take place for acetaldehyde and propionaldehyde. Hydrogen and an acid are produced in each case (328).

G. CARBOXYLIC ACIDS

Formic and acetic acids are the two most thoroughly studied acids, and because their reactions appear to be typical, we shall consider them in some detail.

1. FORMIC ACID

The stoichiometry of the hydrogen-atom and hydroxyl-radical reactions of dilute (10^{-4} to 10^{-2} M) formic acid in deaerated solution is (328, 338)

$$HCOOH \rightarrow H_2 + CO_2 . \tag{228}$$

In solutions containing hydrogen peroxide, radiolysis proceeds by a chain reaction having the stoichiometry

$$HCOOH + H_2O_2 \rightarrow 2H_2O + CO_2 , \tag{229}$$

but the chain reaction is inhibited if oxygen is present by the net reaction

$$HCOOH + O_2 \rightarrow H_2O_2 + CO_2 . \tag{230}$$

Reactions 228 and 230 are not chain reactions.

The dotted line in Fig. 18 shows the rate of decomposition of dilute deaerated formic acid. The carbon dioxide and hydrogen yields are equal and are given by

$$G(H_2) = g(H) + g(H_2), \tag{57}$$

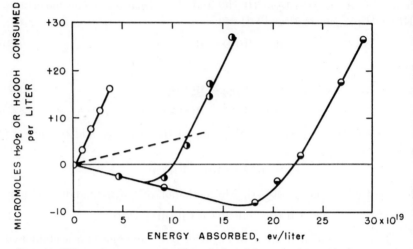

FIG. 18. Effect of oxygen on the X-ray induced decomposition of hydrogen peroxide in aqueous solution containing 0.01 M formic acid, 0.00003 M hydrogen peroxide, and 0.001 N sulfuric acid (338). KEY: ○ oxygen-free; ◑ 4.8 × 10^{-6} M O$_2$; ◕ 10.1 × 10^{-6} M O$_2$.

so that each hydrogen atom removes a hydrogen atom from the formic acid molecule. The slope of this formic acid curve contrasts strikingly with the hydrogen peroxide – formic acid curve of Fig. 18 which rises steeply from the origin. Whereas $G(CO_2)$ in pure aqueous formic acid at this pH is 3.2, $G(CO_2)$ in formic acid containing hydrogen peroxide reaches values as high as 175 (338). However, in formic acid – hydrogen peroxide solutions even a trace of oxygen—as little as 10^{-6} M—inhibits this chain radiolysis. Note in Fig. 18 how hydrogen peroxide continues to form until all of the oxygen is exhausted, and how the uninhibited chain-decomposition of reaction 220 then proceeds with the same high yield as shown for the oxygen-free solution.

The $G(H_2O_2)$ is zero in oxygen-free formic acid solutions. Because of the high yield for the decomposition of formic acid via reaction 229, hydrogen peroxide cannot accumulate at all in irradiated deaerated formic acid. This behavior, not uncommon in aqueous organic radiolyses, is typical of those cases for which $G(H_2O_2) < g(H_2O_2)$ (see Table XVI); that is, when $G(H_2O_2)$ is smaller than $g(H_2O_2)$ it is usually negligibly small.

Reactions 75, 77, and 182 explain the free radical part of the reaction providing a $G(H_2) = G(CO_2)$. And since molecular H$_2$ equals molecular H$_2O_2$ for this system the equivalence of $G(H_2)$ and $G(CO_2)$ is maintained by virtue of reaction 229 converting formic acid to carbon dioxide.

$$H + HCOOH \rightarrow H_2 + COOH \tag{77}$$

$$OH + HCOOH \rightarrow H_2O + COOH \tag{75}$$

$$COOH + COOH \rightarrow HCOOH + CO_2 . \tag{182}$$

Hydrogen atoms react selectively with the hydrogen atom on the carbon atom. This follows from the fact that irradiation of deuteroformic acid (the D atom being the one attached to C) gives hydrogen deuteride as the principal product (301, 339):

$$H + DCOOH \rightarrow HD + COOH. \tag{231}$$

The H_2O_2 reacts by the chain-propagation step:

$$COOH + H_2O_2 \rightarrow CO_2 + H_2O + OH, \tag{232}$$

a COOH radical then being regenerated by reaction 75. When oxygen is present, reaction 77 must compete with 42

$$H + O_2 \rightarrow HO_2 . \tag{42}$$

Chain propagation is terminated by

$$COOH + O_2 \rightarrow CO_2 + HO_2 . \tag{79}$$

The hydroperoxy radicals are removed by

$$HO_2 + HO_2 \rightarrow H_2O_2 + O_2 , \tag{36}$$

because of the relative stability of this radical and the high rate constant for reaction 36 compared to that for reaction of HO_2 with HCOOH.

The formic acid – oxygen system measures the basic radiation yields $g(H)$, $g(OH)$, $g(H_2)$, and $g(H_2O_2)$. Some characteristically linear dose curves are given in Fig. 19 for Co^{60} γ-rays. In a dilute solution—with comparable concentrations of oxygen and formic acid—the radicals H, OH, HO_2 , and COOH disappear exclusively by reactions 42, 75, 36, and 79, respectively, and then it follows at once (340) that

$$g(H) = 2G(-O_2) - G(CO_2) \tag{233}$$

$$g(H_2) = G(H_2) \tag{234}$$

$$g(OH) = G(CO_2) \tag{235}$$

$$g(H_2O_2) = G(H_2O_2) - G(-O_2). \tag{236}$$

Table XVIII presents $g(H)$, $g(OH)$, $g(H_2)$, and $g(H_2O_2)$ as a function of formic acid concentration. [See Tables XI and XII for these yields, also secured by the formic acid system, as a function of pH (247).] The yields

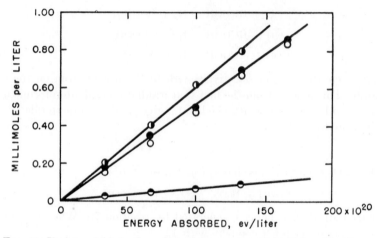

FIG. 19. Various yields in the radiolysis by γ-rays of 0.01 M formic acid containing 1.24 mM oxygen (339). KEY: $\bigcirc$ CO_2 ; $\ominus$ H_2 ; $\bullet$ $-$ O_2 O_2 ; $\oplus$ H_2O_2 .

TABLE XVIII

BASIC YIELDS IN WATER RADIOLYSIS BY THE FORMIC ACID METHOD (340)

HCOOH (M)	1.0	0.01	0.0001
pH	1.77	2.70	2.70
$g(H)$	3.52	2.88	2.64
$g(OH)$	3.52	2.88	2.64
$g(H_2)$	0.44	0.44	0.33
$g(H_2O_2)$	0.44	0.44	0.33

agree well with those obtained by the methanol-ferric sulfate system (Table XVII). In acid solutions, $g(H_2O_2) > g(H_2)$ and $g(H) > g(OH)$.

The data in Tables XI and XII prove that the basic radiation yields are unaffected by pH above about 3.0. However this statement requires qualification. If one assumes that $g(H)$ is given by $G(HD)$ for the D_2–H_2O system, one concludes that $g(H)$ decreases appreciably in the pH range above 9 contrary to the $HCOOH$–O_2 results. It should be emphasized that the formic acid – oxygen system cannot distinguish between an HO_2 formed by reaction 42 and one formed from O_2^- following electron attachment to O_2 (reaction 173). We can therefore conclude only that the sum of these two contributions equals $g(H)$.

Contrasting with their simplicity in dilute formic acid solutions, the reactions in 0.25 M solutions are very complex indeed. The products and 100 ev yields found in the densely ionizing 35-Mev helium-ion irradiation are: glyoxylic acid, 0.30; mesoxalic acid, 0.20; oxalic acid, 0.13; tartronic acid, 0.06; glycolic acid, 0.03; tartaric acid, 0.006; formaldehyde, 0.002; and glyoxal, 0.12. A possible set of free-radical reactions that explains these products is:

$$HCOOH + H \text{ (or OH)} \rightarrow COOH + H_2 \text{ (or } H_2O) \tag{77}$$

$$HCOOH + \epsilon^- \rightarrow HCO + OH^- \tag{237}$$

$$HCO + HCOOH \rightarrow HCHO + COOH \tag{238}$$

$$HCO + COOH \rightarrow CHOCOOH \tag{239}$$

$$HCO + HCO \rightarrow CHOCHO \tag{240}$$

$$CHOCOOH + COOH \rightarrow CHOHCOOH + CO_2 \tag{241}$$

$$HCHO + COOH \rightarrow CHOHCOOH \tag{242}$$

$$2CHOHCOOH \rightarrow COOHCHOHCHOHCOOH \tag{243}$$

$$HCO + HCOOH \rightarrow H_2 + COCOOH \tag{244}$$

$$COOH + COCOOH \rightarrow COOHCOCOOH \tag{245}$$

$$HCO + COOH \rightarrow HCOOH + CO. \tag{246}$$

Note that many radical-radical reactions are included. Although these proposed steps certainly have not been substantiated, radical-radical reactions are to be expected, since the tracks of these high-LET particles will have comparatively large densities of free radicals and molecular products.

2. ACETIC ACID

In acetic acid radiolysis, hydrogen atoms abstract mainly hydrogen atoms attached to the methyl group, for hydrogen deuteride is formed by the irradiation of CH_3COOD in D_2O (164). Succinic acid is the principal organic product in the radiolysis of air-free acetic acid solutions (164, 328, 341, 342). Hydrogen atoms and hydroxyl radicals both react preferentially with the hydrogen atom on the methyl group:

$$H + CH_3COOH \rightarrow CH_2COOH + H_2 \tag{169}$$

$$OH + CH_3COOH \rightarrow CH_2COOH + H_2O \tag{170}$$

$$2CH_2COOH \rightarrow COOHCH_2CH_2COOH. \tag{171}$$

These products or radicals undergo subsequent reactions with hydrogen peroxide. This is suggested by low hydrogen peroxide yield of 0.38 since $g(H_2O_2)$ is 1.0 or greater for 35-Mev helium ions.

Glyoxylic and glycolic acids replace succinic acid as the chief products in oxygenated solutions. The reactions appear to be

$$CH_2COOH + O_2 \rightarrow O_2CH_2COOH \tag{247}$$

$$2O_2CH_2COOH \rightarrow 2OCH_2COOH + O_2 \tag{248}$$

followed by disproportionation of the last radical to give glyoxylic and glycolic acids:

$$2OCH_2COOH \rightarrow CH_2OHCOOH + CHOCOOH. \tag{249}$$

3. MISCELLANEOUS ACIDS

Radiolysis of lactic acid forms pyruvic acid with a yield of 0.7 in air-free solutions and one of 3.0 in oxygen-saturated solutions (343). Acetaldehyde is a minor product.

Solutions of α-hydroxy acids form carbon dioxide as an initial product of the radiolysis (Table XIX). Therefore attack by the radicals again must be on the hydrogen atom or hydroxyl group attached to the α-carbon atom. In general, the higher the state of oxidation of the acid, the greater is $G(CO_2)$. Acids having a methylene carbon atom alpha to the carboxyl group do not liberate carbon dioxide upon irradiation (Table XIX).

Aqueous benzoic acid undergoes a complex radiolysis. The principal products are the simple hydroxylation isomers, o-, m-, and p-hydroxybenzoic acid; they are formed in the ratio 5:2:10, respectively (344, 345). These hydroxylation products are observed in the irradiation of many aromatic compounds in aqueous solution. Benzoic acid also forms benzene (by decarboxylation), benzyl alcohol, benzaldehyde, phenol, diphenyl, and a number of hydroxyphenylbenzoic acids.

H. NITROGEN COMPOUNDS

1. ALIPHATIC AMINES

Aliphatic amines lose the amine group on irradiation in oxygenated solution. Above pH 7, oximes and nitroparaffins are also formed from primary and secondary amines (346).

Acetaldehyde is the main product of the radiolysis of ethylamine, diethylamine, and triethylamine. Attack by radicals formed in the water removes the amino group and in basic solution the presence of oxygen gives a high yield of acetaldehyde (3.2 at pH 11 to 12, but only 0.77 at pH 2 to 3)

The oximes and nitroparaffins result from radical attack at a hydrogen atom bound to the nitrogen atom:

TABLE XIX

GAS YIELDS IN THE X-RAY^a RADIOLYSIS OF ORGANIC ACIDS
IN DILUTE AQUEOUS SOLUTION (328)

Acid	Structure	$G(H_2)$	$G(CO_2)$
Formic	HCOOH	3.3	3.3
Acetic	CH$_3$COOH	2.7	0.0
$\left\{ \begin{array}{l} \text{Propionic-Caproic} \end{array} \right.$	$C_nH_{2n+1}COOH$ $\left. \begin{array}{l} \\ n = 2, 3, 4, \text{ or } 5 \end{array} \right\}$	2.7	0.0
Oxalic	COOHCOOH	0.6	6.4
Malonic	COOHCH$_2$COOH	2.6	0.0
Succinic	COOH(CH$_2$)$_2$COOH	2.6	0.0
Lactic	CH$_3$CHOHCOOH	3.8	0.43
α-Hydroxyisobutyric	(CH$_3$)$_2$COHCOOH	1.2	0.86
Tartaric	COOH(CHOH)$_2$COOH	2.7	1.3

^{a} 110 kv; $\lambda_{eff} = 0.35$ A.

$$RCH_2NH_2 + OH \rightarrow RCH_2NH + H_2O \tag{250}$$

$$RCH_2NH + O_2 \rightarrow RCH_2NHO_2 . \tag{251}$$

This radical may then be oxidized to the nitroparaffin or reduced to the oxime (346).

2. AMINO ACIDS

Deamination dominates the radiolysis of aqueous solutions of the simple amino acids, giving ammonia, hydrogen, and the corresponding oxy-acid:

$$RCHNH_2COOH + H_2O \rightarrow RCOCOOH + H_2 + NH_3 . \tag{252}$$

Table XX presents a list of products and their yields for glycine and alanine (347, 349–354). Data in this table show that for glycine the presence of oxygen reduces $G(H_2)$ and increases the amount of aldehyde and hydrogen peroxide, but it does not change $G(NH_3)$. Consequently, both oxidative and reductive cleavage of the amino group takes place in the glycine molecule. Methylamine, formic acid and formaldehyde are formed from the —CH$_2$— carbon atom, whereas carbon dioxide is produced from the carboxyl carbon atom (347).

Since the glycine radiolysis is very complex we shall indicate only the principal radical reactions that account for the products. They are:

$$H + NH_2CH_2COOH \rightarrow H_2 + NH_2CHCOOH \tag{253}$$

$$H + NH_2CH_2COOH \rightarrow NH_3 + CH_2COOH \tag{254}$$

$$OH + NH_2CH_2COOH \rightarrow H_2O + NH_2CHCOOH \tag{255}$$

$$CH_2COOH + NH_2CH_2COOH \rightarrow CH_3COOH + NH_2CHCOOH \tag{256}$$

$$2NH_2CHCOOH \rightarrow NH=CHCOOH + NH_2CH_2COOH \tag{257}$$

$$NH=CHCOOH + H_2O \rightarrow NH_3 + CHOCOOH . \tag{258}$$

TABLE XX

INITIAL YIELDS IN RADIOLYSIS OF AQUEOUS AMINO ACIDS[a, b]

		G	
Amino Acid	Product	O_2-absent	O_2-present (Saturated Solution)
1 M Glycine	H_2	2.02	0.45
	CO_2	0.90	
	NH_3	3.97	4.01
	CH_3NH_2	2.10	
	CH_3COOH + combined CH_2COOH groups	~1.4	0.0
	HCOOH	0.085	
	HCOCOOH	2.10	4.5
	HCHO	0.53	
	H_2O_2	0.0	3.4
1 M Alanine	H_2	1.10	
	CO_2	0.59	
	NH_3	4.48	
	CH_3CHO	0.59	
	$CH_3COCOOH$	1.92	
	CH_3CH_2COOH	1.04	
	$CH_3CH_2NH_2$	0.17	

[a] See References 347–349.

[b] 50-kv X-rays.

Hydrogen, acetic acid, and ammonia result from these radical reactions while ammonia and glyoxylic acid result from the hydrolysis of the iminoacetic acid. Hydrogen peroxide is of course formed with a yield $g(H_2O_2)$ in the water, but it is not found in irradiated air-free glycine solutions; this suggests that the following radical-hydrogen peroxide reaction occurs:

$$NH_2CHCOOH + H_2O_2 \rightarrow NH{=}CHCOOH + H_2O + OH. \qquad (259)$$

It would be followed by hydrolysis of the iminoacetic acid as written above. According to this mechanism, ammonia is formed by reaction of both hydrogen and hydroxyl radicals with glycine molecules. With radical-radical recombination reaction 257 to give iminoacetic acid,

$$G(NH_3) = \tfrac{1}{2}[g(H) + g(OH)].$$

Ammonia is also derived from 259 followed by 258 in an amount $g(H_2O_2)$. But in view of 254, 255, and 257 ammonia is produced in yield greater than

$$G(NH_3) = \tfrac{1}{2}[g(H) + g(OH)] + g(H_2O_2) \qquad (260)$$

by the extent to which ammonia is formed in 254. It is not possible to compare experimental with expected yields, since the basic radical yields are not well established in 1 M glycine for 50-kv X-rays.

It may be noted that some of the same steps undoubtedly participate in the radiolysis of solid glycine (cf. Section III.E.2).

Radical-radical reactions incorporating amino nitrogen in the products must also occur. For example, the reactions

$$CH_2COOH + NH_2CHCOOH \rightarrow COOHCH_2CH(NH_2)COOH \tag{261}$$

$$2NH_2CHCOOH \rightarrow COOHCH(NH_2)CH(NH_2)COOH \tag{262}$$

account for the aspartic and diaminosuccinic acids observed (349).

The presence of oxygen does not alter $G(NH_3)$, but it lowers $G(H_2)$ to a value coincident with $g(H_2)$ (347). Consequently hydrogen atoms do not abstract hydrogen from the glycine molecule. Instead,

$$H + O_2 \rightarrow HO_2 \tag{42}$$

$$HO_2 + HO_2 \rightarrow H_2O_2 + O_2 \tag{36}$$

$$NH_2CHCOOH + O_2 \rightarrow NH{=}CHCOOH + HO_2 . \tag{263}$$

In the hydrolysis of $NH{=}CHCOOH$ a single molecule of ammonia is produced. And since each hydroxyl group produced one glycyl radical by 255, we expect that $G(NH_3) = g(OH) + g(H_2O_2)$. The yield close to $g(OH) + g(H_2O_2)$ for a 1.0 M solution is therefore explained.

The yield of ammonia from irradiated 0.1 M alanine solutions has a maxima at pH 3 and 9 (cf. Fig. 20). Ease of removal of ammonia appears to be related to the concentration of the zwitterion. At the isoelectric point there is a pronounced minimum in $G(NH_3)$, whereas maximum yields are obtained at pH near either pK-value of the zwitterion:

$$CH_3CH(NH_3)^+COO^- + H^+ \rightleftharpoons CH_3CH(NH_3)^+COOH \qquad (pK = 2.35) \tag{264}$$

$$CH_3CH(NH_3)^+COO^- + OH^- \rightleftharpoons CH_3CH(NH_2)COO^- + H_2O \qquad (pK = 9.87). \tag{265}$$

The decrease in yield at very high pH may be due to the sharp decrease in $g(H)$, discussed previously.

Aromatic amino acids are deaminated and also undergo hydroxyl-radical substitution in the aromatic ring without deamination (356, 357). β-Phenylalanine irradiated in aerated solutions produces o-, m-, and p-tyrosine, and phenylpyruvic acid:

$$\tag{266}$$

as well as $C_6H_5CH_2COCOOH$ and $C_6H_5CH_2CHO$.

The low values of $G(NH_3)$ of about 0.3 indicate that the aromatic ring

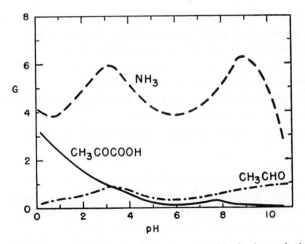

FIG. 20. Yields in radiolysis of oxygen-free 0.1 M alanine solution. (50-kev X-rays; constant dose of 1.5×10^{22} ev/liter (355)).

of β-phenylalanine is readily attacked by hydrogen and hydroxyl free radicals (356).

I. HALOGEN COMPOUNDS

Chlorinated aliphatic hydrocarbons produce hydrochloric acid on irradiation in aqueous solution (358–362). In air-free solutions of chloroform, $G(HCl)$ depends on the chloroform concentration, reaching a yield of 6.3 at 0.07 M chloroform (362). Under these conditions $G(CO_2)$ is 0.4 and $G(H_2O_2)$ is 1.22, showing that hydrogen peroxide does not enter into these reactions, the first steps in the mechanism are

$$CHCl_3 + H \rightarrow CHCl_2 + HCl \qquad (267)$$

$$CHCl_3 + OH \rightarrow H_2O + CCl_3 , \qquad (268)$$

and these radicals may then undergo reactions with each other. Hydroxyl radicals from the Fe^{++}–H_2O_2 reaction remove the H atom from $CHCl_3$ but they do not react with CCl_4 . Therefore reaction 268 seems likely. Also reaction of CCl_3 with a hydroxyl radical can produce HCl and carbon dioxide:

$$CCl_3 + OH \rightarrow CCl_3OH \rightarrow COCl_2 + HCl \qquad (269)$$

$$COCl_2 + H_2O \rightarrow CO_2 + 2HCl. \qquad (270)$$

Since $G(H_2O_2) > g(H_2O_2)$, hydrogen peroxide must be produced, probably as a hydrolysis product. Hypochlorous acid may be formed by reaction

$$OH + Cl^- \rightarrow OH^- + Cl \qquad (271)$$

followed by

$$OH + Cl \rightarrow HOCl. \qquad (272)$$

Its subsequent hydrolysis produces hydrogen peroxide.

Yields of hydrochloric acid and carbon dioxide are greater in aerated solutions. In the 0.07 M chloroform-air system, $G(HCl)$ is 26.6, $G(H_2O_2)$ is 2.04, and $G(CO_2)$ is 8.4. $G(HCl)$ is independent of oxygen concentration from 0.065 to 1.3 mM oxygen. Thus we have a chain reaction producing hydrochloric acid and carbon dioxide. A proposed mechanism is (362):

$$CCl_3 + O_2 \rightarrow CCl_3O_2 \qquad (273)$$

$$CCl_3O_2 \rightarrow COCl_2 + ClO \qquad (274)$$

$$ClO + CHCl_3 \rightarrow COCl_2 + HCl + Cl \qquad (275)$$

$$Cl + CHCl_3 \rightarrow HCl + CCl_3 . \qquad (276)$$

The evidence is conflicting but it is reported that $G(HCl)$ depends on $I^{-1/2}$, which would show that radical-radical (probably of the CCl_3O_2 radical) termination occurs (358). Carbon dioxide and hydrochloric acid are formed by the hydrolysis of phosgene as is explained above.

Aqueous chloral hydrate, $CCl_3CH(OH)_2$, decomposes by a chain mechanism, liberating hydrochloric acid. $G(HCl)$ reaches values as high as 600 at a dose rate of 6×10^{19} ev/liter hour. At this dose rate the average chain lifetime is about 0.1 second. $G(HCl)$ is decreased by a factor of 5 by the removal of oxygen (363, 364).

The chief goal of these studies was to test the chloral hydrate–water system as a potential sensitive dosimeter, but little is known about the mechanism. Photochemical studies of the chlorine atom reaction with chloral (CCl_3CHO) have shown that the over-all reaction is

$$CCl_3CHO + Cl \rightarrow CCl_4 + CO + HCl, \qquad (277)$$

and that the chain-propagating radical is CCl_3CO (365).

Irradiation of aqueous chlorobenzene (0.008 M forms hydrochloric acid, phenol, diphenyl, and o-, m-, and p-chlorophenol. Chlorine removal is independent of pH whereas the introduction of the hydroxyl group is pH dependent. The three chlorophenols are formed in approximately equal amounts at pH 2 and 12, but the p-isomer comprises 50 to 60 % of the total at pH 6. Proposed steps in the mechanism are (366)

$$C_6H_5Cl + H \rightarrow C_6H_5 + HCl \qquad (278)$$

$$C_6H_5 + OH \rightarrow C_6H_5OH \qquad (279)$$

$$2C_6H_5 \rightarrow C_6H_5C_6H_5 \qquad (201)$$

$$C_6H_5Cl + OH \rightarrow C_6H_4Cl + H_2O \tag{280}$$

$$C_6H_4Cl + OH \rightarrow C_6H_4ClOH. \tag{281}$$

If oxygen is present dehydrochlorination increases. The intermediate organic radicals react with oxygen by a reaction capable of removing chlorine as hypochlorous acid. The following reaction is proposed (366)

$$C_6H_5Cl + OH \rightarrow C_6H_5 + HOCl, \tag{282}$$

although OH does not remove Cl from $CHCl_3$. The chlorine atom has an orienting effect on entering hydroxyl radicals similar to that of the nitro and carboxyl groups in these free-radical reactions.

J. Thiols and Disulfides

Ionizing radiations oxidize organic thiols to the corresponding disulfides (367–372). The general stoichiometric reaction is

$$2RSH \rightarrow RSSR + H_2 \tag{283}$$

For cysteine, $G(-\text{cysteine})$ is 74 in aerated solutions, but it drops to 9 in the absence of dissolved oxygen (372). Substantially all of the cysteine oxidized appears as the disulfide, cystine (370, 371). The reaction is

$$2\ COOHCH(NH_2)CH_2SH \rightarrow$$
$$COOHCH(NH_2)CH_2SSCH_2CH(NH_2)COOH + H_2 . \tag{284}$$

Such uncomplicated oxidation shows that the sulfhydryl group is readily attacked by the free radicals, but primary attack need not be on this group. Radical transfer may occur by reactions such as

$$COOHCH(NH_2)CH_2SH + COOHCH(NH_2)CH_2SH \rightarrow$$
$$COOHCH(NH_2)CH_2SH + COOHCH(NH_2)CH_2S. \tag{285}$$

Some hydrogen peroxide is produced in air-free cysteine irradiations. Apparently not all cysteine radicals react with hydrogen peroxide in the absence of oxygen. However, quantitative data are lacking on this point. Every hydrogen and hydroxyl radical must be effective in oxidizing cysteine. Thus we have

$$RSH + H \rightarrow RS + H_2 \tag{286}$$

$$RSH + OH \rightarrow RS + H_2O \tag{287}$$

and $G(-RSH)$ should be equal to $g(H) + g(OH)$, or 6.3. However, if hydrogen peroxide is effective, the $G(-RSH)$ may be increased to about 8.0 since two cysteine molecules may be oxidized by each molecule of hydrogen peroxide. Therefore the air-free radiolysis is not a chain reaction.

The yield in air-saturated solutions, $G(-RSH) = 74$ shows the action of a chain reaction. This probably proceeds via the hydroperoxy free radical

$$RSH + HO_2 \rightarrow RS + H_2O_2 \tag{288}$$

$$RS + O_2 \rightarrow RSO_2 \tag{289}$$

$$RSO_2 + RSH \rightarrow RSSR + HO_2. \tag{290}$$

Cystine loses sulfur in the form of hydrogen sulfide. During the initial stages of cysteine irradiations, quantitative conversion to cystine occurs, but on prolonged irradiation there is an appreciable radical attack on cystine releasing hydrogen sulfide (373). The yield of hydrogen sulfide increases sharply at pH 8.

Other thiols—including glutathione; 2,3-dimercaptopropanol; propane-1,3-dithiol; and N-phenylaminopropane dithiol—undergo similar oxidation to the corresponding disulfides (367).

Much remains to be learned about the radiation chemistry of thiols, disulfides, and more complex organic compounds before their mechanisms can be understood. However, the fact of the simple oxidation of a single sensitive group such as SH in a complex molecule affords hope of progress in the understanding of these reactions. It is possible that the radical transfer reaction depicted in 285 from an intermediate specie (produced by the very reactive H and OH radicals) to a free radical specie of lower reactivity is a very general principle simplifying the radiation chemistry of complex organic compounds.

VII. References

1. Warburg, E., *Jahrb. Radioakt. u. Elektronik* **6,** 181 (1909).
2. Lind, S. C., "The Chemical Effects of Alpha Particles and Electrons." Chemical Catalog Company, New York, 1st ed., 1921; 2nd ed., 1928.
3. Mund, W., "L'action chimique des rayons alpha en phase gazeuse." Hermann, Paris, 1935.
4. Mund, W., Chapter I in ref. 6.
5. Haissinsky, M. (ed.), "Actions chimiques et biologiques des radiations," Vol. 1. Masson, Paris, 1955. Chapter I (pp. 1–91): Gray, L. H., "Aspects physiques de la radiobiologie." Chapter II (pp. 93–204): Lefort, M., "Chimie des radiations des solutions aqueuses." Chapter III (pp. 205–243): Dale, W. M., "Modern Trends in Radiation Biochemistry."
6. Haissinsky, M. (ed.), "Actions chimiques et biologiques des radiations," Vol. 2. Masson, Paris, 1956. Chapter I (pp. 1–64): Mund, W., "Les effets chimiques produits par les rayons ionisants en phase gazeuse." Chapter II (pp. 65–143): Ageno, M., "Phénomènes de luminescence provoqués par des rayonnements de grande énergie." Chapter III (pp. 145–211): Miller, N., "Introduction à la dosimétrie des radiations."
7. Haissinsky, M. (ed.), "Actions chimiques et biologiques des radiations," Vol. 3. Masson, Paris, 1958. Chapter I (pp. 1–61): Burton, M., "Radiolyse de liquides organiques." Chapter II (pp. 63–140): Chapiro, A., and Magat, M., "Poly-

mérisations amorcées par les radiations ionisantes." Chapter III (pp. 141–211):
Charlesby, A., "Effets des rayonnements de grande énergie sur les polymères."

8. Haissinsky, M., "La chimie nucléaire et ses applications." Masson, Paris, 1957.
9. Burton, M., *Ann. Rev. Phys. Chem.* **1,** 113 (1950).
10. Dainton, F. S., and Collinson, E., *Ann. Rev. Phys. Chem.* **2,** 99 (1951).
11. Allen, A. O., *Ann. Rev. Phys. Chem.* **3,** 57 (1952).
12. Weiss, J., *Ann. Rev. Phys. Chem.* **4,** 143 (1953).
13. Hart, E. J., *Ann. Rev. Phys. Chem.* **5,** 139 (1954).
14. Willard, J. E., *Ann. Rev. Phys. Chem.* **6,** 141 (1955).
15. Hochanadel, C. J., and Lind, S. C., *Ann. Rev. Phys. Chem.* **7,** 83 (1956).
16. Garrison, W. M., *Ann. Rev. Phys. Chem.* **8,** 129 (1957).
17. Lefort, M., *Ann. Rev. Phys. Chem.* **9,** 123 (1958).
18. Magee, J. L., *Ann. Rev. Nuclear Sci.* **3,** 171 (1953).
19. Dainton, F. S., *Ann. Rev. Nuclear Sci.* **5,** 213 (1955).
20. Lea, D. E., "Actions of Radiations on Living Cells," Chapter II. Cambridge
Univ. Press, London and New York, 1946.
21. Bacq, Z. M., and Alexander, P., "Fundamentals of Radiobiology," Chapters
1–3. Butterworths, London, 1955.
22. Glockler, G., and Lind, S. C., "The Electrochemistry of Gases and Other Di-
electrics." Wiley, New York, 1939.
23. Massey, H. S. W., and Burhop, E. H. S., "Electronic and Ionic Impact Phenomena." Clarendon, Oxford, 1952.
24. Platzman, R. L., *in* "Radiation Biology and Medicine" (W. Claus, ed.), Chapter
2. Addison-Wesley, Reading, Mass., 1958.
25. Fano, U., *in* "Symposium on Radiobiology" (J. J. Nickson, ed.), Chapter 2.
Wiley, New York, 1952.
26. Platzman, R. L., *in* "Symposium on Radiobiology" (J. J. Nickson, ed.), Chapter 7. Wiley, New York, 1952.
27. Dienes, G. J., and Vineyard, G. H., "Radiation Effects in Solids." Interscience,
New York, 1957.
28. Spencer, L. V., and Fano, U., *Phys. Rev.* **93,** 1172 (1954).
29. McGinnies, R. T., *Natl. Bur. Standards (U.S.) Circ.* **597** (1959).
30. Platzman, R. L., *Radiation Research* **2,** 1 (1955).
31. Magee, J. L., and Burton, M., *J. Am. Chem. Soc.* **72,** 1965 (1950).
32. Hurst, G. S., and Bortner, T. E., *Radiation Research Suppl.* **1,** 547 (1959).
33. Carter, R. J., Hamill, W. H., and Williams, R. R. Jr., *J. Am. Chem. Soc.* **77,**
6457 (1955).
34. Kasha, M., *Discussions Faraday Soc.* **No. 9,** 14 (1950).
35. Sponer, H., *Radiation Research Suppl.* **1,** 558 (1959).
36. Reid, C., *Quart. Rev. Chem. Soc.* **12,** 205 (1958).
37. Field, F. H., and Franklin, J. L., "Electron Impact Phenomena." Academic
Press, New York, 1957.
38. Mohler, F. L., Dibeler, V. H., and Reese, R. M., *J. Chem. Phys.* **22,** 394 (1954).
39. Rylander, P. N., Meyerson, S., and Grubb, H. M., *J. Am. Chem. Soc.* **79,** 842
(1957).
40. Krauss, M., Wahrhaftig, A. L., and Eyring, H., *Ann. Rev. Nuclear Sci.* **5,** 241
(1955).
41. Lumry, R., and Eyring, H., *in* "Radiation Biology" (A. Hollaender, ed.), Vol.
III, Chapter 1. McGraw-Hill, New York, 1956.
42. Weissman, S. I., *J. Chem. Phys.* **10,** 214 (1942).
43. Franck, J., and Livingston, R., *Revs. Modern Phys.* **21,** 505 (1949).

44. Vladimirov, I. A., and Konev, S. V., *Biophysics* **2**, 1 (1957).
45. Tal'roze, V. L., and Frankevitch, E. L., *Trudy Pervogo Vsesoyuz. Soveshchaniya po Radiatsion. Khim. (Akad. Nauk S.S.S.R., Otdel Khim. Nauk), Moscow, 1957* p. 13. (English transl., *Proc. 1st All-Union Conf. on Radiation Chem., Moscow, 1957*, p. 11, Consultants Bureau, New York, 1959.)
46. Stevenson, D. P., *J. Phys. Chem.* **61**, 1453 (1957).
47. Eyring, H., Hirschfelder, J. O., and Taylor, H. S., *J. Chem. Phys.* **4**, 479 (1936).
48. Massey, H. S. W., *Advances in Phys.* **1**, 395 (1952).
49. Varley, J. H. O., *Proc. 1st Intern. Conf. Peaceful Uses Atomic Energy, Geneva, 1955* **7**, 642 (1956).
50. Livingston, R., and Zeldes, H., "The Effects of Gamma Irradiation on Single Crystals of Calcium Hydroxide." Paper presented at the Informal Discussion of the Faraday Society, Sheffield, England (September, 1958).
51. Ramsay, D. A., *Ann. N. Y. Acad. Sci.* **67**, 485 (1957).
52. Norman, I., and Porter, G., *Proc. Roy. Soc.* **A230**, 399 (1955).
53. Gordy, W., *in* "Handbuch der Physik," Vol. 28, p. 1. Springer-Verlag, Berlin 1957.
54. Livingston, R., Zeldes, H., and Taylor, E. H., *Discussions Faraday Soc.* **No. 19**, 166 (1955).
55. Gordy, W., *in* "Symposium on Information Theory in Biology" (H. P. Yockey, ed.), p. 241. Pergamon, London, 1958.
56. Livingston, R., *Radiation Research Suppl.* **1**, 463 (1959).
57. Lea, D. E., *Brit. J. Radiol. Suppl.* **1**, 59 (1947).
58. Samuel, A. H., and Magee, J. L., *J. Chem. Phys.* **21**, 1080 (1953).
59. Fricke, H., *Ann. N. Y. Acad. Sci.* **59**, 567 (1955).
60. Magee, J. L., *J. chim. phys.* **52**, 528 (1955).
61. Schwarz, H. A., *J. Am. Chem. Soc.* **77**, 4960 (1955).
62. Ganguly, A. K., and Magee, J. L., *J. Chem. Phys.* **25**, 129 (1956).
63. Flanders, D. A., and Fricke, H., *J. Chem. Phys.* **28**, 1126 (1958).
64. Monchick, L., Magee, J. L., and Samuel, A. H., *J. Chem. Phys.* **26**, 935 (1957).
65. Dyne, P. J., and Kennedy, J. M., *Can. J. Chem.* **36**, 1518 (1958).
66. Platzman, R. L., *Radiation Research* **3**, 340 (1955). (Also forthcoming, more detailed publication.)
67. Brattain, K. G., *J. Phys. Chem.* **42**, 617 (1938).
68. Günther, P., and Leichter, H., *Z. physik. Chem. (Leipzig)* **B34**, 443 (1936).
69. Zubler, E. G., Hamill, W. H., and Williams, R. R. Jr., *J. Chem. Phys.* **23**, 1263 (1955).
70. Lind, S. C., and Livingston, R., *J. Am. Chem. Soc.* **58**, 612 (1936).
71. Schwarz, H. A., Williams, R. R., Jr., and Hamill, W. H., *J. Am. Chem. Soc.* **74**, 6007 (1952).
72. Ogg, E. F., *J. Phys. Chem.* **43**, 399 (1939).
73. Eyring, H., Hirschfelder, J. O., and Taylor, H. S., *J. Chem. Phys.* **4**, 570 (1936).
74. Schissler, D. O., and Stevenson, D. P., *J. Chem. Phys.* **24**, 926 (1956).
75. Bates, D. R., *in* "The Earth As a Planet" (G. P. Kuiper, ed.), Chapter 12. Univ. of Chicago Press, Chicago, 1954.
76. Lind, S. C., and Bardwell, D. C., *J. Am. Chem. Soc.* **51**, 2751 (1929).
77. Busse, W. F., and Daniels, F., *J. Am. Chem. Soc.* **50**, 3271 (1928).
78. Capron, P. C., *Ann. soc. sci. Bruxelles* **55B**, 222 (1935).
79. Dorfman, L. M., and Shipko, F. J., *J. Phys. Chem.* **59**, 1110 (1955).
80. Mund, W., Huyskens, P., and Lories, R., *J. chim. phys.* **48**, 202 (1951).
81. Thompson, S. O., and Schaeffer, O. A., *J. Am. Chem. Soc.* **80**, 553 (1958).

82. Mund, W., and Van Tiggelen, A., *Bull. soc. chim. Belg.* **46**, 129 (1937).
83. Hirschfelder, J. O., and Taylor, H. S., *J. Chem. Phys.* **6**, 783 (1938).
84. Porter, F., Bardwell, D. C., and Lind, S. C., *J. Am. Chem. Soc.* **48**, 2603 (1926).
85. Götzky, S., and Günther, P., *Z. physik. Chem. (Leipzig)* **B26**, 373 (1934).
86. Harteck, P., and Dondes, S., *J. Chem. Phys.* **26**, 1727 (1957).
87. Lind, S. C., and Bardwell, D. C., *J. Am. Chem. Soc.* **47**, 2675 (1925).
88. Harteck, P., and Dondes, S., *J. Chem. Phys.* **23**, 902 (1955).
89. Dorfman, L. M., and Hemmer, B. A., *J. Chem. Phys.* **22**, 1555 (1954).
90. Schiflett, C. H., and Lind, S. C., *J. Phys. Chem.* **38**, 327 (1934).
91. Harteck, P., and Dondes, S., *Nucleonics* **14**, No. 7, 22 (1956).
92. Pshezhetsky, S. Y., and Dmitriev, M. T., *Soviet J. Atomic Energy* **3**, 1189 (1957).
93. Jesse, W. P., and Sadauskis, J., *Phys. Rev.* **107**, 766 (1957).
94. Gedye, G. R., *J. Chem. Soc.* **1931**, 3016.
95. Harteck, P., and Dondes, S., *Nucleonics* **14**, No. 3, 66 (1956).
96. Lind, S. C., Bardwell, D. C., and Perry, J. H., *J. Am. Chem. Soc.* **48**, 1556 (1926).
97. Firestone, R. F., *J. Am. Chem. Soc.* **79**, 5593 (1957).
98. Duane, W., and Scheuer, O., *Radium* **10**, 33 (1913).
99. Shiflett, C. H., Steidlitz, M. E., Rosen, F. D., and Davis, W. Jr., *J. Inorg. & Nuclear Chem.* **7**, 210 (1958).
100. Collinson, E., and Swallow, A. J., *Chem. Revs.* **56**, 471 (1956).
101. Lampe, F. W., *J. Am. Chem. Soc.* **79**, 1055 (1957).
102. Lind, S. C., and Bardwell, D. C., *J. Am. Chem. Soc.* **48**, 2335 (1926).
103. Honig, R. E., and Sheppard, C. W., *J. Phys. Chem.* **50**, 119 (1946).
104. Lampe, F. W., *J. Phys. Chem.* **61**, 1015 (1957).
105. Henri, V. P., Maxwell, C. R., White, W. C., and Peterson, D. C., *J. Phys. Chem.* **56**, 153 (1952).
106. Yang, K., and Manno, P. J., *J. Phys. Chem.* **63**, 752 (1959).
107. Heisig, G. B., *J. Am. Chem. Soc.* **54**, 2328 (1932).
108. Heisig, G. B., *J. Am. Chem. Soc.* **53**, 3245 (1931).
109. Dorfman, L. M., and Shipko, F. J., *J. Am. Chem. Soc.* **77**, 4723 (1955).
110. Rosenblum, C., *J. Phys. Chem.* **52**, 474 (1948).
111. Lind, S. C., and Bardwell, D. C., *J. Am. Chem. Soc.* **48**, 1575 (1926).
112. Manion, J. P., and Burton, M., *J. Phys. Chem.* **56**, 560 (1952).
113. Meisels, G. G., Hamill, W. H., and Williams, R. R. Jr., *J. Phys. Chem.* **61**, 1456 (1957).
114. Tal'roze, V. L., and Lyubimova, A. K., *Doklady Akad. Nauk S.S.S.R.* **86**, 909 (1952).
115. Dorfman, L. M., *J. Phys. Chem.* **62**, 29 (1958).
116. Lind, S. C., *Radium* **8**, 289 (1911).
117. Pshezhetsky, S. Y., Myasnikov, I. Y., and Buneev, N. A., *in* "Sbornik Rabot po Radiatsionnoi Khimii," p. 133. Akad. Nauk S.S.S.R., Moscow, 1955 (English transl., "Symposium on Radiation Chemistry," p. 111).
118. Hochanadel, C., *J. Am. Chem. Soc.* **76**, 2675 (1954).
119. Hochanadel, C. J., Ghormley, J. A., and Sworski, T. J., *J. Am. Chem. Soc.* **77**, 3215 (1955).
120. Tolbert, B. M., and Lemmon, R. M., *Radiation Research* **3**, 52 (1955).
121. Dewhurst, H. A., *J. Phys. Chem.* **61**, 1466 (1957).
122. Hamashima, M., Reddy, M. P., and Burton, M., *J. Phys. Chem.* **62**, 246 (1958).
123. Dewhurst, H. A., *J. Phys. Chem.* **62**, 15 (1958).

124. Schoepfle, C. S., and Fellows, C. H., *Ind. Eng. Chem.* **23**, 1396 (1931).
125. Brodsky, A. M., Kolbanovsky, Yu. A., Filatova, E. D., and Tchernysheva, A. S., *Intern. J. Appl. Radiation and Isotopes* **5**, 57 (1959).
126. Polak, L. S., Topchiev, A. V., and Cherniak, N. Ya., *Doklady Akad. Nauk S.S.S.R.* **119**, 307 (1958).
127. Schuler, R. H., and Allen, A. O., *J. Am. Chem. Soc.* **77**, 507 (1955).
128. Dewhurst, H. A., *J. Chem. Phys.* **24**, 1254 (1956).
129. Shida, S., Yamazaki, H., and Arai, S., *J. Chem. Phys.* **29**, 245 (1958).
130. Gordon, S., and Burton, M., *Discussions Faraday Soc.* **No. 12**, 88 (1952).
131. Gordon, S., Van Dyken, A. R., and Doumani, T. F., *J. Phys. Chem.* **62**, 20 (1958).
132. Patrick, W. N., and Burton, M., *J. Am. Chem. Soc.* **76**, 2626 (1954).
133. Colichman, E. L., and Gercke, R. H. J., *Nucleonics* **14**, No. 7, 50 (1956).
134. Colichman, E. L., and Fish, R. F., *Nucleonics* **15**, No. 2, 72 (1957).
135. Adams, G. E., and Baxendale, J. H., *J. Am. Chem. Soc.* **80**, 4215 (1958).
136. McDonell, W. R., and Gordon, S., *J. Chem. Phys.* **23**, 208 (1955).
137. McDonell, W. R., and Newton, A. S., *J. Am. Chem. Soc.* **76**, 4651 (1954).
138. Meshitsuka, G., and Burton, M., *Radiation Research* **8**, 285 (1958).
139. Adams, G. E., Baxendale, J. H., and Sedgwick, R. D., *J. Phys. Chem.* **63**, 854 (1959).
140. Newton, A. S., and McDonell, W. R., *J. Am. Chem. Soc.* **78**, 4554 (1956).
141. Bach, N. A., and Sorokin, J. I., *in* "Sbornik Rabot po Radiatsionnoi Khimii," p. 163. Akad. Nauk. S.S.S.R., Moscow, 1955 (English transl., "Symposium on Radiation Chemistry" p. 135).
142. Newton, A. S., *J. Phys. Chem.* **61**, 1485 (1957).
143. Newton, A. S., *J. Phys. Chem.* **61**, 1490 (1957).
144. Patrick, W. N., and Burton, M., *J. Phys. Chem.* **58**, 424 (1954).
145. Ausloos, P., and Paulson, J. F., *J. Am. Chem. Soc.* **80**, 5117 (1958).
146. Smithies, D., and Hart, E. J., unpublished results.
147. Burr, J. G., *J. Phys. Chem.* **61**, 1481 (1957).
148. Bach, N. A., and Saraeva, V. V., *in* "Sbornik Rabot po Radiatsionnoi Khimii," p. 145. Akad. Nauk S.S.S.R., Moscow, 1955 (English transl., "Symposium on Radiation Chemistry", p. 175).
149. Newton, A. S., *J. Chem. Phys.* **26**, 1764 (1957).
150. Schuler, R. H., and Petry, R. C., *J. Am. Chem. Soc.* **78**, 3954 (1956).
151. Hornig, E. O., and Willard, J. E., *J. Am. Chem. Soc.* **79**, 2429 (1957).
152. Schuler, R. H., and Hamill, W. H., *J. Am. Chem. Soc.* **74**, 6171 (1952).
153. Lefort, M., Bonét-Maury, P., and Frilley, M., *Compt. rend.* **226**, 1904 (1948).
154. Zimin, A. V., and Egorova, Z. S., *in* "Sbornik Rabot po Radiatsionnoi Khimii," p. 207. Akad. Nauk S.S.S.R., Moscow, 1955 (English transl., "Symposium on Radiation Chemistry," p. 241).
155. Schulte, J. W., *J. Am. Chem. Soc.* **79**, 4643 (1957).
156. Bach, N. A., *Radiation Research Suppl.* **1**, 190 (1959).
157. Bach, N., *Proc. 1st Intern. Conf. Peaceful Uses Atomic Energy, Geneva, 1955* **7**, 538 (1956).
158. Dewhurst, H. A., and Winslow, E. H., *J. Chem. Phys.* **26**, 969 (1957).
159. Burton, M., and Patrick, W. N., *J. Phys. Chem.* **58**, 421 (1954).
160. Burton, M., Chang, J., Lipsky, S., and Reddy, M. P., *Radiation Research* **8**, 203 (1958).
161. Burton, M., and Lipsky, S., *J. Phys. Chem.* **61**, 1461 (1957).

162. Schuler, R. H., *J. Phys. Chem.* **61**, 1472 (1957).
163. Magat, M., Bouby, L., Chapiro, A., and Gislon, N., *Z. Elektrochem.* **62**, 307 (1958).
164. Garrison, W. M., Bennett, W., Cole, S., Haymond, H. R., and Weeks, B. M., *J. Am. Chem. Soc.* **77**, 2720 (1955).
165. Breger, I. A., and Burton, V. L., *J. Am. Chem. Soc.* **68**, 1639 (1946).
166. Gevantman, L. H., and Williams, R. R. Jr., *J. Phys. Chem.* **56**, 569 (1952).
167. Hanrahan, R. J., and Willard, J. E., *J. Am. Chem. Soc.* **78**, 2434 (1957).
168. Seitz, F., *Revs. Modern Phys.* **26**, 7 (1954).
169. Henderson, G. H., and Bateson, S., *Proc. Roy. Soc.* **A145**, 563 (1934).
170. Henderson, G. H., and Turnbull, L. G., *Proc. Roy. Soc.* **A145**, 582 (1934).
171. Henderson, G. H., Mushkat, C. M., and Crawford, D. P., *Proc. Roy. Soc.* **A158**, 199 (1937).
172. Castner, T. G., and Känzig, W., *J. Phys. Chem. Solids* **3**, 178 (1957).
173. Burns, W. G., and Williams, T. F., *Nature* **175**, 1043 (1955).
174. Pringsheim, P., *J. Chem. Phys.* **23**, 369 (1955).
175. Hochanadel, C. J., and Davis, T. W., *J. Chem. Phys.* **27**, 333 (1957).
176. Cunningham, J., and Heal, H. G., *Trans. Faraday Soc.* **54**, 1355 (1958).
177. Hennig, G., Lees, R., and Matheson, M. S., *J. Chem. Phys.* **21**, 664 (1953).
178. Heal, H. G., *Trans. Faraday Soc.* **53**, 210 (1957).
179. Heal, H. G., *Can. J. Chem.* **31**, 91 (1953).
180. Dole, M., Keeling, C. D., and Rose, D. G., *J. Am. Chem. Soc.* **76**, 4304 (1954).
181. Dole, M., Milner, D. C., and Williams, T. F., *J. Am. Chem. Soc.* **80**, 1580 (1958).
182. Chapiro, A., *J. chim. phys.* **52**, 246 (1955).
183. Charlesby, A., *Proc. Roy. Soc.* **A222**, 60 (1954).
184. Wall, L. A., and Brown, D. W., *J. Phys. Chem.* **61**, 129 (1957).
185. Burton, M., and Patrick, W. N., *J. Chem. Phys.* **22**, 1150 (1954).
186. Wall, L. A., and Brown, D. W., *J. Research Natl. Bur. Standards* **57**, 131 (1956).
187. Whitehead, W. L., Goodman, C., and Breger, I. A., *J. chim. phys.* **48**, 184 (1951).
188. Cauchois, Y. (ed.), "Action des rayonnements de grande énergie sur les solides." Gauthier-Villars, Paris, 1956.
189. Lintner, K., and Schmid, E., *Ergeb. exakt. Naturw.* **28**, 302 (1955).
190. Taylor, E. H., and Kohn, H. W., *J. Am. Chem. Soc.* **79**, 252 (1957).
191. Taylor, E. H., and Wethington, J. A. Jr., *J. Am. Chem. Soc.* **76**, 971 (1954).
192. Schulman, J. H., Etzel, H. W., and Allard, J. G., *J. Appl. Phys.* **28**, 792 (1957).
193. Bovey, F. A., "The Effects of Ionizing Radiation on Natural and Synthetic High Polymers." Interscience, New York, 1958.
194. Alexander, P., and Charlesby, A., *Proc. Roy. Soc.* **A230**, 136 (1955).
195. Breger, I. A., *J. Phys. Chem.* **52**, 551 (1948).
196. Dale, W. M., Davies, J. V., and Gilbert, C. W., *Biochem. J.* **45**, 93 (1949).
197. Ghosh, D. K., and Whiffen, D. H., *Mol. Phys.* **2**, 285 (1959).
198. Box, H. C., and Freund, H. G., *Nucleonics* **17**, No. 1, 66 (1959).
199. Shields, H., and Gordy, W., *J. Phys. Chem.* **62**, 789 (1958).
200. McCormick, G., and Gordy, W., *J. Phys. Chem.* **62**, 783 (1958).
201. Gordy, W., and Shields, H., *Radiation Research* **9**, 611 (1958).
202. Gordy, W., *Radiation Research Suppl.* **1**, 491 (1959).
203. Willard, J. E., *Ann. Rev. Nuclear Sci.* **3**, 193 (1953).
204. Barnes, J. W., Burgus, W. H., and Miskel, J. A., *in* "Radioactivity Applied to Chemistry" (A. C. Wahl, ed.), Chapter 8. Wiley, New York, 1951.
205. Baulch, D. L., and Duncan, J. F., *Quart. Revs. (London)* **12**, 133 (1958).

206. Riehl, N., *Atomkernenergie* **1**, 297 (1956).
207. Bohr, N., *Kgl. Danske Videnskab. Selskab, Mat.-fys. Medd.* **18**, No. 8 (1948) (cf. Section 5.4).
208. Monchick, L., Funabashi, K., and Magee, J. L., *J. Chem. Phys.* **27**, 734 (1957).
209. Szilard, L., and Chalmers, T. A., *Nature* **134**, 462 (1934).
210. McKay, H. A. C., *Progr. in Nuclear Phys.* **1**, 168 (1950).
211. Green, J. H., *Revs. Pure and Appl. Chem. (Australia)* **1**, 235 (1951).
212. Evans, J. B., and Willard, J. E., *J. Am. Chem. Soc.* **78**, 2908 (1956).
213. McCauley, C. E., Hilsdorf, G. J., Geissler, P. R., and Schuler, R. H., *J. Am. Chem. Soc.* **78**, 3246 (1956).
214. Goldhaber, S., and Willard, J. E., *J. Am. Chem. Soc.* **74**, 318 (1952).
215. Snell, A. H., and Pleasonton, F., *Phys. Rev.* **100**, 1396 (1955).
216. Pleasonton, F., and Snell, A. H., *Proc. Roy. Soc.* **A241**, 141 (1957).
217. Snell, A. H., and Pleasonton, F., *Phys. Rev.* **107**, 740 (1957).
218. Snell, A. H., and Pleasonton, F., *Phys. Rev.* **111**, 1338 (1958).
219. Wolfgang, R. L., Anderson, R. C., and Dodson, R. W., *J. Chem. Phys.* **24**, 16 (1956).
220. Wexler, S., *J. Inorg. & Nuclear Chem.* **10**, 8 (1959).
221. Snell, A. H., Pleasonton, F., and Leming, H. E., *J. Inorg. & Nuclear Chem.* **5**, 112 (1957).
222. Wexler, S., and Hess, D. C., *J. Phys. Chem.* **62**, 1382 (1958).
223. Bonhoeffer, K. F., and Harteck, P., "Grundlagen der photochemie," p. 126. Steinkopff, Dresden and Leipzig, 1933.
224. Matheson, M. S., and Smaller, B., *J. Chem. Phys.* **23**, 521 (1955).
225. Ghormley, J. A., and Allen, A. O., *Oak Ridge Natl. Lab. Rept.* **ORNL-128** (September 1948).
226. Ghormley, J. A., and Stewart, A. C., *J. Am. Chem. Soc.* **78**, 2934 (1956).
227. Grossweiner, L. I., and Matheson, M. S., *J. Chem. Phys.* **20**, 1654 (1952).
228. Grossweiner, L. I., and Matheson, M. S., *J. Chem. Phys.* **22**, 1514 (1954).
229. Ghormley, J. A., *J. Chem. Phys.* **24**, 1111 (1956).
230. Jones, W. M., *J. Chem. Phys.* **20**, 1974 (1952).
231. Geisel, F., *Ber.* **35**, 3608 (1902); **36**, 342 (1903).
232. Cameron, A. T., and Ramsey, W., *J. Chem. Soc.* **91**, 931 (1907); **92**, 966 (1908).
233. Debierne, A., *Compt. rend. acad. sci.* **148**, 703 (1909).
234. Kernbaum, M., *Compt. rend. acad. sci.* **148**, 705 (1909); **149**, 116 (1909).
235. Usher, F. L., *Jahrb. Radioakt. Elektronik* **8**, 323; *Chem. Abstr.* **6**, 322 (1912).
236. Kailan, A., *Monatsh.* **33**, 71, 1329 (1912); **34**, 1245 (1913); *Wiener Ber.* **120**(2a), 1213, 1373 (1911).
237. Fricke, H., and Petersen, B. W., *Strahlentherapie* **26**, 329 (1927).
238. Fricke, H., and Morse, S., *Phil. Mag.* [7] **7**, 129 (1929).
239. Hart, E. J., *J. Chem. Educ.* **36**, 266 (1959).
240. Weiss, J., *Nature* **153**, 748 (1944).
241. Allen. A. O., U. S. Atomic Energy Commission Rept. MDDC-363 9/16/46; "The Science and Engineering of Nuclear Power" (C. Goodman, ed.). Addison-Wesley, Reading, Mass., 1949.
242. Allen, A. O., *J. Phys. & Colloid Chem.* **52**, 479 (1948).
243. Barr, N. F., and Schuler, R. H., *Radiation Research* **7**, 302 (1957).
244. Schwarz, H. A., Private communication (1959).
245. Armstrong, D., Collinson, E., Dainton, F. S., Donaldson, D. M., Hayon, E., Miller, N., and Weiss, J., *Proc. 2nd Intern. Conf. Peaceful Uses Atomic Energy, Geneva, 1958* **29**, 80 (1959).

246. Hart, E. J., *J. Am. Chem. Soc.* **81,** 6065 (1959).
247. Hart, E. J., *J. Am. Chem. Soc.* **76,** 4198 (1954).
248. Hart, E. J., McDonell, W. R., and Gordon, S., *Proc. 1st Intern. Conf. Peaceful Uses Atomic Energy, Geneva, 1955* **7,** 593 (1956).
249. Allen, A. O., and Schwarz, H. A., *Proc. 2nd Intern. Conf. Peaceful Uses Atomic Energy, Geneva, 1958* **29,** 30 (1959).
250. McDonell, W. R., *U. S. Atomic Energy Commission Rept.* **ANL-5205** (1954, declassified 1955).
251. Gordon, S., and Hart, E. J., *Proc. 2nd Intern. Conf. Peaceful Uses Atomic Energy, Geneva, 1958* **29,** 13 (1959).
252. Friedman, H. L., and Zeltman, A. H., *J. Chem. Phys.* **28,** 878 (1958).
253. Gordon, S., and Hart, E. J., *J. Am. Chem. Soc.* **77,** 3981 (1955).
254. Hochanadel, C. J., *Proc. 1st Intern. Conf. Peaceful Uses Atomic Energy, Geneva, 1955* **7,** 521 (1956).
255. Ebert, M., *in* "Radiobiology Symposium, 1954" (Z. M. Bacq, ed.), p. 30. Academic Press, New York, 1955.
256. Dolin, P. I., *in* "Sbornik Rabot po Radiatsionnoi Khimii," p. 7. Akad. Nauk S.S.S.R., Moscow, 1955. (English transl., "Symposium on Radiation Chemistry," p. 1).
257. Fricke, H., *J. Chem. Phys.* **2,** 349 (1934).
258. Hart, E. J., Gordon, S., and Hutchison, D. A., *J. chim. phys.* **52,** 570 (1955).
259. Barr, N. F., and Allen, A. O., *J. Phys. Chem.* **63,** 928 (1959).
260. Dolin, P. I., and Ershler, B. V., *Proc. 1st Intern. Conf. Peaceful Uses Atomic Energy, Geneva, 1955* **7,** 564 (1956).
261. Dolin, P. I., *in* "Sbornik Rabot po Radiatsionnoi Khimii," p. 25. Akad. Nauk S.S.S.R., Moscow, 1955 (English transl., "Symposium on Radiation Chemistry," p. 15).
262. Fricke, H., *J. Chem. Phys.* **3,** 364 (1935).
263. Hart, E. J., and Matheson, M. S., *Discussions Faraday Soc.* **No. 12,** 169 (1952).
264. Johnson, E. R., *J. Chem. Phys.* **19,** 1204 (1951).
265. Dainton, F. S., and Rowbottom, J., *Trans. Faraday Soc.* **49,** 1160 (1953).
266. Ebert, M., and Boag, J. W., *Discussions Faraday Soc.* **No. 12,** 189 (1952).
267. Hochanadel, C. J., *J. Phys. Chem.* **56,** 587 (1952).
268. Toulis W. J., *U. S. Atomic Energy Commission Rept.* **UCRL-583** (1950).
269. Boyle, J. W., Weiner, S., and Hochandel, C. J., *J. Phys. Chem.* **63,** 892 (1959).
270. Pucheault, J., and Ferradini, C., *Proc. 2nd Intern. Conf. Peaceful Uses Atomic Energy, Geneva, 1958* **29,** 24 (1959).
271. Dewhurst, H. A., and Burton, M., *J. Am. Chem. Soc.* **77,** 5781 (1955).
272. Lefort, M., and Tarrago, X., *Compt. rend. acad. sci.* **247,** 454 (1958).
273. Hart, E. J., *J. Chem. Educ.* **34,** 586 (1957).
274. Schuler, R. H., and Allen, A. O., *J. Chem. Phys.* **24,** 56 (1956).
275. Hochanadel, C. J., and Ghormley, J. A., *J. Chem. Phys.* **21,** 880 (1953).
276. Haybittle, J. L., Sanders, R. D., and Swallow, A. J., *J. Chem. Phys.* **25,** 1213 (1956).
277. Cottin, M., and Lefort, M., *J. chim phys.* **53,** 267 (1956).
278. Miller, N., *in* "Actions chimiques et biologiques des radiations" (M. Haissinsky, ed.), Vol. 2, Chapter III. Masson, Paris, 1955.
279. McDonell, W. R., and Hart, E. J., *J. Am. Chem. Soc.* **76,** 2121 (1954).
280. Hart, E. J., Ramler, W., and Rocklin, S. R., *Radiation Research* **4,** 378 (1956).
281. Schuler, R. H., and Allen, A. O., *J. Am. Chem. Soc.* **79,** 1565 (1957).
282. Trumbore, C. N., and Hart, E. J., *J. Phys. Chem.* **63,** 867 (1959).

283. Miller, N., *Radiation Research* **9**, 633 (1958).
284. Schuler, R. H., and Barr, N., *J. Am. Chem. Soc.* **78**, 5756 (1956).
285. Ehrenberg, L., and Saeland, E., *JENER Rept.* **No. 8**, 25 pp. (1954).
286. Keene, J. P., *Radiation Research* **6**, 424 (1957).
287. Fricke, H., and Hart, E. J., *J. Chem. Phys.* **3**, 60 (1935).
288. Rothschild, W. G., and Allen, A. O., *Radiation Research* **8**, 101 (1958).
289. Weiss, J., *Nature* **165**, 728 (1950).
290. Hart, E. J., and Walsh, P. D., *Radiation Research* **1**, 342 (1954).
291. Hart, E. J., *Radiation Research* **2**, 33 (1955).
292. Donaldson, D. M., and Miller, N., *J. chim. phys.* **52**, 578 (1955).
293. Cottin, M., Haissinsky, M., and Vermeil, C., *Compt. rend. acad. sci.* **235**, 542 (1952).
294. Vermeil, C., Cottin, M., and Haissinsky, M., *J. chim. phys.* **49**, 437 (1952).
295. Vermeil, C., *J. chim. phys.* **52**, 587 (1955).
296. Vermeil, C., *Ann. chim. (Paris)* [13] **1**, 641 (1956).
297. Dewhurst, H. A., *J. Chem. Phys.* **19**, 1329 (1951).
298. Dewhurst, H. A., *Trans. Faraday Soc.* **48**, 905 (1952).
299. Hart, E. J., *J. Am. Chem. Soc.* **74**, 4174 (1952).
300. Hart, E. J., *J. Am. Chem. Soc.* **77**, 5786 (1955).
301. Baxendale, J. H., and Smithies, D., *Z. physik. Chem. (Frankfurt)* [N.F.] **7**, 242 (1956).
302. Baxendale, J. H., and Hughes, G., *Z. physik. Chem. (Frankfurt)* [N.F.] **14**, 306 (1958).
303. Baxendale, J. H., and Hughes, G., *Z. physik Chem. (Frankfurt)* [N.F.] **14**, 323 (1958).
304. Donaldson, D. M., and Miller, N., *Radiation Research* **9**, 487 (1958).
305. Sworski, T. J., *Radiation Research* **4**, 483 (1956).
306. Challenger, G. E., and Masters, B. J., *J. Am. Chem. Soc.* **77**, 1063 (1955).
307. Spencer, H. E., and Rollefson, G. K., *J. Am. Chem. Soc.* **77**, 1938 (1955).
308. Sworski, T. J., *J. Am. Chem. Soc.* **78**, 1768 (1956).
309. Sworski, T. J., *Radiation Research* **6**, 645 (1957).
310. Challenger, G. E., and Masters, B. J., *J. Am. Chem. Soc.* **78**, 3012 (1956).
311. Rigg, T., Scholes, G., and Weiss, J., *J. Chem. Soc.* **1952**, 3034.
312. Davis, T. W., Gordon, S., and Hart, E. J., *J. Am. Chem. Soc.* **80**, 4487 (1958).
313. Schwarz, H. A., Losee, J. P., and Allen, A. O., *J. Am. Chem. Soc.* **76**, 4693 (1954).
314. Sworski, T. J., *J. Am. Chem. Soc.* **76**, 4687 (1954).
315. Sworski, T. J., *Radiation Research* **2**, 26 (1955).
316. Schwarz, H. A., and Allen, A. O., *J. Am. Chem. Soc.* **77**, 1324 (1955).
317. Mahlman, H. A., and Schweitzer, G. K., *J. Inorg. & Nuclear Chem.* **5**, 213 (1958).
318. Bakh, N. A., Medvedovskiĭ, V. I., Revina, A. A., and Bityukov, V. D., *Trudy Pervogo Vsesoyuz. Soveshchaniya po Radiatsion. Khim. (Akad. Nauk S.S.S.R., Otdel Khim Nauk), Moscow, 1957* pp. 45–50 (1958) (English transl., *Proc. 1st All-Union Conf. on Radiation Chem., Moscow, 1957* p. 39, Consultants Bureau, New York, 1959).
319. Orekov, V. D., Chernova, A. I., and Proskurnin, M. A., *in* "Sbornik Rabot po Radiatsionnoi Khimii," p. 91. Akad. Nauk S.S.S.R., Moscow, 1955 (English transl., "Symposium on Radiation Chemistry," p. 75).
320. Sowden, R. G., *J. Am. Chem. Soc.* **79**, 1263 (1957).
321. Daniels, M., *133rd Meeting, Am. Chem. Soc., San Francisco, 1958* Abstr. No. 89 (1958).

322. Fricke, H., and Washburn, M., *Phys. Rev.* **40**, 1033 (1932).
323. Fricke, H., and Brownscombe, E. R., *J. Am. Chem. Soc.* **55**, 2358 (1933).
324. Lefort, M., and Lederer, M., *Compt. rend. acad. sci.* **242**, 2458 (1956).
325. Fricke, H., and Hart, E. J., *J. Chem. Phys.* **3**, 596 (1935).
326. Daniels, M., and Weiss, J., *J. Chem. Soc.* **1958**, 2467.
327. Hirschfelder, J. O., *J. Chem. Phys.* **9**, 645 (1941).
328. Fricke, H., Hart, E. J., and Smith, H. P., *J. Chem. Phys.* **6**, 229 (1938).
329. Garrison, W. M., and Rollefson, G. K., *Discussions Faraday Soc.* **No. 12**, 155 (1952).
330. Hasselstrom, T., and Henry, M. C., *Science* **123**, 1038 (1956).
331. Vermeil, C., and Cottin, M., *J. chim. phys.* **51**, 24 (1954).
332. Clay, P. G., Johnson, G. R. A., and Weiss, J., *J. Chem. Soc.* **1958**, 2175.
333. Phung, P. V., and Burton, M., *Radiation Research* **7**, 199 (1957).
334. Daniels, M., Scholes, G., and Weiss, J., *J. Chem. Soc.* **1956**, 832.
335. McDonell, W. R., *J. Chem. Phys.* **23**, 208 (1955).
336. Jayson, G. G., Weiss, J., and Scholes, G., *J. Chem. Soc.* **1957**, 1358.
337. Proskurnin, M. A., Barelko, E. V., and Abramova, L. V., *in* "Sbornik Rabot po Radiatsionnoi Khimii," p. 106. Akad. Nauk S.S.S.R., Moscow, 1955 (English transl., "Symposium on Radiation Chemistry," p. 89).
338. Hart, E. J., *J. Am. Chem. Soc.* **73**, 68 (1951).
339. Hart, E. J., *J. Phys. Chem.* **56**, 594 (1952).
340. Hart, E. J., *J. Am. Chem. Soc.* **76**, 4312 (1954).
341. Garrison, W. M., Haymond, H. R., Morrison, D. C., Weeks, B. M., and Gile-Melchert, J., *J. Am. Chem. Soc.* **75**, 2459 (1953).
342. Garrison, W. M., Haymond, H. R., and Weeks, B. M., *Radiation Research* **1**, 97 (1954).
343. Johnson, G. R. A., Scholes, G., and Weiss, J., *J. Chem. Soc.* **1953**, 3091.
344. Loebl, H., Stein, G., and Weiss, J., *J. Chem. Soc.* **1951**, 405.
345. Stein, G., and Weiss, J. *J. Chem. Soc.* **1949**, 3245.
346. Jayson, G. G., Scholes, G., and Weiss, J., *J. Chem. Soc.* **1955**, 2594.
347. Maxwell, C. R., Peterson, D. C., and Sharpless, N. E., *Radiation Research* **1**, 530 (1955).
348. Sharpless, N. E., Blair, A. E., and Maxwell, C. R., *Radiation Research* **2**, 135 (1955).
349. Weeks, B. M., *U. S. Atomic Energy Commission Rept.* **UCRL-3071** (1955).
350. Garrison, W. M., Weeks, B. M., Jayko, M., Bennett, W., Ward, J., and Cole, S., *U. S. Atomic Energy Commission Rept.* **UCRL-3386** (1956).
351. Maxwell, C. R., Peterson, D. C., and White, W. C., *Radiation Research* **2**, 431 (1955).
352. Stein, G., and Weiss, J., *J. Chem. Soc.* **1949**, 3256.
353. White, W. C., *Arch. Biochem. Biophys.* **47**, 225 (1953).
354. Williams, R. R., Jr., and Hamill, W. H., *J. Am. Chem. Soc.* **72**, 1857 (1950).
355. Sharpless, N. E., Blair, A. E., and Maxwell, C. R., *Radiation Research* **3**, 417 (1955).
356. Nosworthy, J., and Allsopp, C. B., *J. Colloid Sci.* **11**, 565 (1956).
357. Vermeil, C., and Lefort, M., *Compt. rend. acad. sci.* **244**, 889 (1957).
358. Hummel, R. W., Van Cleave, A. B., and Spinks, J. W. T., *Can. J. Chem.* **32**, 522 (1954).
359. Minder, W., Knuchel, H., and Gurtner, P., *Experientia* **4**, 219 (1948).
360. Minder, W., *Discussions Faraday Soc.* **No. 12**, 305 (1952).

361. Taplin, G. V., *in* "Radiation Dosimetry" (G. J. Hine and G. L. Brownell, eds.), Chapter 8. Academic Press, New York, 1956.

362. Teply, J., and Bednar, J., *Proc. 2nd Intern. Conf. Peaceful Uses Atomic Energy, Geneva, 1958* **29,** 71 (1959).

363. Freeman, G. R., Van Cleave, A. B., and Spinks, J. W. T., *Can. J. Chem.* **31,** 1164 (1953).

364. Freeman, G. R., Van Cleave, A. B., and Spinks, J. W. T., *Can. J. Chem.* **32,** 322 (1954).

365. Alexander, W. A., and Schumacher, H. J., *Z. physik. Chem.* (*Leipzig*) **B44,** 5 (1939).

366. Johnson, G. R. A., Stein, G., and Weiss, J., *J. Chem. Soc.* **1951,** 3275.

367. Barron, E. S. G., and Flood, V., *J. Gen. Physiol.* **33,** 229 (1950).

368. Barron, E. S. G., *Radiation Research* **1,** 109 (1954).

369. Dale, W. M., and Davies, J. V., *Biochem. J.* **48,** 129 (1951).

370. Rotheram, M., Todd, N., and Whitcher, S. L., *U. S. Atomic Energy Commission Rept.* **UCLA-119** (1951).

371. Rotheram, M., Todd, N., and Whitcher, S. L., *Naturwissenschaften* **39,** 450 (1952).

372. Swallow, A. J., *J. Chem. Soc.* **1952,** 1334.

373. Whitcher, S. L., Rotheram, M., and Todd, N. R., *Nucleonics* **11,** No. 8, 30 (1953).

CHAPTER 3

The Biochemical Lesion
in Vivo and *in Vitro*

M. G. ORD AND L. A. STOCKEN

Department of Biochemistry, University of Oxford, Oxford, England

CONTENTS

I. Introduction

A. BIOCHEMICAL SEQUELAE

For an understanding of the biochemical changes initiated in living systems by ionizing radiations, the appreciation of certain factors is essential. The physicochemical mechanism by which the energy is transferred to the affected site has been considered elsewhere; either the damage may be due to a release of ionization energy within some sensitive target molecule(s), or it may be communicated to such molecules through the intervention of free radicals. To a first approximation the mechanism by which the changes are produced is irrelevant to their analysis. A more detailed consideration of such phenomena as protection, reversibility, and recovery, however, would be facilitated by a knowledge of how the damage has been caused and how the relative contributions from the "direct" and "indirect" actions vary under different circumstances.

Far more important from the biochemical point of view, however, is the realization that the immediate damage is not a single, specific phenomenon. Radiation affects a number of different biochemical systems simultaneously and to an extent which varies independently for each system according to the dose, so that from the time of reception of the dose the interactions between the systems will be affected, not necessarily in an easily foreseeable manner. In a living organism damage produced in this way is likely to elicit compensatory physiological changes which will themselves affect the biochemistry of the cell. Superimposed on this is the possibility that some of the radiation effects may take time for development. This is well known in radiation studies *in vitro* but is difficult to distinguish *in vivo* because of the factors already discussed. There is also a further group of effects which have been recognized in animals which have survived for a considerable time after irradiation. Little work has so far been done on this aspect of the problem, although accelerated aging is established (1). Unfortunately our knowledge of biochemical changes in "normal" aging is at present rudimentary.

We therefore propose to consider the biochemical sequelae as:

1. Immediate.

2. Secondary—the early consequences of the initial damage to 1.

3. Abscopal—the reaction at a distance from the irradiated volume but within the same organism (2). These effects will be taken to include changes detectable in a tissue which was shielded during irradiation of the rest of the organism and also changes occurring, for example, in the liver as a result of damage to the remaining parts of the body.

4. Delayed—those effects which are due to X-radiation but which require time for their development—for example, the fall in viscosity of deoxyribonucleic acid which continues for up to 24 hours after exposure *in vitro*.

5. Long term—those biochemical changes which are present in animals some time after exposure—e.g., in survivors from lethal doses at times later than 30 days after irradiation.

Associated with the interpretation of the time sequence of the events after X-irradiation is the importance of the size of dose received. Dose-response curves have been determined for the viability of many systems with both single and multiple exposures. Much less information is available concerning the underlying biochemical responses, and work often has been restricted to the effects of doses which produce easily detected changes (50 to 150% of the normal levels). It is obvious that extrapolation from the given dose either upward or downward is often unwarrantable, and so far there are few data which can be directly correlated with the very steep character of the dose-response curve in the whole organism.

It is also fairly clear that, the greater the complexity of the irradiated system, the greater will be the response (3). This is evident when the effects of local irradiation are compared to total-body exposure, and many reports are now available of more generalized changes after whole-body irradiation than with larger doses to a restricted target. The extent to which this can be attributed to abscopal effects is not yet clear.

B. HISTORICAL BACKGROUND

1. DIFFERENTIAL RADIOSENSITIVITY

Another factor which must be taken into account is the variation in sensitivity of different systems to X-radiation. This is evident when the effects of exposure on different organisms are considered and also in the response of the tissues in a single species.

Comparison of the radiosensitivity of different systems depends partly on the method used for measuring radiosensitivity. Early work was based mainly on lethality studies or on histological indications of cell death or, in the case of microorganisms and cell cultures, on inhibition of growth. When function rather than structure is emphasized, there tends to be a decrease in the level of exposure necessary to detect damage, and some biochemical investigations have detected quite definite alterations in tissues normally considered "radioresistant."

a. Different Organisms. Large variations in the exposures required to produce death have been found among different organisms (see ref. 4). A dose of less than 1000 r is required to kill 50% of most mammals, whereas unicellular organisms tend to be very resistant, requiring 10^3 to 10^5 r to produce measurable effects. Bacq and Alexander have drawn attention to certain factors which might underlie these differences:

1. There is a parallelism between sensitivity and the resistance of the organism to cyanide poisoning (5), and if this finding can be extended to insects and other invertebrates they suggest that it might indicate that the first enzyme systems to be affected are those containing heavy metals.

2. There is a difference in the mechanism of osmotic regulation between

invertebrates and vertebrates, the former depending on amino acids and small peptides, and the latter on inorganic ions. Amino acids have been shown to exert a slight protective action (see ref. 4), and this might reduce the sensitivity in invertebrates.

3. Oxygen tension might be lower in invertebrates than in vertebrates, and this would reduce the oxygen effects in the former.

b. Different Tissues. At the present time the bulk of our radiobiochemical knowledge has come from work on animal tissues, and it has long been known that dividing cells are especially sensitive (6). Ellinger (7) provides a table of the relative radiosensitivities of different animal cells, but the small lymphocyte which is usually regarded as one of the most radiosensitive is nondividing. This well-established exception to the Bergonié-Tribondeau law is still unexplained, although factors such as relative nuclear/cytoplasmic volume or the level of cytoplasmic activity have been implicated (8–10). It is possible that the division of the other cell types into "sensitive" and "nonsensitive," depending on their mitotic index, is an oversimplification and that "All cells are similarly affected and only those about to divide register the fact in a recognizable manner after small doses of radiation, the others being able to recover before their time for division arrives" (3).

Because of their greater apparent sensitivity it is not surprising that biochemical changes in thymus, bone marrow, and spleen have been especially examined, although even here there is not a single-cell population and thus only an average response will be recorded. At the moment it is difficult to decide whether the changes in these tissues are unique or whether they can be detected in, for example, brain and liver. It is here that the complications of secondary radiation effects become especially marked, and we cannot yet say why changes which may be found both in thymus and liver are easily reversed in the latter and yet lead to cell death and degeneration in the former.

c. Different Stages in the Cell Cycle. It has been appreciated since 1903 (11) that the response of an organism depends on the stage in its development at which the dose is received. The effects at different stages in mitosis have been studied in great detail, and, although the bulk of this work is morphological, Howard and Pelc (12) and later Lajtha and his colleagues (13) have correlated certain biochemical effects with the time in the mitotic cycle at which the dose is given. Unfortunately, technical difficulties at present restrict the variety of cells which can be studied in this way, but the results to date have been illuminating.

2. BIOCHEMICAL APPROACH

Investigation of the radiobiochemical lesion has been much influenced by contemporaneous research in normal systems. As pathways in carbohydrate catabolism were elucidated between 1930 and 1940, so possible changes resulting from irradiation were examined. Similarly the behavior of individual enzymes was studied. Generally this approach has been disappointing, particularly in our understanding of the immediate consequences of exposure, and more attention is now being given to the synthetic aspects of cell activity. With the development of the concept of oxidative phosphorylation, a failure in generation of ATP has provided an attractive hypothesis which is still being explored. Similarly the availability of evidence regarding processes of protein synthesis and function of nucleic acids has facilitated an extension of the pioneering work of Hevesy and von Euler in 1942. Both here, however, and in the more refined extension into disturbed nuclear-cytoplasmic interactions we are still hampered by our lack of knowledge of normal behavior and, in the case of nuclei, by our incomplete understanding of the manifestations of genetic activity in biochemical terms.

II. Enzyme and Coenzyme Sensitivity *in Vivo* and *in Vitro*

A. EARLY WORK

The earliest systematic attempt to determine if the effects of X-radiation on living systems could be due to inactivation of enzymes is associated with Dale and his collaborators (14, 15). They studied the effects of irradiation *in vitro* on certain purified enzymes—e.g., polyphenol oxidase, D-amino acid oxidase, and crystalline carboxypeptidase. It was found that:

1. The enzymes could be inactivated by irradiation in solution, and the greater the dilution of the protein the greater was the inactivation.
2. This inactivation could be partly or completely prevented if irradiation of the enzyme occurred in the presence of its substrate.
3. In the case of D-amino acid oxidase protection was also afforded by irradiation in the presence of the coenzyme.

Certain other low-molecular-weight compounds, notably thiourea, were found to exert a protective action, as did the presence of "inert" protein in the solution. It was thus evident that irradiation could inactivate enzymes, although the conditions required to produce significant destruction, i.e., high dilution and absence of substrate, were not those which obtain in the cell. Nevertheless, as a result of this work and in accord with the profound metabolic effects which inactivation of a catalytic system would produce, studies were made of the action of radiation *in vivo* on numerous enzymes.

B. THE SULFHYDRYL HYPOTHESIS

1. INACTIVATION *IN VITRO*

The most far-reaching examination of enzyme inactivation after Dale's work was that associated with Barron (16, 17). He and his colleagues showed that certain purified sulfhydryl enzymes (SH enzymes)—such as phosphoglyceraldehyde dehydrogenase, succinic dehydrogenase, yeast hexokinase, and adenosine triphosphatase (ATPase)—were more sensitive to irradiation *in vitro* than some non-SH enzymes—for example, carboxypeptidase, catalase, ribonuclease, cytochrome oxidase, purified lactic dehydrogenase, and crystalline trypsin—and that inactivation could be prevented and, even more significantly, reversed by the addition of cysteine or glutathione.

This led Barron to the suggestion that the effects of X-radiation in living systems might be due to inactivation of SH enzymes. Since these are concerned in many essential catabolic and anabolic processes, their inhibition would offer a simple explanation for the complicated sequelae of exposure. Examination of the respiration of various rat tissues (spleen, thymus, liver, kidney, testes, submaxillary glands, and adrenals) after 100 to 900 r of total-body irradiation indicated that in most tissues, but not thymus, the oxidation of substrates requiring SH enzymes was reduced 4 hours after exposure. In sea urchin (*Arbacia punctulata*) eggs and sperm, Barron and Seki (18) found that 100 to 260 r increased respiration, whereas higher doses reduced it. Since that time, however, many detailed studies of tissues after irradiation have failed to substantiate the inhibition of sulfhydryl enzymes.

One of the most detailed investigations was that by Künkel *et al.* (20). Enzymes from female rat livers were examined, as homogenates in the cases of succinic dehydrogenase and ATPase, and as cell-free supernatants for glycolytic enzymes. They were irradiated at 0°C with 5 to 20 × 10³ r, and neither with SH nor with non-SH enzymes could any inactivation be detected. In an attempt to explain the difference between their findings and those of Barron *et al.*, they showed that with purified glutamic dehydrogenase the inactivation produced by 5 × 10³ r was markedly reduced in the presence of an aqueous liver extract and that, as this extract was diluted, so the protection was diminished.

2. SH ENZYMES *IN VIVO*

Before we consider the details of these experiments it must be noted that, although work with cell-free extracts has not confirmed a generalized inhibition of SH enzymes, lack of inactivation *in vitro* cannot necessarily be extrapolated to cover behavior *in vivo* (see discussion following ref. 20).

A considerable effort has been expended in a search for enzymes affected by *in vivo* irradiation but, so far as SH enzymes are concerned, with marked lack of success. Le May (21) could find no evidence for a depression of rat kidney succinic dehydrogenase 1 to 2 hours after 400 to 800 r, and Ballin and Doull (22) reported no diminution in the activity of a number of SH-oxidizing enzymes from rat liver, brain, heart, and kidney, even at 24 hours after 20,000 r.

In radiosensitive tissues also, no reduction in the activities of SH enzymes could be established. Thomson *et al.* (23) exposed rats to 800 r of γ-radiation and found that 3 hours after the dose there was no marked change in succinic dehydrogenase or ATPase of thymus on a dry-weight basis. In mouse spleen also at 4 hours after 640 r succinic dehydrogenase was unaffected (24), although if the results for 2 hours to 4 days were taken together a fall in activity could be detected (25). Many other SH enzymes have been examined (quoted in ref. 26) with similar negative results, and it seems that inhibition of SH enzymes *in vivo* cannot be supported by the available evidence.

C. CHANGES IN SPECIFIC ENZYMES

A complete review by Errera (26) of enzymes which have been examined after irradiation has appeared; we have therefore considered only a few whose relation to the lesions discussed in the later sections is fairly clear or those which have been implicated as potentially able to modify the initial physicochemical effects.

It is in considering some of this work that the complications discussed in the Introduction first become important; unless the enzymes have been examined within really short time intervals after exposure (30 minutes?), any changes in their activity may be consequential rather than the direct result of the immediate changes in the cell. The basis on which the results are expressed can also alter their interpretation; death and removal of radiosensitive cells in a mixed population will increase relatively the number of nonsensitive cells which may have an entirely different enzymatic constitution from the cells normally predominating. An increase or decrease in organ content may not be reflected by expressing the results on a dry-weight, nitrogen, or DNA basis, and vice versa. Even where a change in enzyme activity in a single-cell population undoubtedly occurs, it is extremely difficult to ascertain whether this is due to an actual increase in enzyme protein, to a removal of inhibitors, to an increase in activators, or to an altered physical state of the enzyme unmasking more active centers. Moreover, in certain cases an altered distribution of enzyme between different cell fractions takes place which may produce an increase in activity in one fraction at the expense of another.

1. ATPASE AND 5'-NUCLEOTIDASE

One of the earliest observations on *in vivo* alteration of enzyme content which could profoundly affect the metabolism of the whole animal was that of DuBois and Petersen (27), who reported that whole-body irradiation increased the ATPase activity of rat and mouse spleens. The effect in rats was linear between 25 and 400 r, was detectable 3 hours after irradiation, and reached a maximum within 72 hours of exposure. Similar results were found for the ATPase of thymus and the 5'-nucleotidase of both tissues. The results were expressed per milligram of tissue, and the ATPase activity was measured both in the presence and in the absence of added Ca. Ashwell and Hickman (24) reported comparable results on a N basis in spleens from rats which had received 640 r 4 hours previously. They observed that by 24 hours the nucleotidase level in the spleen was dropping markedly, although the ATPase content in the spleen was approximately constant. A 30% increase in rat spleen ATPase per milligram of N at 1.25 to 1.5 hours after 1000 r was reported by Ord and Stocken (28). Other workers (25) could not substantiate the increase in ATPase in rat spleen after 800 r when the activity was expressed on a dry-weight basis, but DuBois et al. reported that the increase in spleen dry weight in their experiments did not account for the two- to threefold increase in activity which occurred (27). It is relevant in this connection that at 1 hour after 1000 r of total-body irradiation there is a 40% expulsion of red cells and 10% loss of intracellular potassium from rat spleen (Esnouf, Hastings, Richmond, and Stocken, unpublished observations).

In rat thymus Thomson et al. (23) did not detect an increased ATPase on a dry-weight basis with or without Ca before 24 hours after 800 r. Similarly with the ATPase associated with nucleoprotein in rat thymus no change in activity was detectable 2 hours after 1000 r, although an increase was apparent by 24 hours (29).

The ATPase assay used (30) is nonspecific, and Ashwell and Hickman (31) attempted to characterize the enzyme more precisely, particularly with reference to Ca^{++} and Mg^{++} activation. They concluded that the radiation effect was not due to selective destruction of an "ATPase" inhibitor, and although they thought that it might be due to a rise in the relative amount of connective tissue it was difficult to produce experimental evidence for this. Investigation of the intracellular site of ATPase activity (32) showed that it was widely distributed through the different cell fractions, that the ATPase of each fraction was similarly affected by Ca^{++}, Mg^{++}, and F^-, that the activity of each fraction increased after irradiation, and that there were insignificant changes in the distribution of activity after exposure.

Later experiments by Petersen and DuBois (33) have shown that shielding the thorax during exposure diminishes the rise in spleen ATPase, and it is completely prevented if the spleen only is irradiated, even with doses up to 800 r. It has also been reported (28) that 800 to 1600 r of irradiation in vitro did not increase spleen ATPase in either homogenates or mitochondria. It was therefore concluded (33) that "The X-ray induced increase in phosphatase activity of the spleen could not be accounted for on the basis of direct damage to the spleen." At the present time, however, although the increase in ATPase in spleen may be associated with abscopal changes, it is not yet established whether this is the case also in thymus or how this rise in ATPase and 5'-nucleotidase is related in time to changes in generation of ATP (*vide infra*).

2. CATALASE

The interest in catalase lies in the fact that H_2O_2 is formed by the action of ionizing radiation on water and is highly toxic to most biological systems. A considerable effort has been expended in attempts to demonstrate accumulations of peroxides *in vivo* and changes of catalase activity both *in vivo* and *in vitro*.

Forssberg (34) reported a slight activation of rat liver and Jensen sarcoma catalase after 83,000 r, but crystalline beef catalase in dilute aqueous solution was inhibited. The study of the kinetics and mechanism of catalase behavior after irradiation *in vitro* has been extended by Dale and Russell (35) and by Sutton (36), and the activation of intracellular yeast catalase after 10^5 to 10^6 r was investigated by Aronson and his colleagues (37).

Other workers have investigated the catalase activity of tissues taken from irradiated animals. Ludewig and Chanutin could find no change in the enzyme activity in rat liver up to 1 week after 500 r (38), whereas after 600 r Roth *et al.* observed a reduction of 30 % (39). In mice after 800 r Feinstein *et al.* reported a steady decline to 20 % of normal liver catalase (40).

Kazuo Mori and his associates (41) confirmed the fall in liver catalase in mice on the day after 100 to 200 r but found a rise to normal levels again on the second day with a further fall to a minimum at 5 days postirradiation. The phasic response was not found after 250 to 500 r, which produced an uncomplicated fall in the enzyme level.

In other experiments Voskoboinikov (42) has found that rats subjected to 1000 r of X-rays 24 hours previously had a slight lowering of catalase activity in liver and kidney, no change in spleen, and an increase in muscle. At 15 minutes after 30,000 r the same picture was shown by liver, kidney, and spleen; at 48 hours the muscle had a 46 % increase.

The synergistic experiments of Feinstein *et al.* with H_2O_2 (40) and of Friedberg with 3-amino-1,2,4-triazole (43) led both groups to conclude that there was no reason to suppose that the reduction in catalase activity was responsible for X-ray mortality in mice.

Thus, although it seems clear that the role of catalase in radiation damage cannot at present be ascribed to an inactivation with the consequent generalized toxic effects of H_2O_2, one possibility has not yet been eliminated. All the above measurements were made on whole tissues, but it has been found that nuclei of some tissues have a low catalase content.

Kaplan and Paik have demonstrated (44) that, in yeast, catalase is associated with RNA, and Aronson *et al.* have suggested (37) that irradiation of yeast releases catalase from an RNA complex. Brown has shown (45) that liver contains a bound form of catalase, and preliminary experiments in this laboratory have indicated a fall in the catalase content of nuclei prepared from thymus glands from rats given 50, 200, or 1000 r of X-rays 1 hour previously. The fall ranges from 10 to 45 % and is accompanied by a reduced amount of nuclear RNA.

3. CHOLINESTERASES

Increased motility of rat intestine immediately after irradiation with 100 to 200 r was reported in 1951 by Conard (46). This could be associated with an alteration in intestinal cholinesterases, but measurement of acetylcholine hydrolysis did not indicate any significant change in its activity until 10 hours after exposure, although by this time histological changes are evident. The activity declined from 10 hours to 5 days after exposure, but by then gross changes in the intestines were apparent, and it was concluded that the increased motility and cholinesterase response could not be directly correlated. Burn *et al.* (47) carried out similar experiments with rats and found that 24 hours after 1000 r the acetylcholine threshold of loops of intestine was markedly reduced. Using specific substrates for acetylcholinesterase (AChE) and pseudocholinesterase (pChE), they showed that there was a slight fall in pChE activity in the whole intestine at 24 hours after exposure and a more pronounced fall by 48 hours in both whole intestine and its muscle coat; AChE did not appear to be affected. Later experiments by French and Wall (48) with a wider range of species— rhesus monkeys and guinea pigs as well as rats—have confirmed that in rats and guinea pigs there is a fall in intestinal pChE 48 hours after 650 and 250 r, respectively. In monkeys no change was detected after 800 r. The excitatory responses of rat intestine were unaffected in these experiments.

Changes in pChE in other tissues have been shown; in guinea pig plasma a fall occurs for the first 48 hours after exposure to 1000 r (49); this has been confirmed by Lundin *et al.* (50) and has been detected also in mice (51). Synthesis of pChE is thought to occur in the liver, and Doull and Cummings (52) reported marked changes in rat liver, ileum, spleen, and thymus pChE after lethal exposures. They also noted a sex difference in the liver response, since only in female rats did the enzyme activity decrease. It is known (53) that in normal female rat livers pChE exceeds that in males, and DuBois and co-workers have demonstrated (*vide infra*) that in other cases sex differentiation in a liver enzyme system is altered postirradiation. It is not clear from this preliminary report at what time after irradiation the experiments were performed, and starvation is known to produce a fall in rat liver pChE (54). The increased levels of activity found in spleen and thymus might also be due to indirect changes.

Acetylcholinesterase has sometimes been considered as a factor in ion transport, and, since altered cell permeability may occur postirradiation, Hajdukovic (55) examined AChE and pChE activity in mouse cells after 600 to 5000 r, using a cytochemical technique. There was no alteration in AChE activity in spleeen or bone marrow megakaryocytes or in muscle end plates, and pChE activity in liver, pancreas, and prostate was not affected before 12 hours postexposure. It was therefore concluded that altered permeability could not be directly linked with these enzymes.

4. NUCLEASES

As will be discussed later, a fall in nucleic acid content of tissues, especially DNA in radiosensitive cells, is a well-established consequence of exposure. This could be wholly or partly due to an increased nuclease activity; therefore DNAases and RNAase have been extensively studied.

a. DNAases. Two DNAases are known. DNAase I has an optimum pH around 7.5 and was originally thought to be produced only by the pancreas, but it has now been demonstrated in liver, lung, placenta, kidney, spleen, thymus, etc., provided Mg^{++} is present. DNAase II has an optimal pH around 5.6 and was first considered to be the intracellular DNAase. It is associated with mitochondria or possibly more precisely lysosomes (56) but may also occur in nuclei.

The first indication that DNAase in radiosensitive tissues might be affected after X-irradiation is associated with Douglass and his co-workers (57). They found that 12 to 24 hours after 500 r there was an increase in DNAase II in rat spleen, with little affect on DNAase I, and no effect on either enzyme in liver. The effect was later shown to increase from 0 to 500 r (58), but if the results were expressed as total activity in spleen it was found that the level remained constant. These data were confirmed by Hempelmann and his colleagues (59). They also showed increased DNAase II activity in thymus on a wet-weight basis, the level again remaining constant on an organ basis, although there had been about 50% reduction in the weight of both spleen and thymus. No change could be detected in the enzyme in either liver or kidney. They found in addition that there was a roughly comparable increase in enzyme activity in spleen "pulp" and connective tissue, whereas it is the loss of pulp which mainly produces the loss in weight postirradiation. Earlier work by the same group (60, 61) had shown a release of both DNAase I and II into rat plasma and urine after 350 and 700 r. The effect was marked in the first 18 hours postirradiation.

In attempting to evaluate their results, Okada *et al.* (59) concluded that it was difficult to attribute the rise in lymphoid tissue DNAase II activity to selective retention of the enzyme in the organ and loss of inactive material, since the concomitant release of enzyme into the extracellular fluid after exposure had also to be explained. In addition it has been shown (62) that 30 minutes after 850 r there is a release of rat spleen DNAase II from its bound state. Aqueous homogenates were prepared from control and irradiated rats, and the distribution of enzyme activity between the fraction sedimented by 60,000 × *g* for 2 hours and that remaining in solution was measured. In normal spleens 43 % of the activity was found in the soluble phase, whereas after irradiation 73 % of the DNAase II activity was in the supernatant. Goutier-Pirotte and Thonnard considered it possible that this release of bound DNAase might precede the increased activity found in homogenates at 24 hours after exposure. A change in the binding of the enzyme is also indicated from further experiments of Okada *et al.* (63). Spleens were taken from rats 24 hours after 756 r; part was homogenized in 0.44 *M* sucrose, and part in distilled water. Preparations from control animals showed greater activity in aqueous homogenates than in sucrose, but this difference was less marked after irradiation, although in each medium the activity per milligram of tissue was increased. Irradiation therefore appears to increase the accessibility of the enzyme to its substrate.

Irradiation of mitochondria together with lysosomes in buffered sucrose solutions with 25,300 r *in vitro* produced a slight increase in activity (107 to 127 % of control value); 126,500 r caused a more definite activation (136 to 139 %) (64). Further experiments (65) with rat liver mitochondria confirmed that ionizing radiation causes an increase in mitochondrial DNAase II *in vitro*. High doses of γ-radiation were used, and electron micrographs showed rupture of the mitochondrial membranes and internal structures. The changes could not be produced if whole homogenates were exposed.

At present there would seem to be insufficient facts to permit all these findings to be completely integrated. It would still appear possible, however, that the original premise explored by Hempelmann *et al.* (61) can be maintained and that the release of both types of DNAase in the first 18 hours after exposure is due to cellular destruction. Superimposed on this would be an increase in DNAase II in thymus and spleen whose etiology is so far unknown.

There is, however, one other factor which might play a significant part in the experimental findings. So far as we are aware, no account has been taken of the considerable amount of DNAase II present in intestinal mucosa. This tissue, according to Allfrey *et al.* (66), has six to twenty times the concentration of other organs, and it is possible that this is responsible for the circulating enzyme. It would then only be necessary to suppose that the spleen and thymus had lost cells containing DNAase I.

b. RNAase. Less work has been carried out on RNAase changes after X-irradiation. Roth and his colleagues (39) reported that in rat liver there was an increase 2 to 3 days after 600 r, but in later experiments (67) to explore this further in different cell fractions the increase found in whole liver homogenates was much less evident. It is possible that these experiments are complicated by the presence of an RNAase inhibitor whose concentration was reduced 1 day after irradiation and returned to normal at 2 days.

D. COENZYMES

1. COENZYME A (COA)

The significance of SH groups has been referred to previously (see particularly ref. 4). Although SH enzymes themselves do not appear sensitive *in vivo*, the protective action of SH compounds has stimulated examination of CoA levels postirradiation, especially as Barron (68) found aqueous solutions to be readily oxidized by X-rays *in vitro*. Neither DuBois *et al.* (69), Thomson and Mikuta (70), nor Romantsev and Zhulanova (71) could find any evidence, however, for decreased acetylation of sulfanilamide or *p*-aminobenzoic acid in rats after 400 to 3320 r, and Schreier *et al.* (72) found no interference with hippuric acid synthesis in rats exposed to 700 r. Gardella and Lichtler have shown that even 12,000 r fails to inactivate aqueous solutions of the coenzyme or to reduce the content of liver, thymus, and Yoshida sarcoma when doses of 100 to 1600 r have been received *in vivo* (73). It would thus appear that, although CoA is one of the most potent protectors against radiation damage (74), an insufficiency of the coenzyme is not responsible for the early biochemical lesion.

2. PYRIDINE NUCLEOTIDE—COENZYME (COI)

Swallow (75) and Barron (68) have made extensive studies of the changes produced in DPN$^+$–DPNH systems after irradiation *in vitro*. Very few data are available about pyridine nucleotide coenzyme levels after whole-body exposure. Eichel and Spirtes (76) studied DPN$^+$ and DPNH concentrations in rat livers 5 to 150 hours after 700 to 980 r. No changes were found in DPN$^+$ levels, but 980 r reduced the DPNH concentration by 15 to 32 %. The authors did not consider this fall likely to be of importance in the radiation lesion but are extending their work to radiosensitive tissues where nuclear damage, and therefore possible reduction in CoI synthesis (77), is probable. Concomitant studies of TPN$^+$–TPNH levels would be of interest, since it might be possible for altered metabolic pathways to be adopted if relative coenzyme levels became favorable (78).

3. OTHER COFACTORS

Clear evidence has been provided by Fischer *et al.* (79) that lethal doses of X-radiation fail to produce an immediate fall in the glutathione content of tissues taken from either mice or guinea pigs. Pyridoxine levels in liver also remain unchanged in rats subjected to variations in diet to induce changes in the basic level and then exposed to doses up to 600 r (79a).

Few or no data are available on folic acid and cobalamin, and since there is some suggestion of deficiency of thymine nucleotide for DNA synthesis it would be helpful to know that there is no corresponding lack of either of these vitamins. The only relevant evidence in this connection is that medication with folic acid increased the time of 50 % mortality from 43 to 100 days in mice which had received a dose of 350 r (80).

III. Carbohydrate Metabolism

Although as we have seen it is difficult to pinpoint any particular enzyme concerned in carbohydrate metabolism as being specifically and immediately affected by X-radiation, it is still possible that separately very small alterations in a number of linked reactions might exert a profound effect on glucose catabolism as a whole.

A. ABSORPTION

1. INTESTINAL ABSORPTION IN THE INTACT ANIMAL

Decreased absorption of glucose and other sugars undoubtedly results from total, or especially abdominal, irradiation in rats. In 1931 Buchwald (81) first reported decreased absorption of glucose 20 to 40 hours postirradiation. The exposures used were not stated except that they were sublethal, but the findings were confirmed after as little as 50 r by Barron *et al.* (82). These workers used the Cori technique (83) and gave the glucose by stomach tube. Similar experiments were carried out by Lourau and Lartigue (84) using guinea pigs exposed to 500 r; in this case the animals were not examined until 11 days postirradiation, when maximal alterations in glucose tolerance (*vide infra*) occurred. The interpretation of these and subsequent experiments was modified by the observations of Goodman *et al.* (85) that, after irradiation, gastric emptying time of rats was delayed by 450 r and had not achieved normal values even at 21 days postirradiation. This has since been extensively confirmed (see ref. 86). Farrar *et al.* (87), however, gave sugars by duodenal intubation and also found that glucose and fructose absorptions 4 hours after 1410 r were slightly but significantly reduced, the effect being more marked with xylose and showing a further fall with all three sugars after 20 hours. Moss (88) compared the effects of local irradiation of the bowel with that after total-body exposure with the exteriorized bowel shielded. In the latter case no alteration in glucose absorption occurred, but if the bowel was irradiated and absorption from tied-off loops was measured a decreased disappearance of both glucose and arabinose was evident. Reduction in organophosphate levels of dried mucosa previously reported by Barron et al. (82) was confirmed, but, since arabinose absorption as well as that of glucose was depressed, it was suggested that reduced diffusion was also a significant factor. In mice Dickson (89) could find no failure of glucose absorption from intestinal loops 4 hours after 500 r, but a diminution was apparent by 72 hours. At this time hexokinase activity of intestine homogenates from irradiated animals was not different from levels in control animals.

As all those working in this field have stressed, morphological changes in intestinal mucosal cells after irradiation occur rapidly and edema becomes apparent, and these factors may be involved in the decreased absorption rates.

2. INTESTINAL ABSORPTION *IN VITRO*

Fisher and Stocken (unpublished observations) investigated glucose absorption *in vitro* (90) from intestines taken from rats exposed to 800 r 1 hour or 6 days previously. The results were compared to those from control animals of the same weight, and no differences in absorption could be found. The experiments differ from those in intact animals in two respects: firstly, gastric factors are not concerned; and secondly, the animals here were irradiated from the dorsal aspect to minimize gastrointestinal damage. Unfortunately no histological examination was made for comparison with rats irradiated in the more usual way from the sides or below. A complete study using the same absorption technique has been made by Detrick et al. (91). Here there were profound changes in the histology and later hydration of the gut, but the majority of the rats did not die until 8 to 13 days after exposure (600 r). The absorption was examined daily, and the greatest inhibition occurred from the third to the sixth day, by which time the appearance of the cells had reverted to normal. The decreased glucose uptake could not be correlated with histological changes, and the authors stress that histological recovery from radiation injury is no guarantee of physiologically functional tissue.

3. BLOOD SUGAR LEVELS

Delayed glucose absorption might be expected to affect blood glucose levels postirradiation. Early work in this field is associated with Lourau and Lartigue (92). They found that 6 to 20 days after nonlethal doses to guinea pigs a decreased glucose tolerance developed. This was not detected in the first 4 days, and a return to normal occurred about 1 month after exposure.

The changes were associated usually with observable hemorrhages at post-mortem. At the same time guinea pigs starved for 15 hours were found to have blood sugar levels considerably greater than those of the starved control animals. Kohn (93) found an increase in blood sugar levels in rats 6 hours after 100 to 900 r. The levels reverted to normal by the fifth day, and there was a quicker return if the adrenals or pituitary glands were removed prior to irradiation. Similarly McKee reported (94) that the blood sugar level of fasted rats which had received 1500 r fell less in the following 12-hour starvation period than that of control animals, and Kay and Entenman confirmed the rise in blood sugar in fasted rats at 24 to 48 hours after 500 to 550 r (95). In rabbits, also, X-radiation produced a hyperglycemia (96) and prolonged the hyperglycemic period after glucose administration (94).

Lourau-Pitres (97) used mice exposed to 500 to 2000 r. The animals were injected subcutaneously with C^{14}-glucose immediately or 24 hours after irradiation and were killed 60 to 75 minutes later. There was a decreased rate of appearance of C^{14} activity in the blood of the irradiated mice, which then retained a slightly higher activity than that of the control animals. No detectable difference in blood sugar levels between control mice and those exposed to 2000 r was found in the first hour after irradiation. In 3-day-old chicks no change in blood sugar level was detectable 1 to 5 hours after 1000 r (98).

Comparative biochemistry suggests that factors in the control of blood glucose vary in importance from one species to another and may be changed in relative importance with different nutritional backgrounds. It is therefore difficult to compare results with different species obtained at varying states of inanition or development, but it is established in those mammals so far tested that there is a decrease in glucose tolerance after X-irradiation and an increase in blood sugar level. The relationships between these changes and those in liver glycogen metabolism with which they are probably associated are considered in the next section.

B. GLYCOGEN SYNTHESIS

As can be seen from Table I, there is an increase in liver glycogen in the three mammals extensively examined after exposures of up to 2000 r. The increase appears earliest in mice (30 to 60 minutes after exposure); in rats most workers find little alteration before 12 to 18 hours. The results in guinea pigs are less clear-cut. Lourau considers that doses exceeding 1000 r are required before marked increases in the first 24-hour period can be established (108). She and Lartigue have studied liver glycogen levels in guinea pigs several days after 500 r (107). At these times the levels tended to be lower than in comparable control animals, and there is some indica-

TABLE I

LIVER GLYCOGEN LEVELS AFTER X-IRRADIATION

Species	Dose (r)	Time after exposure	Effect	Comment	Ref.
Rats	500–2000	48 hr	Up		(99)
Rats	500–2000	24 hr	Up, maximum effect	Fasted	(100)
Rats	300	3 hr	Up	Fasted	(101)
Rats	1500	12 hr	Up	Fasted before and after	(94)
Rats	250–1500	5 hr	Up		(102)
	1500	70 hr	Down	Fasted before and after	(102)
Rats	880	24 hr	Up	Fasted	(103)
Rats	550–5000	24 hr	Up	Fasted	(95)
		48 hr	Up		
Rats	200	24 hr	6- to 10-fold increase	Fasted	(104)
Rats	750		No consistent increase before 18 hr	Fasted after X-irradiation	(105)
Guinea pigs	1000	24 hr	Up	Fasted	(106)
Guinea pigs	500	10–20 days	Down	Given glucose, killed 6 hr later	(107)
Guinea pigs	2000	4 hr	Up	Fasted	(108)
		24 hr	Up	Fasted	(108)
	1000	4 hr	Normal	Fasted	(108)
		24 hr	Slightly up	Fasted	(108)
	500	4 hr	Normal	Fasted	(108)
		24 hr	Normal	Fasted	(108)
Mice	600	30–60 min	Maximally up, normal at 6 hr	Fed	(109)
Mice	110,000	Immediately after	Fall		(110)
	60,000	Immediately after	Fall	Fed	(111)

tion of a similar fall in irradiated rats after the first 2 days from exposure (102).

When supralethal exposures are used and the liver is examined as soon as the dose has been received, there is a sharp fall in glycogen content (110–113). With 10,000 r the decrease is evident 10 to 20 minutes after exposure, and it is possible to detect a transient hypoglycemia followed by elevated blood sugar levels. Accelerated glycogenolysis as a result of intense adrenal stimulation seems to be a likely contributor to this finding.

Two factors are certainly concerned in the increase in liver glycogen within 24 hours after lower exposures; the actions of the pituitary-adrenal axis and the tissue degradation which follows total-body irradiation. Both have been explored in great detail. Hypophysectomy or adrenalectomy effectively prevents the postirradiation increase in liver glycogen (100, 102–104). Although there are some discrepancies (95) between the time courses of blood sugar and glycogen increases after exposure, it is possible that irradiation of adrenalectomized animals produces insufficient rise in blood sugar to promote liver glycogen synthesis (104).

Some insight into the mechanism of this synthesis after irradiation has been gained by isotope experiments. Lourau-Pitres found that C^{14}-glucose uptake into mouse liver glycogen was enhanced, the maximal effect occurring 50 minutes after irradiation (97). This agrees well with the time course found in mice by Sherman and Dwyer (109) and in rats by Morehouse and Searcy using C^{14}-acetate (114). Chaikoff and his colleagues have carried out similar experiments with rats and extended the work to a study of C^{14}-glucose and C^{14}-fructose uptake by rat liver slices taken from rats exposed to 1000 r 4 hours previously (115). At 4 hours after irradiation of the rats, liver slices showed an increased rate of oxidation of both glucose and fructose, but at 24, 48, and 72 hours postirradiation there was a marked incapacity to convert C^{14}-glucose to CO_2 and glycogen, whereas fructose metabolism was normal. The authors conclude from this that the radiation lesion is at some point before the triose phosphate stage. The diminished incorporation of glucose into glycogen was confirmed in intact rats given glucose intravenously to avoid the decreased gastrointestinal absorption, and attention was drawn to the similarity between their results at 24 hours postirradiation and those found in diabetes; in this connection Steadman and Grimaldi (96) have stated that postirradiation hyperglycemia in rabbits after 500 to 2000 r could be prevented by insulin. Additional confirmation of this is required.

The most obvious source of precursors for the increased liver glycogen is tissue protein. Kay et al. (116) have followed urinary and plasma levels of certain amino acids in rats after 400 and 2500 r. Exposure to 450 r caused an increased excretion of cysteine metabolites by 24 hours postirradiation, cysteic acid being 100 % increased, and taurine 250 %. The levels returned to normal by the third day. Little effect was found on amino acids except valine and leucine, but 2500 r produced a generalized amino aciduria which was still present on the third day. Slight increases in plasma amino acids were detected. Hallesy and Doull (117) reported similar findings in rat blood after 800 r, using the technique of Moore and Stein (118). The changes were transitory, lasting only 24 to 48 hours, except for the fall in glycine and the increase in threonine, leucine, and isoleucine.

Further experiments (119) showed that the increased urinary excretion of taurine was proportional to the dose received up to 250 r, but above this exposure no further increase occurred. Urea levels also rose, although less markedly than those of taurine. Creatinine excretion was unaffected even with doses of 2500 r. Adrenalectomy prevented the rise in urinary urea levels after irradiation but did not affect that of taurine, which was also not prevented by splenectomy. Essentially similar results were found by Pentz (120), who noted an increase in taurine excretion after irradiation of adrenalectomized rats and no reduction in rats with thymus and spleen removed. The origin of the taurine is so far unexplained, although rather high concentrations are associated with lymphatic tissues; the increased urea excretion would be expected from deamination of liberated amino acids.

Hempelmann and his colleagues (121, 122) have attempted to estimate the size of the amino acid pool after irradiation. Rats were injected with glycine-2-C^{14} and phenylalanine-3-C^{14} before irradiation, and hippuric acid excretion as a result of benzoic acid administration was followed after 750 r. There was no change in the amount of hippuric acid excreted, but the specific activity of the carbon atoms derived from the glycine and phenylalanine moieties increased, especially in the 6- to 24-hours urine collections. It was also found that the C^{14} activity of liver protein was increased at 48 hours, whereas that in muscle, thymus, and spleen decreased. They considered that the increase in liver C^{14} activity could not be accounted for by the loss from spleen and thymus so that the reduction in muscle counts might reflect an important change postirradiation. Morehouse and Searcy (123) followed the incorporation of C^{14}-labeled glycine and alanine and leucine-1-C^{14} uptake into liver glycogen immediately after 1500 r. In fed rats the effect was greatest with alanine, but all acids showed a much greater incorporation if the rats were fasted.

Support for the role of muscle in tissue breakdown after irradiation comes from the work of Caster and Armstrong (124), who studied organ weight changes in rats after 700 r. Their values are expressed on a body weight basis after removal of the fat and gastrointestinal tract. Spleen weights were detectably lower 3 hours after exposure and reached a minimum (36.7 % control) by 4 days; the thymus weight was reduced by 24 hours and was at a minimum by 48 hours (11.5 %). Muscle weight was detectably reduced by 3 hours and reached a minimum by 4 days (80.2 % control). Additional evidence of muscle catabolism postirradiation is provided by studies on creatinuria (125–127). Rats and monkeys exhibited a marked creatinuria, especially in the second day, but in dogs no increase in creatine or creatinine excretion could be detected after 400 to 500 r except possibly immediately before death.

In a long-term experiment with rats surviving for 6 months after 1500 r from Co^{60} γ-rays, the results led the same authors (127) to conclude that there was no interference with creatine synthesis and to suggest that radiation destroyed tissue in which a significant part of the creatine pool was located.

To summarize the experimental results discussed here, it appears that the accumulation of liver glycogen found within 24 hours of X-irradiation is due to enhanced tissue protein breakdown and the consequential storage of amino acid carbon skeletons. This is promoted by the presence of the appropriate hormones, but, although stimulation of the pituitary-adrenal axis may occur as a result of X-radiation, it does not seem that the stimulation *per se* is the cause of the glycogen deposition. A good summary of work on the consequences of direct irradiation of the pituitary and adrenal glands leading to the same conclusion has been given by Cronkite and Bond (128). The suggested importance of muscle protein breakdown is interesting, since there is so far little evidence here of immediate damage; it may well be that, again, undetectably small changes take place which are manifested only because of the major contribution of muscle to the total cell population of the body. Later changes in glucose tolerance and glycogen levels are difficult to interpret, since they occur against a background of generalized tissue reorganization and recovery.

C. GLYCOLYSIS

Some data on tissue glycolysis after X-irradiation are summarized in Table II. There is no change immediately after exposure. By 24 hours a reduction in the glycolytic ability of rat thymus does, however, occur. Hickman and Ashwell extended their work on mouse spleen glycolysis to cover glycolytic phosphorylation also (130). This was found to be markedly reduced by 24 hours postirradiation, which was attributed to a loss of adenine nucleotide as phosphate acceptor.

It has been shown by Perkinson and Irving (131) that irradiation from injected P^{32} can inhibit the anaerobic glycolysis of rat liver by 50 % 24 hours after the injection of 5 μc/gm of rat, and these authors suggest that this inhibition is possibly responsible for the 35 % depression in respiration measured at the same time. Anaerobic glycolysis was depressed even at 2 hours after one-tenth of the dose of P^{32}.

D. RESPIRATION

A selection of tissue respiration studies since 1946 is given in Table III. The lack of confirmation for some of Barron's results has been referred to

TABLE II
TISSUE GLYCOLYSIS AFTER X-IRRADIATION

Tissue	Dose (r)	Time after exposure	Test system	Effect	Ref.
Rat thymus	500	4 hr / 24 hr	CO_2 production	Normal / 40% of control	(16)
Rat intestine	900	4 hr	CO_2 production	Normal	(82)
Rat and rabbit bone marrow	1000	6 and 24 hr / 3–6 days		Normal / Reduced	(129)
Mouse spleen	640	1–9 days	Lactic acid formation	Normal	(130)
Mouse liver	60,000	Immediately after	Lactic acid formation	Normal	(111)
Rat liver	From injected P^{32}, 5 μc/gm	24 hr		50% of control	(131)
Yoshida ascites	20,000 in vitro	Immediately after	Lactic acid production	50% of control	(132)

previously. The data for liver and kidney suggest that in these organs there is very little effect on respiration. Thymus O_2 uptake is also initially unaffected, but in rat spleen and intestine it appears to be depressed. Bone marrow respiration increased markedly immediately after exposure, but this was transient and, like the other radiosensitive tissues, there is a reduction at a later period when tissue damage is apparent histologically. Experiments with mouse tissues seem to indicate a lower sensitivity than those in rat, but additional evidence would be needed to support this.

It is interesting that Sullivan and DuBois (134) found that local irradiation of the spleen did not produce the lowered endogenous respiration found after total-body exposure.

Another effect in respiratory systems is an increased dependence on exogenous cytochrome c. Maxwell and Ashwell (32) found that in normal mouse spleen mitochondria O_2 uptake was not increased by added cytochrome c. After irradiation, respiration and phosphorylation (vide infra) were depressed in its absence. Van Bekkum (143) has investigated this in more detail with rat spleen mitochondria, using succinate as substrate. In this animal cytochrome c apparently increases the O_2 uptake of normal spleen mitochondria, but the effect is much greater with those from irradiated animals, being detectable 30 minutes and 1 hour postirradiation,

TABLE III

Tissue	Dose (r)	Time after exposure	Substrate	Effect	Comment	Ref.
Rat	1000	1–3 days	Basal O_2 consumption	Very slight decrease		(132a)
Rat spleen	200	4 hr	O_2 uptake	73% of control	Dry-weight	(16) contains
	900	4 hr	O_2 uptake	50% of control	basis	many references to early work
Rat spleen	1100	4 hr	Succinate	73% of control	No NaF, N basis	(133)
Rat spleen	400	48 hr	Endogenous O_2 uptake	55% of control	Dry-weight basis	(134)
Exteriorized spleen	400	48 hr	Endogenous O_2 uptake	75% of control		(134)
Rat liver	200	4 hr	Pyruvate Glucose Succinate Pyruvate	Normal Normal Normal	Dry-weight basis	(16)
			Pyruvate uptake	68% of control		
	800	4 hr	Glucose Pyruvate Succinate	82% of control 88% of control Normal-58% of control	Dry-weight basis	(16)
			Pyruvate uptake	69% of control		
Rat kidney	200	4 hr	Succinate	61% of control	Dry-weight	(16)
	400	1–2 hr	Succinate	Normal		(21)
Rat kidney slices	806 600	First 10 days	O_2 uptake	Slight decrease	Dry-weight basis	(135)
Rat thymus	500	4 hr	O_2 uptake	Normal	Dry-weight	(16)
Rat thymus	800	3 hr	Succinate + pyruvate	Normal		(23)
Rat thymus	400	48 hr	Endogenous O_2 uptake	44% of control		(134)
Rat intestine	900	4 hr	Endogenous O_2 uptake	38–66% of control segment		(82)
		24 hr		Normal		
Rat skin	700	1, 2 days 4, 7 days	O_2 uptake	Slight increase Decrease	Wet-weight basis	(136)
Rat and rabbit bone marrow	1000	6–24 hr 3–6 days	O_2 uptake	Normal Reduced		(129)
Rabbit bone marrow	800	Immediately 48 hr 3 days	O_2 uptake	270% increased 93% of control 27% of control	Wet-weight basis	(137)
Rabbit brain	900–1500	Immediately –7 hr	Oxygen tension	Increased		(138) contains many references to Russian work
Guinea pig	250	0–13 days	Whole-body O_2 consumption	Normal		(139)
Mouse spleen	640	4 hr–17 days	Succinate	Normal	Dry-weight basis	(24)
Mouse brain	500–19,000	0–190 hr	O_2 uptake	Normal	Wet-weight basis	(140)
Mouse duodenal mucosa	600	2 hr 20 hr–15 days	Succinate Succinate	Normal 2-fold increase	Dry-weight basis	(141)
Monkey	Over 2500	Immediately	O_2 uptake	Decreased		(142)

and marked 2 hours after 700 r. Simple leakage was eliminated as a factor, since with α-ketoglutarate oxidation addition of DPN⁺ affected control and irradiated mitochondria similarly.

Alterations in tissue citrate accumulation brought about by fluoroacetate injections in rats have been studied by DuBois, Petersen, and their colleagues (reviewed in ref. 144). It may be noted that inhibition of citrate accumulation after 800 r was found in skeletal muscle and pancreas as well as in thymus and spleen, although 100 to 400 r affected these latter two organs only. In liver a sex difference in citrate metabolism normally present is abolished by X-radiation as is the sex difference in pChE levels referred to earlier.

Some work has been performed on respiration during or after irradiation *in vitro* (20, 28, 145–146). Liver, muscle, kidney, spleen, and thymus have been studied, and exposures of 10^5 to 10^6 r were required before appreciable reduction (37 to 50 %) could be detected. These results are in marked contrast to those of Fritz-Niggli using rat liver mitochondria in mannitol solutions (147, 148). Citrate and especially pyruvate oxidation was affected by 50 r. Succinic dehydrogenase, however, was very resistant. If the mannitol concentration was reduced, more inactivation occurred so that 60 to 70 % inhibition of citrate oxidation was found after only 0.1 r. These results may reflect conditions in which it is possible to demonstrate mitochondrial sensitivity *in vitro*, and it will be useful when further data are available on the properties of mitochondria in this system compared to those more commonly used. Experiments where effects *in vitro* are in contrast to those obtained *in vivo* have many possible explanations, although those where similar radiosensitivities are found can be extremely useful in simplifying the factors to be investigated.

IV. The Generation of Adenosine Triphosphate

Although X-radiation does not appear to produce an immediate fall in the respiration of any mammalian tissue so far examined, the catabolism of carbohydrate is also associated with the production of energy. A reduction in substrate level phosphorylation in spleen has already been noted. Parallel with our increasing understanding of the mechanism of oxidative phosphorylation has been the knowledge that oxidation and phosphorylation may easily be dissociated, so that the possibility of such a dissociation after irradiation has been investigated.

Once it was found that such an uncoupling did indeed take place, one of the most important factors to be decided was whether the dissociation is the immediate effect of X-rays or whether it is a consequence of changes which take place even earlier. The time sequence and sensitivity of the effect is therefore of major importance. Van Bekkum (143) has reported that in locally irradiated spleens, although many changes found after total-body irradiation are not present (see DuBois, 33, ATPase), reduced phosphorylation is still produced. It seems probable, therefore, that the uncoupling is an effect on the cells themselves.

A. OXIDATIVE PHOSPHORYLATION IN HOMOGENATES AND CELL FRACTIONS

1. HOMOGENATES AND MITOCHONDRIA

a. Prepared from Irradiated Animals. The first indication of uncoupled oxidative phosphorylation came in 1952. Potter and Bethel (149) found reduced P/O ratios in spleen mitochondria from rats which had received 800 r 1 hour previously. Succinate was used as substrate. Similar results with mouse spleen mitochondria were found 4 hours after 640 r (24, 32). These workers used fluoride to inhibit ATPases, whose concentration increases post irradiation, and concluded that increased ATPase activity was not the cause of the reduced phosphorylation. Thomson *et al.* (23) found a similar reduction in the capacity of thymus homogenates to esterify phosphate 3 hours after a dose of 800 r of γ-radiation had been given to rats. Florsheim and his colleagues (140, 150) could detect no change in mouse brain or liver P^{32} uptake after 18,000 to 20,000 r, but Goldfeder (151) found reduced P/O ratios in mouse liver mitochondria after 700 r, the effect being more marked with males than with females.

Van Bekkum and his colleagues have studied rat spleen and thymus mitochondria in great detail (133, 143, 152, 153). With succinate as substrate, reduced P/O ratios were found 4 hours after 100 r with spleen and after 50 r with thymus. In order to determine the time of onset of this depression 700 r was given and measurements made from 15 minutes after exposure. The earliest significant depression of spleen P/O ratios was found at 2 hours. Other tissues such as liver and regenerating liver were also examined, but no effect could be found at 4 hours, even with considerably higher doses. The effect of cytochrome c on spleen mitochondrial respiration has already been mentioned; after irradiation there was an even greater dependence of the phosphorylating mechanism on added cytochrome c. So far no definite reason for this can be advanced. It was also found that a decrease in phosphorylating capacity could occur in mouse spleen mitochondria after 1100 r with no alteration in their ATPase activity. Throughout the experiments histological examinations were carried out, and it was concluded that "The development of nuclear and cytoplasmic damage ran roughly parallel."

b. Mitochondria Irradiated in Vitro. The effect of X- or γ-irradiation *in vitro* on the phosphorylating ability of mitochondria have also been investigated (28, 143, 149), but no effects have been detected in spleen mitochondria with doses up to 20,000 r. A reduction in phosphorylation by rat or mouse liver mitochondria with succinate as substrate has been claimed with doses of 10^4 r or more (145, 154).

It appears from these results that there is a reduction in mitochondrial capacity for ATP generation in radiosensitive tissues after irradiation *in vivo*. Such a fall will obviously reduce the energy available for synthetic processes, and indeed many such reactions, especially those associated with the nucleus, are known to be affected. Van Bekkum considers that the lack of any effect on isolated mitochondria carries little weight, but it seems to us that, since *in vivo* the effect is not immediate and is subsequent to nuclear damage, cell death is not initiated by a defect in mitochondrial energy generation. The causal relationships between the mitochondrial damage and that to the nucleus are still obscure.

2. NUCLEI PREPARED FROM IRRADIATED ANIMALS

Although mitochondria are regarded as the main sites of ATP generation in the cell, Osawa *et al.* (155) have demonstrated the capacity of calf thymus nuclei isolated in sucrose–$CaCl_2$ to generate ATP at 0°C. The importance of this finding is so far uncertain, but it is unlikely that it can contribute appreciably to the over-all production of ATP in the cell. It may, though, be of extreme importance in synthetic processes within the nucleus itself. Creasey and Stocken (156) have investigated the capacity of nuclei from various rat tissues to generate ATP after X-irradiation. Liver, pancreas, kidney, and brain have so far failed to show ATP production under normal conditions, but in spleen, thymus, bone marrow, lymph nodes, and intestinal mucosa the generation is completely inhibited 1 hour after exposure of the rats to 100 r. A dose of 25 r is sufficient to produce 50 to 80% inhibition, and the effect can be detected 3 to 6 minutes after exposure.

B. CONCENTRATION OF, AND ISOTOPE UPTAKE INTO, ACID-SOLUBLE PHOSPHATES

In an attempt to assess the relation between the fall in oxidative phosphorylation and the reduction in synthetic processes it is important to consider the actual concentrations of high-energy phosphate compounds at different times after exposure.

Forssberg and Hevesy (157) continued the earlier work of von Euler and Hevesy (158) on the distribution of P^{32} after irradiation. Mice were given P^{32} immediately after exposure to 2000 r and killed 15 minutes later. Irradiated livers contained about 40% more counts than the controls, and there was a slight decrease in bone and muscle. Later work (159, 160) showed that 5 minutes after 800 r the specific activity of liver inorganic phosphate had risen to 140 % of the control, that of acid-labile P to 199 %, and that of ATP to 113 %. By 1 hour the figures were 105 %, 142 %, and 86 %, respectively. With 508 r there was an equal rate of disappearance of P[32] from the plasma of control and irradiated animals. Denson et al. (103) found that 24 hours after 1000 r there was a fall in rat liver labile P per 100 gm of liver which returned to normal by 5 days. In Ehrlich ascites tumors (161) after 1250 r there was an increased concentration of ATP + ADP at 35 minutes after exposure with a reduced C[14] uptake from glycine-2-C[14]. By 90 minutes the concentration and specific activity were normal, but the concentration had fallen by 100 minutes and was back again to normal by 140 minutes.

Similar experiments have been carried out in the radiosensitive tissues. Lutwak-Mann (162) found a marked fall in ATP concentration in rabbit bone marrow 3 hours after 1000 r. Ord and Stocken (163) could not detect any difference in concentration or P[32] specific activity of inorganic phosphate or ATP in rat thymus 1 hour after 1000 r. Separation of the nucleotides on Dowex (164) gave similar results—at most a 10 % rise in ATP concentration and a slight fall in that of ADP. AMP was unaffected. The time at which the phosphates are analyzed radically affects the change observed, since by 4 hours after 700 r van Bekkum (164a) found that in both rat thymus and spleen there was a fall in the specific activities of ATP and ADP, although in spleen, on which most of the experiments were performed, the concentration of the adenosine polyphosphates was again unchanged. At still later times (3 days) the ATP content of rat and mouse spleen after 400 to 800 r was reduced (165). In guinea pigs 400 r caused a slower decline in spleen ATP. In rat skin 700 r produced a fall in ATP by 24 hours, and inorganic phosphate and glucose-1-phosphate were increased (136).

Irradiation in vitro of mouse liver slices did not affect the specific activities of the acid-soluble phosphates (159), but much larger doses (20 to 25 kr) to Yoshida tumor cells (132, 166) produced a slight rise in ADP and a fall in ATP content; glycolysis was simultaneously inhibited. These facts together with the concomitant accumulation of fructose diphosphate and dihydroxyacetone phosphate led these authors to conclude that a block had been effected at the triose phosphate dehydrogenase stage. With thymocytes given 950 r Ord and Stocken found a slight increase in specific activity of ATP with no effect on O_2 uptake (146).

These data show that there are marked but transitory changes in acid-soluble phosphates after irradiation. The interpretation of the alterations in liver is complicated by the prominent disturbances in carbohydrate metabolism which are also taking place in this organ, but, although there is little evidence for a pronounced rise in P[32] specific activity or ATP concentration in rat thymus, there is equally no evidence of a fall until sometime after 1 hour post irradiation. This would be in agreement with van Bek-kum's finding that oxidative phosphorylation in spleen mitochondria was not affected in the first hour after 700 r. The cytochrome c effect which he found very soon after exposure may reflect direct damage to the mito-chondrion, again with consequent reduction in oxidative phosphorylation.

V. Anabolic Processes

A. LIPIDS

1. LIVER AND PLASMA

a. Tissue Levels. Probably the most striking evidence of a disturbance in fat metabolism is the finding by Rosenthal (167) that an opalescent ap-pearance of rabbit plasma or serum within 24 hours of irradiation was a reliable indication that the animal would subsequently die. This has been followed up in great detail. Entenman and his colleagues (168, 168a) have shown that the increase in serum lipids can be induced in rats, mice, dogs, and guinea pigs as well as in rabbits. The eliciting dose and the time at which the rise in lipids is detectable varies with the different species; the onset was most rapid in rabbits and required the highest exposure in guinea pigs (but cf. ref. 169). In rabbits 24 hours after 1000 r the greatest increase was in neutral fat; phospholipid increased by 140 to 190%, and cholesterol by 70 to 80% (169, 170). If the plasma lipid fractions were compared from animals which survived and from those which died within 30 days, the in-creases were much greater in the animals which died, and they did not diminish within 48 hours, unlike the levels in animals which survived (171). Local irradiation of a rabbit hind limb with 10,000 to 30,000 r (172) also caused the alteration in plasma lipid. The nature of the opalescence in rab-bit serum was investigated by Hewitt and his associates (173, 174); they showed that it was associated with an alteration in concentration and type of plasma phospholipid, the detailed changes being an idiosyncratic as well as a species response.

Since the bulk of plasma phospholipid synthesis occurs in the liver, it was natural to examine liver lipids after exposure. Bacq et al. (175) had observed a decreased rate of fat disappearance from the carcasses of rats exposed to 1000 r. There were, however, no differences in the quantity or quality of the liver fats, and this latter finding has been repeatedly con-firmed. Coniglio and his colleagues (176, 177) used rats exposed to 500 to 650 r and found that there was no difference between these rats and pair-fed controls with respect to fat absorption (see also ref. 178) and liver cholesterol, total lipid, and phospholipid, Comparable results were found in rhesus monkeys given 325 to 650 r. Buchanan et al. (179) carried out similar experiments and found no change in rat liver phosphatidyl choline after 500 r; 48 hours after 1000 or 2000 r the amount of phospholipid was not significantly different, and the per cent of fat in the liver remained constant, as did the phospholipid/total lipid ratio. An increase in liver weight in rats post irradiation is well-established (cf. ref. 180). Cornatzer *et al.* (181) also found no difference in rat liver cholesterol or phospholipid phosphorus in tissue (wet weight) 18 or 120 hours after 700 r, nor was any difference observed in these constituents in kidney. Weinman *et al.* (182) extended this to show no difference in phospholipid distribution between liver cell fractions 24 hours after 2500 r.

    b. Precursor Uptake into Liver Lipids. Some of the results with different tracers are shown in Table IV. There seems to be good evidence that acetate incorporation into rat liver fatty acids increases both if given to the intact animal or if uptake by slices is measured. A period of 24 to 48 hours seems to elapse before maximal effects are present, and rather high doses are required to produce very marked changes. Coniglio *et al.* (185) found no difference in $C^{14}O_2$ production from acetate between control and irradiated animals, with a twofold increase in fatty acid counts in the livers of the exposed rats. These workers did not find close correlation between the rise in liver glycogen levels and increased C^{14} incorporation (185, 188), although it is improbable that the two phenomena do not interact.

    The results on precursor uptake into liver phospholipids are more difficult to interpret. After total-body irradiation exceeding 700 r, P^{32} incorporation into rat liver slice phospholipids appears to increase (182), and the increase is present in nuclei, mitochondria, microsomes, and supernatant. If, however, the tracer is given to the irradiated animal, no difference in specific activity of liver phospholipids is found between control and irradiated animals. It seems likely that different conditions obtain in these two experiments, since incubation of slices in the medium described almost certainly produces glycogenolysis, whereas *in vivo* glycogen synthesis is occurring. If acetate is used *in vivo*, uptake into the liver phospholipids is either normal or slightly increased, and if glyceryl stearate is used, incorporation into liver phospholipids *in vivo* is decreased. These differences in behavior of precursors for different parts of the phospholipid molecule are not unexpected, in view of the findings of Kline *et al.* (193) that fasting also affects different tracer uptakes into rat liver phospholipids to varying extents. Owing to the complex pathways of phospholipid synthesis (194) and their interdependence on nucleotide, carbohydrate, and simple fat metabolism, it is difficult at the moment to foretell the changes which will occur under pathological conditions.

    Incorporation into liver cholesterol is also markedly affected. Again the effect *in vivo* does not occur immediately, but it is present in incorporation studies in the intact animal and also with cell-free preparations, where it is

TABLE IV

PRECURSOR UPTAKE INTO LIVER LIPIDS POSTIRRADIATION

Species	Dose (r)	Time after exposure	Preparation	Tracer	Effect	Comment	Ref.
Rats	700	18 hr	Slices, phospholipids	P32	None	Fasted	(181)
	1000	24 hr	Slices, phospholipids	P32	40–60% increase	Fasted	(182)
	2500	24 hr	Intact rat	P32	None		(182)
Mice	2000	34, 70 hr	Regenerating liver	P32	None		(183)
	510	30 min	Liver	P32	Large increase		(160)
		6 hr	Phospholipids	P32	Decrease		(160)
Rats	200	24 hr	Slices, fatty acid	Acetate-1-C14	Detectably increased	Fasted	(184)
	2500	24 hr	Slices, fatty acid	Acetate-1-C14	Marked increase	Fasted	(184)
Mice			Slices, fatty acid	Acetate-1-C14	None	Fasted	(184)
Rats	750	22 hr	Intact rat, fatty acid	Acetate-1-C14	Increase	Fasted	(185)
	1500	48 hr	Intact rat, fatty acid	Acetate-1-C14	Increase	Fasted	(186)
	1500	48 hr	Phospholipid	Acetate-1-C14	None	Fasted	(186)
	1500	48 hr	Phospholipid	Acetate-1-C14	Increase		(187)
	750	6 hr	Fatty acid	Acetate-1-C14	Increase	Fasted	(188)
	500	48 hr	Phospholipid	Stearic acid-1-C14	Decrease	Fasted	(186)
	1000	48 hr	Phospholipid		Decrease	Fasted	(186)
	500, 1000	48 hr	Phospholipid	Glyceride	Decrease	Fasted	(186)
Mice	2000, 2500		Fat	Glucose-u-C14a	Increase		(97)
Rats	2400	24 hr	Cholesterol	Acetate-1-C14	5- to 10-fold increase	Fasted	(189)
	2400	24 hr	Slices, cell-free preparation, cholesterol	Acetate-1-C14	10-fold increase	Fasted	(190)
	2400	48 hr	Slices, cholesterol	Acetate-1-C14	Increase		(191)
	2400	48 hr	Homogenate	MVA-2-C14	None		(191)
	2400	Immediate	Liver slices, cholesterol, fatty acid	Acetate-1-C14	Increase	In vitro exposure	(192)

[a] For uniformly labeled compounds, we have used the symbol "u."

the microsomes which are the site of sterol synthesis (195). The experiments of Gould and Popjak (191) make it clear that, as might be expected, the effect is in the steps leading to the formation of mevalonic acid (MVA) or its active form and not on the incorporation of MVA to cholesterol. In normal animals it seems probable that regulation of steroid synthesis occurs between acetyl CoA and MVA rather than at the later stages. Gould *et al.* (196) have found that adrenalectomy does not prevent the increased incorporation of C^{14}-acetate into cholesterol *in vivo*, although it has a marked effect on liver glycogen accumulation post irradiation. It is possible, therefore, that the hypophyseal hormones are of greater significance in the increased fat metabolism than those of the adrenal cortex, or that the blood sugar level found after irradiation of adrenalectomized rats is sufficiently high to permit increased fat turnover but not to allow overt glycogen synthesis.

Little evidence regarding fat mobilization after exposure seems available, but presumably the lipids liberated by tissue destruction enter the body fatty acid "pool," although there is not an increased CO_2 production from acetate nor, in rats, any signs of fatty livers. The increased retention of body fat post irradiation found by Bacq *et al.* (175) may be relevant in this connection, as may be the increase in plasma phospholipid levels.

2. OTHER TISSUES

Morehouse and Searcy (186) found some evidence of decreased glyceryl C^{14}-stearate retention in rat intestine 48 hours after 1000 r, and Coniglio *et al.* (185) also reported a decreased acetate-1-C^{14} uptake into intestinal phospholipids 23 hours after 750 r. In rabbit bone marrow Altman *et al.* (137) detected an immediate rise in acetate-2-C^{14} uptake into saturated and unsaturated fatty acids after 800 r. By 48 hours uptake was normal, but at 72 hours incorporation into the saturated fats had risen threefold, whereas that into unsaturated compounds was down to 18 % of the control value. By 7 days the position was reversed. They considered these changes to be associated with the filling of the hypoplastic marrow with fat and thought that there might be changes in the nature of marrow fat as a result of exposure. Lutwak-Mann (197) found no immediate fall in bone marrow phospholipid, but by 6 hours the amount (wet-weight basis) had begun to fall. By 10 days after 600 r the lipid content was returning to normal. She also noted that spleen lipids were reduced 2 days after 800 r.

Cornatzer *et al.* (181) also found a fall in rat spleen lipids 18 to 120 hours after 700 r, with little effect on cholesterol. In rat thymus Thomson *et al.* (23) showed that P^{32} uptake into phospholipid was unchanged 3 hours after 800 r of γ-irradiation and, after 100 r Harrington and Lavik (198) reported similar findings 3 to 48 hours post irradiation.

It seems, therefore, that phospholipid metabolism is not immediately affected in these tissues and that alterations in lipid content or precursor uptake some days after irradiation may be due to degenerative or regenerative changes in the organs. The immediate effects on bone marrow fat are more difficult to explain, although they are presumably part of the metabolic stimulation in this tissue immediately after exposure.

3. PEROXIDE FORMATION

The possibility of squalene and linoleic acid peroxide formation in liver or other tissues after irradiation has been reviewed (199, 200). Philpot and co-workers (200) concluded that "The facts known to us are consistent with the hypothesis that radiation toxicity in mammals is due to initiation of chain auto-oxidation of essential fatty acids producing lethal doses of peroxides . . . " So far, however, little work had been reported on the effects of toxic amounts of autoxidized linoleic acid on systems in which well-defined biochemical changes are produced by X-radiation.

B. PROTEINS

1. SERUM PROTEINS

Results from the examination of serum protein levels are given in Table V. Most work shows a fall in albumin and γ-globulin and an increase in the α- and β-globulins. Fischer $et\ al.$ (202) remarked that the fall in albumin in

TABLE V

SERUM OR PLASMA PROTEIN CHANGES AFTER X-IRRADIATION

Species	Dose (r)	Time after exposure (days)	Effect	Ref. (for references before end 1952, see ref. 49)
Rats	880	1–3	Fall in total protein, albumin, and γ-globulin; α- and β-globulins increased	(201)
	800	7	Fall in albumin and γ-globulin; rise in β-globulin; no change α-globulins	(202)
	650	3	Fall in γ-globulins; rise in α_2-globulin	(203)
	200–700	1–3	Fall in albumin; rise in α_1- and β-globulins	(204)
Dogs	500	9–11	Fall in A/G ratio	(205)
Mice	300	1–28	No change in albumin, α-, and β-globulins; fall in γ-globulin	(206)

their irradiated rats was probably due to inanition. The fall in γ-globulins may be related to the damage to lymphoid tissue. The rise in α- and β-globulins is perhaps associated with altered liver metabolism which is well established by the time the effects are most pronounced. There is no evidence, however, for decreased production of liver proteins.

2. PRECURSOR UPTAKE INTO HEMOGLOBIN

The effects of total-body irradiation on erythropoiesis are reviewed by Cronkite and Bond (128) and by Lajtha (207). Only effects on hemoglobin synthesis, which do not necessarily parallel those on red blood cell production or iron uptake, are presented here.

Richmond et al. (208), as part of their survey of changes in rabbit bone marrow after exposure, investigated glycine-2-C[14] uptake into hemin and globin of bone marrow and spleen homogenates prepared from rabbits exposed to 800 r. There was an immediate rise in incorporation into hemin, followed by a fall at 48 hours which persisted for 3 weeks. Uptake into globin was increased at 48 hours and had not recovered by 4 weeks, when that into hemin was tremendously raised. In spleen also there are differences between the effects on hemin and globin. Incorporation into spleen hemoglobin hemin increased immediately after irradiation and remained up, but that into globin rose initially and then went down. Nizet et al. (209) induced increased erythropoiesis in dogs. The animals were then bled, and glycine-2-C[14] uptake into blood hemoglobin hemin *in vitro* was measured after 500 r of total-body irradiation or after irradiation of the blood *in vitro*. Under both circumstances increased incorporation occurred, and if plasma from an irradiated dog was incubated with control blood there was again a greater uptake. They therefore concluded that irradiation increased the presence in the circulation of some stimulatory humoral factor. No effect on glycine uptake *in vivo* into erythrocyte globin was detected by Richmond et al. (210) in rats 1 hour after 1000 r.

3. PRECURSOR UPTAKE INTO OTHER TISSUE PROTEINS

Our knowledge of the difference in radiosensitivity between nucleic acid and protein synthesis is mainly due to the experiments of Hevesy (211, 212). These experiments showed that uptake of acetate, which becomes incorporated into both nucleic acids and proteins, was inhibited in the former and unaffected in the latter as a result of X-radiation. Similar experiments by Abrams (213) with glycine-1-C[14] emphasized this difference, as did the results of Holmes and Mee (214) with simultaneous methionine-S[35] and P[32] uptake into rat Jensen sarcoma after irradiation of the tumor, and of Forssberg and Klein (161) with glycine-1-C[14] uptake into mouse ascites tumors. Similarly Hokin and Hokin (215) found in mouse pancreas no reduction in amylase synthesis when incorporation of P^{32} into DNA was reduced, and Aleksandrov (216) found only transient changes in methionine-S^{35} uptake by mouse liver and brain after 500 r, although the relative specific activity of kidney protein was increased over that in control ani mals throughout the week after irradiation.

Hevesy's experiments (212) had also shown a stimulation of acetate incorporation into liver proteins after irradiation; this has been confirmed by Kay and Entenman (217), using glycine-1-C^{14} uptake by slices removed from rats given 2500 r 24 to 72 hours previously. The animals were fasted after irradiation, but the livers would presumably contain glycogen so that the difference from the starved controls might therefore be the result of differences in the availability of precursor rather than a direct effect of X-radiation. The effect is, however, detectable fairly early after exposure, since Butler *et al.* (218) and Richmond *et al.* (210) found slightly increased incorporation of amino acids *in vivo* into various rat liver cell fractions isolated 1 hour after 500 r or 1000 r.

In the thymus, on the other hand, we found (210) that glycine-2-C^{14} and lysine-u-C^{14} incorporations into nuclear proteins were inhibited 1 hour after 1000 r, although uptake into proteins from some cytoplasmic fractions was unaffected. This result is in agreement with other evidence for immediate damage to nuclear synthetic processes which is discussed in the next section, and also with some experiments of Pelc (219) on the incorporation of methionine-S^{35} into mouse trachea epithelial cells. Radioautography was used, and it is possible to differentiate nuclear from cytoplasmic S^{35} uptake. Only the former was inhibited at 4 hours by 200 r or 1000 r of total-body irradiation.

C. Nucleic Acids

Since the discovery by von Euler and Hevesy (158) that there was a decrease in the incorporation of inorganic P^{32} into the DNA of rat Jensen sarcoma after X-irradiation, a wealth of data on this topic has been published. We cannot attempt therefore to cover the whole of the field, which has been comprehensively reviewed by Hevesy and Forssberg (220), Howard (221), Errera (26), Kelly (222), and Hevesy (223), but we shall try to provide some representative data from animal experiments mainly reported since 1953 and to discuss the results in the light of the present outstanding problems.

The quoted results in Tables VI through X have been expressed as per cent of control figures for the sake of uniformity, and often only the results obtained early after exposure have been included.

1. IRRADIATION OF THE INTACT ANIMAL

a. Cell Death and Population Changes. The evidence now available (Tables VI through X) has established clearly that after exposure there is usually a fall in the nucleic acid content of tissues, with DNA being especially affected, and that this fall is accompanied by a decreased rate of incorporation of various isotopically labeled precursors into DNA and sometimes RNA. The present uncertainty is whether these changes are due to a primary action on the DNA-synthesizing mechanism or whether they result from cell death and/or changes in the population in the tissues studied.

Examination of Table VI shows that decreases in DNA and RNA concentrations have taken place as early as 3 hours after irradiation in certain tissues. Too many of the data unfortunately have been obtained at much longer times after exposure, so that any fall is likely to be due to a loss of sensitive cells, especially from tissues such as spleen and thymus. Very often rather similar changes in DNA and RNA content occur, supporting the idea that the changes are caused by disappearance of cells, and this is even more probable by the results of Thomson *et al.* (235) when, after irradiation of rabbit bone marrow, there was no change in the amount of DNA expressed on a nuclear basis.

The results of some of the incorporation studies are shown in Table VII. With the exception of rabbit thymus, when the abdomen only was irradiated and the rest of the body shielded, all the tissues exhibited a decreased precursor uptake into DNA if examined in the first 2 hours after exposure. Most of the doses were in the lethal range, but there is evidence from examination of rat thymus DNA 2 hours after irradiation (163) that a reduction of P^{32} incorporation is certainly produced by 50 r and probably by as little as 25 r. The possibility that these rather early changes are due to an altered cell population seems unlikely, since it has been shown by us (29) that virtually identical inhibition of P^{32} uptake into rat thymus is found from 3 minutes to 2 hours after exposure. Control and irradiated animals were treated similarly except for the irradiation. Table VII also shows that the effects of X-radiation on precursor uptake into DNA are not limited to "radiosensitive" tissues. Other changes—for example, certain enzyme activities—do, however, tend to be confined to spleen, thymus, and bone marrow and not to be present in such tissues as kidney and pancreas.

If the results on precursor uptake and DNA content are compared, it can be seen that, although there is this initial fall in uptake in all tissues, this is not invariably followed by a reduced DNA concentration. The data available are inadequate for a firm conclusion to be reached, but generally it appears that exposures of 400 to 500 r tend to reduce the DNA content of "radiosensitive" tissues only and to have little effect on others.

Relevant to these considerations is the question of recovery. Reduced precursor uptake and nucleic acid content are functions of the dose received, the tissue studied, and the time after exposure at which the tissue is examined. For example, in mice after 800 r, uptake into all the tissues examined was depressed 2 hours after exposure, but by 24 hours the specific activity of intestinal DNA was back to the control level, whereas that in spleen and liver was still depressed (241). A comparison of the extent of the reduction at any one time in a number of different tissues is therefore misleading, and factors such as the normal mitotic rate and the proportion of highly radiosensitive cells have also to be taken into account in comparing the effects of irradiation on DNA synthesis in different tissues.

The greatest weakness in the data provided, however, is that they do not give any answer to the vexing question of cell death. It is highly likely that at times later than 2 hours after exposure dying or dead cells are present in all tissues, especially the "radiosensitive" ones (cf. Trowell, 246), and these dead cells could easily account for the reduced precursor uptake. Most tissues show greater inhibitions by 24 hours after lethal exposures than at times up to 2 hours after irradiation, and by 24 hours changed cell populations are certainly present in spleen and thymus. Unfortunately there are no adequate diagnostic criteria for cell death in immotile cell preparations, and it is probable that histological signs such as pyknosis are late rather than early signs of cell death. Disentanglement between cause and effect by examination of the inhibition of precursor uptake alone is impossible, so that many other approaches have been explored and will be discussed later in this section. (For further discussion, cf. refs. 222 and 247.)

b. The Sensitivity of Precursor Incorporation into RNA. Although uptake into DNA is depressed in all the tissues so far considered, this is not the case for RNA. It would seem that the distinction between radiosensitive and nonsensitive tissues can be substantiated if incorporation into RNA is studied. Liver, kidney, and pancreas all show unaffected incorporation into RNA or even an increase, whereas in spleen, appendix, thymus, and bone marrow it is reduced. The distinction between these two groups of tissues and the marked involution of the "sensitive" tissues after exposure is certainly not coincidental, and it must be noted that doses of 25 and 50 r have definite effects on uptake into rat thymus RNA (163) as well as into DNA.

It is now well known that two broad classes of RNA exist—nuclear RNA (n) and cytoplasmic RNA (c)—and within these classes there is good evidence for fractions with different metabolic activities. It is also possible that some fraction(s) of nuclear RNA may be intimately connected with the synthesis of some part(s) of cytoplasmic RNA. So far, little work has been done on fractionation within the two classes of RNA, but a number of ex-

TABLE VI
Nucleic Acid Content of Tissues after X-Irradiation

Tissue	Species	Dose (r)	Time after exposure (hr)	DNA (% control)	RNA (% control)	Comment	Ref.
Liver	Mouse	600	6	90	90	Food available post-irradiation	(224)
			18	35	90	Dry-weight basis	(225)
		800	48	125	150	Starved post-irradiation; DNA P/ liver	
			17	95	—		
	Rat	500 P^{32} β over 48 hr.	—	100	100	Exposure by toxic doses P^{32}	(226)
Brain	Rat	700	12	88	—	Fat-free, dry-weight basis	(227)
Kidney	Rat	400	48	75	80	Organ basis	(228)
Lung	Rat	400	72	70	70	Organ basis	(229)
Spleen	Mouse	740	24	20.5	—	Reduction/organ or dry-weight basis	(230)
	Rat	1500	2.5	81.5	74.5	Dry-weight basis	(231)
		400	48	20	42	Organ basis	(228)
		500	96	37	64	Wet-weight basis	(162)
		300	6	—	—	Total nucleic acids, 90% of control	(197)
		800	6	—	—	64% of control	(197)
		500	—	58	82	Toxic dose P^{32}	(226)
Intestine	Mouse	800	17	82	—		(225)
		200	24	70	—	Organ basis	(232)
		750	48	67	—	Organ basis	(232)
Thymus	Rat	500	—	48	63	Toxic dose P^{32}	(226)
		400	48	10	20	Organ basis	(228)
		800	3	85	92	DNA P/dry-weight basis	(23)
		100	24	100	—	Wet-weight basis	(233)

Bone marrow	Rat	325	24	50	58	Local irradiation	(234)
		500	6	—	—	Total nucleic acid, 50% of control, wet-weight basis	(162)
	Rabbit	1500	3	56	83	Wet-weight basis	(162)
Appendix	Rabbit	620	48	79	70	Local irradiation; no change/nucleus	(235)
	Rabbit	1000	4	88	100	DNA P/dry-weight basis	(236)
Testes	Rat	500	96	87	85	Wet-weight basis	(162)

TABLE VII

INCORPORATION OF ISOTOPICALLY LABELED PRECURSORS INTO
NUCLEIC ACIDS AFTER X-IRRADIATION

Tissue	Species	Dose (r)	Time after exposure (hr)	Precursor	DNA (% control)	RNA (% control)	Ref.
Bone marrow	Rat	725	48	Formate	1–14 (ad-gua)		(237)
	Mouse	750	4.5	Formate	2 (ad)	25	(238)
					8 (gua)	26 (gua)	
	Rabbit	1000, abdominal exposure	2	P	56	56 (n) 50 (c)	(239)
Spleen	Rat	725	48	Formate	1–14 (ad-gua)	—	(237)
		750	4.5	Formate	6 (ad)	11 (ad)	(238)
					21 (gua)	7 (gua)	
		1000	2	P	40	67	(163)
	Mouse	800	24	P	2.5	—	(240)
		800	2	P	21	—	(241)
Intestine	Rat	725	48	Formate	More than 68	—	(237)
		750	4.5	Formate	41 (ad)	92 (ad)	(238)
					87 (gua)	78 (gua)	
	Mouse	800	4	P	49	—	(241)
		800	1	Thymidine	100	—	(242)
Thymus	Rat	800	3	P	47	60	(23)
		100	24	P	50	—	(233)
				Orotic acid	19–44	—	
				Adenine	100–140	—	
				Formate	60–120 (ad)	—	
				Formate	30–70 (gua)	—	
				Formate	120 (thy)	—	
		1000	0.05	P	49	—	(29)
			0.5	P	61	72 (n) 76 (c)	(29)
			1	P	46	72	*
			2	P	46	57 (n) 65 (c)	(29)
			24	P	2	5 (n) 6 (c)	(29)
	Rabbit	1000, abdominal exposure	2	P	119	100 (n) 112 (c)	(239)
Appendix	Rabbit	1000, abdominal exposure	2	P	41	62 (n) 75 (c)	(239)

* Ord and Stocken, unpublished data.

TABLE VII—*Continued*

Tissue	Species	Dose (r)	Time after exposure (hr)	Precursor	DNA (% control)	RNA (% control)	Ref.
Liver	Mouse	800	24	P	16	—	(240)
		800	2	P	59	—	(241)
		400	96	Adenine	48 (ad) 100 (gua)	104 (ad) 160 (gua)	(243)
		600	2.5	P	67	71 (n) 109 (c)	(244)
	Rat	2500	28.5	P	15	80 (n) 133 (c)	(244)
		1000	2	P	31–97	94 (n) 113 (c)	(163)
		1000	2	P	52	—	(210)
				Glycine	116	—	
Kidney	Mouse	800	24	P	20	—	(240)
			2	P	81	—	(241)
	Rabbit	1000, abdominal exposure	2	P	77	146 (n) 154 (c)	(239)
Lungs	Mouse	800	24	P	5	—	(240)
		800	2	P	42	—	(241)
Pancreas	Mouse	2000	24	P incorporation *in vitro*	50	100	(215)
Chick embryo		400	120	Formate	50 (ad) 50 (gua) 50 (thy)	100 (ad, gua)	(245)

periments with results on n- and c-RNA are available and indicate a similarity in response in the two fractions. Heterogeneity of DNA also is being explored, and Bendich and his colleagues (248) have provided some evidence for metabolic heterogeneity also. Backmann and Harbers have found slightly different radiosensitivities of the two sorts of DNA in rat Walker carcinoma (249, 250). As our knowledge in this field in normal animals is extended, it will be very interesting to see whether differential effects in other tissues are detected.

c. Incorporation into Tumors. The effect of X-radiation on tumors has been studied not only for its intrinsic importance but also as a possible means of eliminating changes due to variations in cell population as a factor in the interpretation of this type of experiment. Ascites tumors have obvious advantages in this respect, and some of the results obtained within the last five years are shown in Tables VIII and IX. Unfortunately there is

TABLE VIII

Nucleic Acid Content of Tumors after X-Irradiation

Tumor	Host	Dose (r)	Time after expo-sure (hr)	DNA (% control)	RNA (% control)	Comment	Ref.
Ehrlich ascites	Mouse	1250	0–50	Very slight increase	Increase	Cell basis	(251)
Ehrlich ascites	Mouse	800	12	120	—	Cell basis	(252)
			48	140	—		
		1400	24	130	—	Cell basis	
Yoshida sarcoma	Rat	1000	24	No change	140	Cell basis	(253)
Walker carcinoma	Rat	5000, local	2	—	—	DNA fractionated DNA$_1$/ DNA$_2$ fell from 2.6 to 0.26	(249)

some disagreement in the results with Ehrlich ascites tumors. Klein and Forssberg (161, 251, 256) found slightly impaired glycine incorporation into both DNA and RNA immediately after exposure, but at 48 hours they found the cells to have an increased volume and RNA content but normal amounts of DNA. They concluded that there was a specific inhibitory effect on DNA synthesis such that incorporation of glycine still occurred but there was no net increase in amount. On the other hand, Kelly and her colleagues (252) could not confirm a failure in DNA synthesis, and Kelly concludes (222) that "Experiments with ascites tumors support the concept that DNA synthesis is relatively radioresistant and can proceed normally for some time after radiation," especially if changes in cell population and mitotic delay are taken into account.

The experiments of Harrington and Lavik (257) are also interesting. They found two conditions necessary to produce an effect on incorporation into Ehrlich ascites tumors—the cells had to have been irradiated; i.e., the introduction of normal ascites cells into an irradiated host did not produce any effect—and, also, contact with irradiated nontumor tissue at some time was essential. Little effect was detectable if the animal was exposed and the tumor then inoculated into and examined in a normal animal. Further evidence for indirect effects are mentioned in the following section.

TABLE IX

INCORPORATION OF ISOTOPICALLY LABELED PRECURSORS INTO THE NUCLEIC
ACIDS OF TUMORS AFTER X-IRRADIATION

Tumor	Host	Dose (r)	Time after exposure (hr)	Precursor	DNA (% control)	RNA (% control)	Ref.
Erlich tetraploid	Mouse	1000	3	P	69	87	(254)
Erlich Lettre hyperdiploid		1000–5000	3	P	95–103	99–104	(254)
6C3HED		1000	3	P	94	115	(254)
		5000	3	P	54	134	
TA3		250	3	P	135	114	(254)
		1000	3	P	74	85	
Mammary carcinoma		800	48	P	52	69 (c)	(241)
Lymphosarcoma		800	4	P	55	—	(241)
Mammary carcinoma		4500–9000, local	0–24	P	53	Depression (n) Unchanged (c)	(255)
Sarcoma 37		400	96	Adenine	100 (ad) 146 (gua)	140 (ad) 165 (gua)	(243)
Erlich ascites		1250	0.5 1	Glycine	72 94	63 73	(161)
		800	12 36	P	150 40	— —	(252)
Walker carcinoma	Rat	5000, local	2	P	50 Control DNA₁/ DNA₂ = 1; irradiation ratio = 1.23	—	(149)

d. Abscopal Effects. Abscopal effects on precursor uptake were first reported by Ahlström *et al.* (258), who observed the depression of P^{32} uptake into DNA of tumors after irradiation of one tumor and examination of a second. These results were confirmed by Holmes (259), Kelly and Jones (260), and Vermund *et al.* (255) in similar experiments, but in the light of later experiments by Ahlström *et al.* (261) the effect of trauma itself cannot be excluded as a contributory factor. Another approach has been the comparison of the effects of whole-body and local irradiation of a given tissue.

Mandel *et al.* (234), for example, studied P^{32} uptake into the bone marrow of rat hind limb and found that 24 hours after 700 r the depression in uptake was approximately the same, but recovery was much slower after total-body irradiation. This is not unexpected in view of the probable formation of essential DNA precursors for DNA, such as the nitrogen bases, in tissues such as liver (262), where grossly reoriented metabolism is known to be produced by whole-body exposures. There is little evidence for damage to the purine-synthesizing mechanism itself.

There is no alteration in the reduction of P^{32} incorporation into rat thymus nucleic acids 2 hours after 1000 r if adrenalectomized animals are exposed (163).

2. THE SITE OF THE LESION IN DNA SYNTHESIS

a. The Relation between DNA Synthesis and Mitosis. The effects of X-radiation on mitosis and the mitotic apparatus are considered in other chapters; unfortunately, too little information is available relating the genetic consequences to biochemical changes. It is, however, obvious that mitotic arrest would itself cause an inhibition in DNA synthesis. The temporal relation between mitosis and DNA synthesis has been explored in several cell types; in the cases to be considered here, synthesis takes place in interphase. It is generally assumed that in dividing cells DNA, once formed, is metabolically stable and that precursor incorporation occurs only at synthesis. The position in tissues with low mitotic indices is less certain, and some evidence is available suggesting that limited precursor uptake can occur unconnected with cell division (263). Most experimental data have come from radioautographic studies in tissue cultures, but chemical analyses in regenerating liver have also been reported.

(i) Regenerating liver. Although normal liver with its low mitotic rate shows only slight precursor uptake into DNA, incorporation into regenerating liver is much more easily measured and has the tremendous advantage that the cells are partly synchronized with DNA synthesis maximal about 24 hours after partial hepatectomy and the peak in the mitotic count 27 to 30 hours after operation. The effects of X-radiation on precursor uptake into this preparation are shown in Table X. Most of the work reported is on rat livers regenerating after surgical hepatectomy. Holmes and Mee (264) and Holmes (270) have established that doses of 450 r given locally to the liver will reduce precursor uptake into DNA except if given during the peak synthetic period, when they exert no effect on incorporation: A much larger dose (2000 r) did, however, reduce the incorporation of P^{32} into DNA regardless of the time of irradiation during the cycle. The inhibition of precursor uptake is not absolute, but rather there is a delayed onset of synthesis and of mitosis, and the whole process eventually goes

TABLE X

THE INCORPORATION OF ISOTOPICALLY LABELED PRECURSORS INTO THE
NUCLEIC ACIDS OF REGENERATING LIVERS AFTER X-RADIATION

Species	Dose (r)	Times from partial hepatectomy to:		Precursor	DNA (% control)	RNA (% control)	Ref.
		Exposure (hr)	Death (hr)				
Rat	450, local	12–17	27–29	P	30	—	(264)
		19	22–23	P	100	—	(264)
		46	49	P	50–92	—	(264)
		48	60	P	20	—	(264)
	2200, local	19	23	P	50	—	(264)
	2200, local	18–25	21–28	Formate	34–58	—	(265)
				P	34–61	—	(265)
	800 γ	24	72	P	41	137 (n) ± (c)	(266)
	1000	28	30	P	26	81 (c)	(163)
		42	44	P	61	126 (n)	(163)
		47	49	P	63	97 (n) 92 (c)	(163)
	500	Immediately before	24	Formate in vitro	29–51 (ad) 65 (gua) 26–46 (thy)	83–4 (ad) 91 (gua)	(267)
		12	24	Formate in vitro	81–92 (ad) 52–87 (gua)	92–109 (ad) 70–113 (gua)	(267)
		24	24	Formate in vitro	133 (ad) 76 (gua) 102 (thy)	157 (ad) 120 (gua)	(267)
	1500	28–29.25	30.5–31.75	Orotic acid	75	—	(268)
	1500	14–15.25	16.5–17.75	Orotic acid	3	—	(268)
Mouse	800	0, 12, 72, 84, 96	12–24 hr later	P	20–60	—	(269)
CCl₄ poisoning	800	24, 41	24 hr later	P	100	—	(269)

forward in an effectively normal manner. Larger exposures appear to inhibit incorporation at any period in the cycle. Rather similar experiments have been carried out by Potter and his colleagues (268), who have been studying the mechanism of pyrimidine incorporation into nucleic acids of regenerating rat liver (271, 272). Initially it was shown that if the rats were irradiated at any time from 6 to 30 hours after hepatectomy and killed 24 hours later, orotic acid incorporation into DNA was reduced. Uptake into c-RNA was unaffected. These results apparently are in contrast with those of Holmes and Mee (264) but, further experiments showed that if incorporation was measured only for 2.5 hours after exposure and irradiation was given between 14 and 15.25 hours after hepatectomy uptake into DNA was almost completely inhibited after 1500 r, whereas if the dose was given 28 to 29.25 hours after operation only about 25 % depression occurred. Some very interesting suggestions were advanced: "The data obtained certainly justify the view that the potentiality for DNA synthesis is rather quickly and directly affected in those cells in which it has not yet begun. . . . It might be suggested that there are [periods of varying sensitivity] in each cycle i.e. a sensitive period in interphase when preparation for DNA synthesis is blocked . . . and [a period of insensitivity which is] pronounced when radiation is delivered at a time when the number of cells engaged in DNA synthesis [is] maximal and the measurement [is] made when these cells [are] the ones chiefly responsible for any DNA synthesis that [can] be observed. This result is interpreted to mean that the so-called insensitive period for the synthesis occurs during the time that synthesis is actually in progress."

The results of Kelly *et al.* (222, 269) with CCl_4-poisoned mice are somewhat at variance with the results in rats, although they could reproduce a delaying effect on DNA synthesis by irradiation during the first 12 hours after CCl_4 administration. No inhibition was found, however, if irradiation with either 800 or 2000 r was given in the synthetic period, but the difference in species and mode of hepatectomy may account for this divergence. The conclusion to be reached from these experiments is that irradiation with doses of 450 r or less produces a delay in DNA synthesis and cell division.

(*ii*) *Bean root tips and bone marrow.* The now classical experiments of Howard and Pelc (12) established that incorporation of P^{32} into DNA of bean root tips (*Vicia faba*) occurred only in cells which were shortly to divide. They could distinguish three periods in interphase—a period (G_1) of about 12 hours immediately after mitosis in which synthesis of DNA did not occur, a synthetic period (S, 6 hours) during which precursor uptake took place, followed by a lapse of about 4 hours (G_2) before mitosis commenced. Irradiation of cells in interphase was most effective in reducing DNA synthesis if exposure occurred in the G_1 period. Much higher doses were required for inhibition if irradiation took place in S. They concluded (273) that "It is questionable whether the effect of such high doses is a primary effect on DNA synthesis or whether it is a consequence of interference with some other process. It would be tempting to assume that the effect of high doses is due to an interference with existing DNA in such a way that the presumed self-duplication is made impossible but there is little evidence for this."

Lajtha and his colleagues (13, 274, 275) have extended this approach in experiments with human bone marrow cultures using adenine or formate as precursors. Similar interphase periods are distinguishable in these cells, and irradiation in G_1 with 200 to 300 rads will cause a 40 to 50 % depression in the number of cells entering the subsequent S period in a given time, whereas exposures to more than 300 rads are required in the S period to inhibit DNA synthesis. After exposure in G_1, DNA synthesis in the cells which actually enter the synthetic period appears unaffected. Lajtha *et al.*

(275) suggest that the effect on DNA synthesis is not simply related to chromosome damage and cell viability, because damage brought about by irradiation in G_1 is saturated by 200 to 300 rads, whereas chromosome damage and cell viability is further dose-dependent. We do not yet know how the possible stages in DNA synthesis are related to these interphase divisions, but the measurements are based on incorporation into DNA in the terminal stage. How far the preliminary association of deoxyribomononucleotides (DMP) occurs in G_1 is unknown also, but from the effect in G_1 Lajtha et al. have concluded: "There is a system connected with but not identical to DNA synthesis which is more radiosensitive than the process of DNA synthesis" (275).

To summarize all these results at recognized periods in interphase, there seems to be fairly good agreement that low doses of irradiation cause a delay in the processes leading to DNA synthesis and in the onset of mitosis, and that larger doses are required to block DNA synthesis itself. If this latter action is associated with damage to the DNA template—an attractive hypothesis—it cannot be established at the present time that it is not also, or indeed consequentially, related to damage to the cell sufficient to cause death.

b. *Irradiation of Other Systems in Vitro.* (i) *The sensitivity of DNA synthesis in vitro.* Besides their use in analysis of the relation of DNA synthesis to mitosis, studies on the incorporation into DNA after irradiation *in vitro* have been carried out on homogenates and cell suspensions in an attempt to obtain systems isolated from any abscopal effects and yielding sufficient material for biochemical analysis.

Totter and his colleagues (276, 277) have studied formate uptake into the DNA of bone marrow homogenates and chick embryo suspensions after irradiation from a Co^{60} source. It was established that over 90 % of the incorporation into DNA was into the methyl group of thymine (278), and this was inhibited by 2400 r in the case of bone marrow (50 % control) and by 5000 to 20,000 r in chick embryo. Glycine incorporation into guanine and thymine of chick embryo DNA was also depressed, but the effects on uptake of this precursor into DNA adenine were variable, and uptake of adenine itself into DNA was unaffected. Lajtha (279) obtained results rather different from those of Totter, using human bone marrow cultures after exposure to 1000 r, since he found equal reduction in the incorporation of both formate and adenine. He also noted "No indication . . . [of] the existence of a pre-synthetic accumulation of low molecular weight precursors using formate C^{14}."

In lymph node cultures we have found that 600 r of X-radiation depressed the uptake of P^{32} into DNA but not RNA in the first 2 hours after exposure (163), and in thymocyte suspensions the uptake was reduced to about 70 % of the control level 30 minutes after 950 r of γ-irradiation, again with no effect on RNA (146). There was some indication of an increased specific activity of ATP and GTP coincidentally with the decrease in specific activity of DNA.

Incorporation of precursors into the DNA of particle-free preparations from liver (280) and ascites tumor cells (281) has now been demonstrated, and uptake of thymidine and adenine into the DNA of the latter system is not affected by 500 r *in vitro*. The relation between the soluble DNA found in these preparations and that in the nucleus is not yet clear, but it may be presumed at least that in the nucleus there is a difference in physical state of the molecules leading to a greater degree of orientation. It is a disturbance of the orientation which has been implicated in X-radiation damage to intact cells.

(*ii*) *Intranuclear protein synthesis.* A very interesting paper on a property closely associated with DNA is that by Ficq and Errera (282), which demonstrates the sensitivity of isolated calf thymus nuclei to 950 r of X-rays. They studied incorporation of phenylalanine-2-C^{14} into these nuclei by radioautography. Little decrease in uptake was apparent 20 minutes after exposure, but by 40 minutes a lowering was detectable, and it was marked by 1 hour, when the incorporation was reduced to 30 to 50 % of the control value. It is particularly important that they were able to find some restoration from X-radiation effects on this process by the addition of DNA after exposure. This recalls the work of Allfrey and Mirsky (283), who first established the metabolic activities of these nuclei isolated in sucrose–$CaCl_2$ and showed that intranuclear generation of ATP, now known to be highly sensitive to X-irradiation *in vivo* (156), is prevented by removal of DNA and can be restored by addition of either DNA or RNA.

It would be enlightening to know if the intranuclear generation of ATP which is blocked by irradiation *in vitro* can be restored by readdition of DNA or whether in the experiments of Ficq and Errera the DNA is acting rather as a template for protein synthesis. No information is yet available regarding the identity of the proteins formed after restoration of their synthetic ability with those formed by control nuclei.

c. The Uniform Susceptibility of Different Precursors. The majority of the experiments carried out on precursor uptake into DNA after irradiation *in vivo* and *in vitro* demonstrates virtually identical sensitivity with all the tracers used. This is extended by many observations that there is little difference in the effects on uptake into the various nucleotides of DNA. Some anomalous results have, however, been reported with adenine; Harrington and Lavik (233) and Passoneau and Totter (277) found that, although uptake of other precursors into rat thymus and chick embryo DNA was blocked, that of adenine was unaffected. Bennett *et al.* (284), however, found that adenine uptake into the DNA of many mouse tissues was lowered after 800 r, and, even more significantly, Lajtha (279), repeating Passoneau and Totter's experiments with human bone marrow, could detect no difference in sensitivity between formate and adenine. It must be stressed, though, that it is now clear (285) that patterns of incorporation into DNA under conditions *in vitro* differ greatly from those obtaining during uptake *in vivo*, and it is probable also that precursor behavior under one set of conditions *in vitro* may differ markedly from that under other circumstances. We also have previously noted (146) that P^{32} distribution in DNA isolated from thymocyte suspensions after incorporation *in vitro* differed significantly from that shown after labeling *in vivo*, since uptake into purine deoxyribonucleotides was relatively much reduced. Earlier experiments (163) with thymocyte suspensions in a different medium showed that although P^{32} incorporation occurred the cells were not radiosensitive *in vitro*, and this was attributable to visible changes in their structure. It would seem, therefore, that experimental conditions may be imposed such that the cells are no longer susceptible to further insult and also that, although sensitivity may be apparent, the behavior of the cells may be demonstrably different from that *in vivo*.

It would seem, therefore, most satisfactory at the present time to consider that different pathways of incorporation into DNA are probably all radiosensitive but that there may be certain conditions under which this sensitivity is not demonstrated and possibly a few ill-defined pathways which are more akin to turnover than synthesis, and which are also less readily affected.

These excepting clauses will include the results on liver found by Richmond *et al.* (210), who could show inhibition of phosphorus uptake into DNA but no sign of an effect if glycine was used. These authors point out that only one experiment was performed with glycine, and the level of activity in liver DNA with this substrate is very low, so that too much weight should not perhaps be attached to the divergence.

d. The Sensitivity of the DNA–Protein Complex. It is now almost universally assumed that DNA occurs in the nucleus in association with proteins and that it is the integrity of the DNA–protein complex(es)(DNAPC) which is essential for any function exerted by the DNA molecule. The behavior of DNA and of protein solutions *in vitro* after X-irradiation is discussed in other chapters. We are only concerned with actual evidence for damage to DNAPC or its components after irradiation *in vivo*.

(i) DNA. Studies on DNA isolated from tissues after exposure have presented serious technical difficulties, since the various procedures for isolation which have been developed almost certainly operate in such a way as to exclude molecules with very different properties, and in particular any

fragments of lower molecular weight which may have been produced. Such evidence as is available (29) suggests that DNA *in vivo* is relatively radio-resistant, although there appear to be delayed effects of lethal exposures on its viscosity and, in the case of mouse spleen DNA, a lowered pyrimidine/purine ratio 2 days after 400 r (228). This change in base composition is not found in kidney, lung, liver, or thymus DNA (29, 224, 228).

(*ii*) *DNAPC*. Although investigation of DNAPC rather than DNA may well be more pertinent to our knowledge of intranuclear conditions, it is even more difficult, since there are few reliable criteria to define the DNA–protein complexes isolated. Bernstein (286) in 1954 reported a change in the properties of calf thymus nuclei irradiated with 250 to 5000 r *in vitro*. After 4 to 6 hours at 2 to 5°C there was a spontaneous loss in viscosity with no change in intrinsic viscosity; he also noted a decreased swelling of the nuclei in water after irradiation with 1000 r. Anderson (287), Butler (288), and Fisher (289) have also shown a fall in the viscosity of rat thymus homogenates after irradiation *in vitro* with as little as 25 r, and Dounce and Monty (290) isolated DNAPC from liver nuclei and showed that the gel produced at pH 9 was less resistant to disruption by water after 300 r than the control preparations.

By far the major contribution to this field is the work on mouse spleen DNAPC by Cole and Ellis. They first showed that it was possible to separate spleen DNAPC from DNA polynucleotides by the solubility of the latter in 0.14 M NaCl (230). Fresh mouse spleen contains 98 % of its DNA as insoluble nucleoprotein and has less than 50 μg of soluble polynucleotide DNA per 100 mg of fresh spleen. They then found that spleen DNAPC isolated immediately after giving the mice 850 r of total-body irradiation exhibited different properties from control preparations; the ability to swell in distilled water at 5°C was unaffected, but if the gel was incubated at 37°C for 1 to 2 hours DNAPC from irradiated mice was no longer viscous and contained appreciable insoluble matter. It was also more susceptible to the action of trypsin (291). By 2 hours after 810 r the content of soluble DNA polynucleotide had risen to 100 μg per 100 mg of fresh spleen, and at 6 hours after exposure it was 450 μg per 100 mg (292, 293). The nature of the soluble polynucleotides liberated at 6 hours after 810 to 850 r was examined by chromatographic separation on calcium phosphate columns, and a component was isolated (294) which was not present in unirradiated samples. Rather similar results were obtained if the DNAPC was irradiated *in vitro* (295), and with the complex isolated from rat bone marrow after 870 r *in vivo* or prepared and then exposed *in vitro* (296). Cole and Ellis interpreted their results as indicating a change in the binding between DNA and protein in DNAPC. This appears to be evident immediately after exposure, although liberation of soluble DNA polynucleotides is not detectable before 2 hours postirradiation. The minimum dose to elicit the damage is not yet reported.

It would be interesting to determine precisely the relation between the dissociation of DNA polynucleotide from DNAPC and the increased DNA-ase activity also prominent in spleen. It will be recalled that there is a liberation of DNAase from its bound form immediately after exposure, and at a slightly later time a rise in the activity of DNAase II. The possibility that these cytoplasmic phenomena are related to the nuclear derangement and can exert an effect as soon as the binding between DNA and its protein is loosened is attractive. The metabolic significance of the DNA–protein complexes is at present unknown, but it is tempting to equate them with the hypothetical DNA template(s) which may be damaged by high exposures in the synthetic period (*vide supra*) and so produce a block in DNA synthesis.

It is also interesting that altered physical properties of nucleohistone isolated from pyknotic nuclei have been described (297), so that a connection between disorganized DNAPC after irradiation and the appearance of pyknotic nuclei becomes increasingly probable.

e. The Dynamic Interference in DNA Synthesis. It has frequently been reiterated that cell death may be the cause of diminished DNA synthesis postirradiation. This is perhaps less likely now that positive results are being reported for accumulation of DNA precursors early after irradiation, coincidentally with inhibited precursor uptakes. Mitchell (298, 299) first detected an accumulation of ribonucleotides in the cytoplasm of various tissues after exposure; it may be significant that this accumulation was greater with doses of less than 750 to 1000 r than with higher exposures. Accumulation of deoxyribose material in *E. coli* after ultraviolet irradiation has been shown by Kanazir and Errera (300), and in rabbit appendix and thymus after 1000 r of X-rays by Bishop and Davidson (236). The increase was definite in both tissues by 4 hours and was attributed to interference in DNA synthesis. In rat thymus an increase in deoxyribonucleotides is present 1 hour after 1000 r (164) and is present both with mono- and triphosphorylated derivatives; no thymidine compounds were detected in either control or exposed preparations, probably because too little material was analyzed, but there was a large increase in the amount of DUMP and a marked increase in DCMP, DCTP, and DUTP.

The inhibition of formate uptake into the methyl group of thymine *in vitro* raises several problems. No information is available from incorporation studies *in vivo* on the relative sensitivities of uptake into adenine, guanine, and thymine in DNA. Adenine and guanine incorporations are equally sensitive with formate, and if P^{32} is used all four nucleotides show the same depression. The interrelationships of cytosine, uracil, and thymine nucleotides are not yet fully established, but it is known that uracil and cytosine deoxyribosides are incorporated into the thymine of DNA (301, 302). It is clear that if there is any interference with the availability of thymine from the nonmethylated precursor the deficiency will result in an observable reduction in DNA synthesis which may affect all the nucleotides.

If, therefore, damage to this step in DNA synthesis is excluded, it would seem that these results indicate that the processes leading to the formation of appropriately phosphorylated deoxy compounds after X-irradiation are unaffected and that, taken together with the results already discussed, they provide strong support for the hypothesis that high doses exert their effect on DNA synthesis by damaging the DNA template, thus preventing the final condensation stage.

3. THE INTEGRATION OF THE RESULTS ON NUCLEAR-CYTOPLASMIC INTER-ACTIONS CONCERNED IN DNA SYNTHESIS

Before attempting to integrate the results on different aspects of DNA synthesis, it must be stressed that only experiments in animals are being considered here. A much more comprehensive and very stimulating treatment covering the effects of ultraviolet and X-radiation on nuclear-cytoplasmic interactions in many species is given by Errera (26). It must also be emphasized that much fundamental biochemical knowledge in this field is still lacking, so that it is quite possible that some of the mechanisms assumed in normal animals may be completely wrong. Moreover, the interpretation put on the results is probably oversimplified by trying to force them into a single picture and is intended to provoke further experiments rather than to be a pontifical assessment of the facts.

The reciprocal interactions between cytoplasmic DNAase and damaged DNAPC and between the accumulation of triphosphates, decreasing oxidative phosphorylation, and increased ATPase have been mentioned earlier; these and other processes believed to be concerned in DNA synthesis are shown in Fig. 1. It will be assumed that in dividing cells the signal for division is biochemically represented by the start of synthesis of some molecule essential for DNA, here taken to be deoxyribomononucleotide(s) (DMP). This process occurs in the cytoplasm (280). It will also be assumed that the synthesis of DNA, n-RNA, and nucleoproteins occurs by a process analogous to the mechanism now becoming probable for cytoplasmic RNA and protein—that is, the formation of an activated nucleotide–amino acid complex, its orientation on a template, and finally its reaction with DMP, ribomononucleotides (RMP), or amino acids (AA) to give DNA, n-RNA, and protein, respectively. For the purposes of this discussion it is immaterial whether the activated complex (DMP–AA; RMP–AA) is identical for the different synthetic processes and also what degree of phosphoryla-

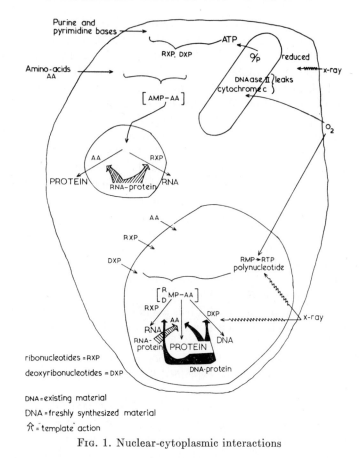

Fig. 1. Nuclear-cytoplasmic interactions

tion is required for the reacting deoxy- and ribonucleotides. It is presumed that existing DNA–protein template(s) affect the synthesis of DNA(s) and n-RNA(s) and possibly nucleoprotein(s), and that RNA–protein complex(es) affects the synthesis of nucleoprotein(s). It also seems likely that some fractions of n-RNA are actively concerned in the formation of c-RNA.

Much more uncertain is the assumption that intranuclear triphosphates (155) are, *inter alia*, essential for the formation or alignment of the activated nucleotide–amino acid complex within the nucleus before synthesis can occur. It is suggested that the processes necessary for the synthesis of DNA which occur in G_1 are those leading to the formation of the activated nucleotide–amino acid complex within the nucleus. In the synthetic period this complex reacts on its template to give new DNA.

We have discussed already the probability that changes in cell population are not likely to be implicated in the effects of X-radiation detected early (say up to 1 to 2 hours) after irradiation, though they become important at later times. The hypothesis that large doses interfere with the template for DNA synthesis has been advanced by many workers and is consistent with the available evidence. This could be the basis for the immediate block in precursor uptake produced by more than 500 r given in the synthetic period itself. We should like to suggest that one of the causes for the delay produced by less than 200 r if given in the presynthetic period (G_1) is an arrest of the processes involved in intranuclear generation of nucleotide triphosphates. These will also be blocked by higher doses, but if low doses are given in the synthetic period the nucleotide–amino acid complex will already be correctly aligned within the nucleus so that only the template reaction is concerned. The G_1 delay in regenerating liver is temporary only, probably not exceeding 12 hours. In bone marrow, Lajtha's work suggests that the delay in G_1 is proportional to the time that the cells would normally still have in this period at the time of exposure; cells at the beginning of G_1 at the time of irradiation are delayed for 20 to 30 hours, whereas those halfway through G_1 are held up by about 12 hours. Nuclear phosphorylation is completely blocked by doses which affect G_1 only, but the 50 % delay can be explained if it is assumed that throughout the whole of G_1 nuclear phosphorylation is required to build up the active complex to its presynthetic level, but once formed and aligned the complex is stable to these exposures. As the delay is temporary, recovery must be possible, and we think that this can be explained by the situation within the cytoplasm.

It is known that up to 1 hour (152, 164) 700 to 1000 r does not reduce the total cell concentration of nucleotide triphosphates, and, although oxidative phosphorylation by spleen and thymus mitochondria is partially inhibited by irradiation, if the block with less than 200 r is not too great there may be sufficient ATP produced to permit cytoplasmic concentrations of nucleotide triphosphates to accumulate in the absence of nuclear utilization. As these concentrations rise, they could become sufficient to re-form essential intranuclear triphosphates and so allow DNA synthesis to recommence. An interaction of this sort between cytoplasmic and nuclear functions, both of which are affected by radiation, but to different extents, may well contribute to the complexities of the biochemical situation after irradiation.

The idea can be extended to cover the responses of tissues such as normal liver and pancreas where an effect on uptake into DNA is produced and there is no reduction of that into nuclear and cytoplasmic RNA and protein. Intranuclear ATP generation in these tissues has not yet been demonstrated, but this could be due to further differences in enzymatic complement. For example, thymus nuclei pyrophosphatase liberates 3.4

μg of inorganic phosphorus per milligram of DNA phosphorus per minute; liver nuclei, 18.5 μg; and regenerating liver nuclei at 23 hours, 30 μg. Thymus ATPase liberates 47.6 μg, and liver 110 μg, both at 37°C; and at 0°C the amount is 3.1 μg and 9.2 μg for thymus and liver, respectively (W. A. Creasey, unpublished observations). If intranuclear generation of triphosphate does occur in these tissues and this is nevertheless blocked by irradiation, then their great cytoplasmic potentialities will enable these cells to produce sufficient triphosphates once more to overcome the block and so to permit n-RNA and protein synthesis to go forward.

Little information is available on the effects of low doses on uptake into DNA in liver, but preliminary experiments indicate that 400 r of total-body irradiation given to rats in G_1 delays DNA synthesis, as expected from the work of Holmes, and also produces an accumulation of deoxyribose material, the increase diminishing by 36 hours when DNA synthesis has recommenced. With doses exceeding 500 r damage to the template would again explain interference in incorporation into DNA. This would imply that nuclear and/or cytoplasmic RNA and protein synthesis can continue even when the DNA template is damaged. This appears quite likely, since already existing DNA and RNA may be concerned with RNA and protein synthesis in resting cells, and only in cells which are proceeding to division will the need for increased amounts of RNA and nucleoprotein be essential.

The ability of added DNA to restore uptake into intranuclear protein in irradiated isolated nuclei has already been mentioned. The obligatory requirement of polynucleotide (283) for the formation of intranuclear triphosphates suggests that a two-stage bimolecular reaction may be involved:

$$\text{RMP} + \text{polynucleotide} \rightarrow \text{RMP-polynucleotide}$$

$$\text{RMP-polynucleotide} + \text{organo(pyro)phosphate (XPP)} \rightarrow$$

$$\text{RTP} + \text{polynucleotide} + \text{X}$$

Oxygen is required for the reaction.

The importance of bound nucleotides in mitochondrial phosphorylation has been suggested (303), and it is fascinating to note the similarities between the conditions for mitochondrial and nuclear phosphorylation and the sensitivity of both processes to radiation, although to different extents.

One final point must be considered. Even after quite small exposures, cells are killed. Lajtha et al. (275) have pointed out the discrepancy between the delay produced in G_1, which is maximal after 200 r, and the increasing effects of doses much greater than this on cell viability. In thymus the presumed parallelism between the probit/log dose-response curve for uptake into DNA and that for thymocyte killing has already been remarked (163). It is, however, most interesting to note that if the data are plotted as a

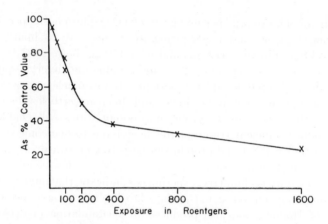

FIG. 2. Effect of total-body X-irradiation on P[32] incorporation into rat thymus DNA 2 hours after exposure.

simple dose-response curve there is a suggestion that two processes are at work (Fig. 2). In the light of our later knowledge of the radiosensitivity of nuclear phosphorylation it is tempting to equate the initial response to less than 200 r with reduction in P[32] uptake into DNA because of inhibited nuclear phosphorylation and to interpret the less sensitive portion of the curve to increasing mitochondrial damage superimposed on increasing template inactivation. Be this as it may, it seems very unlikely that the acion of X-radiation on a process postulated to be so fundamental to the biochemistry of the nucleus as intranuclear triphosphate generation, and possibly caused by disturbed polynucleotide orientation, will not affect dynamically or through structural disorganization the integrity of the nucleus as a whole. We have already discussed how this biochemical effect may be overcome by the response of the cytoplasm, but this also is affected in proportion to the dose received, so that the increase in the number of dead cells will depend on the summation of increasing dynamic and structural disruption of nuclear and cytoplasmic systems offset by a progressively diminishing ability of the cytoplasm to repair the damage.

VI. Electrolyte Distribution and Cell Permeability

A. ELECTROLYTE BALANCE

Studies on electrolytes after radiation have not so far produced entirely unequivocal results. It is evident that the pattern of distribution will be differently affected if the species shows predominantly gastrointestinal symptoms, as in the lethally irradiated rat in the first 3 to 5 days after exposure, from that which will be manifested when hemorrhage is the major factor. It has also been established that variations in the nature of the diet affect the response obtained.

In rats there seems to be fairly general agreement for increased urinary excretions of K^+ and Na^+ (304, 305). Bennett et al. (306) and Kohn (307) found a rise in plasma Na^+, but this was not confirmed by Caster and Armstrong (308) or by Baker and Sellers (309) at times up to 10 days and 136 hours after 700 r and 650 r, respectively. The origins of the urinary losses of Na^+ and K^+ after 700 r were extensively explored by tissue analysis (308). The loss in K^+ appeared to be due to loss of cells, especially muscle. Other experiments (124) had demonstrated that the main contribution to the loss in body weight after exposure comes from muscle, the involution of spleen and thymus being only small factors in the over-all weight loss. Parallel investigations on the DNA content of tissues showed the same general trend as for K^+ and indicated that nuclear changes preceded tissue weight losses, which were most faithfully reflected by altered K balance. The Cl^- distribution was also studied and was found to be strongly influenced by extracellular fluid movements which in their turn were mainly governed by the disturbance of the gastrointestinal tract. Reduction in gastric motility after exposure has been referred to previously. During the first 3 to 12 hours after irradiation, Cl^-, water, and acid moved into the stomach from the body tissues; at 3 hours the Cl^- was mainly derived from connective tissue, liver, and muscle, but by 12 hours there was a decrease in plasma Cl^- (and a rise in HCO_3^-). Increased Cl^- excretion occurred only by 4 days after exposure. The origin of the increased loss of Na^+ was less easy to define than in the cases of K^+ and Cl^- and was partly obscured by the changes in that anion and in water. With all three ions there was a tendency for recovery after 4 to 5 days (308).

Serum changes in rabbits after 600 and 800 r were not striking (310). No change was found in K^+ levels, except for a premortal rise; after 600 r there was a suggestion of increased Na^+ retention on the third day after exposure. In hamsters Fulton and Sudak (311) found a significant fall in serum Na^+ 4 days after 1000 and 1500 r, and with 1000 r again a rise in K^+ just before death. No differences were found with either ion after 600 r. Some data are available from human subjects (312) where there were indications of increased Na^+ and Cl^- excretions after therapeutic exposures. No consistent alterations in plasma Na^+, Cl^-, or phosphate were found, but it was difficult to control variations in food intake.

We could find no change in plasma K^+ in guinea pigs at 120 hours after exposure to 1000 r of total-body X-irradiation (49).

The changes in dogs after 450 to 550 r were examined by McDonald et al. (313). Dietary factors modified the results obtained, but total body water was reduced in most animals, with no corresponding decrease either in plasma water or in intracellular hydration. Excretions of Na^+ and K^+ increased before anorexia had developed, but a negative Cl^- balance was present only in two out of six cases before reduced food intake became a major factor. They concluded that the reduced body water was mainly attributable to oligodipsia and diminished food and that there was no evidence that the changes were not those which would be expected in an animal suffering from diarrhea, fever, etc., attendant upon radiation sickness.

B. CELL PERMEABILITY

Over-all alterations in electrolyte distribution appear to be those expected from tissue destruction and/or major gastrointestinal damage. Much less work has been carried out on alterations in specific tissue permeability or in intracellular distribution of ions. Exposures to 20,000 r *in vitro* reduce K^+ concentrations (314) in erythrocytes, and there is an increase in the loss of K^+ from perfused rabbit heart given 500 to 2500 r (315). Locally irradiated rat forelimb shows a marked extracellular edema after 36.9 to 73.4 kr, but on a dry-weight basis there was no change in intracellular K^+, although Wilde and Sheppard (316) stress that the use of the limb was avoided in the 22 hours intervening between exposure and examination. It would be interesting to know whether the nuclear and mitochondrial changes already referred to are associated with altered K^+ and Na^+ uptakes. Reduced ability for oxidative phosphorylation would be expected to be accompanied by reduced K^+ retention, and the importance of Na^+ to nuclear metabolism has been stressed by Osawa *et al.* (155).

VII. Late Biochemical Consequences

The investigations considered so far have been continued at the most for 2 to 3 months postirradiation. Most commonly, changes found up to 48 hours after exposure have been followed for perhaps 2 to 4 weeks, and frequently the immediate alterations return to normal within this time period. With lethal exposures death intervenes, and very little biochemistry has been carried out on animals which have survived near-lethal doses and are living several months later. A decreased life expectancy and an increased tumor incidence in such surviving animals is now established. Kohn and his co-workers (317) have investigated in detail organ weight and histological changes in male and female mice of two strains surviving an $LD_{50(28)}$ exposure at up to a year from irradiation. Irradiated mice of both sexes and strains had lower body, thymus, kidney, and liver weights; testes and ovaries weighed less, but the effect on heart and submaxillary gland was strain- or sex-dependent. The normal differences between male and female heart, liver, kidney, and submaxillary glands (organs known to be sensitive to available androgens) were reduced by radiation. A preliminary survey of biochemical differences between adult male mice 6 to 10 months after an $LD_{20-30(30)}$ and similarly aged controls has been carried out by Esnouf et al. (318), and the weight changes agree with those reported by Kohn et al. In addition the irradiated mice had less DNA per kidney than the controls, and when P^{32} incorporation into kidney nucleic acids was studied there was an increased RNA/DNA specific activity ratio. An association between these two findings is probable but obscure.

No difference in water, phospholipid, or nitrogen content of the carcasses was found, but the irradiated mice had significantly more fat for a given body weight than the controls. Total fat content of the individual organs examined (heart, liver, kidney, spleen, and testes) was unaffected. Skin and muscle were not studied, but in a preliminary analysis of the weight changes skin weight loss seemed to be a major contributory factor to the reduced weight of the irradiated animals. This is in contrast to the situation in the initial stages of the injury when muscle appears to make the greatest contribution to the decreased weight (124).

Biochemical changes associated with the development of radiation cataract in rabbits have been studied by Pirie and her colleagues (319, 320). There is a loss of glutathione in the lens about 12 to 15 weeks after exposure, before any clinical change is apparent. The activities of glyceraldehyde phosphate dehydrogenase, glyoxalase, and acetaldehyde oxidase—all SH enzymes—are diminished later than the fall in glutathione content and as the opacity develops. Glutathione reductase, which is not an SH enzyme, is also decreased in activity, which may be a contributory factor in the fall in glutathione. Changes in the nature of lens proteins have been studied electrophoretically (321), but alterations were not apparent until after the appearance of the cataract.

At present, studies on long-term biochemical changes after radiation are in their infancy, but it is clear that more information would be advantageous not only with reference to radiation damage itself but also as a pointer to changes that occur in normal animals and in the production under other circumstances of specific lesions such as cataracts.

VIII. Conclusions and Summary

The main pathways which have been investigated as potential sites of the biochemical lesion(s) after X-irradiation in vivo have now been indicated, and it is appropriate to attempt to assess their relative importance. It seems that enzymes per se are largely unaffected by the immediate effects of irradiation. This generalization necessarily excludes many enzymes which may participate in synthetic processes but which are so far undefined, but it would perhaps be surprising if these proteins should be any more sensitive than those catalytic in catabolic reactions. The three hydrolytic enzymes—ATPase, 5'-nucleotidase, and DNAase II—all show increased activity in spleen and thymus after exposure; it is noteworthy that in the case of spleen ATPase the increase is not evidenced after irradiation of the exteriorized spleen with the rest of the body shielded. This suggests that the rise in activity may be an indirect result of total-body irradiation, and, although the increase would be extremely significant if it occurred in the same cells as are present in normal spleens, changes in cell population cannot yet be excluded. The increase in spleen DNAase II is associated with a change in the distribution of the enzyme within the cell, and since it is believed to be located in the mitochondria (or lysosomes) the release from its bound form after irradiation may be another reflection of damage to the mitochondrion rather than a direct effect on the enzyme itself.

Changes in the mechanisms of fat, carbohydrate, or protein breakdown have not been established, and in the liver, where increased glycogen deposition is found, it seems that to a first approximation this may be attributed to an increased availability of precursors after cell destruction, and their consequent utilization for glycogen or lipid synthesis.

The changes which do appear to be concerned in the immediate consequences of X-irradiation and are possibly not attributable to alterations in cell population may be summarized as follows:

1. Release of bound DNAase II from mitochondria.
2. A need for added cytochrome c for mitochondrial oxidation and phosphorylation.
3. Decreased oxidative phosphorylation.
4. Inhibited nuclear formation of nucleotide triphosphates.
5. Inhibited DNA synthesis.

The doses of radiation required to elicit these changes lie in the order $4 < 1, 2, 3 < 5$.

We do not yet know what changes occur in the metabolism of cells during division, but it is clear that irradiation of cells actually in mitosis produces chromosomal damage which may result in immediate cell death or which may exert its effects one or many generations later. The biochemical consequences of such chromosomal damage in cells which may survive are as yet virtually unexplored, so that the bulk of our discussion necessarily deals with cells in interphase or with metabolic pathways which have not so far been defined with reference to the life cycle of the cell.

At this point the suggestion of Spear (3) may be recalled, "that all cells are equally affected but some die more easily than others." If this is the case, we have to explain why the changes become apparent in some tissues and not others. An examination of the reactions affected by exposure suggests that they have two or possibly three common factors:

1. The reacting structures contain bound nucleotides.
2. Oxygen is intimately concerned at the site.
3. Lipid forms part of the structure of the reacting site.

The first of these has been mentioned previously, and it is only necessary to add that the nature of the internucleotide or protein-nucleotide links may be the cause of their sensitivity. If bound nucleotides are a common factor, the resistance of microsomal protein synthesis must be explained and also the lack of any convincing evidence showing immediate impairment of cell permeability.

Within the present limits of our knowledge oxygen may be a second factor implicated in mitochondrial sensitivity and in the generation of nuclear triphosphates. The participation of O_2, possibly in some bound form, in reactions at these sites would produce locally higher concentrations which could then take part in the radiation reaction. This suggestion of the importance of O_2 is in accord with much evidence from other radiobiological research, but it is not meant to imply that biochemical processes in which oxygen takes part will be radiosensitive—in fact, the evidence indicates that generally they are not, but the presence of oxygen in the structures could ensure its availability for the production of oxidizing free radicals which can then attack nearby sensitive linkages.

Philpot has suggested (200) that lipid is concerned in the propagation of a chain reaction initiated by peroxide formation. If peroxides are concerned in the mediation of cell damage, the presence of lipid in affected structures will be important, although the apparent insensitivity of cell membranes must again be noted.

If these factors are to be advanced for further consideration they must be examined for their general applicability. The first three of the changes summarized are found only in lymphoid tissues. Inhibition of DNA synthesis occurs in all tissues so far studied, although some tumors require very high doses before showing an effect. Whether nuclear phosphorylation occurs in all cells is still being explored. Nuclear-cytoplasmic interactions have already been discussed in relation to nucleic acid synthesis, and the suggestion, which has been widely advanced (8–10), of the importance of cytoplasmic volume in radiosensitivity was considered. This must be interpreted in terms of both the volume of the cytoplasm and its metabolic activity, and especially its metabolic reserves. Nondividing cells with great cytoplasmic activity, such as liver parenchymatous cells, are much less affected than either dividing cells or lymphocytes. Their nuclei will be protected by the relatively larger amounts of cytoplasm, and it has been suggested that damage to their nuclei can be restored from the cytoplasm and in any case is less immediately disastrous than in a dividing cell. Liver cytoplasm too, though presumptively as sensitive as elsewhere, has greater reserves for restoring the damage than in lymphoid cells.

In lymphocytes the cytoplasm is comparatively trivial in amount and probably has little reserve activity. Thus the nucleus plays a larger part in the total metabolism of the cell, and the same amount of damage received by a lymphoid and a liver cell will be much more deleterious to the one with the less cytoplasm. If the cell is to divide, then the position will be aggravated by the still greater metabolic activity required for the extra synthesis.

These considerations are advanced to explain lymphoid tissue involution after X-irradiation and the biochemical changes which accompany it. The likely reduction in the number of muscle cells cannot be neglected either in its own right or as the most important single contribution to the increase in liver glycogen postirradiation. The idea of nuclear and cytoplasmic changes, however, which are common to all cells but which become apparent only in circumstances which we have attempted to indicate, and which are inherent in the nature of the cells themselves, is capable of extension to cell types where the relations between nuclear and cytoplasmic factors are less easy to assess.

It is hoped that the present extent of our knowledge of biochemical changes after X-irradiation warrants the attempts which have been made to get some of the common factors underlined so that future investigations may be directed to fill the many gaps in our knowledge and so that we may cease to consider the various effects in isolation but attempt to relate them to their importance within the economy of the cell and of the animal as a whole.

IX. Addendum

During the period which has elapsed since the above was written, work on the biochemical effects of X-radiation has intensified, especially in the nucleic acid field (for recent reviews see ref. 322, 323). Many of the results fall into the pattern discerned earlier and it is only possible in this addendum to mention very briefly those points which are of general interest and provide new examples of, or new ideas about, the biochemical actions of irradiation.

Criteria similar to those discussed in Sections I and II have been presented by Eichel and Roth (324) for consideration when the effects of total body radiation on enzymes are interpreted. Their work on rat spleen RNAase (325) illustrates the redistribution of an enzyme which can occur after release from its normal site and reabsorption onto another particulate fraction. Histochemical studies of rat spleen and thymus DNAase II have shown (326) that the increase in enzyme activity/mg tissue after 756 r is at any rate partly due to localization of the enzyme in radioresistant reticular cells and macrophages.

Brody (327) and Goutier *et al.* (328) have shown that in the early stage of regeneration after partial hepatectomy there was an increase in the acid and neutral DNA-ases. Total body X-irradiation of 850 r given at 6 and 12 hours post-hepatectomy reduced the extent of the increase in enzyme activity which suggested that nucleotides released by the DNAase might be used for DNA synthesis in the same or other cells and that the DNAase release could be related to a slowing down of the rate of DNA synthesis (328).

Benjamin and Yost (329) have examined oxidative phosphorylation in rat spleen and liver mitochondria 24 hours after 800 r X-irradiation. They attribute the uncoupling to an indirect action on the mitochondria following hyperactivity of the pituitary and release of adrenocorticoids and thyroxine. This is interesting in view of van Bekkum's finding (153) that the uncoupling in spleen mitochondria was not immediate. Differences in radiosensitivity of liver mitochondria have been found by different workers (140, 143, 150, 153, 330) although the times of examination after exposure and the concentration of the mitochondria vary. A stimulatory effect of DNA on oxidative phosphorylation by liver mitochondria from irradiated rats has been described (330); the stimulus was reduced by irradiating the DNA (10^5 r *in vitro*). Stern and Timonen (331) have described a similar phenomenon with normal liver mitochondria. Since albumin had the same effect, they ascribe this to a nonspecific stabilization of the mitochondrial suspension. The possibility must be entertained that dilution of mitochondria exacerbates the radiation-induced instability.

While there have been continued reports of an over-all inhibition of the synthesis of DNA (332–338) many of the investigations have been concerned with identifiable stages in DNA synthesis (339) or with new techniques for demonstrating inhibition at a cellular level (340). A careful autoradiographic study of the effects of radiation on hepatocytes in regenerating liver has led Looney *et al.* (341) to suggest that the rate of DNA synthesis is reduced and that this reduction is proportional to the rate of synthesis at the time of irradiation. Confirmation of the biphasic response of DNA synthesis (342, 343) has been reported for C^{14}-thymidine uptake into mouse Erlich ascites tumor in cells *in vitro* (344). Studies in liver regeneration have established that low exposures produce a delay in the appearance of the enzymes required for the phosphorylation of thymidine (345–347). This is associated with an accumulation of deoxycytidine (348) and a delay in the disappearance of thymine-catabolizing enzymes (349, 350). Relevant to these observations is the recent work of Hiatt and Bojarski (351) who demonstrated that injections of thymidine promotes the appearance of thymidylate kinase in normal liver and kidney and of Soska and Karpfel (352) who found an increased mitotic index in bone marrow after administration of deoxycytidylic, thymidylic, and deoxy-adenylic acids. Welling and Cohen (353) have shown that if P^{32} incorporation into RNA is examined in regenerating liver 6 hours after hepatectomy, with 700 r given 2–4 hours after operation, there is an inhibition of uptake. At present it is not possible to say whether the enzymes for the phosphorylation of thymidine are formed adaptively for DNA synthesis or whether they are normally present but inhibited (354, 355) so that irradiation retards the removal of the inhibitor.

Mandel and Chambon (356) have made a comprehensive study of nucleotide concentrations in rat spleen from 12 hours to 21 days after exposure to varying doses of X-rays and suggested that the abnormal ratios of deoxynucleoside triphosphates may explain the occurrence of mutations. Similar work by Soska and Soskova also shows the early accumulation of DNA precursors in rat spleen (357) and an increased amount of deoxycytidine is excreted by rats after 300–600 r (358).

More evidence for possible damage to DNA as a template has also accrued. Irradiation *in vitro* can produce an increase in the ability of DNA to act as a primer for cell-free systems to synthesize DNA; higher doses decrease its ability (359, 360). Changes in the distribution pattern of rat thymus DNA on ECTEOLA columns after 1000 r *in vivo* have been reported (361); van Lancker (362) found that using the cell-free DNA synthesizing system (363) and rat liver nuclei after irradiation *in vivo*, the nuclei showed a diminished capacity to act as a primer. Similar results have been obtained with autoradiography (364). The possibility of breakdown of DNA in irradiated nuclei as a result of DNAase activation is not yet excluded in interpreting these findings; irradiation of nuclei *in vitro* does not appear to affect their priming properties (360).

The dependence of nuclear sensitivity to exposure on the integrity of the DNA-nucleoprotein complex is suggested by a number of recent studies on nuclei irradiated *in vitro*. Kuzin and Shabadash (330) conclude that the sensitivity of lymphoid tissues to X-radiation is determined by the greater number of free phosphate groups in their DNA compared to that of liver or fibrocytes. Unfortunately it is not easy to ascertain the extent to which nuclear behavior after isolation truly represents their behaviour in the intact cell and in particular precursor uptake into DNA is usually slight. Loss of nuclear catalase (365), sodium and potassium (366), and the labilization of DNA to extraction procedures after irradiation (367) is consistent with a general disorganization of nuclear structure. Reduction in the ability of rabbit appendix, liver, and thymus nuclei *in vitro* to take up protein and nucleic acid precursors after 300 rads has been reported by Logan (368) from autoradiographic studies but chemical analysis failed to show any inhibition of uptake either into RNA or DNA. Uptake of phenylalanine and adenine into protein and RNA of calf thymus nuclei was reduced by 50 r with no effect on adenine incorporation into DNA (364). Tchoe and Sibatani found that removal of DNA by prior treatment with DNAase reduced the sensitivity of P^{32} uptake into RNA *in vitro* (369). On the other hand the ability of isolated rat liver, spleen and thymus nuclei to synthesize diphosphopyridine nucleotide after 1500 r was unimpaired, suggesting (370) that nuclear ATP was still available although nuclear phosphorylation is extremely radiosensitive (371).

The picture of the nucleus which emerges from these recent observations is of a highly organized structure in which charged nucleoprotein attracts to itself nucleotides, inorganic phosphate, and possibly amino acids and cations in an ordered array. When nuclei are isolated many factors will operate against the preservation of this order. The rapid breakdown of substrates (155, 372) and release of enzymes from their proper compartments makes difficult the interpretation of the experimental findings. It may be that the contrast between the tight binding of thymidine compounds found by Crathorn and Shooter (373) in mouse ascites tumor cells and the lability of these precursors in mammalian cells is reflected in their different radiosensitivities.

If irradiation takes place *in vivo* the nucleoprotein structure will be partly stabilized by its ionic interactions with low molecular weight compounds, similar to the protection of enzymes by their substrates against exposure *in vitro* (14, 15). Loss of bound material does occur however (365, 366) indicating disruption of the nucleoprotein complex. When thymus nuclei are isolated in a state in which their nucleoside triphosphates have been lost, their ability to replace these through nuclear phosphorylation is greatly impaired because of the disorganization of the binding sites on which the phosphorylation is thought to take place. If such nuclei are irradiated *in vitro*, reformation of ATP is prevented by the increased disarray of the unstabilized nucleoprotein; nuclei isolated with their full complement of triphosphates are very much more radioresistant (Ord and Stocken, unpublished). These views may be correlated with those of Kuzin and Shabadash (330) if it is supposed that the free phosphate groups detected by their histochemical method are normally neutralized through ionic interactions.

In spite of the recent evidence focusing attention on the nuclear lesion the effects of X-radiation on the cell will only be fully appreciated when the interactions and interpendence of the various cell components have been clearly recognized.

Acknowledgment

It is a pleasure to acknowledge the help given to us by Mr. A. Morris in the compilation of the references.

X. References

1. Upton, A. C., J. Gerontol. **12**, 306 (1957).
2. Mole, R. H., Brit. J. Radiol. **26**, 234 (1953).
3. Spear, F. G., "Radiations and Living Cells." Chapman & Hall, London, 1953.
4. Bacq, Z. M., and Alexander, P., "Fundamentals of Radiobiology." Academic Press, New York, 1955.
5. Bacq, Z. M., Mugard, H., and Herve, A., Acta Radiol. **38**, 489 (1952).
6. Bergonié, J., and Tribondeau, L., Compt. rend. **143**, 983 (1906).
7. Ellinger, F., "Medical Radiation Biology," C. C Thomas, Springfield, Illinois, 1957.
8. Trowell, O. A., Ann. N. Y. Acad. Sci. **59**, 1066 (1955).
9. Ord, M. G., and Stocken, L. A., Proc. 3rd Intern. Congr. Biochem., Brussels, 1955 491 (1956).
10. Schjeide, O. A., Mead, J. F., and Myers, L. S., Science **123**, 1020 (1956).
11. Bohn, C., Compt. rend. **136**, 1085 (1903).
12. Howard, A., and Pelc, S. R. Heredity Suppl. **6**, 261 (1953).
13. Lajtha, L. G., Oliver, R., and Ellis, F., in "Radiobiology Symposium, 1954" (Z. M. Bacq and P. Alexander, eds.), p. 216. Academic Press, New York, 1955.
14. Dale, W. M., Biochem. J. **34**, 1367 (1940).
15. Dale, W. M., Ciba Foundation Symposium, Ionizing Radiations and Cell Metabolism 25 (1956).
16. Barron, E. S. G., U. S. Atomic Energy Commission Document **2316** (1946).
17. Barron, E. S. G., Dickman, S., Muntz, J. A., and Singer, T. P., J. Gen. Physiol. **32**, 537 (1948).
18. Barron, E. S. G., and Seki, L., J. Gen. Physiol. **35**, 865 (1952).
19. Ledoux, L., Biochim. et Biophys. Acta **11**, 517 (1953).
20. Künkel, H. A., Höhne, G., Maass, H., and Schubert, G., in "Progress in Radiobiology" (J. S. Mitchell, B. E. Holmes, and C. L. Smith, eds.), p. 52. Oliver & Boyd, Edinburgh, 1956.
21. Le May, M., Proc. Soc. Exptl. Biol. Med. **77**, 337 (1951).
22. Ballin, J. C., and Doull, J., U. S. Air Force Radiation Lab. Quart. Progr. Rept. No. 10, 44 (1954).
23. Thomson, J. F., Tourtellotte, W. W., and Carttar, M. S., Proc. Soc. Exptl. Biol. Med. **80**, 268 (1952).
24. Ashwell, G., and Hickman, J., Proc. Soc. Exptl. Biol. Med. **80**, 407 (1952).
25. Fischer, M. A., Pruvis-Coulter, E., and Costello, M. J., Proc. Soc. Exptl. Biol. Med. **83**, 266 (1953).
26. Errera, M., in "Protoplasmatologia. Handbuch der Protoplasmaforschung" (L. V. Heilbrunn and F. Weber, eds.), Vol. X, No. 3, p. 1. Springer, Vienna, 1957.
27. DuBois, K. P., and Petersen, D. F., Am. J. Physiol. **176**, 282 (1954).
28. Ord, M. G., and Stocken, L. A., Brit. J. Radiol. **28**, 279 (1955).
29. Ord, M. G., and Stocken, L. A., in "Advances in Radiobiology" (G. de Hevesy, A. Forssberg, and J. D. Abbatt, eds.), Oliver & Boyd, Edinburgh, 1957.
30. DuBois, K. P., and Potter, V. R., J. Biol. Chem. **150**, 185 (1943).
31. Ashwell, G., and Hickman, J., J. Biol. Chem. **201**, 651 (1953).
32. Maxwell, E., and Ashwell, G., Arch. Biochem. Biophys. **43**, 389 (1953).

33. Petersen, D. F., and DuBois, K. P., *Federation Proc.* **14,** 378 (1955).
34. Forssberg, A., *Arkiv Kemi Mineral. Geol.* **21,** No. 7, 1 (1946).
35. Dale, W. M., and Russell, C., *Biochem. J.* **62,** 50 (1956).
36. Sutton, H. C., *Biochem. J.* **64,** 447, 456 (1956).
37. Aronson, D. M., Fraser, M. J., and Smith, C. L., *Radiation Research* **5,** 225 (1956).
38. Ludewig, S., and Chanutin, A., *Arch. Biochem.* **29,** 441 (1950).
39. Roth, J. S., Eichel, H. J., Wase, A., Alper, C., and Boyd, M. J., *Arch. Biochem. Biophys.* **44,** 95 (1953).
40. Feinstein, R. N., Butler, C. L., and Hendley, D. D., *Science* **111,** 149 (1950).
41. Kazuo Mori, Seiko Momoki, and Hisashi Itô, *Igaku to Seibutsugaku* **18,** 303 (1951) [*Chem. Abstr.* **45,** 9580 (1951)].
42. Voskoboinikov, G. V., *Med. Radiol.* **1,** 39 (1956) [*Intern. Abstr. Biol. Sci.* **7,** No. 1233 (1957)].
43. Friedberg, W., *Proc. Soc. Exptl. Biol. Med.* **93,** 52 (1956).
44. Kaplan, J. G., and Paik, W. K., *J. Gen. Physiol.* **40,** 147 (1957).
45. Brown, G. L., *Biochem. J.* **51,** 569 (1952).
46. Conard, R. A., *Am. J. Physiol.* **165,** 375 (1951).
47. Burn, J. H., Kordik, P., and Mole, R. H., *Brit. J. Pharmacol.* **7,** 58 (1952).
48. French, A. B., and Wall, P. E., *Am. J. Physiol.* **188,** 76 (1957).
49. Ord, M. G., and Stocken, L. A., *Physiol. Revs.* **33,** 356 (1953).
50. Lundin, J., Clemedson, C. J., and Nelson, A., *Acta Radiol.* **48,** 52 (1957).
51. Luthy, H., *Radiol. Clin.* **22,** 491 (1953).
52. Doull, J., and Cummings, O. K., *Federation Proc.* **13,** 349 (1954).
53. Sawyer, C. H., and Everett, J. W., *Endocrinology* **39,** 307 (1946).
54. Harrison, M. F., and Brown, L. M., *Biochem. J.* **48,** 151 (1951).
55. Hajdukovic, S., *Experientia* **11,** 356 (1955).
56. de Duve, C., Pressman, B. D., Gianetto, R., Wattiaux, R., and Appelmans, F., *Biochem. J.* **60,** 604 (1955).
57. Fellas, V. M., Meschan, I., Day, P. L., and Douglass, C. D., *Proc. Soc. Exptl. Biol. Med.* **87,** 231 (1954).
58. Douglass, C. D., and Day, P. L., *Proc. Soc. Exptl. Biol. Med.* **89,** 616 (1955).
59. Okada, S., Gordon, E. R., King, R., and Hempelmann, L. H., *Arch. Biochem. Biophys.* **70,** 469 (1957).
60. Kowlessar, O. D., Altman, K. I., and Hempelmann, L. H., *Arch. Biochem. Biophys.* **52,** 362 (1954).
61. Kowlessar, O. D., Altman, K. I., and Hempelmann, L. H., *Arch. Biochem. Biophys.* **54,** 355 (1955).
62. Goutier-Pirotte, M., and Thonnard, A., *Biochim. et Biophys. Acta* **22,** 396 (1956).
63. Okada, S., Schlegel, B., and Hempelmann, L. H., *Biochim. et Biophys. Acta* **28,** 209 (1958).
64. Okada, S., and Kallee, E., *Exptl. Cell Research* **11,** 212 (1956).
65. Okada, S., and Peachey, L. D., *J. Biophys. Biochem. Cytol.* **3,** 239 (1957).
66. Allfrey, V. G., Mirsky, A. E., and Stern, H., *Advances in Enzymol.* **16,** 411 (1955).
67. Roth, J. S., *Arch. Biochem. Biophys.* **60,** 7 (1956).
68. Barron, E. S. G., *Radiation Research* **1,** 109 (1954).
69. DuBois, K. P., Cotter, G. J., and Petersen, D. F., *Radiation Research* **2,** 79 (1955).
70. Thomson, J. F., and Mikuta, E. T., *Proc. Soc. Exptl. Biol. Med.* **86,** 487 (1954).
71. Romantsev, E. F., and Zhulanova, Z. I., *Biokhimiya* **21,** 663 (1956) [*Intern. Abstr. Biol. Sci.* **8,** No. 2, 3360 (1958)].
72. Schreier, K., Altman, K. I., and Hempelmann, L. H., *Proc. Soc. Exptl. Biol. Med.* **87,** 61 (1954).
73. Gardella, J. W., and Lichtler, E. J., *Federation Proc.* **15,** 70 (1956).

74. Bacq, Z. M., and Herve, A., *Arch. intern. physiol.* **61,** 434 (1953).
75. Swallow, A. J., *in* "Progress in Radiobiology" (J. S. Mitchell, B. E. Holmes. and C. L. Smith, eds.), p. 317. Oliver & Boyd, Edinburgh, 1956.
76. Eichel, H. J., and Spirtes, M. A., *Proc. Soc. Exptl. Biol. Med.* **88,** 412 (1955).
77. Hogeboom, G. H., and Schneider, W. C., *J. Biol. Chem.* **197,** 611 (1952).
78. Krebs, H. A., *Ciba Foundation Symposium, Ionizing Radiations and Cell Metabolism* 92 (1956).
79. Fischer, P., DeLandtsheer, L., and Lecomte, J., *Bull. soc. chim. biol.* **32,** 1009 (1950).
79a. MacFarland, M. L., Peters, M. V., Ballantyne, R. M., and McHenry, E. W., *Am. J. Physiol.* **163,** 394 (1950).
80. Goldfeder, A., Cohen, L., Miller, C., and Singer, M., *Proc. Soc. Exptl. Biol. Med.* **67,** 272 (1948).
81. Buchwald, K. W., *J. Exptl. Med.* **53,** 827 (1931).
82. Barron, E. S. G., Wolkowitz, W., and Muntz, J. A., *U. S. Atomic Energy Commission Rept.* **MDDC-1241** (1947).
83. Cori, C. F., *J. Biol. Chem.* **66,** 691 (1925).
84. Lourau, M., and Lartigue, O., *Arch. sci. physiol.* **5,** 83 (1951).
85. Goodman, R. D., Lewis, A. E., and Schuck, E. A., *Am. J. Physiol.* **169,** 242 (1952).
86. Swift, M. N., Taketa, S. T., and Bond, V. P., *Am. J. Physiol.* **182,** 479 (1955).
87. Farrar, J. T., Small, M. D., Bullard, D., and Ingelfinger, F. J., *Am. J. Physiol.* **186,** 549 (1956).
88. Moss, W. T., *Am. J. Roentgenol. Radium Therapy Nuclear Med.* **78,** 850 (1957).
89. Dickson, H. M., *Am. J. Physiol.* **182,** 477 (1955).
90. Fisher, R. B., and Parsons, D. S., *J. Physiol. (London)* **110,** 36 (1949).
91. Detrick, L. E., Upham, H. C., Highby, D., Debley, V., and Haley, T. J., *Radiation Research* **2,** 483 (1955).
92. Lourau, M., and Lartigue, O., *Arch. sci. physiol.* **4,** 197 (1950).
93. Kohn, H. I., *Am. J. Physiol.* **165,** 27, 43 (1951).
94. McKee, R. W., *Federation Proc.* **11,** 256 (1952).
95. Kay, R. E., and Entenman, C., *Proc. Soc. Exptl. Biol. Med.* **91,** 143 (1956).
96. Steadman, L. T., and Grimaldi, A. J., *U. S. Atomic Energy Commission Rept.* **UR-205,** No. 6 (1952).
97. Lourau-Pitres, M., *Arkiv Kemi* **7,** 211 (1954–55).
98. Bernstein, E. K., Stearner, S. P., and Brues, A. M., *Am. J. Physiol.* **186,** 543 (1956).
99. North, N., and Nims, L. F., *Federation Proc.* **8,** 119 (1949).
100. Nims, L. F., and Sutton, E., *Am. J. Physiol.* **177,** 51 (1954).
101. Ross, M. H., and Ely, J. O., *J. Cellular Comp. Physiol.* **37,** 163 (1951).
102. McKee, R. W., and Brin, M., *Arch. Biochem. Biophys.* **61,** 390 (1956).
103. Denson, J. R., Gray, E. J., Gray, J. L., Herbert, F. J., Tew, J. T., and Jensen, H., *Proc. Soc. Exptl. Med. Biol.* **82,** 707 (1953).
104. Mole, R. H., *Brit. J. Exptl. Pathol.* **37,** 528 (1956).
105. Coniglio, J. G., Kirschman, J. C., and Hudson, G. W., *Federation Proc.* **16,** 166 (1957).
106. Ord, M. G., and Stocken, L. A., *Chem. & Ind. (London)* **1951,** 1166.
107. Lourau, M., and Lartigue, O., *J. physiol. (Paris)* **43,** 593 (1951).
108. Lourau, M., *Compt. rend.* **236,** 422 (1953).
109. Sherman, F. G., and Dwyer, F. M., *Federation Proc.* **15,** 169 (1956).
110. Levy, B., and Rugh, R., *Proc. Soc. Exptl. Biol. Med.* **82,** 223 (1953).
111. Lelièvre, P., *Compt. rend. soc. biol.* **151,** 412 (1957).
112. Lelièvre, P., and Betz, E. H., *Compt. rend. soc. biol.* **149,** 1296, 2034 (1955).

113. Lelièvre, P., Betz, H., and Jehotte, J., *Compt. rend. soc. biol.* **149**, 1077 (1955).
114. Morehouse, M. G., and Searcy, R. L., *Science* **122**, 158 (1955).
115. Hill, R., Kiyasu, J., and Chaikoff, I. L., *Am. J. Physiol.* **187**, 417 (1956).
116. Kay, R. E., Harris, D. C., and Entenman, C., *Am. J. Physiol.* **186**, 175 (1956).
117. Hallesy, D. W., and Doull, J., *Federation Proc.* **15**, 433 (1956).
118. Moore, S., and Stein, W. H., *J. Biol. Chem.* **192**, 663 (1951).
119. Kay, R. E., Early, J. C., and Entenman, C., *Radiation Research* **6**, 98 (1957).
120. Pentz, E. I., *J. Biol. Chem.* **231**, 165 (1958).
121. Haberland, G. L., Schreier, K., Altman, K. I., and Hempelmann, L. H., *Biochim. et Biophys. Acta* **25**, 237 (1957).
122. Lauenstein, K., Haberland, G. L., Hempelmann, L. H., and Altman, K. I., *Biochim. et Biophys. Acta* **26**, 421 (1957).
123. Morehouse, M. G., and Searcy, R. L., *Federation Proc.* **16**, 223 (1957).
124. Caster, W. O., and Armstrong, W. D., *Proc. Soc. Exptl. Biol. Med.* **91**, 126 (1956).
125. Haberland, G. L., Schreier, K., Bruns, F., Altman, K. I., and Hempelmann, L. H., *Nature* **175**, 1039 (1955).
126. Krise, G. M., Williams, C. M., and Anderson, D. R., *Proc. Soc. Exptl. Biol. Med.* **95**, 764 (1957).
127. Williams, C. M., Krise, G. M., Anderson, D. R., and Dowben, R. M., *Radiation Research* **7**, 176 (1957).
128. Cronkite, E. P., and Bond, V. P., *Ann. Rev. Physiol.* **18**, 483 (1956).
129. Lutwak-Mann, C., and Gunz, F. W., *Biochem. J.* **44**, 3P (1949).
130. Hickman, J., and Ashwell, G., *J. Biol. Chem.* **205**, 651 (1953).
131. Perkinson, J. D., and Irving, C. C., *Radiation Research* **5**, 589 (1956).
132. Höhne, G., Künkel, H. A., Maass, H., and Rathgen G. H., *in* "Advances in Radiobiology" (G. de Hevesy, A. Forssberg, and J. D. Abbatt, eds.), p. 43. Oliver & Boyd, Edinburgh, 1957.
132a. Mole, R. H., *Quart. J. Exptl. Physiol.* **38**, 69 (1953).
133. van Bekkum, D. W., Jongepier, H. J., Nieuwerkerk, H. T. M., and Cohen, J. A., *Brit. J. Radiol.* **27**, 127 (1954).
134. Sullivan, M. F., and DuBois, K. P., *Radiation Research* **3**, 202 (1955).
135. Huang, K. C., Almand, J. R., and Hargan, L. A., *Federation Proc.* **13**, 368 (1954).
136. Mandel, P., Gros, C. H., and Rodesch, J., *in* "Radiobiology Symposium, 1954" (Z. M. Bacq and P. Alexander, eds.), p. 210. Academic Press, New York, 1955.
137. Altman, K. I., Richmond, J. E., and Salomon, K., *Biochim. et Biophys. Acta* **7**, 460 (1951).
138. Snezhko, A. D., *Biophysics* **2**, 70 (1957).
139. Smith, F., Buddington, W. G., and Grenan, M. M., *Proc. Soc. Exptl. Biol. Med.* **81**, 140 (1952).
140. Florsheim, W., Doernbach, C., and Morton, M. E., *Proc. Soc. Exptl. Biol. Med.* **81**, 121 (1952).
141. Szönyi, S., and Várterész, W., *Nature* **179**, 51 (1957).
142. Brooks, P. M., Richey, E. O., and Pickering, J. E., *Radiation Research* **6**, 430 (1957).
143. van Bekkum, D. W., *Ciba Foundation Symposium, Ionizing Radiations and Cell Metabolism* 77 (1956).
144. DuBois, K. P., and Petersen, D. F., *Ann. Rev. Nuclear Sci.* **4**, 351 (1954).
145. Pauly, H., and Rajewsky, B., *in* "Progress in Radiobiology" (J. S. Mitchell, B. E. Holmes, and C. L. Smith, eds.), p. 32. Oliver & Boyd, Edinburgh, 1956.
145a. Rajewsky, B., Gerber, G., and Pauly, H., *in* "Advances in Radiobiology" (G. de Hevesy, A. Forssberg, and J. D. Abbatt, eds.), p. 25. Oliver & Boyd, Edinburgh, 1957.

146. Ord, M. G., and Stocken, L. A., *Biochem. J.* **68**, 410 (1958).
147. Fritz-Niggli, H., *Naturwissenschaften* **42**, 585 (1955).
148. Fritz-Niggli, H., *Naturwissenschaften* **43**, 113, 425 (1956).
149. Potter, R. L., and Bethell, F. H., *Federation Proc.* **11**, 270 (1952).
150. Florsheim, W. H., and Morton, M. E., *Am. J. Physiol.* **176**, 15 (1954).
151. Goldfeder, A., *in* "Progress in Radiobiology" (J. S. Mitchell, B. E. Holmes, and C. L. Smith, eds.), p. 69. Oliver & Boyd, Edinburgh, 1956.
152. van Bekkum, D. W., *Biochim. et Biophys. Acta* **16**, 437 (1955).
153. van Bekkum, D. W., and Vos, O., *Brit. J. Exptl. Pathol.* **36**, 432 (1955).
154. Yost, H. T., and Robson, H. H., *Biol. Bull.* **113**, 198 (1957).
155. Osawa, S., Allfrey, V. G., and Mirsky, A. E., *J. Gen. Physiol.* **40**, 491 (1957).
156. Creasey, W. A., and Stocken, L. A., *Biochem. J.* **69**, 17P (1958).
157. Forssberg, A., and Hevesy, G., *Arkiv Kemi* **5**, 93 (1953).
158. von Euler, H., and Hevesy, G., *Kgl. Danske Videnskab. Selskab, Biol. Medd.* **17**, 1 (1942–43).
159. Sherman, F. G., and Forssberg, A., *Arch. Biochem. Biophys.* **48**, 293 (1954).
160. Sherman, F. G., and Almeida, A. B., *in* "Advances in Radiobiology" (G. de Hevesy, A. Forssberg, and J. D. Abbatt, eds.), p. 49. Oliver & Boyd, Edinburgh, 1957.
161. Forssberg, A., and Klein, G., *Exptl. Cell Research* **7**, 480 (1954).
162. Lutwak-Mann, C., *Biochem. J.* **49**, 300 (1951).
163. Ord, M. G., and Stocken, L. A., *Biochem. J.* **63**, 3 (1956).
164. Ord. M. G., and Stocken, L. A., *Biochim. et Biophys. Acta* **29**, 201 (1958).
164a. van Bekkum, D. W., *Biochim. et Biophys. Acta* **25**, 487 (1957).
165. Uyeki, E. M., *Federation Proc.* **13**, 413 (1954).
166. Maass, H., Höhne, G., Künkel, H. A., and Rathgen, G. H., *Z. Naturforsch.* **12b**, 553 (1957).
167. Rosenthal, R. L., *Science* **110**, 43 (1949).
168. Entenman, C., Neve, R. A., Supplee, H., and Olmstead, C. A., *Arch. Biochem. Biophys.* **59**, 97 (1955).
168a. Goldwater, W. H., and Entenman, C., *Radiation Research* **4**, 243 (1956).
169. Steadman, L. T., and Thompson, H. E., *U. S. Atomic Energy Commission Rept.* **UR-103**, 20 (1949).
170. Elko, E. E., and Di Luzio, N. R., *Federation Proc.* **17**, 41 (1958).
171. Di Luzio, N. R., and Simon, K. A., *Radiation Research* **7**, 79 (1957).
172. Milch, L. J., Stinson, J. V., and Albaum, H. G., *Radiation Research* **4**, 321 (1956).
173. Hewitt, J. E., Hayes, T. L., Gofman, J. W., Jones, H. B., and Pierce, F. T., *Am. J. Physiol.* **172**, 579 (1953).
174. Hewitt, J. E., and Hayes, T. L., *Am. J. Physiol.* **185**, 257 (1956).
175. Bacq, Z. M., Burg, C., Chevallier, A., and Heusghem, C., *J. physiol. (Paris)* **43**, 640 (1951).
176. Coniglio, J. G., Darby, W. J., Wilkerson, M. C., Stewart, R., Stockwell, A., and Hudson, G. W., *Am. J. Physiol.* **172**, 86 (1953).
177. Coniglio, J. G., Darby, W. J., Efner, J. A., Fleming, J., and Hudson, G. W., *Am. J. Physiol.* **184**, 113 (1956).
178. Mead, J. F., Decker, A. B., and Bennett, L. R., *J. Nutrition* **43**, 485 (1951).
179. Buchanan, D. J., Darby, W. J., Bridgforth, E. B., Hudson, G. W., and Efner. J. A., *Am. J. Physiol.* **174**, 336 (1953).
180. Supplee, H., Weinman, E. O., and Entenman, C., *Am. J. Physiol.* **185**, 583 (1956).
181. Cornatzer, W. E., Davison, J. P., Engelstad, O. D., and Simonson, C., *Radiation Research* **1**, 546 (1954).

182. Weinman, E. O., Lerner, S. R., and Entenman, C., *Arch. Biochem. Biophys.* **64,** 164 (1956).

183. Jardetzky, C. D., Barnum, C. P., and Vermund, H., *J. Biol. Chem.* **222,** 421 (1956).

184. Lerner, S. R., Warner, W. L., and Entenman, C., *Federation Proc.* **12,** 85 (1953).

185. Coniglio, J. G., McCormick, D. B., and Hudson, G. W., *Am. J. Physiol.* **185,** 577 (1956).

186. Morehouse, M. G., and Searcy, R. L., *Federation Proc.* **13,** 267 (1954).

187. Morehouse, M. G., and Searcy, R. L., *Federation Proc.* **15,** 316 (1956).

188. Coniglio, J. G., Kirschmann, J. C., and Hudson, G. W., *Am. J. Physiol.* **191,** 350 (1957).

189. Gould, R. G., Lotz, L. V., and Lilly, E. M., *Federation Proc.* **15,** 264 (1956).

190. Bucher, N. L. R., Loud, A. V., and McGarrahan, K., *Federation Proc.* **16,** 17 (1957).

191. Gould, R. G., and Popjak, G., *Biochem. J.* **66,** 51P (1957).

192. Popjak, G., *in* "Progress in Radiobiology" (J. S. Mitchell, B. E. Holmes, and C. L. Smith, eds.), p. 71. Oliver & Boyd, Edinburgh, 1956.

193. Kline, D., McPherson, C., Pritchard, E. T., and Rossiter, R. J., *J. Biol. Chem.* **222,** 219 (1956).

194. Dawson, R. M. C., *Biol. Revs. Cambridge Phil. Soc.* **32,** 188 (1957).

195. Bucher, N. L. R., and McGarrahan, K., *J. Biol. Chem.* **222,** 1 (1956).

196. Gould, R. G., Bell, V. L., and Lilly, E. H., *Radiation Research* **5,** 609 (1956).

197. Lutwak-Mann, C., *Biochem. J.* **52,** 356 (1952).

198. Harrington, H., and Lavik, P., *Federation Proc.* **16,** 192 (1957).

199. Chevallier, A., and Burg, C., *in* "Radiobiology Symposium, 1954" (Z. M. Bacq and P. Alexander, eds.), p. 1. Academic Press, New York, 1955.

200. Horgan, V. J., Philpot, J. St., Porter, B. W., and Roodyn, D. B., *Biochem. J.* **67,** 551 (1957).

201. Westphal, U., Priest, S. G., Stets, J. F., and Selden, G. L., *Am. J. Physiol.* **175,** 424 (1953).

202. Fischer, M. A., Magee, M. Z., and Coulter, E. P., *Arch. Biochem. Biophys.* **56,** 66 (1955).

203. Höhne, G., Künkel, H. A., and Anger, R., *Klin. Wochschr.* **33,** 284 (1955).

204. Winkler, C., and Paschke, G., *Radiation Research,* **5,** 156 (1956).

205. Cornatzer, W. E., Engelstad, O., and Davison, J. P., *Am. J. Physiol.* **175,** 153 (1953).

206. Werder, A. A., Hardin, C. A., and Morgan, P., *Radiation Research* **7,** 500 (1957).

207. Lajtha, L. G., *Physiol. Revs.* **37,** 50 (1957).

208. Richmond, J. E., Altman, K. I., and Salomon, K., *J. Biol. Chem.* **190,** 817 (1951).

209. Nizet, A., Lambert, S., Herve, A., and Bacq, Z. M., *Arch. intern. physiol.* **62,** 129 (1954).

210. Richmond, J. E., Ord, M. G., and Stocken, L. A., *Biochem. J.* **66,** 123 (1957).

211. Hevesy, G., *Nature* **163,** 869 (1949).

212. Hevesy, G., *Nature* **164,** 269 (1949).

213. Abrams, R., *Arch. Biochem.* **30,** 91 (1951).

214. Holmes, B. E., and Mee, L. K., *Brit. J. Radiol.* **25,** 273 (1952).

215. Hokin, M. R., and Hokin, L. E., *J. Biol. Chem.* **219,** 85 (1956).

216. Aleksandrov, S. N., *Doklady, Akad Nauk S.S.S.R.* **106,** 569 (1956) [*Intern. Abstr. Biol. Sci.* **8,** No. 1, 975 (1957–58)].

217. Kay, R. E., and Entenman, C., *Arch. Biochem. Biophys.* **62,** 419 (1956).

218. Butler, J. A. V., Cohn, P., and Crathorn, A. R., *in* "Advances in Radiobiology"

(G. de Hevesy, A. Forssberg, and J. D. Abbatt, eds.), p. 33. Oliver & Boyd, Edinburgh, 1957.

219. Pelc, S. R., *Nature* **178,** 359 (1956).
220. Hevesy, G., and Forssberg, A., *Proc. 3rd Intern. Congr. Biochem., Brussels, 1955* 479 (1956).
221. Howard, A., *Ciba Foundation Symposium, Ionizing Radiations and Cell Metabolism* 196 (1956).
222. Kelly, L. S., *Progr. in Biophys. and Biophys. Chem.* **8,** 144 (1957).
223. Hevesy, G., *Brit. J. Radiol.* **29,** 465 (1956).
224. Paigen, K., and Kaufmann, B. P., *J. Cellular Comp. Physiol.* **42,** 163 (1953).
225. Kelly, L. S., *U. S. Atomic Energy Commission Rept.* **UCRL-2881,** 38 (1954).
226. Harrington, H., and Lavik, P. S., *J. Cellular Comp. Physiol.* **46,** 503 (1955).
227. Caster, W. O., Redgate, E. S., and Armstrong, W. D., *Radiation Research* **8,** 92 (1958).
228. Berenbom, M., and Peters, E. R., *Radiation Research* **5,** 515 (1956).
229. Berenbom, M., *Radiation Research* **5,** 650 (1956).
230. Cole, L. J., and Ellis, M., *Cancer Research* **14,** 738 (1954).
231. Bećarević, A., Kaćanski, K., Mančić, D., and Hadžić, L., *Experientia* **12,** 23 (1956).
232. Mole, R. H., and Temple, D. M., *Nature* **180,** 1278 (1957).
233. Harrington, H., and Lavik, P. S., *Arch. Biochem. Biophys.* **54,** 6 (1955).
234. Mandel, P., Gros, C. M., Rodesch, J., Jaudel, C., and Chambon, P., *in* "Advances in Radiobiology" (G. de Hevesy, A. Forssberg, and J. D. Abbatt, eds.), p. 59. Oliver & Boyd, Edinburgh, 1957.
235. Thomson, J. F., Tourtellotte, W. W., Carttar, M. S., and Storer, J. B., *Arch. Biochem. Biophys.* **42,** 185 (1953).
236. Bishop, C. W., and Davisdon, J. N., *Brit. J. Radiol.* **30,** 367 (1957).
237. Erickson, C. A., Main, R. K., and Cole, L. J., *Radiation Research* **5,** 332 (1956).
238. Main, R. K., Cole, L. J., and Bond, V. P., *Arch. Biochem. Biophys.* **56,** 143 (1955).
239. Smellie, R. M. S., Humphrey, G. F., Kay, E. R. M., and Davidson, J. N., *Bio-J.* **60,** 177 (1955).
240. Kelly, L., and Payne, A., *Federation Proc.* **12,** 76 (1953).
241. Kelly, L. S., Hirsch, J. D., Beach, G., and Payne, A. H., *Radiation Research* **2,** 490 (1955).
242. Sherman, F. G., Brecher, G., Cronkite, E. P., and Quastler, H., *Federation Proc.* **17,** 148 (1958).
243. Way, J. L., Mandel, H. G., and Smith, P. K., *Cancer Research* **14,** 812 (1954).
244. Payne, A. H., Kelly, L. S., and Entenman, C., *Proc. Soc. Exptl. Biol. Med.* **81,** 698 (1952).
245. Lavik, P. S., *Federation Proc.* **12,** 236 (1953).
246. Trowell, O. A., *J. Pathol. Bacteriol.* **64,** 687 (1952).
247. Patt, H. M., *Ann. N. Y. Acad. Sci.* **59,** 649 (1955).
248. Bendich, A., *Exptl. Cell Research Suppl.* **2,** 181 (1952).
249. Harbers, E., and Backmann, R., *Exptl. Cell Research* **10,** 125 (1956).
250. Backmann, R., and Harbers, E., *Biochim. et Biophys. Acta* **16,** 604 (1955).
251. Klein, G., and Forssberg, A., *Exptl. Cell Research* **6,** 211 (1954).
252. Kelly, L. S., Hirsch, J. D., Beach, G., and Petrakis, N. L., *Proc. Soc. Exptl. Biol. Med.* **94,** 83 (1957).
253. Gardella, J. W., and Lichtler, E. J., *Cancer Research* **15,** 529 (1955).
254. Harrington, H., Rauschkolb, D., and Lavik, P. S., *Cancer Research* **17,** 34 (1957).
255. Vermund, H., Barnum, C. P., Huseby, R. A., and Stenstrom, K. W., *Cancer Research* **13,** 633 (1953).

256. Forssberg, A., *Ciba Foundation Symposium, Ionizing Radiations and Cell Metabolism* 212 (1956).
257. Harrington, H., and Lavik, P. S., *Cancer Research* **17**, 38 (1957).
258. Ahlström, L., von Euler, H., and Hevesy, G., *Arkiv. Kemi Mineral. Geol.* **19A**, No. 13, 1 (1945).
259. Holmes, B. E., *Brit. J. Radiol.* **22**, 487 (1949).
260. Kelly, L. S., and Jones, H. B., *Proc. Soc. Exptl. Biol. Med.* **74**, 493 (1950).
261. Ahlström, L., von Euler, H., and Hevesy, G., *Arkiv. Kemi Mineral. Geol.* **24A**, No. 12, 1 (1947).
262. Lajtha, L. G., and Vane, J. R., *Nature* **182**, 191 (1958).
263. Pelc, S. R., *Exptl. Cell Research* **14**, 301 (1958).
264. Holmes, B. E., and Mee, L. K., *in* "Radiobiology Symposium, 1954" (Z, M. Bacq and P. Alexander, eds.), p. 220. Academic Press, New York, 1955.
265. Mee, L. K., *in* "Progress in Radiobiology" (J. S. Mitchell, B. E. Holmes, and C. L. Smith, eds.), p. 12. Oliver & Boyd, Edinburgh, 1956.
266. Thomson, J. F., Carttar, M. S., and Tourtellotte, W. W., *Radiation Research* **1**, 165 (1954).
267. Sibatani, A., *Biochim. et Biophys. Acta* **25**, 592 (1957).
268. Beltz, R. E., van Lancker, J., and Potter, V. R., *Cancer Research* **17**, 688 (1957).
269. Kelly, L. S., Hirsch, J. D., Beach, G., and Palmer, W., *Cancer Research* **17**, 117 (1957).
270. Holmes, B. E., *Ciba Foundation Symposium, Ionizing Radiations and Cell Metabolism* 225 (1956).
271. Hecht, L. I., and Potter, V. R., *Cancer Research* **16**, 988, 999 (1956).
272. Takagi, Y., Hecht, L. I., and Potter, V. R., *Cancer Research* **16**, 994 (1956).
273. Pelc, S. R., and Howard, A., *Radiation Research* **3**, 135 (1955).
274. Lajtha, L. G., Oliver, R., and Ellis, F., *in* "Advances in Radiobiology" (G. de Hevesy, A. Forssberg and J. D. Abbatt, eds.), p. 54. Oliver & Boyd, Edinburgh, 1957.
275. Lajtha, L. G., Oliver, R., Kumatori, T., and Ellis, F., *Radiation Research* **8**, 1 (1958).
276. Totter, J. R., *Abstr. 19th Intern. Physiol. Congr.* 833 (1953).
277. Passonneau, J. V., and Totter, J. R., *Radiation Research* **3**, 304 (1955).
278. Totter, J. R., *Federation Proc.* **12**, 281 (1953).
279. Lajtha, L. G., *Nature* **180**, 1048 (1957).
280. Canellakis, E. S., and Montsavinos, R., *Biochim. et Biophys. Acta* **27**, 643, 661, (1958).
281. Smellie, R. M. S., McArdle, A. H., Keir, H. M., and Davidson, J. N., *Biochem. J.* **69**, 37P (1958).
282. Ficq, A., and Errera, M., *Exptl. Cell Research* **14**, 182 (1958).
283. Allfrey, V. G., and Mirsky, A. E., *Proc. Natl. Acad. Sci. U. S.* **43**, 589 (1957).
284. Bennett, E. L., Kelly, L., and Krueckel, B., *Federation Proc.* **13**, 181 (1954).
285. Davidson, J. N., Thomson, R. Y., Paul, J., Smellie, R. M. S., and Goutier, R., *Biokhimiya* **22**, 157 (1957).
286. Bernstein, M. H., *Nature* **174**, 463 (1954).
287. Anderson, N. G., *Federation Proc.* **13**, 3 (1954).
288. Butler, J. A. V., *Radiation Research* **4**, 20 (1956).
289. Fisher, W., quoted by Hollaender, A., *Ciba Foundation Symposium, Ionizing Radiations and Cell Metabolism* 73 (1956).
290. Dounce, A. L., and Monty, K. J., *J. Biophys. Biochem. Cytol.* **1**, 155 (1955).
291. Cole, L. J., and Ellis, M. E., *Radiation Research* **1**, 128 (1954).
292. Cole, L. J., and Ellis, M. E., *Radiation Research* **7**, 508 (1957).

293. Cole, L. J., and Ellis, M. E., *Federation Proc.* **15,** 411 (1956).
294. Main, R. K., Cole, L. J., and Ellis, M. E., *Nature* **180,** 1285 (1957).
295. Cole, L. J., and Ellis, M. E., *Radiation Research* **5,** 252 (1956).
296. Ellis, M. E., and Cole, L. J., *Federation Proc.* **17,** 366 (1958).
297. Vendrely, R., Alfert, M., Matsudaira, H., and Knobloch, A., *Exptl. Cell Research*
     14, 295 (1958).
298. Mitchell, J. S., *Brit. J. Exptl. Pathol.* **23,** 296 (1942).
299. Mitchell, J. S., *J. Colloid Sci.* **11,** 317 (1956).
300. Kanazir, D., and Errera, M., *Biochem. et Biophys. Acta* **14,** 62 (1954).
301. Friedkin, M., and Roberts, D., *J. Biol. Chem.* **220,** 653 (1956).
302. Reichard, P., and Estborn, B., *J. Biol. Chem.* **188,** 839 (1951).
303. Siekewitz, P., and Watson, M. L., *Biochim. et Biophys. Acta* **25,** 274 (1957).
304. Edelmann, R., *Federation Proc.* **8,** 39 (1949).
305. Caster, W. O., and Armstrong, W. D., *Proc. Soc. Exptl. Biol. Med.* **90,** 56 (1955).
306. Bennett, L. R., Bennett, V. C., and Howland, J. W., *Federation Proc.* **8,** 350
     (1949).
307. Kohn, H. I., *Am. J. Physiol.* **165,** 27 (1951).
308. Caster, W. O., and Armstrong, W. D., *Radiation Research* **5,** 189 (1956).
309. Baker, D. G., and Sellers, E. A., *Can. J. Biochem. and Physiol.* **34,** 835 (1956).
310. Goodman, R. D., and Vogel, M., *Am. J. Physiol.* **175,** 29 (1953).
311. Fulton, G. P., and Sudak, F. N., *Am. J. Physiol.* **179,** 135 (1954).
312. Court-Brown, W. M., and Mahler, R. F., *Proc. Roy. Soc. Med.* **46,** 245 (1953).
313. McDonald, R. E., Jensen, R. E., Urry, H. C., Bolin, V. S., and Price, P. B., *Am.
     J. Roentgenol. Radium Therapy Nuclear Med.* **74,** 701 (1955).
314. Sheppard, C. W., and Beyl, G. E., *J. Gen. Physiol.* **34,** 691 (1950).
315. Ellinwood, L. E., Wilson, J. E., and Coon, J. M., *Proc. Soc. Exptl. Biol. Med.*
     94, 129 (1957).
316. Wilde, W. S., and Sheppard, C. W., *Proc. Soc. Exptl. Biol. Med.* **88,** 249 (1955).
317. Kohn, H. I., Kallman, R. F., Berdjis, C. C., and de Orne, K. B., *Radiation Re-
     search* **7,** 407 (1957).
318. Esnouf, M. P., Ord, M. G., and Stocken, L. A., in preparation.
319. Pirie, A., Van Heyningen, R., and Boag, J. W., *Biochem. J.* **54,** 682 (1953).
320. Van Heyningen, R., Pirie, A., and Boag, J. W., *Biochem. J.*, **56,** 372 (1954).
321. Rupe, C. O., Monsul, R. W., and Koenig, V. L., *Radiation Research* **8.** 265 (1958).
322. Lajtha, L. G., *in* "Nucleic Acids" (E. Chargaff and J. N. Davidson, eds.),
     Vol. 3, p. 527. Academic Press, New York, 1960.
323. Errera, M., *Am. Naturalist* **44,** 111 (1960).
324. Eichel, H. J., and Roth, J. S., *Radiation Research* **12,** 258 (1960).
325. Roth, J. S., and Eichel, H. J., *Radiation Research* **11,** 572 (1959).
326. Aldridge, W. G., Hempelmann, L. H., and Emmel, V. M., *Radiation Research*
     12, 49 (1960).
327. Brody, S., *Nature* **182,** 1386 (1958).
328. Goutier, R., Goutier–Pirotte, M., and Ciccarone, P., *in* "Immediate and Low
     Level Effects of Ionizing Radiations" (A. A. Buzzati-Traverso, ed.), p. 93.
     Taylor and Francis, London, 1960.
329. Benjamin, T. L., and Yost, H. T., *Radiation Research* **12,** 613 (1960).
330. Kuzin, A. M., and Shabadash, A. L., *Prog. in Nuclear Energy* [6] **2,** 364 (1959).
331. Stern, H., and Timonen, S., *Exptl. Cell Research* **9,** 101 (1955).
332. Nygaard, O. F., and Potter, R. L., *Radiation Research* **10,** 462 (1959).
333. Nygaard, O. F., and Potter, R. L., *Radiation Research* **12,** 120, 131 (1960).
334. Yen, C. Y., Anderson, E. P., and Smith, P. K., *Radiation Research* **11,** 7 (1959).

335. Uyeki, E. M., Leuchtenberger, C., and Salerno, P. R., *Exptl. Cell Research* **17**, 405 (1959).
336. Mole, R. H., and Temple, D. M., *Intern. J. Radiation Biol.* **1**, 28 (1959).
337. Cooper, E. H., *Intern. J. Radiation Biol.* **1**, 43 (1959).
338. Cattaneo, S. M., Quastler, H., and Sherman, F. G., *Radiation Research* **12**, 587 (1960).
339. Sherman, F. G., and Quastler, H., *Exptl. Cell Research* **19**, 343 (1960).
340. Seed, J., *Proc. Roy. Soc.* **B152**, 387 (1960).
341. Looney, W. B., Campbell, R. C., and Holmes, B. E., *Proc. Natl. Acad. Sci. U. S.* **46**, 698. (1960).
342. Ord, M. G., and Stocken, L. A., *Nature* **182**, 1787 (1958).
343. Lajtha, L. G., Oliver, R., Berry, R., and Noyes, W. D., *Nature* **182**, 1787 (1958).
344. Berry, R. J., Hell, E., Lajtha, L. G., and Ebert, M., *Nature* **186**, 563 (1960).
345. van Lancker, J. L., *Biochim. et Biophys. Acta.* **33**, 587 (1959).
346. Bollum, F. S., Anderegg, J. W., McElya, A. B., and Potter, V. R., *Cancer Research* **20**, 138 (1960).
347. Beltz, R. E., and Applegate, R. L., *Biochem. Biophys. Research Communs.* **1**, 298 (1959).
348. Jaffe, J. J., Lajtha, L. G., Lascelles, J., Ord, M. G., and Stocken, L. A., *Intern. J. Radiation. Biol.* **1**, 241 (1959).
349. Okada, S., and Hempelmann, L. H., *Intern. J. Radiation Biol.* **1**, 305 (1959).
350. Stevens, L., quoted by Stocken, L. A., *in* Symposium on Initial Effects of Ionizing Radiations in Living Cells, Moscow, 1960.
351. Hiatt, H. H., and Bojarski, T. B., *Biochem. Biophys. Research Communs.* **2**, 35 (1960).
352. Soska, J., and Karpfel, Z., *Folia Biol.* **6**, 172 (1960).
353. Welling, W., and Cohen, J. A., *Biochim. et Biophys. Acta* **42**, 181 (1960).
354. Bianchi, P., Butler, J. A. V., Crathorn, A. R., and Shooter, K. V., *Biochem. J.* **77**, 15P (1960).
355. Smellie, R. M. S., *Biochem. J.* **77**, 15P (1960).
356. Mandel, P., and Chambon, P., *in* "Immediate and Low Level Effects of Ionizing Radiations" (A. A. Buzzati-Traverso, ed.), p. 71. Taylor and Francis, London, 1960.
357. Soska, J., and Soskoya, L., *Folia Biol.* **5**, 425 (1959).
358. Paricek, J., Arient, M., Dienstbier, Z., and Skoda, J., *Nature* **182**, 721 (1958).
359. Okada, S., *Nature* **185**, 193 (1960).
360. Wheeler, C. M., and Okada, S., *Intern. J. Radiation Biol.* **3**, 23 (1961).
361. Ord, M. G., and Stocken, L. A., *Biochim. et Biophys. Acta* **37**, 352 (1960).
362. van Lancker, J. L., *Biochim. et Biophys. Acta* **45**, 57, 63 (1960).
363. Bollom, F. J., and Potter, V. R., *J. Biol. Chem.* **233**, 478 (1958).
364. Logan, R., Errera, M., and Ficq, A., *Biochim. et Biophys. Acta* **32**, 147 (1959).
365. Creasey, W. A., *Biochem. J.* **77**, 5 (1960).
366. Creasey, W. A., *Biochim. et Biophys. Acta* **38**, 181 (1960).
367. Hagen, U., *Nature* **187**, 1123 (1960).
368. Logan, R., *Biochim. et Biophys. Acta* **35**, 251 (1959).
369. Tchoe, Y-T., and Sibatani, A., *Nature* **183**, 1335 (1959).
370. Myers, D. K., *Nature* **187**, 1124 (1960).
371. Creasey, W. A., and Stocken, L. A., *Biochem. J.* **72**, 519 (1959).
372. Ord, M. G., and Stocken, L. A., quoted by Stocken, L. A., Symposium on Initial Effects of Ionising Radiations on Living Cells, Moscow, 1960.
373. Crathorn, A. R., and Shooter, K. V., *Nature* **187**, 614 (1960).

CHAPTER 4

Cytological Effects

THEODORE N. TAHMISIAN

*Division of Biological and Medical Research, Argonne National
Laboratory, Argonne, Illinois*

CONTENTS

I. Introduction

One cannot overemphasize the importance of the cytological effects of
ionizing radiation. The ultimate radiation effects must be referred to physicochemical changes caused immediately in the molecules and atoms that
compose the cell. The constituents of the cell, e.g., organelles, granules,
and fibers, bridge the gap between physicochemical and biological phenomena. It is not sufficient to study the effect of radiation on pure substances,
although such investigations are of extreme importance to the cytologist.
It is apparent that organized intracellular entities such as nucleoli, mitochondria, and the Golgi apparatus are the sites of specific effects. Therefore, the study of radiation effects is concerned not only with molecules but
also with these organized systems of molecules. The biological system, unlike inert physical systems, is constantly in a state of flux; through a dy-

* This work was prepared under the auspices of the U. S. Atomic Energy Commission.

namic equilibrium the cell is capable of building up and tearing down materials. These metabolic processes endow the cell with attributes peculiar to the living system, such as growth, duplication, and differentiation. Information on these aspects of radiobiology is fairly meager and represents a field deserving of much attention in the future. The writer of this chapter had drawn heavily on his own observations and on those of his associates.

If an external force such as radiation is applied to an organized system, then, depending on the degree of disorganization that results, rates of processes will be altered, or function will be abolished. Such changes are reflected as changes or breakdowns of form; this is the basis of cytological observations. Before the electron microscope became available, the cytologist could observe only the larger organelles. With the electron microscope having, theoretically, the capacity to resolve 8 to 10 A, it may in time be possible to study molecular ecology; the cross section of a molecule of water—one of the smaller of the molecules in a living system—is about 3 A. The ultimate task now confronting us is to recognize and describe the changes in the structure of various subcellular systems after radiation, with the aim of recognizing them as reflecting altered molecular arrangement.

II. The Nucleus as Affected by Radiation

Studies of the cytological effects of radiation have for the most part dealt with the nucleus. There are many reasons for such observations. The nucleus is the largest cellular organelle, it is the seat of anabolic processes, it undergoes more striking morphological changes during cell division than any other organelle, it is of genetic interest, and, studied by the usual techniques in an injured or abnormal cell, its morphological deviations have been observed. The nuclear contents, which are separated from the cytoplasm by a double membrane (1), consist of the karyoplasm made up of matrix, nucleoli, and chromatin. The chromatin is usually in long strands made up of DNA and histones or protamines and other proteins (2, 3); it constitutes the main substance of the chromosomes. The chromosomal material exhibits a high degree of organization as shown by the number and shape of the chromosomes; it is highly species-specific and does not vary greatly under normal conditions.

A. CHROMATIN

Morphologically, the nucleus of an irradiated cell has a different appearance from that of an unirradiated cell. The chromosomes are swollen, and, if the dose is high enough, the nucleus becomes homogeneous several days after irradiation. The distinction between chromatin and matrix disappears, and the nuclear contents appear to be highly solated (4) as determined by the high rate of Brownian movement (5). The increased rate of Brownian movement within the nucleus (5) suggests that radiation has caused fragmentation of the nuclear contents. The solation of the nucleus is a secondary radiation effect; it does not appear immediately on irradiation, even with a dose as high as 200,000 r (6). When such nuclei are fixed and stained, the fixed nucleus appears pyknotic owing to extracting of the proteins by the salts in the fixing solution.

In some cases the chromonemata appear to be widely separated with apparent solation between them (5), probably due to partial solation of the nucleus after irradiation. When such cells are fixed, chromatids appear widely displaced from each other.

The DNA content of the nucleus is affected by irradiation. The increase in nuclear DNA which normally occurs in ascites tumor cells over 48 hours *during the growth period* was not observed when the cells were irradiated (7). The same investigators found that incorporation of C^{14}-labeled glycine into the DNA of the nucleus was very low compared to that in nonirradiated cells (8). This indicates that the synthesis of DNA after irradiation may be suppressed. Before the nucleus becomes homogeneous and pyknotic the various constituents of the karyoplasm are segregated (6). A separation between Feulgen-positive and Feulgen-negative constituents takes place. In the main body of the Feulgen-positive portion of the nucleus one finds spherules of osmophilic material. The presence of such material in the DNA portion of the pyknotic nucleus suggests that lipoproteins that were distributed in an organized fashion in the chromosomal element have been displaced from their topological pattern and become isolated as cohesive droplets. Similarly isolated osmophilic material also appears in irradiated chromosomes (5).

This segregation of the karyoplasmic constituents suggests that molecular organization is disturbed after radiation. Since the disorganized state does not appear immediately after irradiation, the delay indicates that it may not be a primary result of irradiation damage but that metabolic changes may precede the observed alterations.

B. THE RESTING NUCLEUS

Some grasshopper embryos normally enter a state of suspended animation called diapause, during which they are in a basal metabolic condition (9, 10); mitosis ceases, and the cells are uniformly in the resting stage with all nuclei at interphase. Unless diapause is interrupted, the embryos die. In some eggs diapause is broken at room temperature, but almost 100 % interruption can be accomplished by chilling the eggs for 3 months at 1° to 3°C. It can also be interrupted by puncturing the eggs, by immersing them in fat solvents for a few minutes (11), or by deliberately dropping them.

Because diapause embryos contain only interphase nuclei they have provided interesting material for determining the effect of irradiation on the resting cell (12). Doses between 1000 and 200,000 r do not alter the appearance of the nucleus immediately after irradiation. If the cells are kept at developmental temperatures after radiation, nuclei that receive 10,000 to 100,000 r become pyknotic. It is apparent that this change in the state of the nuclei takes place during subsequent metabolic activity. These cells with pyknotic nuclei die eventually, although respiration continues for 20 to 40 days. Those that receive 200,000 r show very little morphological change when observed with a light microscope, but physiologically they are dead as though they had been fixed. Such cells must have widespread molecular injury after irradiation.

In grasshopper embryos, if the dose of radiation is high enough to cause pyknosis of nuclei, eventually the whole embryo gradually diminishes in size. Respiration of such material appears normal or enhanced in spite of the fact that the intranuclear components are pyknotic. The fact that respiration is unaffected, although the cell diminishes in size, indicates that anabolic processes are prevented when the nucleus is pyknotic but catabolism is not affected. Although these cells are in their normal position with all their nutrient yolk material available, they are not able to utilize the anabolites even to maintain the status quo (which is all that the cell under basal conditions does normally). The cell diminishes in size and dies because it uses up its contents. Respirometric determinations indicate that catabolism is affected only at a dose of 200,000 r or more. Thus anabolic processes are more sensitive to radiation than the catabolic processes; although respiration is abolished in a few days after radiation with 200,000 r, the cells remain unchanged morphologically.

Embryonic cells of grasshopper embryos in diapause that are exposed under basal conditions to 2500 to 5000 r appear normal, but when diapause is interrupted by cold treatment and the cells are returned to developmental temperature, many chromosomal aberrations become apparent. As long as the embryonic cells are maintained under basal conditions prior to interruption of diapause, even though they are maintained at developmental temperatures, radiation injury is not apparent. When diapause is interrupted, cells that have received 2500 to 5000 r begin mitotic division again; the embryo grows, but tissue differentiation does not occur. There is no differentiation of the cells into striated muscle, neurons, connectives, commissures, or apodemes. This indicates that in grasshopper embryos cell division is less sensitive to radiation than the process of cell differentiation. Cell division goes on, with some chromosomal aberrations; there are undoubtedly many genetic effects even in cells that appear normal.

C. MITOSIS

The reader is referred to Schrader's "Mitosis" (13) for a concise description of the events that occur during normal cell division. It is a matter of general knowledge that irradiation of the cell causes deviations in the normal mitotic pattern, which may yield pyknotic nuclei in the daughter cells.

Early in this century Bergonié and Tribondeau (14) enunciated the principle that the radiosensitivity of cells is proportional to their degree of reproductive activity and inversely proportional to the degree of differentiation. Their "law" suffers, of course, from the fact that radiosensitivity is not easily defined; also, numerous exceptions have been found in subsequent research (15, 16). It has been found that one of the most readily destroyed tissue layers in embryos is that composed of the cells that have completed division and are in the process of differentiation (17–19). The periods of induction and differentiation have been determined as periods of particularly great sensitivity in a number of other situations (17–19). It is also known that spermatids are more sensitive to irradiation than are spermatogonia or spermatozoa (20). It would seem legitimate to conclude that the effects of radiation on living systems cannot be considered in the same light as those on purely physical systems (21), but rather that the dynamic equilibrium in which living matter exists imposes quite different conditions. Delicately balanced processes may be upset by injury occurring at a critical stage—of which mitosis is one—or injury may be observable only after metabolic changes or cell division has intervened.

The radiosensitivity of the dividing cell is related to the degree of intracellular differentiation that is associated with the division process. The function of the interphase cell—self-maintenance—has been altered to one of self-duplication. This change necessitates a series of changes in form, since a new function cannot be undertaken without a corresponding change in form. The internal morphology of the cell about to divide undergoes drastic and systematic changes. Some organelles exhibit progressive changes in form; some disappear, and others are established. The nuclear membrane breaks down, centrioles move apart, the spindle is formed, and when the daughter chromosomes separate interzonal fibers appear between them. The chromosomal fibers arrange themselves from the kinetochore to the centriole. The mitochondria are apportioned between the daughter cells, chromosomes are distributed equally, and a new nuclear membrane is formed about each chromosomal mass as the cleavage furrow advances, dividing the cell. All these morphological changes during cell division (e.g., the formation of chromatids, their physical displacement and distribution to daughter cells, the breakdown and buildup of the nuclear membrane, the duplication and displacement of centrioles, and the formation and dissolution of the spindle fibers) by necessity are associated with internal differentiation and, therefore, with considerable reapportionment at the molecular level (22–25). The obligatory sequential events throughout this process could easily be upset by structural change or physical displacement of an essential molecule, and the result could be an abnormal cell. Thus in the larger sense the sensitivity of dividing cells is related to internal mobilization and remobilization during the mitotic cycle. Although this is part of the dynamic equilibrium of cell function, it constitutes differentiation, whether the process involved be gene duplication, chromatid duplication, organelle division or union, or molecular redistribution. In one species or another, every stage of cell division has been observed to be sensitive to radiation. It may be suggested that the stage of mitosis that appears most radiosensitive in a given cell very likely is the stage at which the process of internal reorganization is most active.

Radiation causes partial or complete degradation of the mitotic spindle. If the spindle is completely absent after radiation, it may have been destroyed after it was formed, or the centers and substrates necessary for its formation may have been injured prior to the differentiation of the spindle fibers. The spindle fibrils, unlike some other organelles such as centrioles and mitochondria, are not self-perpetuating. Their formation depend on the interaction of chromosomal kinetochores, centrioles, cytoplasm, and, probably, karyoplasm. If the spindle is formed at all, it is probably complete. Although at present there is no direct evidence that the spindle can be partially inhibited, evidence can be cited that other cytoplasmic organelles follow an "all-or-none" pattern (see Fig. 2). When spindle formation is inhibited with colchicine, the chromosomal integrity is not lost (26, 27); however, when the spindle is degraded by X-irradiation, individual chromosomes lose their identity in grasshopper embryonic cells (5). The loss of chromosomal identity accompanying the loss of the spindle after irradiation may be due to nonspecific simultaneous effects of irradiation on both the spindle and the chromosome, whereas colchicine inhibition appears to be specific for spindle formation. It may be that colchicine affects only the formation of the spindle fibers. In any case the radiation effect on the spindle-chromosome relationship is quite different from the colchicine effect.

Two types of partial loss of the spindle have been observed: (i) bilateral loss (5) (see Fig. A) and (ii) unilateral loss (28). In such cases the spindle may have been present at the time of irradiation. When only half a spindle is present on each side of the metaphase plate (bilateral loss), the chromosomes on the injured side clump (see Fig. A) and appear pyknotic (5). After unilateral loss of the spindle, anaphase does not occur; the cell divides, with one daughter having no nucleus (28).

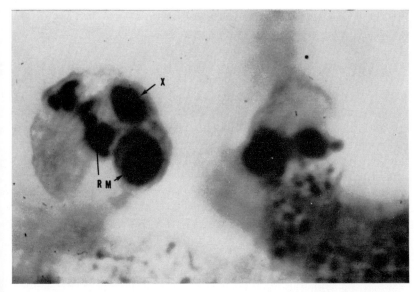

Fig. A. Grasshopper embryo neuroblast that received an equivalent of 200 r of
β-irradiation from strontium-90 solution surrounding the egg at the time of irradiation. Neuroblast cell in metaphase with the right half of the spindle destroyed bi-
laterally. The accessory chromosome (X) and the right half of the metaphase plate
(RM) show chromosomal pyknosis. Chromosomes at the left that are attached to the
spindle maintain their integrity. Flemming's triple stain and fixative. 2500×.

The fact that division of the cell occurs without the presence of a
mitotic spindle is well known (29, 30). After irradiation, some cells on dividing tend to apportion the chromosomal mass between the two daughter
cells. In this case there is a complete loss of chromosomal identity; it is
not known whether the newly formed cells produced by anastrous division
can survive. The constriction of a cell without the presence of a spindle
indicates that the cleavage furrow is independent of the spindle. Stroud
et al. (31) in tritium-irradiated tissue culture cells have a time-lapse cine-
matographic recording in which the spindle becomes detached and, with
the metaphase plate intact, moves up and down within the cell. As cleavage
begins, the spindle with the metaphase plate of chromosomes promptly
moves to the plane of cleavage and the cell divides. Here again, it is apparent
that cleavage is independent of the spindle as far as any mechanical effect of the asters or spindle fibers is concerned.

D. Meiosis

The effect of radiation on gametogenesis has been widely studied in
both animals and plants. There are many reviews on the subject (32–35).
Luning and Jonsson (20) have shown that the metamorphosis of the sperma-

tid to the spermatozoon is more sensitive to irradiation than the meiotic divisions. A similar investigation has been carried out over the last four years in this laboratory (36); our own unpublished material leads to the same conclusion.

When meiosis is altered by radiation, the development of primary and secondary spermatocytes is so affected that cells with double nuclei or fused giant nuclei appear. There is fragmentation and eventual abnormal sperm head development (see Figs. 9 and 10). The genetic effect of radiation during meiosis needs further investigation. The question arises: Is it possible to elicit genetic effects of meiotic rather than spermatogonial origin? Under such conditions a parent with radiation-induced genetic damage incurred at or beyond the meiotic stages of spermiogenesis should produce mutant offspring only at the first mating after irradiation; subsequent progeny should have the normal genetic constitution.

III. Radiation Effects on the Cytoplasm

The cytoplasm of the cell contains the major portion of the protoplasm, in comparison with the nucleus. Because it contains many organelles as well as the cytoplasmic matrix, it might be expected that radiation damage would be mostly of cytoplasmic origin (37). The classic experiments of Duryee are well known (38); he was able to show that the frog egg nucleus was very resistant to irradiation, but in the presence of small amounts of cytoplasm sensitivity increased greatly. The basis of his test for nuclear sensitivity was the appearance of nucleolar lesions, which appeared only after 60,000 r. He showed that the greatest portion of radiation damage is of cytoplasmic origin; he was able to produce radiation-type injuries in the nucleus of nonirradiated cells by injection of minute amounts of irradiated cytoplasm into these normal cells. Zirkle and Bloom (39), using microbeams of α-particles, demonstrated chromosome breakage if the beam traversed the nucleus; when the cytoplasm adjacent to the nucleus was bombarded, nuclear aberrations were not observed. The discrepancies may, however, be explained. In the former case the irradiated cytoplasm came from a cell in which all the cytoplasm was irradiated, and in the latter case the heavy ionization track left much of the cytoplasm not irradiated.

The cytoplasm of the cell contains most of the respiratory enzymes. The mitochondria are very rich in enzymes that are necessary for energy metabolism from the dehydrogenases up. The Golgi apparatus in *Helix aspersa* is very rich in dehydrogenase content. The centrioles, neutral red bodies, and endoplasmic reticulum are specific organelles present in the cytoplasm. In addition to this, metabolites are present either as integral parts of the cytoplasm or en route to the nucleus. The diverse substances of the cytoplasm constitute a multitude of targets. Most of the cytological studies of radiation effects are biochemical in nature, and these are discussed elsewhere. The reason for the lack of morphological observations of radiation-induced anomalies in cytoplasmic constituents stems from the limits imposed by the light microscope. Fortunately a great field of investigation is now open with the advent of electron optics.

In our laboratory we have studied the effects of irradiation on cytoplasmic organelles with the aid of the electron microscope. The study was on spermiogenesis in the insect *Melanoplus differentialis differentialis* Thomas. The reason for the choice of spermiogenesis was that many well-defined intracellular morphological changes in organelles occur during the development of the sperm (40). The germ cell undergoes metamorphosis accompanied by distinct characteristic morphological changes in organelles.

All metabolites that enter the cell must be incorporated into the structure of the cell through anabolic processes. Even on the catabolic side we are aware, for example, of the changes in the molecular structure of dextrose to fructose before this saccharide is degraded stepwise, ending as CO_2 and H_2O and yielding energy. Such processes may be looked upon as the analogs of differentiation at the molecular level, and they form a continuous process in all cells that are actively metabolizing. The interdependence between organelles (41) and enzymes, substrates, and end products, where an end product of one enzyme is the substrate of the next enzyme, leads us to investigate larger organelles, which are easily observed with the electron microscope, in the hope of finding leads toward explaining morphological radiation effects on a molecular basis.

A. CYTOPLASMIC ORGANELLES

1. CENTRIOLES

In animal cells the centrioles are associated with spindle formation during mitotic and meiotic cell divisions. Normally a cell has two centrioles which migrate to opposing poles as the spindle is formed between them. One function of the centriole in cell division is to radiate fibers in all directions, but in the differentiation of the spermatozoon the filaments are unidirectioned. As spermiogenesis begins, the centrioles are at the base of the nucleus. As centriole 2 moves down toward the region where the sperm tail will form, a bundle of tail filament fibrils is formed which eventually passes through the ring centriole (40) and forms the tail fibrils. The centriole is a self-perpetuating organelle, in that each daughter obtains one centriole which later divides. On fertilization the centriole from the sperm enters the egg, so that complete diploidy is achieved.

If a cell is given a sublethal dose (200 to 400 r), it can still divide; but when it is required to differentiate, the differentiation is abnormal, yield-

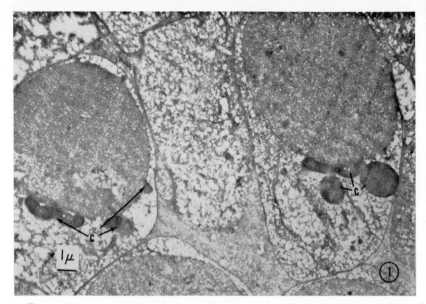

Fig. 1. Electron micrograph of grasshopper spermatid showing effect of 600 r of X-irradiation. Both cells contain supernumerary centrioles (C). Since centrioles normally are self-perpetuating, it is concluded that division and growth of centriolar material is radiation-induced. 8000×.

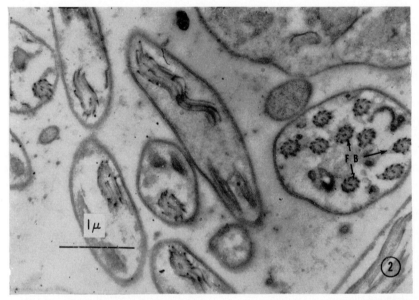

Fig. 2. A high magnification of the cross section of sperm tails showing tail filament bundles (FB). Sperm tail to the left contains nine tail filament bundles. Eight additional tail filament bundles were induced 18 days after 400 r of X-irradiation. This indicates that radiation can cause induction and differentiation of intracellular organelles, since the tail bundle normally is differentiated and is not self-perpetuated. Each bundle has the nine peripheral pairs and two central filaments. From this and other preparations, it is concluded that filament bundles are always complete as to number of filaments, and therefore the differentiation is all-or-none. 30,000×.

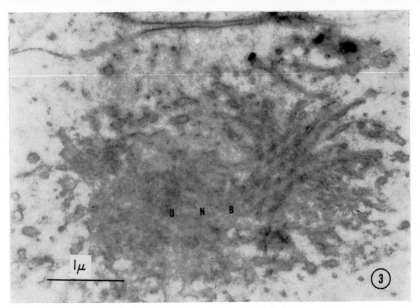

Fig. 3. Grasshopper spermatid 18 days after administration of 200 r of X-irradiation. Electron micrograph showing undifferentiated mitochondrial *Nebenkern* (UNB) which is degenerating because of X-irradiation. Palade fixative in Belar solution. 31,500×.

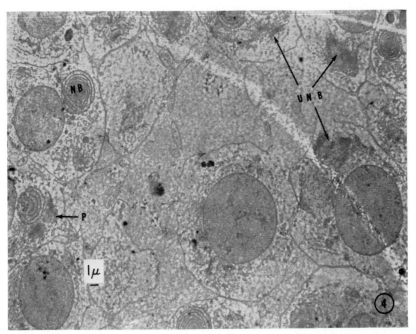

Fig. 4. Grasshopper spermatid 18 days after 200 r of X-irradiation. Electron micrograph showing inability of filamentous mitochondria (UNB) to differentiate into the mitochondrial *Nebenkern*. Other cells show partial (P) or total (NB) mitochondrial *Nebenkern* differentiation. Palade fixative in Belar solution. Note: At the time the testes were irradiated no maturation divisions were present. The meiotic divisions leading to the formation of the spermatids shown must not have been affected by irradiation. 3500×.

ing a malformed cell or gamete. In our experiments the grasshoppers were irradiated two instars prior to becoming adults. The gonads of such insects had only spermatocytes, with no meiotic divisions in progress. After 200 r, mitosis and meiosis occurred; many spermatids were present, but the differentiation from spermatids to spermatozoa was markedly abnormal.

For the centrioles themselves, the abnormality consisted in an increase over the normal number (see Fig. 1). When the single or supernumerary centriole was in contact with the nuclear membrane, each centriole gave rise to a tail filament bundle. If the centriole was not in direct contact with the nuclear membrane, it grew in size tremendously but no filaments were formed. Radiation in this case must have induced centriole formation by some such process as division, since centrioles ordinarily are derived from pre-existing ones. It caused topological displacement of the centriole so that the latter could not act synergistically with the nuclear membrane to form the tail bundle. The ecological relations within the cell, specifically those of the nucleus and centriole, were disturbed. In the interpretation of such findings as these it is useful to bear in mind Weiss' concept (42) of molecular ecology. In the light of this concept it is interesting to consider the devastating consequences of small disturbances on a much finer level, especially in processes such as differentiation.

2. FILAMENTS

Neither the fibers of the mitotic and meiotic spindle nor the tail filament bundles are self-perpetuating; they are formed each time through synergistic action of organelles together with the cytoplasm. It is not known whether injury to centrioles and other cell constituents may lead to a partial spindle formation. Tail filament bundles were always complete as far as the number of fibrils was concerned. Partially formed bundles were never found; each bundle always had nine peripheral pairs and two central fibrils (see Fig. 2). This suggests that tail filament bundle formation is an "all-or-none" phenomenon.

Many of the spermatozoa that developed in irradiated animals had supernumerary tail filament bundles; others had supernumerary tails (43). Among spermatozoa with supernumerary tail filament bundles in one tail, many were found to have four bundles. It is inconceivable that irradiation injured identical regions in each cell. Since the formation of the bundle is preceded by a chain of events, a nonspecific injury must yield a specific end result. The synergistic action between the centriole and nuclear membrane for the production of the tail filament bundle was mentioned above. In the formation of supernumerary bundles in a single cell, intracellular induction must occur in order for the differentiation of the second or nth tail bundle to occur. It may be assumed that at some point a displacement or separation of molecules has occurred which accounts for the disturbance of the eventual relation between organelles. If the bundle is formed, it must have differentiated; and if supernumerary tail bundles are differentiated after irradiation, they must have been induced. The pattern of intracellular induction and differentiation must be comparable to tissue differentiation as observed in embryonic induction and differentiation.

3. MITOCHONDRIA

Mitochondria are self-perpetuating organelles, and they are known to fuse and to divide (44). When a cell divides, mitochondria are apportioned between the two daughter cells. In insect spermatogenesis, as observed especially in Orthoptera, the distribution and fusion are very complex (40, 45–47) and precise (48). The fusion of the mitochondria to form the *Nebenkern* is again an example of a change of form to fit specific functional requirements, during which many molecules must be mobilized and redistributed. We are speaking here of the mitochondrial differentiation involved in the formation of the neck piece of the sperm tail. In irradiated spermatocytes the mitochondrial complex is affected in such a manner that normal events are often halted (Figs. 3 and 4). Some mitochondria remain in the filamentous stage; they are incapable of aggregating to form the chromophobic (45) *Nebenkern*. In others the *Nebenkern* breaks up completely and is sloughed off. In this case the normal course of differentiation is upset, but enzymatic function, though disoriented, may not be altered quantitatively. It becomes important to determine the morphological position of these organelles after radiation as well as the quantitative potencies of their constituents.

Although no quantitative variation may be observed, the topological arrangement determines the normality of the cell. Morphological changes in mammalian mitochondria were found by J. F. Thomson of this laboratory (see, compare Figs. 7 and 8). Mitochondria of thymocytes of nonirradiated 2-month-old Sprague-Dawley rats appear normal; but exposure to 600 r was followed within 24 hours by intramitochondrial breakdown as well as vacuolization and probably disintegration.

4. GOLGI BODIES AND ACROSOMES

The Golgi bodies or dictyosomes are found in many cells; the voluminous literature on the subject prohibits extensive citations; the study by Gatenby *et al.* may suffice as to historical and morphological aspects (48). We have not observed any morphological effects on the fine structure of the Golgi body after irradiation. The reason for its normal appearance after irradiation may lie in the high concentration of reducing substances in this organelle.

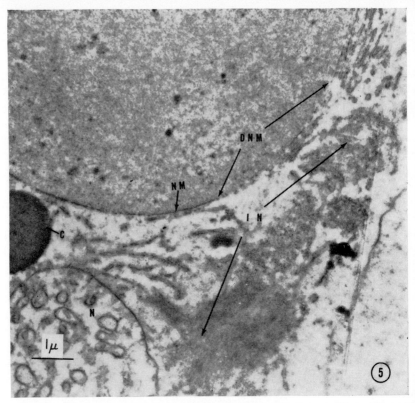

Fig. 5. Grasshopper spermatid 18 days after X-irradiation at 200 r while testis contained no spermatocytes. Electron micrograph of spermatid formed after irradiation. Shows partial breakdown of nuclear membrane (DNM). One half of the mitochondrial *Nebenkern* (N) has differentiated; the other half (IN) shows mitochondria remaining in the filamentous state inhibited from further differentiation. The centriolar complex (C), inhibited from making contact with the nuclear membrane (NM), has increased in size at the expense of forming a tail filament bundle. 17,000×.

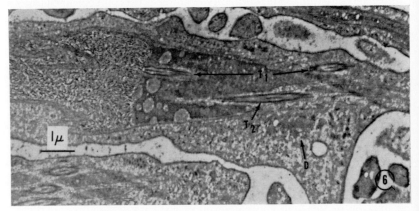

Fig. 6. Abnormal spermatozoon caused by 400 r of X-irradiation at spermatogonial stage. The nuclear portion shows trifurcation. Vacuolization of the centriolar complex and the presence of two tail filament bundles $T_1 + T_2$. At lower left cross section of three tail bundles is shown. Dictyosome (D) being sloughed off. 13,500×.

346

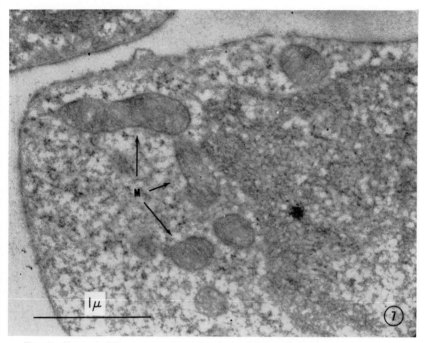

FIG. 7. Control. Thymocytes from 2-month-old Sprague-Dawley rat ♀ showing normal mitochondria (M). Courtesy of J. F. Thomson. 32,000×.

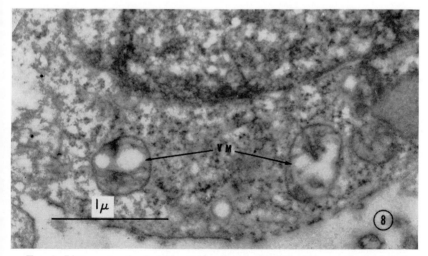

FIG. 8. Littermate of rat of Fig. 7, irradiated with 600 r 3 days prior to sacrifice. Note vacuolization of mitochondria (VM) caused by X-irradiation and almost complete internal breakdown. Courtesy of J. F. Thomson. 32,000×.

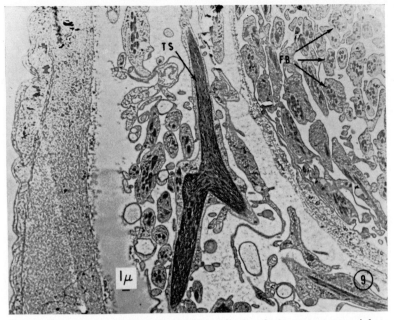

Fig. 9. Spermiogenesis after 400 r of X-irradiation during spermatogonial stage. Cross section of many sperm tails shown at the upper right-hand corner. Usually each tail has three or four filament bundles (FB); some have only one. In the center of the figure a sperm head shows tripolarity (TS), and the chromatin content has assumed a peculiar form quite different from the normal fusiform condition. 2900×.

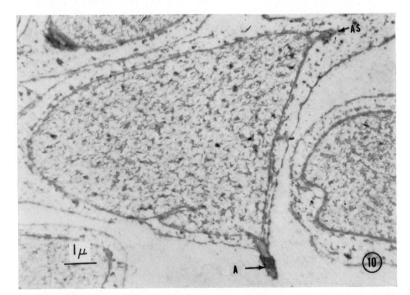

Fig. 10. Bipolar sperm head caused by 400 r of X-irradiation during spermatogonial stage. Electron micrograph of grasshopper sperm shows a complete acrosome (A) at the lowest corner of the sperm head. There is indication of a second acrosome (AS) at the upper corner, but only a portion of the acrosome stalk is present in the section. Since the acrosome is related to the Golgi apparatus, this indicates that more than one can be caused to differentiate after irradiation. 13,500×.

The Golgi body gives rise to the sperm acrosome (49), and normally as the proacrosome develops the Golgi body disintegrates. The proacrosome is formed in the concave surface of the Golgi body; under normal conditions it appears as a group of granules, which then form an amorphous spherical body with a limiting membrane. The proacrosome moves onto the nuclear membrane and proceeds until it is opposite the centrioles and tail filament. At this region the amorphous spherule differentiates into a spearhead-like form which appears to be made up of many lamellae in close proximity. In irradiated material one finds two and sometimes three acrosomes on one sperm (see Fig. 10), indicating that after irradiation the Golgi is capable of producing more than one acrosome. Instead of the induction of only one acrosome followed by disintegration of the Golgi complex, the disintegration process must be abolished by 200 to 400 r of irradiation, so that additional proacrosomes are induced and differentiated into typical acrosomes. The sperm, however, is abnormal. The fact that radiation causes not only abolition but induction and differentiation of supernumerary organelles is additional suggestive evidence that displacement of molecular systems occurs and that the process of intracellular differentiation is analogous to embryonic differentiation and response.

Subsequent to irradiation of the cell, the cytoplasmic stroma appears to contain large spaces comparable to vacuoles. The vacuolization may be caused by regional breakdown of organized structure into an amorphous disoriented region. In some cases, such areas of protein breakdown appear as amorphous dense regions after fixation of the cell. In other cases the complete absence of material after fixation (vacuolization) suggests that the region probably was filled with water or fluid that was removed during the fixing and dehydration process.

B. Undifferentiated Cytoplasm

If the cell is exposed to radiation at doses below 400 r just prior to intracellular differentiation, some organelles as mentioned above are so affected that their differentiation is incomplete. For instance, filamentous mitochondria may not form a *Nebenkern* but may be left as long filaments. In other cases the transition of the *Nebenkern* from the chromophilic to the chromophobic state does not occur. Some organelles are induced from the undifferentiated cytoplasm in abundance, e.g., supernumerary centrioles and tail filament bundles. The induction of these organelles suggests that at a responsive period topological displacement of an organelle allows it to grow and divide. The supernumerary centrioles, in conjunction with the nuclear membrane and cytoplasmic constituents, transform part of the undifferentiated cytoplasm to tail filament bundles.

As we have seen, inhibition of differentiation may occur when synergistic organelles are displaced from their normal position by the effect of irradiation. The displacement of the centrioles from the nuclear membrane inhibits tail bundle formation in grasshopper sperm. The centriole continues to grow to an abnormally large size when displaced from the vicinity of the nuclear membrane, as though the metabolites which would ordinarily yield a tail bundle were being used for centriolar growth only.

These observations have been emphasized because in the case of the sperm intracellular differentiation is spectacular, and the organelles are large and distinct enough to be observed by phase and light as well as electron microscopy. In cells such as those of the intestinal mucosa, where organization of metabolites into new cells must occur every 30 to 60 hours, such intracellular differentiation at the molecular level must also be occurring at a high rate; however, the changes are difficult to discern with instruments now available.

IV. Biological Basis of Radiation Damage

In other chapters in this book the biological bases of irradiation damage with respect to "ionization" and "target" theory are presented in detail. Here we wish to discuss the sort of radiation damage that may occur secondarily through molecular disarrangements or that may be due to alteration in the morphology of the molecule initiated by local disturbances of Van der Waals forces.

As we have observed above, the precise spatial arrangement of molecules (molecular ecology) is important in determining chemical processes especially in relation to morphological development. Any disturbance in the molecular ecology, as well as in other circumstances as, for example, local hydrogen ion concentration, may have far-reaching consequences. For optimal reaction rates and in the determination of specific end reactions, molecular arrangement is critical and must fall within very precise limits. Many of the effects will be observable only after cell metabolism or such processes as cell division or differentiation have progressed for some time. Only in the case of chromosomal or genetic damage has this been fully appreciated. An important question relates to whether ionization or activation of molecules can produce crucial effects of this sort without accompanying detectable chemical changes. It would appear so in analogy to the denaturation of protein by ionization or activation affecting only a few secondary bonds (50). It seems quite possible, for example, that the solation of the nuclear contents after irradiation involves such effects. Dr. Pinset, at Saclay, informed the author that the zeta potential of monolayers can be altered with a dose of less than 100 r *in vitro* (51).

Although increasing knowledge is being gained on the molecular level as to the nature of the physicochemical actions of radiation on cell constituents, the biologist is also concerned with the processes by which these actions are translated into the profound cytological change that occurs, for example, in differentiation: changes which, as we have seen, may have a topological basis, intervening between a small physicochemical change and a striking morphological result. It is hoped that this brief review of the subject will stimulate further interest in the various promising approaches to bridge this gap between molecular configuration and ecology and those changes now readily observed by the electron microscopist.

V. References

1. Watson, M. L., *J. Biophys. Biochem. Cytol.* **1,** 257 (1955).
2. Felix, K., Fischer, H., Krekels, A., and Rauen, H. M., *Z. physiol. Chem.* **286,** 67 (1950).
3. Alexander, P., *Biochim. et Biophys. Acta* **10,** 595 (1953).
4. Errera, M., *Cold Spring Harbor Symposia Quant. Biol.* **12,** 60 (1947).
5. Tahmisian, T. N., and Gasvoda, J., *Trans. Illinois State Acad. Sci.* **44,** 235 (1951).
6. Tahmisian, T. N., and Adamson, D. M., *Proc. Soc. Exptl. Biol. Med.* **78,** 597 (1951).
7. Forssberg, A., and Klein, G., *Exptl. Cell Research* **7,** 480 (1954).
8. Forssberg, A., and Révész, L., *Biochem. et Biophys. Acta* **25,** 165 (1957).
9. Henneguy, L. F., "Les Insectes: Morphologie Reproduction Embryologie." Masson, Paris, 1904.
10. Slifer, E. H., *J. Exptl. Zool.* **102,** 333 (1946).
11. Bodine, J. H., *Physiol. Zool.* **2,** 91 (1929).
12. Tahmisian, T. N., *J. Exptl. Zool.* **112,** 449 (1949).
13. Schrader, F., "Mitosis." Columbia Univ. Press, New York, 1946.
14. Bergonié, J., and Tribondeau, L., *Compt. rend.* **143,** 983 (1906).
15. Patt, H. M., and Brues, A. M., *in* "Radiation Biology" (A. Hollaender, ed.), Vol. I, p. 927. McGraw-Hill, New York, 1955.
16. Bloom, W., *in* "Radiation Biology" (A. Hollaender, ed.), Vol. I, p. 1133. McGraw-Hill, New York, 1955.
17. Evans, T. C., *Physiol. Zool.* **9,** 443 (1936).
18. Tahmisian, T. N., Passonneau, J. V., and Adamson, D. M., *J. Natl. Cancer Inst.* **14,** 941 (1954).
19. Hicks, S. P., Brown, B. L., and D'Amato, C. J., *Am. J. Pathol.* **33,** 459 (1957).
20. Luning, K. G., and Jonsson, S., *Nature* **178,** 1123 (1956).
21. Butler, J. A. V., *Radiation Research* **4,** 20 (1956).
22. Brachet, J., *Arch. biol. Paris* **44,** 159 (1933).
23. Brachet, J., *Arch. biol. Paris* **48,** 529 (1937).
24. Brachet, J., *Embryol. Chim.* (Ed. Desoer) Liège, 1947.
25. Pelc, S. R., *Exptl. Cell Research* **12,** 320 (1957).
26. Gaulden, M. E., and Carlson, J. G., *Exptl. Cell Research* **2,** 416 (1951).
27. Gaulden, M. E., and Carlson, J. G., *Genetics* **32,** 87 (1947).
28. Davis, M., and Smith, C. L., *Exptl. Cell Research* **12,** 15 (1957).
29. Fankhauser, G., *Ann. N. Y. Acad. Sci.* **49,** 684 (1948).
30. Brues, A. M., *Am. J. Cancer* **30,** 504 (1937).
31. Stroud, A. S., and Brues, A. M., *Texas Repts. Biol. and Med.* **12,** 931 (1954).
32. Lea, D. E., "Actions of Radiations of Living Cells," 2nd ed. Cambridge Univ. Press, London, 1955.
33. Bacq, Z. M., and Alexander, P., "Fundamentals of Radiobiology." Academic Press, New York, 1955.

34. Hollaender, A., ed., "Radiation Biology," Vols. I and II. McGraw-Hill, New York, 1955.
35. Nickson, J. J., ed., "Symposium on Radiobiology," Wiley, New York, 1952.
36. Tahmisian, T. N., and Devine, R. L., *Biophys. Biochem. Cytol.* in press (1961).
37. Errera, M., and Vanderhaeghe, F., *Exptl. Cell Research* **13,** 1 (1957).
38. Duryee, W. R., *J. Natl. Cancer Inst.* **10,** 735 (1949).
39. Zirkle, R. E., and Bloom, W., *Science* **117,** 487 (1953).
40. Johnson, H. H., *Z. wiss. Zool.* **115,** (1931).
41. Ehret, C. F., *in* "Symposium on Information Theory in Biology" (H. P. Yockey, ed.), pp. 218–229. Pergamon, New York, 1958.
42. Weiss, P., *Yale J. Biol. and Med.* **19,** 235 (1947).
43. Gatenby, J. B., and Wigoder, S., *Proc. Roy. Soc.* **B104,** 351 (1929).
44. Chèvremont, S., Firket, H., Chèvremont, M., and Frederic, J., *Acta Anat.* **30,** 175 (1957).
45. Gatenby, J. B., *Proc. Roy. Irish Acad.* **B47,** 149 (1941).
46. Makino, S., and Nakanishi, Y. H., *Chromosoma* **8,** 212 (1956).
47. DeRobertis, E., and Raffo, H. F., *Exptl. Cell Research* **12,** 66 (1957).
48. Tahmisian, T. N., Powers, E. L., and Devine, R. L., *J. Biophys. Biochem. Cytol. Suppl.* **2,** 341 (1956).
49. Gatenby, J. B., Tahmisian, T. N., Devine, R. L., and Beams, H. W., *Cellule rec. cytol. histol.* **59,** 29 (1958).
50. Platzman, R., and Franck, J., *in* "Symposium on Information Theory in Biology" (H. P. Yockey, ed.), pp. 262–275. Pergamon, New York, 1958.
51. Pinset, I., interviewed by the author, Saclay, France.

CHAPTER 5

Effects on Subcellular Units and Free-Living Cells

Tikvah Alper

*Medical Research Council, Experimental Radiopathology
Research Unit, Hammersmith Hospital, London, England*

Contents

I. Introduction

The use of homogeneous populations of single cells or subcellular units has obvious advantages for the study of radiobiological mechanisms, since it avoids many uncertainties which may arise in working with organized tissues. Investigations have been made on numerous types of test materials in suspension, varying from biologically active DNA ("transforming principle") to mammalian cells. The range of effects which have been studied is wide, and it is perhaps more surprising that there should be any common features in radiation effects on test objects with greatly different biochemical properties than that there should be large variations in their response.

This chapter will be concerned mainly with developments in the field since the appearance of the classic works of Lea (1) and of Timoféeff-Ressovsky and Zimmer (2). These provided outstanding reviews of the work done up to about 1944, and both of them developed and refined the "target principle" which had been evolved in the fifty years since ionizing radiation had been discovered and used therapeutically. In the period since these two books appeared, much research has been devoted to investigating conditions which change or appear to change radiosensitivity, and it has sometimes quite mistakenly been assumed that the possibility of such modification *ipso facto* invalidates the whole of the target theory. The basis of the theory is that there are certain vital "targets," i.e., molecules or structures, the integrity of which is essential to the function which is being used as the test of radiation damage. This function may be disrupted if one or a few ionizations take place within or very near to such a target, and the theory assigns a probability to the effectiveness of one *or more* ionizations or ion clusters. The probability may be one or very near to one in some instances, but it may also be significantly less than one, as may be determined if suitable data are available. Another misconception sometimes encountered is that the success of the theory depends on the identification of the "target" in a cell with its genetic apparatus. This is a complete misunderstanding of the status and usefulness of the theory, which enables deductions to be made as to the shape and size of targets; their identification rests not on the radiobiological data but on the available knowledge of cellular biochemistry and genetics.

Since the target concept is a valuable aid in describing the first steps involved in the development of radiation damage, and since its validity has not been seriously challenged, it will be the basis of much of the ensuing treatment of various topics concerned with radiation effects on viruses, biologically active nucleic acid, and single-cell populations.

II. Lethal Effects of Radiation: General Remarks

A. DEFINITION OF LETHALITY

Two of the predominating drives behind research in radiobiology are protection against harmful effects of radiation and the improvement of radiotherapy. The conditions which bring about cell death and hereditary changes in surviving cells have therefore received considerable attention. As usually applied to viruses or individual cells, the notion of lethality is restricted but well defined. A cell or virus particle may be said to have suffered lethal damage if it fails to reproduce a clone of like organisms in conditions in which it would normally do so, if it had not been affected by the radiation. It is well recognized that damage which is lethal in this restricted sense may leave many other measurable functions almost unimpaired, such as adaptive enzyme synthesis (3), other enzyme activities (4), respiration rate (5, 6), or the support of virus growth (7, 8). Nevertheless it is both convenient and meaningful to apply the phrase "lethal effect of radiation" in the sense which has been defined. This concept is relevant to the killing of animals by radiation, since this often results from the failure of bone marrow cells to reproduce. Different criteria of lethality are often applied to protozoa, as in some cases they may be observed individually, and various criteria such as loss of motility and cytolysis may be used to define death, rather than failure to reproduce (9). The doses required to cause death of this type are, as with other cells, considerably higher than those which cause "delayed death" (i.e., death at division) or failure to infect (10).

B. Dose-Effect Curves

Some general remarks apply to all investigations of lethal effects, no matter what test object or what type of radiation may be used. A point which has frequently and justly been stressed is the importance of establishing "dose-effect" or survival curves, whatever parameter is being investigated. Although this technique has been generally adopted, reports still sometimes appear in which the effects of different treatments are described in terms of the ratios between surviving populations after a given fixed dose. The significance of such ratios, however, cannot be judged unless data are available to indicate both the shape of the survival curve and the extent to which the given dose has affected survival.

Figures 1A, B, and C, all indicating "semilog" plots of survival against dose, represent types of survival curves of which numerous examples may be found. Each pair of curves has been drawn so that any given level of survival attained with dose D in one case requires dose 2D in the other; i.e., the lower curve of each pair represents a radiosensitivity which is twice as great as that represented by the upper curve. Point X on each of the upper curves marks the 10 % survival level, and point Y on each of the lower curves marks the survival level for the same dose. Although each of the lower curves represents the same increase in the effectiveness of the treatment (by a factor of 2), the ratios $X:Y$ are, respectively, 10, 3, and 100.

It is an important aspect of some treatments which modify radiation damage that dose-effect curves will bear to each other the same relationship

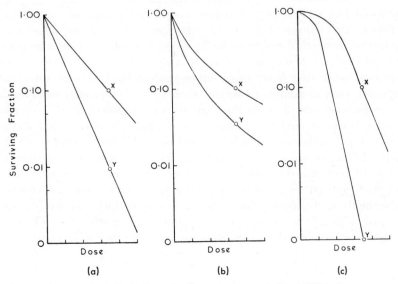

Fig. 1. Hypothetical survival curves, types A, B, and C (12).

as any of the pairs of curves of Fig. 1. In such a case a treatment may be regarded as a "dose-reducing" or a "dose-multiplying" agent; i.e., the effect of any dose with the modifying treatment is equal to that of a constant multiple of the dose without it (11). As will be seen below, the question whether a modifying treatment acts as a dose-modifying agent is very relevant to its mechanism of action.

C. Interpretation of Survival Curves

The types of survival curves illustrated in Figures 1A, B, and C were named A, B, and C, respectively, by Gunter and Kohn (12), and this convenient nomenclature will be adopted.

The interpretation of the three types of curve merits brief consideration.

1. *Type A: Survival Curves of Exponential Form*. Lea (Chapter 3 of ref. 1) has discussed possible interpretations of such curves, and it will suffice here to adopt the common view that the action of radiation in such cases is of the type for which Gray (13) coined the word "monotopic," implying that lethality has resulted from an event taking place in a single site. A frequently used term, "one-hit curve," is perhaps misleading in giving a somewhat colored implication of the mechanism involved. The equation usually applied to such curves is

$$f = e^{-\lambda D} \tag{1}$$

where f represents the fraction of the population surviving after dose D, and one aspect of the interpretation of such survival curves which has perhaps not received sufficient consideration is that λ may represent a sum of separate exponents, i.e., that an exponential survival curve may represent a summation of different monotopic events leading to cell death. It might be more correct to rewrite equation 1 in many cases as

$$f = e^{-\Sigma\lambda D} \qquad (2)$$

2. *Type B: Survival Curves with a "Resistant Tail."* These may be interpreted as being due to inhomogeneity in the radiosensitivity of the irradiated population, but in different test systems this inhomogeneity has different origins. For example, the "resistant tail" commonly found in survival curves with haploid yeast appears to be due to the presence of buds, since treatment which causes the buds to separate from the mother cells, while inhibiting further budding, also extends the initial exponential portion of the survival curve (14).

It is sometimes assumed that if a type B survival curve is found with a population of microorganisms derived from a single clone, the "tail" is due to the presence of mutants which are more resistant to radiation than the wild type. In such a case, it should be possible to select resistant mutants from the survivors of radiation doses which are large enough to kill all the more sensitive cells. With some strains, attempts to do this have failed. Gunter and Kohn (12), for example, found that the survival curve for *Escherichia coli* K12 (variant W1485) was of type B. Colonies were selected which had grown from the survivors of large doses of radiation, but these yielded populations of the same sensitivity as the parent strain, and the survival curves were again type B. The widely used strain *E. coli* B/r was selected by Witkin (15) from among the survivors of *E. coli* B cells which had been exposed to large doses of radiation, but she estimated that the rate of mutation to radiation resistance was only about 10^{-5} mutation per bacterium per generation, which was too low to account for the appearance of the tail. From survival curves usually obtained with *E. coli* B, it may be deduced that as many as 1 %, or in some conditions even 10 %, of the original population are "resistant." Factors other than mutation have been found by Alper and Gillies (16) to contribute to the resistant portion of the survival curves often found with *E. coli* B, one of these being the fact that a population in the logarithmic phase of growth is more sensitive than a stationary-phase one, so that a population containing cells in both stages of growth will be heterogeneous in respect of its radiosensitivity. Another factor contributing to the shape of the survival curve with *E. coli* B is its response to postirradiation culture conditions (16), which will be discussed in a later section.

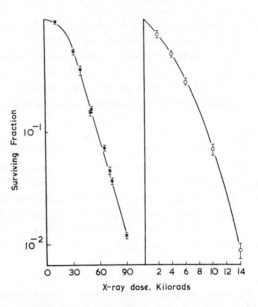

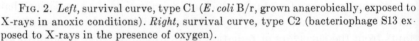

FIG. 2. *Left*, survival curve, type C1 (*E. coli* B/r, grown anaerobically, exposed to X-rays in anoxic conditions). *Right*, survival curve, type C2 (bacteriophage S13 exposed to X-rays in the presence of oxygen).

3. *Type C: "Sigmoid" Survival Curves.* The term "sigmoid" for these curves refers to their shape on a linear plot. Many discussions have been devoted to the interpretation of this type of curve, often previously referred to as "multitarget" or "multihit," and the theory has been dealt with in Chapter 1. It may be noted that curves of this general shape may be divided into two subgroups: C1, in which an initial threshold dose is required before an exponential form of curve is established; and C2, in which no such form is established, since the proportion of the surviving population killed by any increment of dose always increases as the dose increases (Fig. 2). Type C1 survival curves are obtained with *E. coli* B/r, (15), for example, or with human tumor cells (17); type C2 curves are obtained with dilute suspensions of bacteriophage exposed to X-rays in conditions in which H_2O_2 is formed in the suspension (18). It will readily be appreciated that type C1 curves will be obtained with suspensions of organisms in which a proportion are clumped, or contain discrete viable units which have not separated, although the lethal event for any viable unit is monotopic in nature.

In numerous examples, however, sigmoid survival curves are found to occur with cells which are demonstrably single viable units at the time of irradiation. Furthermore, the shape of the survival curve may depend on the method of culture, a phenomenon which is particularly common with strain *Escherichia coli* B and its mutants. Thus the resistant mutant B/r cultured in different conditions before irradiation gives rise to survival curves of differing threshold dose but of equal final slope (19, 20); the same is true of survival curves obtained by imposing different culture conditions on cells of this strain *after* irradiation (21). Fig. 3 shows how survival curves constructed from colony counts on a mutant of *E. coli* B may be either of exponential form, or sigmoid, depending on the plating medium used. It is clear that if the sigmoid nature of the curve had been due to the existence of multiple morphologically discrete targets (e.g., a multinucleate structure) within the cell, this would have been reflected in both survival curves.

Consideration of these and allied phenomena have led to the proposal (21a) that the intercept obtained by extrapolating the exponential portion of a type C1 curve to zero dose should be referred to as the "extrapolation number," rather than as a "hit" or "target" number, unless there is supporting evidence that this number can be identified with specific entities which can plausibly be regarded as targets of radiation damage.

Survival curves of type C2 will arise when lethality is due to an ac-

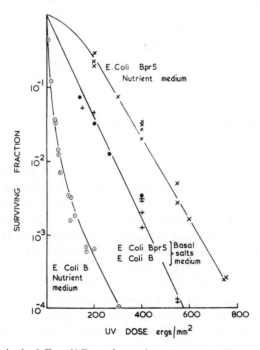

FIG. 3. Survival of *E. coli* B, and a resistant mutant, *E. coli* Bpr5 (21), after exposure to ultraviolet: ⊙ *E. coli* B, plated on nutrient medium. ● *E. coli* B, plated on basal salts medium. + *E. coli* Bpr5, plated on basal salts medium. × *E. coli* Bpr5, plated on nutrient medium.

cumulation of damaging events, and von Borstel and Rogers (22), working on the hatchability of *Habrobracon* eggs, interpreted in this way their dose-effect curve for death due to irradiation by α-particles of the cytoplasm only. This type of survival curve will also be obtained in conditions in which the irradiation of the suspending medium leads to an accumulation of some damaging substance. Thus, when the small bacteriophage S13 was irradiated in dilute aqueous suspension, exponential survival curves were obtained in anoxic conditions (23), indicating that the reaction between phage and the short-lived free radicals formed from water was monotopic in nature; when irradiation took place in the presence of oxygen, however, survival curves were of type C2; this was found to be due to the fact that the phage particles were "part-inactivated," i.e., sensitized (by the monotopic action of free radicals) to the action of the H_2O_2 formed as a stable product in these conditions, so that the slope of the survival curve increased with dose (see Section III.C.2*b*).

In many experiments the accuracy of the observations does not permit a clear distinction to be made between survival curves of types C1 and C2. With some experimental material, as shown by Uretz (24), a high degree of accuracy in determining the shape of the survival curve reveals the fact that a "final slope" is not approached even when the survival level is as low as 10^{-4} of the original population. As this author pointed out, false deductions as to "target number" can easily be made if it is assumed that the final slope is given by a portion of a survival curve which appears straight.

III. Lethal Effects on Subcellular Units

A. General Remarks

An arbitrary decision has been taken as to which objects of radio-biological study to include under this heading. The criteria used will be: (1) that the particles are unable to reproduce themselves unless they have access to the metabolic apparatus of a host cell; (2) that they can be manipulated quantitatively in extracellular form; and (3) that they show evidence of genetic continuity when they are reproduced.

These conditions are fulfilled by plant, animal, and bacterial viruses, by "transforming principle" (TP), which is now believed to be almost pure deoxyribonucleic acid, and by paramecin, which is secreted by certain strains of *Paramecium* and is able to kill others (25). Only inactivation of these particles will be discussed, since no genetic changes have been observed to take place in viruses exposed in the free state to ionizing radiations. This in itself is important and has to be taken into account when the mechanism by which radiation induces genetic changes in cells is discussed.

The activity of TP is assessed in terms of its ability to bring about genetic changes in the bacterial cells which are exposed to it, and, by definition, a preparation of TP which has lost a certain fraction of its transforming ability will have been inactivated to that extent. Animal and plant virus preparations are titrated by counting the number of lesions to which they give rise in the tissues of the hosts, and methods of assay were described by Lea (Chapter 4 of ref. 1). To these must be added the technique devised by Dulbecco (26), in which a dilute suspension of animal virus is applied to a sheet of mammalian cells growing in tissue culture. When an active virus particle is replicated within and destroys a cell, the progeny so released invade neighboring cells, and a "plaque" of lysed cells can eventually be observed. These are quite analogous with the plaques formed by active bacterial virus (or bacteriophage) particles in a lawn of the host bacteria.

The nature of the steps involved in the ultimate replication of a virus particle within the host cell have been investigated within the last few years. The particle must be able to adsorb, to inject its infective material into the cell, and to bring about a change in the host metabolism so that new virus material is synthesized instead of the host's own characteristic protein and nucleic acid. These various steps have been studied with a wide range of viruses (27). Similarly, TP must (presumably) be able to enter the recipient cell, and the genetic markers it carries must then be incorporated within the cell's own hereditary substance, if its effect is to be detected. An interference with any of the steps will be scored as an "inactivation," and it is probable that different inactivating treatments will bring about the final result in different ways.

When subcellular particles are in aqueous suspension, they may in some circumstances be affected by the products of radiolysis of water (Chapter 2). This is commonly called the "indirect effect" of radiation and was so described by Dale (28) when reporting on the effects of radiation on enzymes in solution. These effects may in suitable experiments be distinguished from "direct effects," which by hypothesis are the result of energy absorbed within the sensitive volume of the particle.

The primary decomposition products of water, namely the free radicals H· and OH·, may react with other solutes present (notably gases), and in some circumstances products may be formed which are considerably more stable than the primary radicals themselves. The reactions these undergo with oxygen and hydrogen have been described in Chapter 2. When hydrogen peroxide or organic peroxides are formed by reactions of free radicals with oxygen and with organic solutes, these long-lived products may have marked biological effects on subcellular particles (18, 29). By contrast, the effects of peroxides formed in the suspending medium are usually negligible with whole cells, particularly when these produce catalase, since their reproductive integrity is affected by doses which are too low to form peroxides in sufficient concentration to affect them. A few exceptional cases have been reported, however, in which hydrogen peroxide in the suspending medium has affected complete cells (30, 31).

Particles in suspension may be protected against indirect action mediated by free radicals or peroxides, if a second solute is present which is able to react with these and so prevent their reaching the particles under test. Most organic substances are effective as protective agents, or "radical scavengers," and it is common to use mixed material such as nutrient broth or peptone, if direct action alone is to be studied. The "inactivation dose," usually defined as that dose which will reduce the active population to e^{-1} (or 37 %), is less, sometimes by a considerable factor, if indirect action takes place, since the particles are affected by energy absorbed in the solvent as well as that absorbed within the particles themselves. The efficiency of indirect action per ionization is usually considerably less than that of direct action, however.

Whether or not the particles in suspension have been fully protected against indirect action can be ascertained by determining whether an increase in the concentration of the protective material effects an increase in the inactivation dose. If the concentration is high enough, all the radicals will be captured before they can react with the particles under test, and the inactivation dose will in general be the same as that observed with dry material. With viruses, the concentration of protective protein needed to afford full protection has been found to be about 1 to 10 gm/l. Ephrussi-Taylor and Latarjet (32) found that it was much more difficult to protect TP completely: even with 100 gm/l of yeast extract present (sufficient to be toxic), some of the inactivation of TP was found to be due to indirect effects.

B. INACTIVATION BY DIRECT EFFECT

1. THE "SENSITIVE VOLUME"

The methods which had been established for determining target sizes from radiation data were reviewed by Lea (Chapter 3 of ref. 1), who introduced some important refinements and pointed out the necessity for examining sensitivity to ionizing radiations of different quality in order to obtain a reliable estimate of both size and shape of the sensitive volume. The target sizes of some of the smaller (roughly spherical) bacteriophages, calculated by Lea from the radiation data, agreed very well with the sizes of the whole viruses as estimated by other techniques. With these strains it could be deduced that almost the whole virus formed the target volume, which was an indication that an ionization anywhere within its volume was sufficient to inhibit replication. Timoféeff-Ressovsky and Zimmer (Chapter

14 of ref. 2) drew attention to a series of plant viruses for which the calculated target, or sensitive volume, was considerably smaller than that of
the whole virus as determined by other means, and pointed out that this
disagreement might arise from the fact that these possessed a structure,
and that certain regions might be preferentially sensitive, although this
did not imply a cell-like morphology. This suggestion is of course now known
to be correct, since a wide variety of plant and bacterial virus strains
have been shown to possess a nucleic acid core coated with viral protein.
Considerable use of ionizing radiation has been made by Pollard and his
collaborators (33) to determine structure in a range of virus strains, in
some of which the sensitive volume may amount to as little as one-twentieth
of that of the whole virus. The identification of the sensitive volume with
the nucleic acid fraction seems well justified, and a particularly suitable
material for this study is afforded by tobacco mosaic virus, which is sep-
arable into the protein and nucleic acid fractions, the latter retaining the
infectivity of the particle (34). Ginoza and Norman (35) found that the
target volume for inactivation, as estimated from the survival curve taken
on the infective fraction alone, was the same as that for inactivation of the
complete virus. The calculated volume agreed well with estimates made
by other methods of the molecular weight of the ribonucleic acid (RNA)
fraction of the particle. It was concluded that a single ionization anywhere
within the infective component (i.e., the RNA) would inactivate a virus
particle.

Studies on the direct effect of ionizing radiation on transforming principle have been directed at estimating the "molecular weight" or target
size of the particular genetic marker under test. Dose-effect curves have
been observed by various authors (32, 36, 37) to be of type B (Section
II.C.2). It was shown by Ephrussi-Taylor and Latarjet (32) that the
"resistant tail" was not due to genetic heterogeneity, and Guild and De-
Filippes (37) showed that it was not due to heterogeneity in particle size
or in sensitivity of the preparation before it was dried. The estimates of
"molecular weights" by the various authors who have worked with this
difficult material have varied from about 3.10^5 to 2.10^6 for individual
markers or combinations of markers. In view of the great dependence of
observed sensitivity on methods of preparation and drying (37) and of the
apparently uncontrolled variations in sensitivity observed even with
material prepared by the same method (38), the poorness of the agreement
does not cast a reflection on the validity of the method, which assumes that
an inactivation takes place as the result of a single ionization (32) or an
ion cluster (37) left anywhere within the marker. An elucidation of the
reasons for the "break" in the survival curve would be helpful from the
radiobiological as well as the genetic point of view.

From a study of the properties of coliphage particles inactivated by the direct action of X-rays, Watson (39) reported that inactive particles were still able to adsorb to bacteria and to initiate "lysis from without" but had lost the ability to multiply within the bacteria or to exclude another type of bacteriophage. He interpreted the results to mean that two stages were involved in the early period of phage multiplication and called the first stage "adsorption" and the second "invasion." It could be deduced, therefore, that the invasive stage was preferentially inactivated. This interpretation has been justified by the later work of Puck and his coworkers (40) on the various stages of attachment of viruses to host cells and the splitting of bacteriophage into DNA and protein components, and also by the work of Hershey and Chase (41), who demonstrated that phage nucleic acid was injected into the host, but the protein coat remained outside the bacterium. It has been shown by various authors that it requires far larger doses of radiation to disrupt the function of attachment than to inactivate the nucleic acid component; i.e., the former has a much smaller "target size" (42, 43).

2. MODIFICATIONS OF THE "DIRECT EFFECT"

a. Effect of Oxygen. In recent years a large volume of work has been done on the enhancing effect of oxygen on radiation damage to cells. Hewitt and Read (44) looked for an effect of oxygen on the inactivation by X-rays of a coliphage and reported that none could be detected. Other subcellular units for which inactivation doses (in conditions of direct effect) have been found to be independent of oxygen concentration are the dysentery phage S13 (45), pneumococcal transforming principle (32, 38), and bacteriophage T2 (46). The absence of an effect of oxygen on the radiosensitivity of biologically active DNA is of great importance in relation to the mechanism by which radiation induces lethal and genetic effects on cells.

b. Temperature and Physical State. It was reported by Bachofer *et al.* (47) that the radiosensitivity of bacteriophage T1 showed some temperature dependence: the inactivation dose was about 60 % higher at $-196°C$ than at 37°C. In a later paper, Bachofer (48) reported that a temperature dependence of the inactivation dose was observed with lyophilized as well as with vacuum-dried preparations and that the inactivation dose was greater for the latter, by an average factor of 2.4, at each of the temperatures tested.

Data of this nature are of value in showing how the probability of the effectiveness of an ionizing event may be reduced in different physical conditions. Thus it may be inferred from Bachofer's results that for roughly every three ionizations which are effective in the lyophilized preparation only one is effective in the vacuum-dried one; and for every three ionizations which are effective at 37°C only one inactivates a phage particle at −196°C. An estimate of the "sensitive volume" of T1 from Bachofer's data is on less sure ground, since such an estimate depends on accurate dosimetry. The source of radiation was unfiltered 50-kv X-rays, and these present difficult problems of dosimetry. Bachofer *et al.* (47) did not themselves place great reliance on the absolute doses quoted. Furthermore, an estimate of sensitive volume should be based on a knowledge of the probability, p, that every ionization will be effective. One test for finding whether $p = 1$ is to make observations on the effectiveness of radiations of different quality. If p is not known, however, but is assumed to be 1, then the estimate of sensitive volume deduced from the inactivation dose may be compared with estimates from other data, and if the result appears too low it may be inferred that p is in fact less than 1.

In the most sensitive condition in which the bacteriophage T1 was used in these experiments, the inactivation dose was 111 kr. The calculated target diameter is of course dependent on the quality of radiation used, and this again is difficult to assess with unfiltered 50-kv X-rays. A rough estimate of target diameter in these conditions is 40 mμ, however (Lea, Chapter 3 of ref. 1). If it is assumed that the sensitive volume represents the nucleic acid fraction, this estimate leads to the result that 0.2 of the phage particle consists of nucleic acid. This would be rather low, when compared with the fraction as deduced by other methods. The calculation may therefore reflect an error in assuming $p = 1$ and may imply that perhaps two or three ionizations are required for each inactivation. The estimate of sensitive volume depends too critically, however, on a knowledge of inactivation dose and quality of radiation for this implication to carry much weight.

c. Protection by Chemical Substances. Doermann (49) discovered that bacteriophage particles were less sensitive when irradiated in the presence of cysteine, and this result was confirmed by Epstein and Schardl (50), working with coliphage 2Tr. Ginoza and Norman (35) reported that, if the nucleic acid of tobacco mosaic virus was frozen or dried in the presence of 2 % glutathione, the radiosensitivity was less by a factor of more than 2. Marcovich (46) has reported that cysteamine acted as a protective agent for bacteriophage T2. None of these compounds could have been acting as a scavenger of radicals formed from water molecules, since indirect action did not contribute to the effects of radiation in any of these experiments. None of the protective agents could be presumed to act by oxygen depletion, since direct action on viruses is not influenced by the presence of oxygen (Section III.B.2a). The mechanism therefore must be related to some means of energy or electron transfer within the ionized structure (see

Vol. II, Chapter 3), and it may be significant that sulfur is present in all the compounds which have been found to protect bacteriophage in conditions of direct action.

3. POSSIBLE MECHANISM OF DIRECT ACTION ON SUBCELLULAR UNITS

"It is the opinion of the present author . . . that the validity of the target theory is as certain as a scientific theory ever is in a rapidly developing subject, in the case of the inactivation of small viruses by radiation . . . ." (Chapter 3 of ref. 1). Since Lea wrote this, work done on the inactivation of viruses by ionizing radiation has fully justified his opinion. During this time there have been considerable advances in our knowledge of the structure of viruses, and the "sensitive targets" have been convincingly identified with their nucleic acid components. It should be possible to push radiobiological theory a step further and to account for the well-substantiated fact that an individual ionization or ion cluster left *anywhere* within the sensitive volume can inhibit multiplication in the host cell.

It has for some time been very puzzling that the efficiency of a single ionizing event within a virus particle should be greater than that of a single disintegration of a P^{32} atom incorporated into the viral nucleic acid. As reported by Stent and Fuerst (51), the probability that a disintegration will lead to the inactivation of a bacteriophage particle varies from 0.05 at $-196°C$ to 0.3 at $65°C$. They interpreted this rather low efficiency at the lower temperatures to mean that inactivation occurred only when both polynucleotide chains in the DNA molecule were broken. The recoil energy after a P^{32} disintegration is considerably higher, however, than that absorbed in the formation by X-rays of an average-sized ion cluster, and there is no a priori reason for supposing that the ionization should be the more efficient in breaking both polynucleotide chains simultaneously.

Recent physicochemical investigations with herring-sperm DNA have shown that it is in fact unlikely that a single ionization can bring about a complete break in the DNA molecule. The relevant data are those which have been obtained with DNA preparations irradiated in conditions in which they were highly protected against indirect action. Alexander and Stacey (52) first showed that "hidden" breaks occurred in DNA molecules irradiated "dry" (i.e., with about 10 to 15% moisture), and that the production of a break in a single polynucleotide strand required fewer ionizations than a complete break of the molecule. They pointed out that a decrease in the molecular weight of DNA would be observed only if breaks occurred close together in the two strands. In the discussion after their paper, Peacocke (53) gave evidence pointing to the same conclusion, though he attributed the breaks observed to the action of free radicals, in his experiments. In a later paper Peacocke and Preston (54) have substantiated the conclusion that a fracture in the molecule occurs only when two independent and approximately opposite breaks occur, one in each of the two polynucleotide chains. These conclusions were based on viscosity and light-scattering measurements, the irradiations being carried out on DNA solutions of 0.2 to 0.4%. No attempt was made by the authors to distinguish between direct and indirect action, but at the concentrations they used both types must have been operative. This assumption seems justified by results of Butler et al. (55), who reported on the effects of radiation on the viscosity of DNA solutions. The concentrations they used varied from 0.01% to 100%, and for all those above 1% the results were the same, which would imply that indirect action was playing only a small part in radiation effects at these concentrations. Butler et al. (55) found that the decrease in viscosity was independent of dose rate and that the dose-effect curves were the same for 15-Mev electrons and unfiltered 140-kv X-rays. The number of ionizations required to halve the viscosity varied from 14 to 200 per molecule, depending on the preparation used. If halving the viscosity corresponds to halving the weight average molecular weight, the results imply that at most one in seven ionizations will break both polynucleotide chains. It cannot be reasoned that the initiation of a complete break requires a large cluster of ions, or a dense electron "tail," since the results were the same with both types of radiation.

If, then, we accept the facts that (1) a single ionization or ion cluster will inactivate a virus particle, and (2) a single ionization will break a double-stranded DNA molecule only if by chance it appears opposite the site of another ionization, it must follow that the inactivation of viruses does not depend to any great extent on fractures of the double DNA strand. An attractive possible explanation for the great effectiveness of a single ionization in a virus particle is suggested by a report of Alexander and Stacey (56). They found that, if herring-sperm heads were irradiated before the extraction and separation of nucleic acid and protein, bonds had been formed which might be covalent crosslinks. Since the nucleic acid in a virus particle is closely coiled, it seems plausible that a single ionization might cause a crosslink, which in its turn would cause inactivation, either because the nucleic acid molecule, with its new geometry, would fail to enter the host cell, or because it could not replicate without the molecule's unfolding. Data of Alexander et al. (57) and Alexander and Lett (57a) demonstrate satisfactory parallelism between the cross-linking phenomenon and the inactivation of small viruses: the presence of oxygen decreases the amount of cross-linking; α-rays are much less efficient than X-rays; and cysteamine is a good protective agent against this effect.

In terms of this hypothesis, Stent and Fuerst's report (51) that virus particles are inactivated by only about one in ten P^{32} disintegrations no longer seems discordant with data which show that a single ionizing event may inactivate a virus particle. In spite of the greater energy change involved in a P^{32} disintegration than in the formation of an ion cluster, there is no reason to suppose that either the transmutation of the P^{32} atom or the recoil energy would lead to crosslinking.

Alexander and Stacey's discovery (56) may also provide the clue to the "break" observed in the dose-effect curves obtained with transforming principle: the initial sensitive component may perhaps pertain to parts of the DNA which are coiled and susceptible to crosslinking, whereas the insensitive component pertains to the fraction of DNA which is already unfolded, as suggested by the evidence of Ephrussi-Taylor and Latarjet (32) on the difficulty of protecting the TP against radical action.

C. Indirect Actions of Radiation

1. efficacy of various radical species

It may be assumed that the indirect action of radiation on particles in aqueous suspension is due to the decomposition products of water (Chapter 2). Since it is not known a priori whether the inactivation of biologically active particles is due to oxidative or to reductive changes, information on this point must be deduced from the experimental arrangements. It is broadly true that indirect action which operates by effecting oxidations will be enhanced if oxygen is present during irradiation, and conversely, if the presence of oxygen diminishes the effect observed, this is likely to have resulted from the reducing action of radicals on the materials under test. A complication which arises with some biologically active units is that reaction with free radicals may make them more sensitive than non-irradiated material to stable products formed in the suspending medium by the radiation. In particular, there may be an increased sensitivity to hydrogen peroxide, which in most conditions is accumulated in water only if oxygen is present during the irradiation. In such a case an irradiation performed in the presence of oxygen may appear to have been more effective than one in anoxic conditions by virtue of the reactions with free radicals, whereas in fact the apparent enhancing action of oxygen has been mediated by the peroxide acting on the sensitized particles. In experiments with the small bacteriophage S13, Alper (23) was able to distinguish between inactivation due to the immediate reactions of the particles with free radicals and that due to subsequent reactions with hydrogen peroxide. For this purpose it was necessary to deliver the radiation within a time which was short compared with that needed for the action of hydrogen peroxide, and to initiate adsorption to the host cells within a few seconds of the end of the irradiation. When experiments on the indirect effects of

X-rays on the bacteriophage S13 were done under these conditions, it could be deduced from the data that H radicals were the most effective inactivating agents. This conclusion was based in part on the following evidence:

1. Inactivation doses in the presence of pure hydrogen, pure nitrogen, oxygen, and a mixture of hydrogen and oxygen, respectively, were in the ratios 1:2:5:10. The increased effectiveness of irradiation in the presence of hydrogen was presumed to arise from the conversion of OH to H radicals ($H_2 + OH \rightarrow H + H_2O$), and the increased protection exerted by a mixture of oxygen and hydrogen was attributed to the removal of H radicals by the mechanisms $H + O_2 \rightarrow HO_2$ and $H + HO_2 \rightarrow H_2O_2$. The conclusion that H radicals and, to a smaller extent, O_2^- radical ions were effective inactivating agents was substantiated by the finding that the immediate effects of irradiation on the phage were in exact inverse relation to the production of H_2O_2, in the varying conditions used (58).

2. Experiments on the inactivation of bacteriophage suspended in buffer at different pH values yielded results which accorded with predictions based on the assumption that H radicals and O_2^- radical ions were the inactivating agents (59).

3. Ascorbic acid at concentration 10^{-5} M inactivated 50% of a dilute nonirradiated suspension of phage particles in 40 minutes. No effect of dehydroascorbic acid was observed, and the oxidizing agents KIO_3 and $KClO_3$, when used in concentration 10^{-3} M, were without effect on the phage particles (60). It was concluded that they were much more sensitive to inactivation by reduction than by oxidation.

Oxygen has been found to exert a protective effect if present during irradiation of dilute suspensions of several strains, viz., coliphages T1 (61) and T3 (23), the temperate coliphage λ (62), and the *Salmonella* phage P22 (63). Kimball reported that paramecin irradiated outside the cells was protected by the presence of oxygen (25).

Apart from the investigations reported above with the dysentery phage S13, only phage T1 has been examined in the variety of conditions necessary for deducing which radical species are most active (64). Unfortunately the T series of phages are not suitable for use in experiments in which gas bubbling techniques are used, as they are rapidly inactivated by this treatment. In experiments with T1, Bachofer and Pottinger (64) found it necessary to introduce the bacteriophage particles into the diluting medium after the completion of gas bubbling. Although they noticed sensitivity of the phage to reducing agents in general, the authors concluded that it was not particularly sensitive to H radicals, because in their conditions the inactivation dose in the presence of hydrogen was no less than in the presence of nitrogen. It should be noted, however, that an extremely small admixture of oxygen to the hydrogen, which might have been introduced with the nonbubbled phage preparation, would be sufficient to afford some protection to the bacteriophage (58).

As will be seen below, there is some rather tenuous evidence that free radicals may inactivate bacteriophage particles by interfering with their ability to adsorb to the host cells. If this is so, it seems plausible that bacteriophage particles should be strong oxidizing agents, and therefore subject to inactivation by reducing agents, since bacteria themselves are easily killed by oxidation.

Experiments on the inactivation of transforming principle by free radicals have failed to demonstrate either an enhancing or a protective effect of oxygen (32, 38). Latarjet (65) reported also that no effect of hydrogen had been observed but said that the conditions of gas control had not been rigorous. The technical difficulties of working with this material are very great (38), and the experimental techniques do not permit of the sort of handling which enables a clear-cut distinction to be made between immediate and possible delayed effects of the radiation.

2. THE ACTION OF PEROXIDES ON SUBCELLULAR UNITS

a. Action on Nonirradiated Material. Since peroxides are formed in water or in aqueous solutions when these are irradiated in the presence of oxygen, it is natural that their role in the biological effects of radiation has frequently been considered. It is now well established that the doses which exert profound effects on whole cells are not usually high enough to produce damaging concentrations of peroxides in the suspending media, particularly if the cells produce catalase. If subcellular units are used in dilute suspensions which contain little protective organic matter, however, hydrogen and organic peroxides may exert a marked effect. The inactivation of bacteriophage particles by hydrogen peroxide has been found to proceed exponentially with time (18, 60). This form of survival curve was found also with coliphage T2 inactivated by succinic peroxide (65) and with transforming principle inactivated by hydrogen peroxide (29). When TP was treated with succinic peroxide, the survival curve was of the type B form reminiscent of dose-effect curves for X-ray inactivation in conditions of direct or indirect action.

b. Part-Inactivation. This term was applied to a phenomenon first observed with the bacteriophages S13 and T3, in which some particles exposed to radical action would give rise to plaques if they came into contact immediately with the host bacteria but would gradually lose their activity if they remained in the suspending buffer (23). If these part-inactivated phage particles were exposed to the action of hydrogen peroxide or ascorbic acid after the irradiation, they were inactivated at a much higher rate than the nonirradiated particles. The postirradiation survival curve was of type B, and this could be resolved into two exponential components: the steeper was assumed to pertain to the part-inactivated fraction; the less steep component was parallel to the survival curves for nonirradiated bacteriophage and was presumed therefore to indicate the presence of a fraction of the population which had not been affected by the active radicals. The most favorable conditions in which to observe part-inactivation were found to be: (1) after irradiation delivered at a high dose rate; (2) after irradiation delivered in anoxic conditions; (3) after a dose of radiation in which only a small fraction of the bacteriophage particles had been completely inactivated (66).

It was reported by Maxwell (67) that the phenomenon of part-inactivation occurred also with coliphages T2, T4, and λ, and that pretreatment with hydrogen peroxide or with cumene peroxide, as well as with the radicals formed in the X-irradiation of water, would sensitize the phage particles to further inactivation by hydrogen peroxide or ascorbic acid. Latarjet et al. (29) searched for the part-inactivation effect with transforming principle but failed to find any.

3. FUNCTIONS DISRUPTED BY INDIRECT ACTIONS

It is not unlikely that the direct and indirect actions of ionizing radiation cause inactivation of virus particles by interfering with different functions. The part-inactivation phenomenon, for example, does not occur in conditions where the phage particles are fully protected against radical action (23). Watson (68) attempted a systematic study of the properties of bacteriophage inactivated by indirect action, using techniques of the same type as he had used in studying inactivation by direct effect (39). He concluded that the *survivors* of an irradiation adsorbed to bacteria at a slower than normal rate: however, if the part-inactivation phenomenon was operative, the apparently diminished adsorption rate may in fact have been due to continuing inactivation, which Watson assumed did not occur if the particles were removed from the irradiated medium. The ability of *inactivated* phage particles to adsorb was tested by mixing them in the ratio of 250 particles to one heat-killed bacterium. Whether or not the inactive particles had adsorbed was then judged by the capacity of these bacteria to adsorb bacteriophage of another strain. Watson concluded that the inactive particles had lost most of their capacity to adsorb; but this result, too, is open to some doubt, as far as the mechanism of inactivation by radicals is concerned, since it is evident from the shape of the survival curve, and the level to which the active population was reduced, that a high proportion of the particles must have been inactivated by peroxides formed in the medium.

Latarjet and Frédéricq (42) suggested briefly that bacteriophage particles inactivated by indirect action had lost proportionately much more of their ability to kill bacteria than had inactive particles which had been irradiated in conditions of direct effect. They suggested that the bactericidal activity of a bacteriophage particle might be associated with a colicine-like particle located in the tail, and that this was readily "inactivated" by indirect action. Feingold and Plough (63) reported evidence which indicated a reduced ability of the *Salmonella* phage P22 to adsorb when they had been heavily irradiated in aqueous suspension.

IV. Effects on the Course of Replication

A. Division Delay and Change in Growth Rate

One effect of radiation which has been observed with all types of cells is an inhibition in the processes leading to division. This applies to cells which would be classed as survivors, if lethality were the test of damage, as well as to those cells which ultimately fail to produce a viable clone. It follows that this test of damage is usually more sensitive than the observation of lethal effects, and in one case observations on a change in growth rate have been made with doses as low as 10^{-3} rad (69). When populations of microorganisms are studied, the rate of growth may be determined in two ways: The total mass of the population may be measured, as, for example, when change in the turbidity of a culture is used to estimate growth. Alternatively, the effect of irradiation on division may be observed by making viable counts at intervals. These methods present very different pictures of the course of growth after or during irradiation.

1. OBSERVATIONS ON CELLS UNDERGOING CONTINUOUS IRRADIATION

Forssberg (69) has made extensive use of the fungus *Phycomyces blakesleeanus* to study effects of low doses of irradiation on growth rate. In controlled conditions the sporangiophore elongates at a steady rate, which is easily altered by certain stimuli, such as a flash of light. The actively growing zone is located just below the sporangium, and a beam of ionizing radiation directed momentarily at this zone causes an immediate reduction in growth rate, which is reversible: when the source of radiation is removed, the decrease is exactly compensated for by a wave of increase in the growth rate. If the zone is continuously irradiated, the growth rate settles down to a steady value which is less than normal: this again returns to normal when irradiation is stopped. Effects may be observed with doses as low as 10^{-3} r, and alteration in growth rate varies linearly with dose, up to a total dose of 1 r (69a). The radiation appears to affect a substance important for growth which is transported in the cell wall; if the radiation is directed below the active zone, there is a delay before the effect is observed.

The observations of Forssberg (69, 69a) were made by studying individual organisms. With bacteria and yeast, whole populations have been used to determine effects of radiation on growth and division.

Various strains of *Escherichia coli* (70–72) and a strain of *Saccharomyces* (72) have been used in investigations of this nature. In one respect, the same conclusion was reached in all three reports, namely that the total cell mass of the irradiated culture in each case increased at the same or nearly the same rate as that of the control culture. According to Lea *et al.* (70), who irradiated *E. coli* with γ-rays at 1500 r/hr, this increase in total cell mass occurred without any division taking place in the organisms, in which the viable count slowly fell. This general conclusion corresponds with that of Spoerl *et al.* (72), who used dose rates of 16,000 and 30,000 r/hr, respectively, on *E. coli* B and *Saccharomyces cerevisiae*. In each case they found a large increase in the average cell mass through the first part of the irradiation period which lasted for $1\frac{1}{2}$ hours with the *coli* and 4 hours with yeast. During the latter half of the irradiation the average cell mass decreased, and by the end of the irradiation period there was a slight decrease in the total dry weight of the cultures, as compared with the controls. The increase in total cell mass which occurred without divisions, in these experiments, indicated that the irradiated cells developed into giant forms; this is general with most types of cell which have been studied, including plant and mammalian cells. A very different result, however, was reported by Rubin (71) for *E. coli* B/r. Viable counts on cultures irradiated at 5000 r/hr gave results which indicated that in cultures inoculated with logarithmic stage cells, and irradiated throughout the period of growth, the final number of viable organisms was the same as in nonirradiated cultures. According to the data presented, the only difference observed between continuously irradiated and nonirradiated cultures was in the delay which occurred before the beginning of the increase in total mass or in viable count.

2. OBSERVATIONS AFTER A SINGLE DOSE OF RADIATION

A few dose-effect curves have been reported pertaining to delay in division after a single dose of radiation, and these appear to be of similar form, although they were obtained with very dissimilar materials and methods (73–75). From these curves, it can be seen that low doses of radiation are relatively much more effective in prolonging the time until the first division (or until first cleavage, in the case of *Arbacia* eggs) than high doses. Henshaw (74), in presenting his results on cleavage delay in these eggs, found a straight-line relationship when he plotted the logarithm of the delay until first cleavage against the logarithm of the dose. From growth curves established by taking viable counts on bacteria cultured after irradiation in nutrient broth, Alper (75) found that generation times for the first few divisions after the initial prolonged period of lag were *shorter* than those observed in the control cultures. A faster growth rate after X-irradiation was also observed in *E. coli* B by Laser and Thornley (76) in special conditions of growth. Cells which were normally grown in medium containing inorganic salts, glucose, and ammonium chloride were able to utilize maltose only if glutamic acid was provided. After irradiation, cells grown in the medium containing maltose and glutamate multiplied much faster than the unirradiated controls.

An extensive series of observations on individual cells was made by Burns (77), who used haploid, diploid, and tetraploid yeast, irradiated with doses up to 7000 r. Observations on the haploid yeast at doses above 2500 r were difficult because of their great radiosensitivity, and most of the data were taken on the diploid cells. These gave rise to the first buds after irradiation at the normal rate, the major delay occurring before the second budding, and most of the lethality was observed in the second generation after irradiation. The cells which were budding at the time of irradiation required five to six times as large a dose as the nonbudding cells to produce the same delay. Burns concluded from his observations that lethality and division delay followed a qualitatively different pattern, but that there was some interdependence of these effects.

According to Kimball (78), ciliates differ from bacteria and yeasts in that they are not more sensitive to inhibition of division than to lethal effects. Changes (i.e., reductions) in the fission rate of various protozoa after irradiation have been widely used as a test of damage, and sometimes the term "recovery" is used in this context as meaning recovery of the normal division rate.

3. MODIFICATIONS IN DIVISION DELAY

Although the effect of oxygen has been widely studied in relation to various tests of radiation damage, little seems to have been reported as regards delay in division. The increase in the lag phase imposed on *Shigella flexneri* and *Escherichia coli* B has been found to depend on oxygen to precisely the same extent as the lethal effect (45). Growth curves (by viable counts) were taken on cells which had been exposed to three times as high a dose under anoxia as in aerobic conditions, and these could be exactly superimposed, showing that the survival had been reduced and the lag phase of the survivors prolonged to the same extent (Fig. 4). Evans *et al.* (79) found that oxygen affected the mitotic delay imposed by a given dose

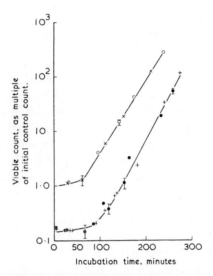

FIG. 4. Growth of *Shigella flexneri*, Y6R, irradiated and nonirradiated: ○ non-irradiated, after oxygen bubbling. × nonirradiated, after nitrogen bubbling. ● after 4000 rads of X-rays, under oxygen bubbling, lag phase prolonged by 45 minutes. + after 12,000 rads of X-rays, under nitrogen bubbling, lag phase prolonged by 45 minutes.

of radiation on cells in *Vicia faba* root tips: according to their report, the oxygen enhanced the effectiveness of the dose by a somewhat smaller factor for this than for other tests of damage.

Powers (80) reported observations on the rate of fission in irradiated *Paramecia*. Division rates were greatly reduced for a period of time which was dose-dependent. After all doses, however, about the same period of time was taken to return to normal division rates, once the division rates in the irradiated cells had reached about 0.3 of the normal. The time taken for this latter portion of the recovery to normal division rate depended on temperature, being twice as long for animals kept at 17.5°C as for those kept at 32.5°C.

Daniels (81, 82) made a series of observations on cell division in the giant amoeba *Pelomyxa*. He studied the effects on division rate of fusing the irradiated cells with parts of nonirradiated ones. In every case, fusion with the nonirradiated protoplasma shortened the time until division started. This effect appeared to be independent of which parts of the non-irradiated amoebae were used; however, there was slight evidence of more effect from fusion with the nucleated than with the "light" halves from animals which had been centrifuged at 6000 × *g*.

Ducoff (83) studied the effects of various nutrients on the division delay imposed on *Tetrahymena* by X-irradiation. He concluded that some recovery from delay took place if purines and pyrimidines were supplied, even in the absence of amino acids.

It should be noted that recovery from division delay is not necessarily correlated with higher survival from lethal effects. Indeed, exactly the reverse may be true. As will be seen in Section V.D, many treatments which have been found to increase survival or to decrease genetic changes are of a nature to prolong division delay in both irradiated and nonirradiated cells. An example may be seen in the work of Powers (80), quoted above, where treatment by higher temperatures after irradiation was found to shorten the time taken for return to normal division rates but to increase the lethal effect of the radiation.

B. Virus-Host Relationships

1. development of virulent phage

It was found by Friedewald and Anderson (7) that heavily irradiated animal cells which could no longer divide were still able to support virus growth; Rouyer and Latarjet (8) made an analogous observation with bacterial cells and viruses. Use was made of this fact by Latarjet (84), and later by Tobin (85), to attempt to follow the course of bacteriophage replication within infected cells by irradiating these and following their survival as infective (i.e., bacteriophage-producing) centers. The interpretation of such survival curves depends on a knowledge of the changes in configuration (and hence probably of radiosensitivity) of the viral nucleic acid, once it has invaded the host cell. Latarjet (84) concluded from his data that the radiosensitivity of the bacteriophage particles decreased by a factor of about 2 in the latter half of the period of replication. The curves altered in shape as well as in slope during the whole period, however, and they may require re-interpretation when a better understanding has been achieved of the mechanism of inactivation both of free bacteriophage and of the invading nucleic acid.

Bacteriophage particles (coliphage T1) which have survived inactivation, i.e., are still able to multiply, have been found by Pollard et al. (86) and by Davis and Pollard (87) to have suffered an increase in latent period after exposure to X-rays, slow electrons, deuterons, or α-particles. This occurred with phage irradiated dry, as well as in conditions where indirect effects operated. According to Davis and Pollard (87), the function of the particle which controls the latent period is "situated deep within the virus." The implication is that a densely ionizing particle may pass through a phage particle without inactivating it. This is puzzling, in view of the constancy of "cross section" of the phage reported by Pollard et al. (86)

for radiations of linear energy transfer (LET) greater than 100 kev/μ, and the report of Fluke and Brustad (88) that inactivation doses for this phage decrease with radiations of LET higher than 100 kev/μ.

An increase in latent period in phage which had survived the indirect effects of radiation was observed by Pollard *et al.* (86) only after doses which had reduced the surviving fraction to 0.13. From the survival curve presented, it is evident that a considerable fraction of the total inactivation at this level must have been due to hydrogen peroxide (18, 60).

2. LYSOGENESIS

a. Dose-Effect Relationships. After the discovery that lysogenic bacteria could be "induced," i.e., caused to yield infective bacteriophage, by ultraviolet light (89), Latarjet (90) found that X-rays, too, could be used as an inducing agent. With a lysogenic strain of *Bacillus megaterium*, he found that, in terms of energy absorbed, X-rays were considerably more efficient than ultraviolet, as has been found with other tests of radiation damage (Chapter 4 of ref. 1). Studies on the dose-effect relationship of induction by X-rays have been carried out by Tobin (85) on a lysogenic strain of *Pseudomonas pyocyanea*, and by Marcovich (91) on *Escherichia coli* K12(λ). A typical curve is shown in Fig. 5. It will be noted that the ordinary "survival curve" (in terms of colony counts) represents the proportions of cells which have *not* been affected by given doses of radiation, whereas the curve of induction represents the proportions of cells which *have* been

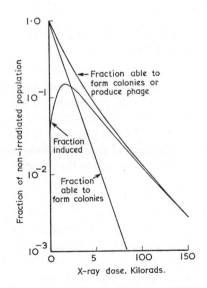

FIG. 5. Typical curve for "induction" of *E. coli* K12 (λ) by X-rays.

affected, in terms of ability to produce infective phage. The curve of induction, with its "peaked response," may therefore be regarded as the difference between two survival curves—one representing survival in terms of either colony-forming or phage-forming ability, the other showing survival in terms of colony-forming ability only. The peak in the induction curve occurs also when the results of ultraviolet irradiation are presented in this way. When induction is presented as the difference between two survival curves, it becomes evident that, even at the lowest irradiation doses used, a proportion of the bacteria have been affected by the radiation so that they can produce neither colonies not infective phage.

Marcovich (91) made a complete study of the induction of *E. coli* K12(λ) by low doses of radiation. Observations on low numbers of phage-producing cells are complicated by the fact that spontaneous induction occurs, even without irradiation. Marcovich devised a technique, however, by which the disturbing effect of these spontaneous inductions was largely suppressed, and he was then able to establish that at very low doses the number of induced bacteria increased linearly with the dose, and that the passage of a single electron of 0.5 Mev was sufficient to cause induction.

b. Effect of Oxygen on Lysogenesis. It has been found by Miletić and Alper (62) that the effectiveness of X-rays in inducing *E. coli* K12(λ) is enhanced by a factor of about 3, if oxygen is present during irradiation (see Section V.A.1*a*). This result contradicts a report of Marcovich (91) that induction of *E. coli* K12(λ) was not oxygen-sensitive, but his conditions for producing anoxia were not rigorous (92).

V. Lethal and Genetic Effects of Ionizing Radiation on Cells: Modifications of Radiosensitivity

In recent years much research has been devoted to investigating conditions which change or appear to change the radiosensitivity of cells; such studies are of great importance for understanding the steps between the initial absorption of energy and the manifestation of its effects. As pointed out by Zelle and Hollaender (93), the observed radiosensitivity of microorganisms has been found to depend greatly on conditions before, during, and after irradiation, though on the whole the response seems rather more susceptible of modification after ultraviolet than after ionizing radiation. Fewer examples occur of methods of modifying the sensitivity of higher cells, but this may be because they cannot be subjected to so much variation in methods of handling them. Where comparable changes of environment have been made—for example, irradiation in the presence or in the absence of oxygen—modification of radiosensitivity has been found to be much the same in microorganisms and in higher cells. Very frequently, modification of the lethal effects of radiation is matched by modification of the genetic effects, so to avoid repetition these will be considered together.

It will be convenient to consider modifications to these forms of radiation response under four headings.

A. Modifying Agents Which Must Be Present during Irradiation

1. GASES

a. Oxygen. It was recognized by radiotherapists early in this century that tissues are more radiosensitive when well oxygenated than when anoxic. Experimental studies on the interaction between radiosensitivity and oxygen (e.g., refs. 94–96) were followed by the investigations of Giles and Beatty (97) and of Read (11), who showed that radiosensitivity varies steeply with oxygen concentration at the lowest concentrations used, and at high concentrations reaches a maximum which cannot be exceeded by increasing the concentration. Read (11) demonstrated that the oxygen present during irradiation acts as a "dose-multiplying agent" (Section II.B). If the production of a given effect requires dose D in anoxic conditions, it will require dose D/r in the presence of oxygen, r being greater than 1: the oxygen has effectively multiplied the dose (or increased the radiosensitivity) by the factor r. This characteristic of the oxygen effect has been so amply verified, with a wide range of cell types and of tests of damage (20, 98, 99), that any apparent departure therefrom should be closely examined in case complicating factors have been introduced by the techniques employed.

It has been shown (20, 100) that the form of curve established for plant tissues by Giles and Beatty (97) and by Read (11) may be accurately described by the equation

$$r = (m[O] + k)/([O] + k) \qquad (3)$$

where [O] represents the oxygen concentration required to increase the radiosensitivity above that for anoxic cells by the factor r, which approaches a maximum value, m, asymptotically at high oxygen concentrations. It is readily seen that at low concentrations

$$dr/d[O] = \text{Constant}/k \qquad (4)$$

so that k is a measure of the initial slope of the curve (Fig. 6). The constant k, expressed as an oxygen concentration, is that concentration at which r becomes equal to $(m + 1)/2$; i.e., it is the concentration at which the sensitivity is midway between the minimum and maximum values it assumes for anoxic and well-oxygenated conditions, respectively. The ratio m will be referred to as the "maximum enhancement ratio."

The relationship expressed by equation 3 was established for lethal effects on bacteria and yeast irradiated in well-controlled conditions of gas equilibration. For these microorganisms k was found to be about 4 μM/l,

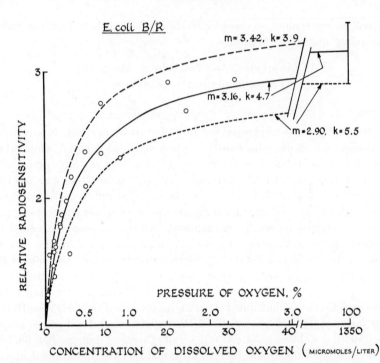

FIG. 6. Variation in radiosensitivity of *E. coli* B/r with oxygen concentration. Dotted lines give theoretical curves for equation 3 with highest and lowest experimentally determined values of *m*. From Howard-Flanders and Alper (20).

this being the concentration of oxygen in water equilibrated with an atmosphere which contains 0.3 % oxygen. With *k* equal to 4 μM/l, and *m* = 3 *r* becomes equal to 0.9 *m* when [O] is about 23 μM/l, i.e., when the suspending buffer is in equilibrium with an atmosphere containing 1.7 % oxygen. Since a difference in radiosensitivity of only 10 % is usually difficult to measure with biological materials, it may be said that as little as 2 % oxygen is sufficient to confer effectively the maximum radiosensitivity on microorganisms. Deschner and Gray (101) have found that equation 3 applies also to the radiosensitivity of Ehrlich mouse ascites tumor cells as measured by the production of chromosome aberrations after irradiation *in vitro*; both *m* and *k* were found to have about the same values as those established for microorganisms.

When anoxic conditions are required in radiobiological experiments, it is often the practice to flush with nitrogen. If this is not carefully freed from oxygen contamination, the lowest possible radiosensitivity may not be attained. By applying equation 3 it may be calculated that where [O] = 0.1 % O_2 in the gas, i.e., 1.3 μM/l dissolved in water, *r* is 1.5. It has been found by Kihlman (102) that the presence of this proportion of oxygen in "tank" nitrogen is sufficient to affect markedly the radiosensitivity of cells in organized tissues (bean roots), if respiration is inhibited, and that k for this material has about the same value as for microorganisms (103.)

A few reports have been made on the effect of oxygen on lethal damage to dry spores of microorganisms. Stapleton and Hollaender (104) reported on the results of irradiating dry and wet spores of *Aspergillus terreus* in the presence and absence of oxygen. Enhancement ratios of about 1.5 for both the wet and dry spores may be deduced from their data. Tallentire (105) reported that very dry spores of *Bacillus subtilis* were considerably more radiosensitive when irradiated in air than in vacuum (0.002 mm Hg). Using dried spores of *B. megaterium*, Powers *et al.* (106) found an effect of oxygen which varied with the temperature of the spores at the time of irradiation. Enhancement of radiosensitivity was not observed at temperatures below $-120°C$; above this, the enhancement ratio increased to a maximum value of 2.5 at 77°C.

The enhancement by oxygen of ionizing radiation effects on cells is now recognized as being very general in radiobiology, applying to widely differing types of cells and tests of damage. Many genetic effects of ionizing radiation have been found to be enhanced by oxygen, although genetic effects in free cell populations have not been widely studied from this point of view. Anderson (107) reported the interesting result that in *Escherichia coli* B/r the X-ray induction of back-mutation to streptomycin nondependence was sensitive to oxygen, whereas induction of back-mutation to purine nondependence was the same under anoxic and aerobic conditions. The genetic effect in single-cell populations which has mainly been studied for the influence of oxygen is the induction of dominant and recessive lethal mutations (e.g., refs. 108, 109) which may be related to chromosome structural changes.

Effects of oxygen in enhancing the induction of lysogenic bacteria, and on radiation-induced delay before division, were reported in Section IV.

With vegetative or "wet" cells, oxygen must be present during irradiation to exert its effect. Howard-Flanders and Moore (110) were unable to detect an effect on the sensitivity of bacteria irradiated in anoxic conditions if oxygen was introduced within the shortest time after irradiation possible with their experimental conditions, viz., after 20 msec. Effects of anoxia after irradiation have been noted, but this type of postirradiation modification would seem to be the result of metabolic processes in the case of vegetative cells (see Section V.D). For example, anoxia imposed after exposure to UV may affect survival (21), although anoxia during UV-irradiation is without effect.

By contrast with vegetative cells, those which are in a dry form (seeds,

TABLE I
OXYGEN ENHANCEMENT RATIOS WITH X-RAYS AND FAST NEUTRONS

Author and ref.	Material	Test of damage	Enhancement ratio for radiations in the presence of oxygen	
			X-rays	Fast neutrons
				(2 Mev deuterons-Be)
Gray et al. (99)	Ascites tumor cells	Anaphase ab-normalities	(200 kv) 3.7	1.3
Howard-Flanders and Alper (20)	Shigella flexneri	Lethal effect	(1.5 Mev) 3.0	1.4
Howard-Flanders and Alper (20)	Saccharomyces cerevisiae ("starved" for 4 hours)	Lethal effect	(200 kv) 2.4	1.7
Alper and Gillies (113)	Escherichia coli B	Lethal effect, medium "D"	(200 kv) 3.0	1.7
Alper and Gillies (113)	Escherichia coli B	Lethal effect, medium "O"	(200 kv) 2.1	1.5
Hornsey et al. (113a)	Ascites tumor cells	Anaphase abnormalities	(200 kv) 2.5	1.3
				(15 Mev deuterons Be)
Hornsey and Silini (113b)	Ascites tumor cells	Lethal effect	(200 kv) 3.1	1.8

spores) may demonstrate changes in their biological response to radiation if they are exposed subsequently to oxygen (e.g., 106, 110a). It would appear that as long as cells are dry there may be a postponement of the metionic reaction, i.e., of the chemical reaction which Alper (111) postulated to ensue because of the highly reactive state of the ionized target molecules. The phenomenon of interaction of oxygen with dry materials previously irradiated has been demonstrated by electron spin resonance (e.g., see reference 111a).

It is an important aspect of the oxygen effect that the enhancement ratio, m, varies with the type of radiation used, being highest with radiations of lowest LET (Chapter 1). From the available evidence it would appear that m varies continuously from a maximum value (often 3 to 4) with lightly ionizing radiation to a value near to 1 with heavy particles. The first observations pertaining to the interdependence of oxygen and radiation quality in biological effects of radiation appear to have been made by Read (112), who reported a value for m of about 1.2 in the effect of α-particles on the growth rate of bean roots. Not many single-cell populations have been investigated in respect of the oxygen effect with radiations other than γ- or X-rays. Some relevant data are presented in Table I.

As a consequence of the variation in m with radiation quality, observations on the relative effectiveness of different types of radiation will be affected by the oxygen concentration in the cells under test. It is to be expected that the effectiveness of heavy radiations relative to light ones (i.e., γ- and X-rays) will always be greater in anoxic than in aerobic conditions. A striking example of this was afforded by observations with *Shigella flexneri* Y6R. The effectiveness of fast neutrons relative to 1.5-Mev X-rays was greater than 1 for anoxic irradiations, but less than 1 in fully oxygenated conditions (20).

b. Other Gases. If oxygen exerts its radiobiological effects by reacting with radicals induced by radiation, other substances might be able to react in a similar fashion (111). From a consideration of its properties, Howard-Flanders predicted that nitric oxide would act as an agent for enhancing radiation damage in the absence of oxygen and showed that when present during irradiation this gas enhanced the effects of X-rays on *Shigella flexneri* Y6R. The dependence of the enhancement ratio on the concentration of nitric oxide was similar to that of oxygen (114). Nitric oxide has subsequently been found to enhance the effects of ionizing radiation on bean roots (102) and on ascites tumor cells (115).

Although these studies have shown that the action of nitric oxide may simulate that of oxygen, differences in the effects of the two gases have been demonstrated when dry biological materials have been used. Sparrman *et al.* (115a) found that dry plant seeds irradiated and stored in nitric oxide were less affected by radiation than if they were irradiated in the presence or the absence of oxygen. When the moisture content of the seeds exceeded 8%, however, the nitric oxide acted as an enhancing agent, and it was at least as effective as oxygen when the moisture content exceeded 12%. Similarly, Powers *et al.* (106) found that although nitric oxide could act as a sensitizing agent for the spores of *B. megaterium* when it was present during irradiation, it was protective when admitted to spores which had been irradiated in anoxic conditions. If the spores were irradiated in the presence of oxygen, the admission of nitric oxide afterwards was without effect.

In ordinary circumstances no gases other than oxygen and nitric oxide have been found to influence the radiosensitivity of homogeneous populations of single cells. The case of hydrogen is of special interest. This gas plays an important part in the radiation chemistry of water (cf. Chapter 2), but has been shown in several studies to be without effect on radiation damage to single-cell populations (20, 116). An exceptional state of affairs occurs when hydrogen under pressure is applied to ascites tumor cells during irradiation (117). If at the same time air is present, the effect of the oxygen is suppressed by hydrogen at pressures of 100 atmospheres and more. Hydrogen gas is not so efficient in this respect, however, as nitrogen, argon, or krypton. The authors assume as a working hypothesis that, in order to exert its effect on radiosensitivity, oxygen must be adsorbed at specific sites. The gases which are most effective in suppressing the oxygen effect are therefore presumed to be the most effective in displacing oxygen from the postulated sites.

2. CHEMICAL PROTECTION (SEE CHAPTER 3, VOLUME II)

It follows from what has been said in Section V.A.1 that a variety of chemical substances added to cell suspensions may affect the observed result of radiation through their influence on the oxygen concentration. In some circumstances they may assist the cells to remove oxygen which is present in low concentration. Thus, if a dense suspension of respiring cells is used as test material, the addition of metabolites may cause them to deplete the medium of oxygen by increasing the respiration rate (118). Chemical substances may also deplete the suspending fluid of oxygen if they are autoxidizable. Two substances which are commonly regarded as protective agents for a variety of biological test materials, cysteine and cysteamine, have been shown by Gray to remove oxygen efficiently from neutral water (119), and these substances are considered by some investigators to exert their protective action by this mechanism (120, 121).

A safe criterion for regarding a chemical protector as acting independently of the oxygen effect would be its ability to protect in anoxic conditions. Marcovich (121) has tested the protective action of cysteamine on *Escherichia coli* B/r, both in the presence and in the absence of oxygen. He observed a slight additional protection afforded by cysteamine beyond that obtained by oxygen removal, but this may be ascribed to the fact that his conditions of anoxia were not rigorous (92). He concluded that the protective action of cysteamine was a consequence of its ability to deplete the medium of oxygen.

Many chemical protective agents for *Escherichia coli* B/r have been used by Hollaender and his co-workers (122). They ascribe the action of a large proportion of these to their influence on the oxygen content of the suspensions but consider that a different protective mechanism applies to the two compounds cysteamine and β-mercaptoethanol. It is apparent from the data presented that cysteamine did not act as a dose-reducing agent. Survival curves for unprotected bacteria were exponential, whereas in the presence of cysteamine they were sigmoid. It can be inferred from the dose-effect curves with and without β-mercaptoethanol that this compound reduced the effectiveness of all doses by a factor of 5 to 6. From other reports from the same laboratory on experiments with *E. coli* B/r it may be deduced that anoxia in their conditions reduces the effectiveness of X-rays by a factor of about 4 (123), so that the latter compound appears to have given more protection than could be attained by anoxia alone. A direct comparison of the radiosensitivity of *anoxic* bacterial suspensions in the presence and in the absence of these compounds would be of very great interest.

The alcohols seem to form a special class of protective agents. Goucher *et al.* (118) reported that the protective action of 0.2 *M* ethanol on *Escherichia coli* B/r was dissimilar to that of succinate. The respiration rate of the bacteria with ethanol present was only one-fifth of its value in the presence of succinate, yet ethanol protected suspensions of cells in concentrations which were too low to deplete the medium of oxygen even when succinate was present. On the other hand, equilibration with oxygen immediately before irradiation abolished the protective effect of the ethanol. However, Marcovich (124), who examined the protective action of glycerol, ethanol, methanol, mannitol, and glycol, found that their protective action was not abolished by equilibration with oxygen immediately before irradiation, although they gave no protection to anoxic suspensions. The protective action of all these alcohols was about equal for equimolar concentrations, reaching a maximum effect at about 1 *M*. Glycerol was found by Dewey (124a) to protect *Serratia marcescens* even in anoxic conditions, with a dose-reduction factor of 2.7 when the concentration was 0.8 *M*.

B. Physical Conditions at the Time of Irradiation

1. temperature (above 0°c)

a. Vegetative Cells. In considering the application of target theory to lethal effects of radiation on microorganisms, Lea (Chapter 9 of ref. 1) considered it important that radiosensitivity had been found to be independent of temperature, and he quoted the supporting evidence which was available at that time. Many examples of temperature dependence of the radiosensitivity of cells in organized tissues must now be ascribed to changes in oxygen gradient which occur with changes in respiration rate (102), and even suspensions of single cells may be subject to changes in radiosensitivity which appear to depend on temperature change but are in fact attributable either to oxygen depletion because of increased repiration rate, or to an increased supply of oxygen when the respiration rate is lowered, if the conditions of the experiment are such that rapid equilibration with the atmosphere is not achieved. However, a few investigations which have been made with single-cell suspensions in controlled gas conditions have suggested that a small but real variation in radiosensitivity might occur between 0° and 40°C. Stapleton and Edington (123) examined the sensitivity of *Escherichia coli* B/r to the lethal effects of X-rays at temperatures between −196° and +40°C in both anoxic and aerobic conditions. Their data show that the radiosensitivity of aerobic and anoxic cells were, respectively, 25 % and 50 % greater at 40°C than at 30°C, though it remained essentially constant between 0° and 30°C. No data were given as to the survival of nonirradiated bacteria held for the requisite period of time at 40°C, as compared with the general control suspension kept at ice-bath temperature. Deschner and Gray (101) have used *in vitro* suspensions of Ehrlich mouse ascites tumor cells, the test of damage being chromosomal abnormalities. The investigation was designed mainly to examine the effect of oxygen in various concentrations, and particular attention was paid to problems of equilibration. An increase of about 30 % was observed in the sensitivity of both anoxic and aerobic cells irradiated at 37°C over that of cells irradiated at 3°C.

Wood (125) examined the radiosensitivity of haploid yeast cells over a range of temperature from −10° to +50°C. He observed some increase in radiosensitivity (about 13 %) between 0° and 40°C. There was a marked increase in radiosensitivity as the temperature of the cells was raised to 50°C and above, but it was observed that the nonirradiated cells were killed very quickly at the higher temperatures.

b. Bacterial Spores. Lea *et al.* (70) reported that the sensitivity of *Bacillus mesentericus* to β- and γ-rays was essentially the same when irradiated at 0° and 37°C. In other studies considerably wider ranges of temperature have been used. Houtermans (126) examined the sensitivity to both α- and X-rays of moist and dry spores of *B. subtilis* and observed little change between −20° and +40°C. The changes observed below −20°C will be discussed in the next section. Webb *et al.* (127) have described experiments in which dry spores of *B. megaterium* were irradiated, in anaerobic conditions, at temperatures up to 131°C. They observed a gradual increase by about 7 % in radiosensitivity over the range −20° to 36°C. At 36°C there was quite a sharp maximum, the sensitivity decreasing with temperature to 100°C, after which it increased once more. It was necessary, however, to maintain the spores at the higher temperatures for periods of 20 minutes or more in order to change their sensitivity. In aerobic conditions the dependence of radiosensitivity on temperature followed a different course (106). There was an over-all increase of about 15 % as the temperature was increased from −20° to +36°C, but the sharp fall in radiosensitivity noted at higher temperatures in anoxic conditions was not observed when oxygen was present.

2. FREEZING

It was shown by Houtermans (128) that *Escherichia coli* cells were protected by freezing from the lethal effects of both α- and X-rays. The effect of the freezing was similar with both radiations in that there was a large decrease in radiosensitivity over a small temperature range, the "half-value" dose increasing by a factor of 2 in each case. There was a dissimilarity, however, in that with α-rays the transition occurred at 0°C, and the radiosensitivity remained constant between 0° and −200°C, whereas with X-rays the transition occurred at about −10°C, and radiosensitivity decreased with decreasing temperature until at −200°C it was less than that for cells above 0°C by a factor of about 3. The pattern reported by Houtermans (128) with X-rays is similar to that found by Stapleton and Edington (123) with *E. coli* B/r under aerobic conditions. In anoxic conditions, however, the sensitivity of frozen cells changed little, if at all, with decreasing temperature. It is noteworthy that some effect of oxygen on radiosensitivity was detected at all temperatures tested, but the ratios of radiosensitivities in the presence and in the absence of oxygen decreased with temperature, which follows from the fact that the radiosensitivity had a larger temperature coefficient in aerobic than in anaerobic conditions.

In experiments with haploid yeast cells, Wood (125) found a discontinuity in radiosensitivity as the state changed. This author was able to keep the suspensions of yeast cells supercooled and so to compare the sensitivities of liquid and frozen cells at the same temperatures. It could be seen that it was the change in state, and not the temperature, which afforded the decrease in radiosensitivity. In later work Wood and Taylor (129) have examined the effect of both phase state and anoxia on the radiosensitivity of two lines of yeast descended from the same parent haploid strain. The interesting observation was made that the enhancement of radiosensitivity by oxygen differed considerably in the two lines, and that the degree of protection afforded by anoxia alone was less for the cells of the line with which freezing gave greater protection in the absence of oxygen. Oxygen appears to enhance radiation damage almost as effectively when the cell is frozen, but near 0°C, as when it is liquid, as shown by the results of both Stapleton and Edington (123) and of Wood and Taylor (129).

The general conclusion can be drawn that the freezing of microorganisms protects them against the lethal effects of radiation, and that with vegetative cells a rather sudden change in radiosensitivity occurs as the state changes. With *Escherichia coli* in aerobic conditions, radiosensitivity decreases throughout the range of temperatures below freezing which have been tested. An anomalous result for yeast cells was reported by Wood and Taylor (130) in that radiosensitivity was at a minimum at about −30°C and increased with lower temperatures. However, the control cells were themselves severely affected by the lower temperatures, only 50% surviving one hour at −50°C, and 15% at −72°C. In this connection it may be remembered that Wood (125) had previously reported a marked increase in the sensitivity of yeast cells irradiated at temperatures above 50°C, at which a drastic inactivation of the nonirradiated controls was observed (see section V.B.1a).

When bacterial spores have been used, no sudden transition in X-ray sensitivity at temperatures near 0°C seems to have been observed. Houtermans (126), working with *Bacillus subtilis* spores, reported a gradual increase in sensitivity in the temperature range −200° to 0°C, with no great difference in this respect between wet and dry spores, although with the latter the increase seems to have been somewhat sharper between −200° and 50°C, whereas the radiosensitivity remained rather more constant between −50° and 0°C. Houtermans (126) also investigated the change in sensitivity to α-rays over the same temperature range. Only the dry spores showed a change, which consisted of a sharp increase in sensitivity between −40° and 0°C. Webb *et al.* (131) used dry spores of *B. megaterium*, irradiated by X-rays *in vacuo* over the range −268° to +36°C. The radiosensitivity was constant up to −194°C; then it gradually increased by 25% over the whole range up to 36°C.

Nothing can be said about the effects of freezing on the lethal effects of radiation on higher cells. Fabergé (132) showed that ripe pollen of *Tradescantia* was protected by freezing against radiation-induced chromosome aberrations. He found also that oxygen enhanced radiation damage at −192°C. There is no reason to suppose, therefore, that the phenomenon of protection by freezing is not generally applicable to lethal effects on cells. The effect of freezing on the induction of mutations does not seem to have been examined.

3. MOISTURE CONTENT

Not many types of cell can be dried without loss of viability, and it is difficult to draw a general conclusion from the few investigations which have been made into the comparative radiosensitivities of wet and dry cells. The possibility must be considered that in some experimental arrangements radiosensitivity may be changed by an inadvertent change in oxygen concentration, if, for example, the supply is limited by the respiration rate, which is very likely to be different if the moisture content of the cells is changed.

The eggs of the blue shrimp, *Artemia*, are very suitable material for the study of the effect of moisture content on radiosensitivity (133), since they can survive within capsules, in the blastula stage, for periods as long as 15 years in a dry environment. Rugh and Clugston (133) measured the percentages which hatched after 24 and 48 hours after various doses of X-rays delivered to wet and to dry eggs. More of the eggs hatched after all doses if irradiated while dry; however, the shapes of the dose-effect curves were different, so that the water did not act as a dose-multiplying agent. The curve pertaining to the eggs irradiated wet was roughly of exponential form, whereas the dry eggs gave a sigmoid curve, with a threshold to a dose level of 10^5 r. With greater doses the slope of the curve was equal to that for the hydrated eggs. *Artemia* eggs were used also by Iwasaki (134), who reported an investigation into the effect of X-rays on the hatchability at 72 hours of eggs of differing moisture content. The results were analogous to those which have been obtained with plant seeds, in that the radiosensitivity varied in a complex way with water content, 16% giving the minimum sensitivity. Furthermore, eggs which were hydrated at 0°C had to be soaked for longer in order to reach the same radiosensitivity as those hydrated at 27°C. The author concluded that the water was important in setting the stages of physiological development rather than in radiation chemical reactions.

One or two investigations on the effect of moisture content have been carried out with spores of microorganisms. Stapleton and Hollaender (104), using *Asperigillus terreus*, found that radiosensitivity increased with increasing moisture content, but in this case, too, the survival curves showed that the water did not act as a dose-multiplying agent. Houtermans (126) used spores of *Bacillus subtilis* to examine the interaction of moisture content and temperature with radiosensitivity. Moist spores were *less* sensitive to X-rays than dry ones at all temperatures down to that of liquid air, but the difference decreased with decreasing temperature.

An anomalous result was reported by Bellamy and Lawton (135) with *Streptococcus faecalis*. Bacteria dried in the mass were less sensitive to radiation than when hydrated; but if they had been freeze-dried on millipore filters they were considerably more sensitive, particularly at the higher doses. Survival curves were presented for the latter case, and these showed that the removal of water did not act as a simple dose-multiplying agent.

Rather complicated effects of drying on the sensitivity of bacteria were reported by Moos (136), who irradiated *Pseudomonas aeruginosa* suspended in, and dried from, distilled water and broth. Radiosensitivities were about the same for the cells irradiated in broth and dried from the water suspension but were higher for the cells suspended in water and very much lower for the cells dried from broth.

Although it has sometimes been assumed to be generally true that dried cells are less radiosensitive than wet ones, the examples quoted show that no simple principle can be stated. It would appear that the modifying effect of varying moisture content on the radiosensitivity of cells is in a different category from the presence of oxygen during irradiation, or the effect of freezing, both of which are dose-modifying agents. It may well be that such effects of moisture content as have been observed are mainly due to alterations in the physiological state, as suggested by Iwasaki (134).

C. Physiological and Morphological Factors

1. Mammalian Cells: Morphology and Division Stage

We shall consider here only data on populations of single cells which are able to divide, since we are concerned with genetic and lethal effects (as defined in Section II.A). Techniques for growing separate clones from single mammalian cells have been developed by Puck and his co-workers (137, 138), and some data are now available on survival curves constructed from viable counts on free cells irradiated *in vitro*. The dose-effect curve for human carcinomatous cells (HeLa cells) exposed to X-rays was found by Puck and Marcus (17) to be accurately described by the equation

$$S = 1 - (1 - e^{D/D_0})^2 \qquad (5)$$

where D is the dose and D_0 the increment which reduces surviving fraction S to $.037S$, when the curve has become exponential. The D_0 for HeLa cells was equal to 96 r.* The dose-effect curve was carried down to $S = 10^{-3}$, and the experimental points fitted the theoretical curve accurately throughout the range tested. The authors interpreted the fit of this equation to their experimental curve as implying that the lethal effect of the X-rays was due to single ionizing events, one of which had to occur in each of two equivalent loci per cell (probably chromosomes) to cause cell death.

In a later paper, Puck *et al.* (139) presented survival curves for human cells of different types, cultured from normal tissues. Although the scatter of the points about a defined curve was much greater for some cell types than was the case with HeLa cells, the survival curve was in each case of the same nature, viz. type C1 as defined in Section II.B.3. In any interpretation of this type of curve, it is assumed that the population is homogeneous as regards its radiosensitivity, the initial shoulder being due to aggregates, or to a multiplicity of "hit number" or "target number." If some of the population were inherently more resistant than the rest, there should be evidence of a "resistant tail" (see Section II.B.2). In the experiments of Puck and his co-workers, the methods of preparing the cells for irradiation were such that cells in all division stages must have been in-

---

* The original dosimetry was found to be in error, and these doses should be multiplied by the factor 1.45 (139a).

cluded. It may be deduced, therefore, that sensitivity to the lethal effect of radiation is independent of the division stage of the cells, at least to a level of one in a thousand.

A further deduction from the work of this group is that cell morphology has only a small influence on sensitivity, since the 37% doses varied only between 75 and 166 r.* for human cells of such varying types as epitheloid and fibroblastic, originating from skin, spleen, conjuctiva, and lung. It may be noted, however, that Warburg *et al.* (140) have reported on respiration measurements with rabbit kidney cells kept in tissue culture, from which they deduced that after some generations in culture all mammalian cells acquired certain of the properties of tumor cells.

A technique has been developed by Hewitt and Wilson (141) for establishing survival curves on leukemic cells of mice, irradiated *in vivo*. They have found that the survival curve is accurately exponential to a surviving fraction of 10^{-5}. The sensitivity of the cells was found to be about the same as that reported by Puck and his co-workers (17, 139) for human cells.

Until Puck and his collaborators had developed techniques for growing separate clones from single mammalian cells, only Ehrlich mouse ascites tumor cells had been used in quantitative radiobiological investigations on dividing cells irradiated *in vitro* (99, 142, 143). The tumor is customarily harvested from mice while the number of cells is increasing, and all stages of division are therefore present. Hornsey and Silini (113b) constructed survival curves for these cells based directly on observations of viability, which was assessed in terms of the ability of the cells to originate solid tumors in young mice. Tumor cells were irradiated *in vitro* by X-rays and by fast neutrons to survival levels of about 10^{-4}, the effects of oxygen being examined in both cases. All four survival curves had extrapolation numbers of about 12, and approached an exponential form, with no evidence of a resistant tail. Hewitt and Wilson (144) looked specifically for signs of a fraction of leukemia cells which might be resistant (by virtue of anoxia); they would have been able to detect a resistant fraction as small as 10^{-3}, but there was no evidence of such a fraction, although again cells must have been in all stages of division since the mice were irradiated before the cells were harvested. It seems to be a generality that survival curves taken on asynchronous populations of mammalian cells fail to reveal even a small fraction which is more resistant than the majority.

Dependence of radiosensitivity on division stage is a well-known phenomenon (145), but the studies on which such observations are based have been carried out for the most part with germ cells in known stages of mitosis or meiosis. The apparent homogeneity in radiosensitivity of somatic mammalian cells indicates that there is no special phase of marked *resistance* to lethal effects of radiation as the cells proceed through the division cycle, although small fractions of specially *sensitive* cells may not have been detectable by the techniques used in constructing survival curves. With this reservation, it seems likely that the sensitivity of somatic mammalian cells to lethal effects of radiation remains uniform through the cell cycle. It is apparently fallacious, therefore, to extrapolate from data obtained with specialized cells in making the assumption that variation in radio-sensitivity with division stage is characteristic of all cells for all tests of damage.

Many radiobiologists are of the opinion that lethal effects of radiation on higher cells are closely related to the induction of chromosomal defects (17, 146), and, if this is so, it is to be expected that the influence of division stage would be the same, whichever of these tests of damage were used. Results of Revell (147) with meristematic cells of *Vicia faba* roots show that when sensitivity to X-rays is determined by scoring chromatid breaks at anaphase the response is constant for cells at all stages of the division cycle. The author's previous observation (147a) of a peak of sensitivity just before mitosis was later attributed by him to the fact that the scoring of breaks was done on metaphase cells. He found that this method led to the inclusion of spurious "chromatid breaks." The data of Deschner and Gray (101) on the induction of anaphase abnormalities by X-rays in Ehrlich mouse ascites tumor cells show that the number of abnormalities observed depended on the time of fixing after irradiation, a broad maximum being observed with cells fixed between 10 and 20 hours after reinoculation. These results exclude the possibility that a small fraction of cells was selectively *sensitive* to this test of damage, since that situation would have been observed as a sharp, narrow maximum. If the timing curves of Deschner and Gray are indicative of a variation in sensitivity with cell cycle, the variation must be such that the resistant phase occupies the minor part of the cell cycle, and it would follow that cell killing and the induction of chromosomal defects are separate tests of damage with no causal relationship.

2. *Habrobracon* EGGS

This chapter is concerned with radiation effects on homogeneous populations of individual units of biological organization, and very little material of this type is available from plants or insects. A considerable volume of work has been done, for the most part by Whiting and her co-workers, on the cytological and lethal effects of ionizing radiation on *Habrobracon* eggs. The cytological aspects will be discussed elsewhere (see Chapter 4), but certain data are relevant to the present discussion. Although they do not refer to eggs irradiated *in vitro*, the techniques developed by Whiting include methods of handling the females so that populations of eggs may be harvested which are uniform as regards their division stage at the time of irradiation (148). Meiotic metaphase eggs are obtained by causing the female to store them in the uterine sac, and in this stage the eggs may be regarded as free-living cells. The great difference in the radiosensitivity of *Habrobracon* eggs at different stages of the meiotic cycle was established by Whiting (148) and confirmed by Kenworthy (149), who compared the hatchability of eggs irradiated in meiotic metaphase stage with that of eggs irradiated in prophase. Dose-effect curves were very well matched when doses to the prophase eggs were about twenty-two times as high as those to the metaphase eggs, so that the physiological difference acted as a dose-modifying agent. Furthermore, the radiosensitivity in both stages was enhanced to an equal extent by the presence of oxygen, the enhancement ratio being 3 throughout the whole range of doses tested for eggs in both stages of development.

3. YEAST CELLS

a. Ploidy. Mortimer (150) has reported fully on the dependence of radiosensitivity of *Saccharomyces cerevisiae* on ploidy, describing the methods used to obtain cells of different ploidies, with certain genetic markers, up to hexaploid cells. The data confirm results from other laboratories (151, 152) which have shown that sensitivity, as judged by the final slopes of the sigmoid survival curves, increases as ploidy is increased from the diploid stage. Lucke and Sarachek (151), working with haploid, diploid, triploid, and tetraploid *Saccharomyces*, found that the "multiplicities" of the survival curves agreed with the ploidy, but that haploids were about twice as sensitive (as judged by slopes of the survival curves) and the triploids twice as resistant as the diploid and tetraploid cells. Mortimer's data (150) agree well with those of Magni (152) in demonstrating an increase in radiosensitivity from the diploid to the hexaploid cells. Mortimer and Magni differ somewhat, however, in the interpretation of their results. The former considers that his data are consistent with the view that, in diploid cells and those of higher ploidy, most of the lethal effects are due to the induction of dominant lethal mutations, whereas haploid cells are killed by recessive lethals. Magni, on the other hand, inclines to the view that nongenetic damage is responsible for much of the lethal effect of radiation and points out that with this material the concept of "genetic defect" has been only operationally defined. Lucke and Sarachek (151) consider that their data eliminate the possibility that dominant lethals can be responsible for killing cells of ploidy higher than one and incline to the view that there is a complicated interrelationship of genetic and nongenetic effects.

b. The Effect of Budding. It was reported by Beam *et al.* (14) that the radioresistant fraction of a young, freshly harvested population of yeast cells consisted of the budding cells, and that incubation of the cells in a medium which contained a source of carbon, but no nitrogen, would increase the proportion of more sensitive cells to a greater and greater extent as "starvation" proceeded. At the same time microscopic examination showed that the percentage of budding cells observed was in excellent agreement with the percentage of cells estimated to be radioresistant from the survival curves.

It can be deduced from the papers of Beam *et al.* (14) and of Elkind and Beam (153) that the radiosensitivity of the budding cells is low, when compared not only with that of nonbudding haploid cells but also with the sensitivities of the strains of higher ploidy tested by Mortimer (150). According to the final slopes of the curves presented in the papers in question, the budding cells required a larger dose to reduce the population from 10^{-3} to 10^{-4} of the controls than that required to reduce Mortimer's most resistant strain (diploid) from 10^{-1} to 10^{-2}. Alper (154) has postulated that the high resistance of the budding cells is due to a change in the main target for cell killing, once the cell has budded. This is discussed in more detail in Section VI.A.

c. Interaction between Physiological State and the Effect of Oxygen. Birge and Tobias (155) examined the radiosensitivity of yeast cells grown anaerobically and, in experiments in which survival was followed to 20 % of the control population, found that the radiosensitivity was the same as for aerobically grown cells, whether irradiated in the absence or in the presence of oxygen. Beam (156) found that the enhancement of radiosensitivity by oxygen was the same for yeasts of all ploidies examined; with the haploid yeast, it was the same ($m = 2$) for the more sensitive and more resistant cells. Alper (157) has found, however, that freshly harvested yeast cells, before starvation, demonstrated a considerably higher oxygen enhancement ratio ($m = 3.6$) than cells which had been starved by the procedure of Beam *et al.* (14). The ratio decreased as the starvation period was prolonged, reaching a minimum value of $m = 2$ after 2 days' starvation. The change in the oxygen enhancement ratio was due to a change in the anoxic sensitivity, whereas that of the fully oxygenated cells remained unchanged. These results may be compared with those reported by Laser (158), who found that a period of nitrogen starvation abolished the oxygen effect observed with freshly harvested cells. The criterion of damage used by Laser was reduction in growth rate of the cells, as measured by oxygen uptake on reinoculation into growth medium.

Alper (154) has also found that the oxygen enhancement ratio for budding yeast cells, as judged by the lethal effect of 8-Mev electrons, is only about 1.7, i.e. about one-half of the maximum enhancement ratio observed with fresh single cells.

4. BACTERIA

a. *Stages of Division and Growth.* If a population of bacteria is harvested in the logarithmic stage of growth and washed and resuspended in buffer solution, it will contain cells in all stages of division, unless special measures have been taken to induce synchrony. Since exponential survival curves are obtained with many such populations, it must be concluded that the radiosensitivity of bacteria does not change throughout the division stage. Marcovich (92) has specially examined logarithmic-stage cultures of *Escherichia coli* B/r and K12(S) for evidence of varying radiosensitivity in the population but has failed to find any.

The growth of a population of bacteria which has been freshly inoculated into liquid medium is normally characterized by an initial lag phase, a logarithmic phase during which multiplication occurs at a constant rate, when averaged over the population, and a stationary phase in which the population has reached a maximum for the particular conditions of growth. A detailed survey was made by Stapleton (159) of the variation

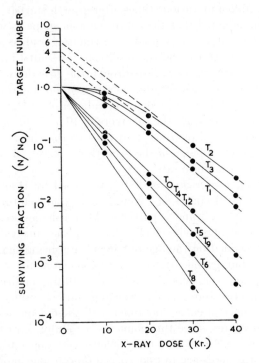

FIG. 7. Survival of *E. coli* B/r harvested at various times after commencement of incubation. Times T1, T2, etc., indicate hours of incubation. By courtesy of Dr. G. E. Stapleton (159).

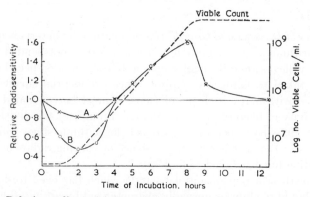

FIG. 8. Relative radiosensitivity of *E. coli* B/r as a function of time of incubation. Calculated from data of G. E. Stapleton (159). *Curve A:* Radiosensitivity defined as inverse of dose to give 10% survival. *Curve B:* Radiosensitivity in terms of final slopes. *Dotted curve:* viable count during 12 hours of incubation.

in radiosensitivity of *E. coli* B/r throughout the period of growth. The survival curves, taken at various times after growth started, are presented in Fig. 7. It will be noted that the curves vary in shape as well as in final slope. Two criteria have been used in estimating radiosensitivity from Stapleton's survival curves, and the results are presented in Fig. 8. Curve *A* shows how radiosensitivity varies through the growth cycle, if the final slopes of the survival curves are used as a measure of radiosensitivity; the data for curve *B* were derived by defining radiosensitivity as the reciprocal of the dose required to reduce the survivors to 10 % of the original population. It is of interest, and puzzling, that most of the change in sensitivity takes place during the 6 hours of the logarithmic phase, when the bacteria are multiplying at a uniform rate.

Another strain, *Escherichia coli* HIG, was used by Houtermans (160) in comparing survival curves of "young" and "old" cultures, irradiated with ultraviolet, X-rays, and α-particles. Microcolonies were counted to determine the level of survival. The shape of the survival curves after X-irradiation depended on the age of the culture, being sigmoid for 6- or 7-hour cultures, but exponential or near-exponential for "old" cultures. The final slopes, however, were about the same. In the conditions described, the "young" cultures were just entering the stationary phase. The initial shoulder to the survival curves obtained with these could not be ascribed to chains or aggregates, since this point was carefully controlled.

The sensitivity of *E. coli* B to ultraviolet is very dependent on its stage of growth, and it is necessary to take special precautions in order to ensure that a "logarithmic-phase" culture does not in fact contain cells which have already entered the stationary phase (16). It has been found that a mixture of logarithmic-phase and stationary-phase cells give a curve of type B (Section II.C.2) with a very pronounced break indeed. This phenomenon has been discussed by Meynell (161) with reference to various lethal agents of bacteria. Preliminary experiments on the dependence of X-ray sensitivity on stage of growth (45) have shown that there is an interaction between the oxygen concentration at the time of irradiation, the plating medium used after irradiation, and the stage of growth. The difference observed in the sensitivity of logarithmic-stage and stationary-stage *E. coli* B cells was greatest when they were irradiated in anoxic conditions and cultured afterward on a medium which was suboptimal for their growth (see Section V.D, below).

When bacterial spores have been used to study effects of ionizing radiations, the radiosensitivity has in general been of a lower order than that of vegetative bacterial cells. Stuy (162) investigated the sensitivity of germinating spores of *Bacillus cereus* and reported that 1 minute after germination had commenced the sensitivity had increased by a large factor, and it continued to increase until 3 hours after germination; by this time it had become equal to that of the vegetative cells.

An important difference between vegetative bacteria and spores was reported and discussed by Lea (Chapter 9 of ref. 1), who was interested in variation in the response to ionizing radiations of different linear energy transfer (LET; see Chapter 1). With vegetative cells (*Escherichia coli*) the lethal effectiveness of the radiation decreased with increasing LET, whereas the reverse was true of spores of *Bacillus mesentericus*. The general nature of this finding with spores has since been confirmed by Donnellan and Morowitz (163) and by Powers *et al.* (164). It is known that the oxygen concentration at the time of irradiation has an important bearing on the observed relative effectiveness of different types of radiation (20, 142), since oxygen enhances radiation effects less and less as the LET of the radiation increases (20, 99, 112). It would be of great interest if data were available on the interactions of oxygen with radiations of different LET on a bacterial strain examined both in the spore and the vegetative stages.

b. Radiosensitivity of Bacterial Mutants. Mutants of the strain *Escherichia coli* B have been selected specifically for their resistance to radiation (15, 21), and these will be discussed in Section V.D.2. Apart from these specifically radioresistant variants, such bacterial mutants as have been tested appear to have the same radiosensitivity as the wild-type strains. Examples are *E. coli* 15, and its thymine-requiring mutant 15T⁻, which have the same sensitivity to ultraviolet if thymine is provided in the culture medium (165), and various mutants of *E. coli* K12 with biochemical deficiencies, which are like the wild type in their sensitivity to X-rays (45) if complete medium is used for plating all the strains. Moustacchi (166) compared the sensitivity to X-rays of two strains of *E. coli*, and two of *Saccharomyces*, with mutants of each which were deficient in their respiratory enzyme systems. Her investigation was designed to test for a possible difference between the wild type and the deficient mutants in the extent to which oxygen affected the lethal damage. The respiratory enzyme deficiency did not affect the enhancement by oxygen of radiosensitivity in any of the four mutants; and the absolute radiosensitivity was the same for each mutant as for its parent strain, except in the case of the "petite" haploid yeast, which was more sensitive than the wild type, both in anoxic and in aerobic conditions.

D. POSTIRRADIATION CONDITIONS OF CULTURE

1. GENERAL REMARKS

Numerous reports have been made of modification of radiation response by varying the treatment of the test material after irradiation. Most of these pertain to investigations with ultraviolet, but sufficient data are available on the modification of the effects of ionizing radiation to justify an attempt to discern a unifying principle. As before, only results on uniform single-celled populations will be considered, and, at this point, only modifications of lethal or genetic effects on cells. Various reports on methods of modification have been Summarized in Table II. Reports of postirradiation modification of division delay have been excluded from this table, as they were discussed in Section IV.

It is a feature of the results tabulated that the great majority of treatments which reduce the response can be described as providing an environment which is suboptimal for the growth of the cells in question. An exception is provided by the resistant mutants of *E. coli* B and of other *E. coli* strains. Stapleton *et al.* (172) first reported that *E. coli* B/r gave lower colony counts after X-rays if the cells were cultured on a salts-glucose than on a complete medium. With strains which demonstrate this property, survival curves from counts on different media differ in extrapolation number only (21, 45), the final slopes of the curves being parallel. The strain *E. coli* B and its radio-resistant mutants have been widely used in radiobiological studies and therefore merit special discussion.

2. ESCHERICHIA COLI B AND ITS RADIORESISTANT MUTANTS

The observed radiosensitivity of these strains is strongly dependent on conditions of culture before and after irradiation, and they cannot be considered typical of vegetative bacteria in this respect. It has been found that *E. coli* B cells demonstrate less effect of all types of radiation if they are cultured after irradiation in suboptimal conditions, and it was sug-

TABLE II

MODIFICATIONS OF EFFECTS BY CONDITIONS OF CULTURE AFTER IRRADIATION

Author and ref.	Material and test of damage	"Normal" handling	Postirradiation treatment, Observed radiosensitivity		Treatment as dose-modifying agent
			Increased by	Reduced by	
Cook (167)[a]	*Ascaris* eggs —failure to hatch	Incubation at 25°C		Holding at 5°C	No data
Latarjet (168)	*Saccharomyces*—lethal effect	Incubation at 30°C		Holding at 5°C	No data
Schrek (169)	Mammalian cells—loss of viability	Incubation at 37°C, pH ∼ 7		Incubation at 7°–17°C; incubation at 45°C; low pH	No data
Stapleton *et al.* (170)	Strains of *E. coli*—lethal effect	Incubation at 37°C		Incubation at suboptimal temperatures	Yes (170) No (45)
Powers (80)	*Paramecium* —death at 1st and 2nd divisions	Incubation at 26°C	Incubation at 37°C	Incubation at 16°C	No
Anderson and Billen (171)	Auxotrophic variants, *E. coli*— reversions to protrophs	Incubation at 37°C			No data
	1. Purineless			Incubation below 37°C	
	2. Tyrosineless			Incubation below 15°C	
	3. Arginineless		Incubation at 24°C	Incubation below 15°C	
	4. Prolineless		Incubation at 24°C	Incubation at 6°–12°C	
Stapleton *et al.* (172)	*E. coli* B/r, grown in nutrient medium— lethal effect	Growth on nutrient medium	Growth on basal salts medium		Yes (172) No (21, 45)

TABLE II—*Continued*

Author and ref.	Material and test of damage	"Normal" handling	Postirradiation treatment, Observed radiosensitivity Increased by	Reduced by	Treatment as dose-modifying agent
Wainwright and Nevill (173)	Streptomyces spores —lethal and genetic effects	Immediate plating on nutrient medium		Incubation in distilled water at 37°C; incubation with metabolic inhibitor	No
Kimball (25), Kimball *et al.* (174), Kimball (175)	*Paramecium* —induction of lethal mutations			Near toxic amounts, H₂O₂ . Low temperature	No data
				Streptomycin	Yes
Pahl and Bachofer (176)	*Parascaris* eggs—failure to hatch.	Aerobic incubation		Anaerobic incubation	No
Alper and Gillies (16)	*E. coli* B— lethal effect	Growth on medium containing peptone, 20 gm/l, NaCl, 5 gm/l		Growth on medium with less peptone, less NaCl	No
Gillies and Alper (177)	*E. coli* B— lethal effect	Immediate plating, nutrient medium		Plating on nutrient medium + chloramphenicol, then nutrient medium	No

a Recently Pahl (178) has reported that he was unable to repeat Cook's observations.

gested (16) that some procedures which have been regarded as specifically "restorative" have exerted their effect rather nonspecifically by their effect in slowing growth. *E. coli* B/r cells, as well as those of other *coli* strains, were found by Stapleton *et al.* (170) to survive X-irradiation better if they were cultured after irradiation at suboptimal temperatures. In this respect, therefore, the response of *E. coli* B/r appears to correspond to the general principle which has been suggested. As regards nutrients supplied after irradiation, however, the resistant mutants of *E. coli* B behave differently from the parent strain. A resistant mutant of *E. coli* B, called *E. coli* Bpr5 (21), was found to have the same sensitivity to ultraviolet as *E. coli* B, if they were plated after irradiation on a basal salts medium. As shown by Fig. 3, however, they gave evidence of very different radiosensitivities if they were plated on medium of high nutritive quality. The difference in radiosensitivity between *E. coli* B and its resistant mutants seems to be connected with the effect of certain growth factors, when complete medium is used. These factors have the effect of increasing the extrapolation numbers of survival curves pertaining to the resistant strains, and therefore, perhaps, of providing alternative pathways when particular synthetic processes have been affected. In the parent strain, on the other hand, the utilization of organic growth factors by the irradiated cell causes certain synthetic pathways to get out of step, and thereby brings to light a fraction of the radiation damage which is not manifested when basal medium is used. In particular, active amino acid metabolism after ultraviolet irradiation is damaging to *E. coli* B. Gillies (179) has demonstrated this clearly by using auxotrophic mutants with requirements either for a single amino acid, for thymine, or for thymine as well as an amino acid. All the strains, like the prototrophic parent, showed low survival when cultured after ultraviolet irradiation on a "complete" medium which contained salts, glucose, and a mixture of amino acids and bases; considerably higher survival was shown on a salts-glucose medium (to which, of course, the appropriate required factor was added). Irradiated auxotrophic cells were maintained for varying periods on medium which was "complete" except for the strain's requirement, then transferred to complete medium also containing the requirement. Those strains which required an amino acid, and could therefore not synthesize protein in its absence, were rescued from ultraviolet damage by withholding the amino acid for a period immediately following irradiation. If the period was long enough, survival was as high as on salts-glucose medium. When a thymine-requiring strain was used, however, no rescue was effected by withholding thymine. Strains which required both thymine and an amino acid were rescued to about the same extent by withholding the amino acid and thymine and by withholding only the amino acid.

Various microorganisms have been investigated for an effect of medium on survival after ionizing radiation. Negative results were reported for *Serratia indica* (180), spores of *Bacillus subtilis* (163), *Shigella flexneri* Y6R, *E. coli*, strain 86, and variants of *E. coli* K12 (16). It should be noted also that *E. coli* B was not affected in the same way by ultraviolet and by X-rays. With the latter, there was a large difference in survival on two "complete" media of different quality, but survival on basal salts medium was the same as on the poor-quality nutrient medium (45). After ultraviolet, however, survival was considerably higher on the basal salts medium.

3. POSTIRRADIATION MODIFICATION AND DOSE-EFFECT CURVES

Culture conditions which affect the survival of *Escherichia coli* B after irradiation change the shape of the dose-effect curve, as well as the initial slope (Figs. 9A and 9B). The ratios of surviving fractions observed on two different media reach a maximum after a certain dose of ultraviolet, neutrons, or X-rays, and thereafter the dose-effect curves under the different conditions are parallel. It has in fact been shown by various authors (112, 181, 182) (see also Fig. 3) that conditions may be imposed after ultraviolet or ionizing radiation which will cause the observed survival curve

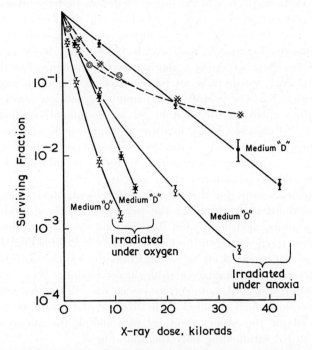

FIG. 9A. Survival of *E. coli* B after X-irradiation: ⊠ irradiated under oxygen, plated on medium "0." ○ irradiated under oxygen, plated on medium "D." ◗ irradiated anoxically, plated on medium "0." ● irradiated anoxically, plated on medium "D." ◎ $\dfrac{\text{surviving fraction, medium "O"}}{\text{surviving fraction, medium "D"}}$, irradiations under oxygen. ✳ $\dfrac{\text{surviving fraction, medium "O"}}{\text{surviving fraction, medium "D"}}$, anoxic irradiations.

for this organism to be of exponential form, or even slightly sigmoid. Thus the well-known "break" in the survival curve of *E. coli* B, so often mistakenly attributed to the presence of resistant mutants, is in fact connected with its response to the conditions of growth.

Changes in the shape of dose-effect curves due to changes in post-irradiation conditions of culture seem, in fact, to be fairly general. As an example, the data of Wainwright and Nevill (173) have been used to construct two survival curves, one of which represents the survival of *Streptomyces* spores plated immediately after X-irradiation, the other showing survival when the spores were incubated in distilled water for 3 hours at 37°C before plating (Fig. 10). It can be seen that the ratio between doses necessary to produce the same effect was not constant. Twice the dose was necessary to reduce the surviving population to 40%, if the

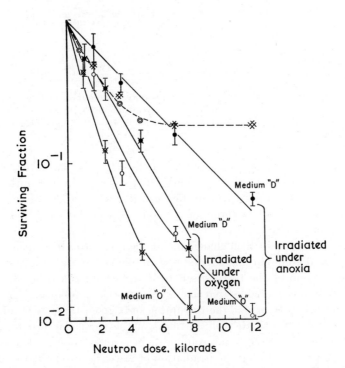

FIG. 9*B*. Survival of *E. coli* B after fast neutron irradiation: ⊠ irradiated under oxygen, plated on medium "O." ⊠ irradiated under oxygen, plated on medium "D." ○ irradiated anoxically, plated on medium "O." ● irradiated anoxically, plated on medium "D." ◎ $\frac{\text{surviving fraction, medium "O"}}{\text{surviving fraction, medium "D"}}$, irradiations under oxygen. ✳ $\frac{\text{surviving fraction, medium "O"}}{\text{surviving fraction, medium "D"}}$, anoxic irradiations.

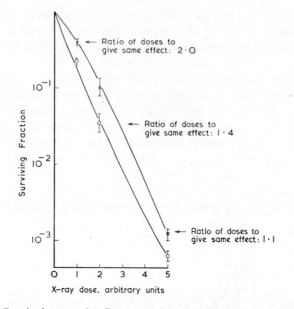

Fig. 10. Survival curves for *Streptomyces* spores. From data of Wainwright and Nevill (173). ○ spores plated immediately. × spores incubated for 3 hours in distilled water at 37°C before plating. The 95% confidence limits shown have been calculated from the data presented.

postirradiation treatment was applied; at the 0.1 % survival level, however, only 1.1 times the dose was necessary. It was shown by the authors that the effectiveness of the treatment diminished even more sharply with dose, when it was assessed in terms of its ability to modify (i.e., reduce) the induction of genetic changes.

Since procedures which change metabolic rates after irradiation seldom act as true dose-modifying agents, it is unlikely that their effects are due to a restoration of the target itself to its preirradiation condition in the cell; it is more probable that metabolic processes following irradiation determine whether or not the disruption of a given target will affect the subsequent history of the cell, in terms of the particular test of damage used. By contrast, oxygen, for example, acts as a true dose-modifying agent when it is present during the irradiation of wet cells, or even after irradiation if the cells are dry (Section V.A.1). It is plausible that a dose-modifying agent acts before metabolic processes are affected. Damage to an ionized target which would otherwise be restored to normal functioning may be made permanent by interaction with the agent, or, conversely, the probability of restoration of the target to its normal condition may be increased (111).

4. INTERACTION OF THE OXYGEN EFFECT WITH POSTIRRADIATION CULTURE
CONDITIONS

Alper and Gillies (16), working with *E. coli* B, reported that the survival observed after X-rays or neutrons depended on the medium used for plating, being least on the medium on which growth of normal or irradiated cells was fastest. The fraction of damage brought to light by the factors which increased the growth rate was very little influenced by oxygen during irradiation (113) (Figs. 9A and 9B). In consequence, the over-all oxygen effect was dependent on culture conditions after irradiation. A variety of postirradiation treatments which led to survival curves of different slope concomitantly changed the oxygen-enhancement ratio (m), which varied from 1.6 to 3.7 with the various treatments used. The greatest value for m was observed when conditions were used which gave the greatest 37% dose (182). There was a linear relationship between m and D_{37}, which supported the postulate (16, 113) that in *E. coli* B there are at least two main targets of radiation damage, A and B. Damage to A is the residue seen when maximum "rescue" of the cells has taken place, and this damage is considerably influenced by oxygen. Damage to B is brought to light in conditions of active growth (21), and is incurred to much the same extent whether or not oxygen is present during irradiation. The modification of damage by culture conditions after exposure to ultraviolet at 2537 A suggest that the target for the action of UV is akin to target B, which may therefore be tentatively assumed to be a part of the nucleic acid complex. It would follow that the cell may easily be rescued from that type of damage, and it seems probable that A is chemically of a different nature.

The restoring effect of incubating irradiated cells of *E. coli* B/r at 19° (170) is also dependent on whether or not oxygen is present during irradiation (45). With this strain, cells are rescued to a much smaller extent when irradiation has been delivered in anoxic conditions. The over-all result of incubating the cells at 19° is therefore to *reduce* the oxygen-enhancement ratio. Incubation at 19° does not restore cells of *E. coli* B/r which have been exposed to ultraviolet, and it would follow that low temperature incubation rescues the cell from damage to a target which is oxygen-sensitive; whereas another target, which is akin to that for ultraviolet damage, is much less oxygen-sensitive.

5. THE TERMS "REVERSAL," "REACTIVATION," "RECOVERY," AND "RESTO-
RATION"

Latarjet and Gray (183) discussed the propriety of using various terms to indicate modification of radiation damage and proposed terminology which would distinguish clearly between *protection* ("a diminution of the observable lesion resulting from a treatment or procedure which is operative before the beginning of irradiation") and *restoration* ("achieved by treating the cell in some way after the beginning of radiation"). They remarked also that "it may well be that restoration is more often achieved by blocking the development of the lesion at some point in the latent period than in the restoration of the precise chemical condition of the cell prior to irradiation."

At the present time, there is a dearth of sufficiently exact knowledge of cell chemistry, as well as of sufficiently exact techniques, to allow conclusions to be drawn on this point. An observed reduction in radiation response may be regarded either as evidence of a positive "repair mechanism" or as evidence that a part of the radiation damage has been prevented from coming to light; this is more than a semantic difference, since it lies at the root of our understanding of radiobiological mechanisms. There is undoubtedly evidence that in some cases a reduction in radiation response may be brought about *without* "restoration of the precise chemistry of the cell." In numerous radiobiological studies, lethal effects, as defined in Section II, are the test of damage. A cell is counted as a survivor if it is successful in giving rise to *one* viable daughter, since this process will lead to formation of a clone. It is known, however, that very abnormal yeast and bacterial cells can give rise to clones (75, 184, 185), and these would automatically be counted as "survivors" in terms of macrocolony formation. Furthermore, there are clear indications with some cells that a treatment which has been correlated with greater survival has at the same time caused other changes which may fairly be regarded as evidence of further damage to the survivors (21). There are good grounds, therefore, for avoiding the use of such words as "reversal," "reactivation," and "recovery" (all of which carry the implication of a positive repair mechanism), except in cases where such a mechanism can be shown to operate.

VI. Possible Mechanism of Lethal and Genetic Effects on Cells

A. The Location and Identification of Sensitive Sites

The application of formal "target theory" to the interpretation of radiobiological data has been discussed in Chapter 1 and briefly in Section III of this chapter. When the inactivation of a virus or of a specific cellular enzyme is under investigation, the "target" is well defined. When lethal and genetic effects on cells are the tests of radiation damage, however, the nature or even the existence of "vital targets" can only be postulated, because of the dearth of knowledge of the conditions which bring about cell division or genetic change. Nonetheless, the target concept is a useful aid in describing qualitatively the steps involved in the development of damage to cells by ionizing radiation. The postulate that the reproductive integrity of the cell depends on certain unique molecules or structures seems the simplest way of accounting for the fact that the passage of a single ionizing particle may destroy this integrity (91, 186) and also for the many dose-effect curves which accord accurately with very simple formulations, such as those of equation 2 (Section II.C.1), or equation 5 (Section V.C.1).

This postulate does not imply any mechanism by which the energy from the ionizing radiation is conveyed to the sensitive site. This will be discussed below. We may attempt, however, to come to some tentative conclusions as to the location and identification of these unique sites or "targets," the disruption of one of which may, by hypothesis, have profound effects on the life of the cell.

There is good evidence, recently reviewed by Gray (187), that when disturbance of reproductive or hereditary integrity of cells is the test of radiation damage, energy absorbed in cell nuclei is much more effective than that absorbed in cytoplasm. Although some exceptions have been noted (188), these have been with cells which are extremely radioresistant, as compared with bacteria, yeast, or the cells of higher plants or animals. It may be assumed, therefore, that, in these, the vital targets for lethal or genetic effects are located within the cell nuclei. Furthermore, it has been noted that genetic and lethal effects are frequently modified by the same agents and conditions, and in the same sense; the simplest hypothesis for the time being is therefore that the targets for these two types of damage are closely related. It seems plausible that genes, the units of hereditary continuity, may be the vital targets in question, because at some stages at any rate each gene is unique within the cell. It is nowadays widely postulated that genes are DNA molecules, or parts of DNA molecules. If this is so, and if the vital targets are genes, it would follow that ionizations in or near the DNA are the ones which determine that the cell shall die. This hypothesis is tempting; indeed, it is not uncommon to find it accepted as proven fact. We cannot doubt that damage to DNA must play at least some part in the killing of cells by radiation; but examination of various lines of evidence raises doubts as to whether radiation-induced cell death occurs through damage to DNA in the majority of a population exposed to radiation, or whether it is true that damage to DNA is the critical factor for the majority of cell types.

If the radiation does affect cells mainly by virtue of its effects on the DNA, the mechanism might be elucidated by studying the effects of radiation on DNA *in vitro*; if this can act as a model for the killing of cells by radiation, we should observe comparable effects, with comparable doses, and agents which modify radiation damage should do so in the same sense in both systems. We find, however, that DNA irradiated *in vitro* fails in at least two important ways to act as a model for the killing of cells. Firstly, most of the changes in the DNA molecule *in vitro*, tested biologically or physicochemically, occur in the proportion of about one observable change for between one to ten ionizations in the DNA (189); whereas the doses required to kill cells are such that with few exceptions several hundred ionizations at least must take place in the cellular DNA for an average of one lethal event per cell. Secondly, the almost universal and very important part played in cell killing by the presence of oxygen during irradiation is not usually observed with DNA irradiated *in vitro*; oxygen can even in certain circumstances act protectively on DNA *in vitro* (Section II.C.1). In very special circumstances a slight enhancing action of oxygen on radiation damage to DNA *in vitro* has been found (190), but this is much smaller than the usual magnitude of its effect on the living cell. It is to be expected that if the main target for the lethal effect of radiation is cellular DNA, then it is here that the oxygen effect should be expressed.

The postulate that DNA alone carries the genetic code of the cell implies a constant structure, since by hypothesis the genetic constitution of the cell is in control at all stages of its life. At some stages each gene must be present in duplicate, so that each daughter receives its full complement of genes, but the DNA molecule, however it may be coiled, stretched, or unwound, is assumed to maintain its integrity in terms of the sequence of bases. Any very large variations in the effectiveness per ionization, through the life of the cell, are therefore not to be expected if the mechanism of killing is mainly damage to the DNA. Yet, as shown by Whiting and her colleagues (148, 149), metaphase eggs of *Habrobracon* are more sensitive than the prophase eggs by the large factor of nearly 22 (Section V.C.2). This implies that for every ionization which is effective in the metaphase egg, 22 are required to kill the prophase egg. If the cells are killed because lethal mutations are inflicted, then at least 21 out of 22 ionizations are ineffective in bringing these about when the egg is irradiated in prophase. It seems very unlikely that any change in the configuration of the chromosomes could account for the marked change in the effectiveness of an ionization; and if physiological conditions can effect "repair" in more than 95 % of "damaged" sites, then clearly ionizations in other structures must acquire some relative importance.

Another example of a cell which varies markedly in radiosensitivity through its cycle is afforded by haploid yeast (Section V.C.3). Comparison of dose-effect curves shows that it requires an average of nearly eight times as many ionizations per lethal event in the budding as in the single cell, if oxygen is present during irradiation. As with the *Habrobracon* eggs, we might again postulate a physiological difference, once the cell has budded, which enable it to repair otherwise fatal lesions in the DNA. However, there are three experimental observations which, taken together, seem to offer a more plausible hypothesis. First, Elkind and Beam (153) found that the two types of cell behaved differently when exposed to X-rays and α-rays; the X-rays were more effective in killing the single cells, while the α-rays were more effective on the dividing cells. Second, the extent to which oxygen enhances the action of X-rays is very different for the two types of cell (154). These facts seem to argue that a type of lesion which is of major importance in killing the single cell does not play much part in killing the budding cell; if it were simply a question of the same type of lesion in both cases, with repair taking place in one state, but not in the other, then we should expect the change in the quality of radiation, and the modifying action of oxygen, to influence the results in the same way. The third observation is that sensitivity to ultraviolet does not differ in the two types of cell to nearly the same extent as does sensitivity to ionizing radiation (191). Ultraviolet at 2537 A can very plausibly be assumed to be specifically effective on the nucleic acid, which absorbs at this wavelength. It may be postulated, therefore, that the killing of the single cells by ionizing radiation is due to a lesion in some component other than the DNA, whereas once the cell has budded this form of damage is no longer of importance, and the effective damage may then very well be mainly to the nucleic acid. This would accord with the large reduction in the effect of oxygen when the cell buds, the change in the relative effectiveness of the two qualities of radiation, and the fact that cells in the two states barely differ in their sensitivity to ultraviolet at 2537 A.

Evidence for the concept that cells of strain *E. coli* B may be killed by the effect of radiation on one of at least two types of target which differ chemically was described in Section V.D.4. The fraction of damage which may well be to the nucleic acid or its components is at the same time the fraction which can be bypassed by various forms of postirradiation treatment. Furthermore, resistant mutant strains of *E. coli* B differ from their parent precisely in not being subject to that fraction of damage (Section V.D.2). It would follow that these resistant strains are normally able to bypass the effects of the majority of ionizations occurring in the DNA, of which the parent and mutant strains contain the same quantity per cell, when these are in the logarithmic phase (192, 192a).

These various examples suggest that either (i) it is a structure other than the "gene" which frequently acts as a target for cell killing, and even for the induction of mutation, or (ii) the gene as functionally defined must include chemical substances other than DNA (or parts thereof).

B. Transfer of Absorbed Energy to Sensitive Sites

The "subcellular units" discussed in Section III permit examination of radiation effects by the "indirect" as well as the "direct" mechanism; in suitable conditions these can be clearly distinguished. Since the discovery of "activated water," i.e., of the active radicals produced by ionizing radiation in the decomposition of water, and the demonstration that these could affect solutes of biological interest (28), the suggestion has been widely canvassed that ionizing radiation could also affect vital targets within cells through the mechanism of "indirect actions." If the $H \cdot$ and $OH \cdot$ radicals which arise from the water decomposition are considered to be important vectors of radiation damage, an additional mechanism must be invoked with radiations of high LET, since the yield of H and OH radicals is much reduced with these; the biological effectiveness for some tests of damage, however, is greater with "heavy" radiations that with those of low LET. It is known that hydrogen peroxide is produced at high LET values, and that the yield becomes less dependent on oxygen concentration as LET increases, in a manner which is paralleled by the increasing independence on oxygen of biological damage, as LET increases. It might appear, therefore, that this species, together with H and OH radicals, might act as "intermediates," as suggested by Zirkle and Tobias (193). Although this mechanism might conceivably apply to types of cells such as *Escherichia coli*, in which the effectiveness of radiation delivered *in aerobic conditions* decreases as LET increases (Chapter 9 of ref. 1), it would not appear plausible as a method of explaining the effect of radiations on the cells for which the "diffusion model" was invoked. These were yeast and algal cells, which were more effectively damaged by radiations of high than of low LET, in fully aerobic conditions. In these conditions, however, the yield of all species of intermediates suggested as vectors of absorbed energy is less with radiations of high than of low LET.

The "indirect effect" postulate for cells also fails to account for the oxygen effect. It is true that the presence of oxygen increases the yield of oxidative changes in aqueous solutions *at low pH values*, but the reactions concerned, which are generally agreed to proceed in part via the reaction $H + O_2 \rightarrow HO_2$, would not be likely to occur in neutral solutions, in which the HO_2 radicals are probably mostly dissociated (194).

There is now a considerable body of chemical, physical, and biological evidence to show that oxygen may affect the changes observed in organic molecules irradiated in the absence of water, i.e., by direct effect. This has been observed in experiments on the inactivation of enzymes, e.g., of trypsin (195) and of lysozyme (196). With the latter, it is particularly striking that an oxygen effect was observed *only* in conditions of direct ionization, but *not* with lysozyme in aqueous suspension and inactivated by indirect effect. Observations on the electron spin resonance spectra of irradiated dry organic material have indicated that the admission of oxygen after irradiation may change the nature of the radicals formed, or eliminate them (111a, 197). Examples of dried spores with which an oxygen effect has been demonstrated were quoted in Section V.A.1.*a*, and it is of particular interest that the enhancement by oxygen of the lethal effect of radiation on spores of *Aspergillus torreus* was about the same, whether they were wet or dry (104). At the present time, therefore the simplest hypothesis would appear to be that the major part of lethal and genetic effects on cells is due to ionizations taking place within the vital molecules or structures themselves.

The dependence of biological effectiveness on the LET of radiations may be examined within the framework of this postulate. If the results of an experiment performed with different qualities of radiation show that the effectiveness per ionization decreases when the ionizations occur closer together, it may be assumed that a single ionization will suffice to disrupt the target, but a second ionization in the same target will be "wasted." If the reverse is true, this may be regarded as evidence that the target can be disrupted only if several ionizations occur simultaneously within its volume. With certain strains of bacteria, the first-mentioned condition has been found to hold, provided the radiation has been delivered in aerobic conditions (20, 198). When *Shigella flexneri* was irradiated with X-rays and fast neutrons, however, the latter were more effective in anaerobic conditions (20). It may be inferred that in these cells singly occurring ionizations have a high probability of disrupting some target, provided oxygen is present. In anaerobic conditions, however, many of these single ionizations will be without permanent effect, and the effective ionizations will be those which occur close together, perhaps because neighboring ionized molecules react irreversibly with each other (111).

Results of LET studies with cells of many different types allow of a rough division into three patterns (199). Plant cells suffer an increase in the effectiveness of radiation, to a factor of about 10, with increasing LET. Biological effectiveness of radiation damage to animal cells increases by a factor of 3 to 4; while with vegetative bacteria effectiveness decreases with increasing LET. In terms of the suggestion made above, it would follow that the main targets of damage are of a different chemical or structural nature in these three sorts of cells: in plant cells, even ionizations which are made more effective by the presence of oxygen have less probability of damaging the cell than the interactions between ionized molecules lying close together. In the bacterial cell, on the other hand, targets for cell death are such that single ionizations have a high probability of being effective. Despite these differences, the metionic reaction with oxygen is evidently similar in nature, whatever the difference in the nature of the targets in different cell types, since, as shown in Section V.A.1, the relationship of oxygen concentration to enhancement of radiation effect is similar in detail for examples of each cell type.

Acknowledgments

I should like to express my appreciation to Mrs. S. Hornsey, Dr. K. A. Stacey, and Dr. M. Sterne for helpful discussions of parts of the text. I am grateful to the following for permission to quote work not yet published: Dr. N. E. Gillies, Dr. B. Miletić, Mrs. S. Hornsey, and Dr. G. Silini.

VII. References

1. Lea, D. E., "Actions of Radiations on Living Cells," 2nd ed. Cambridge Univ. Press, London, 1955.
2. Timoféeff-Ressovsky, N. W., and Zimmer, K. G., "Das Trefferprinzip in der Biologie." Hirzel, Leipzig, 1947.
3. Spiegelman, S., Baron, L. S., and Quastler, H., *Federation Proc.* **10**, 130 (1951).
4. Aldous, J. G., and Steward, K. D., *Rev. can. biol.* **11**, 49 (1952).
5. Brandt, C. L., Freeman, P. J., and Swanson, P. A., *Science* **113**, 383 (1951).
6. Billen, D., Stapleton, G. E., and Hollaender, A., *J. Bacteriol.* **65**, 131 (1953).
7. Friedewald, W. F., and Anderson, R. S., *J. Exptl. Med.* **78**, 285 (1943).
8. Rouyer, M., and Latarjet, R., *Ann. inst. Pasteur* **72**, 89 (1947).
9. Back, A., and Halberstaedter, L., *Am. J. Roentgenol. Radium Therapy* **54**, 290 (1943).
10. Kimball, R. F., *in* "Radiation Biology" (A. Hollaender, ed.), Vol. II, Chapter 8. McGraw-Hill, New York, 1955.
11. Read, J., *Brit. J. Radiol.* **25**, 89, 154 (1952).
12. Gunter, S. E., and Kohn, H. I., *J. Bacteriol.* **71**, 571 (1956).
13. Gray, L. H., *Prog. in Biophys. and Biophys. Chem.* **2**, 240 (1951).
14. Beam, C. A., Mortimer, R. K., Wolfe, R. G., and Tobias, C. A., *Arch. Biochem. Biophys.* **49**, 110 (1954).
15. Witkin, E. M., *Proc. Natl. Acad. Sci., U. S.* **32**, 59 (1946).
16. Alper, T., and Gillies, N. E., *J. Gen. Microbiol.* **18**, 461 (1958).
17. Puck, T. T., and Marcus, P. I., *J. Exptl. Med.* **103**, 653 (1956).
18. Alper, T., *Nature* **162**, 615 (1948).
19. Hollaender, A., Stapleton, G. E., and Martin, F. I., *Nature* **167**, 103 (1951).
20. Howard-Flanders, P., and Alper, T., *Radiation Research* **7**, 518 (1957).
21. Alper, T., and Gillies, N. E., *J. Gen. Microbiol.* **22**, 113 (1960).
21a. Alper, T., Gillies, N. E., and Elkind, M. M., *Nature* **186**, 1062 (1960).
22. von Borstel, R. C., and Rogers, R. W., *Radiation Research* **8**, 248 (1958).
23. Alper, T., *Brit. J. Radiol.* **27**, 50 (1954).
24. Uretz, R. B., *Radiation Research* **2**, 240 (1955).
25. Kimball, R. F., *Ann. N. Y. Acad. Sci.* **59**, 638 (1955).
26. Dulbecco, R., *Proc. Natl. Acad. Sci., U. S.* **38**, 747 (1952).
27. Fildes, Sir Paul, and van Heyningen, W. E., eds., "The Nature of Virus Multiplication." Cambridge Univ. Press, London, 1953.
28. Dale, W. M., *Biochem. J.* **34**, 1367 (1940).

29. Latarjet, R., Rebeyrotte, N., and Demerseman, P., *in* "Organic Peroxides in Radiobiology" (R. Latarjet and M. Haïssinsky, eds.), p. 61. Pergamon, London, 1958.
30. Kimball, R. F., and Gaither, N., *Proc. Soc. Exptl. Biol. Med.* **80**, 525 (1952).
31. Adler, H. I., *Radiation Research* **9**, 451 (1958).
32. Ephrussi-Taylor, H., and Latarjet, R., *Biochim. et Biophys. Acta* **16**, 183 (1955).
33. Pollard, E., *Advances in Virus Research* **2**, 109 (1954).
34. Fraenkel-Conrat, H., Singer, B. A., and Williams, R. C., *in* "The Chemical Basis of Heredity" (W. D. McElroy and B. Glass, eds.), p. 501. Johns Hopkins Press, Baltimore, 1957.
35. Ginoza, W., and Norman, A., *Nature* **179**, 520 (1957).
36. Marmur, J., and Fluke, D. J., *Arch. Biochem. Biophys.* **57**, 506 (1955).
37. Guild, W. R., and DeFilippes, F. M., *Biochim. et Biophys. Acta* **26**, 241 (1957).
38. DeFilippes, F. M., and Guild, W. R., *Radiation Research* **11**, 38 (1959).
39. Watson, J. D., *J. Bacteriol.* **60**, 697 (1950).
40. Puck, T. T., *Cold Spring Harbor Symposia Quant. Biol.* **18**, 149 (1953).
41. Hershey, A. D., and Chase, M., *J. Gen. Physiol.* **36**, 39 (1952).
42. Latarjet, R., and Frédéricq, P., *Virology* **1**, 100 (1955).
43. Pollard, E., and Setlow, J., *Radiation Research* **4**, 87 (1956).
44. Hewitt, H. B., and Read, J., *Brit. J. Radiol.* **23**, 416 (1950).
45. Alper, T., unpublished work.
46. Marcovich, H., *Radiation Research* **9**, 149 (1958).
47. Bachofer, C. S., Ehret, C. F., Mayer, S., and Powers, E. L., *Proc. Natl. Acad. Sci. U. S.* **39**, 744 (1953).
48. Bachofer, C. S., *Science* **117**, 280 (1953).
49. Doermann, A., unpublished work (see ref. 39).
50. Epstein, H. D., and Schardl, D., *Nature* **179**, 100 (1957).
51. Stent, G. S., and Fuerst, C. R., *J. Gen. Physiol.* **38**, 441 (1955).
52. Alexander, P., and Stacey, K. A., *in* "Progress in Radiobiology" (J. S. Mitchell, B. E. Holmes, and C. L. Smith, eds.), p. 105. Oliver & Boyd, Edinburgh, 1956.
53. Peacocke, A. R., *in* "Progress in Radiobiology (J. S. Mitchell, B. E. Holmes, and C. L. Smith, eds.), p. 109. Oliver & Boyd, Edinburgh, 1956.
54. Peacocke, A. R., and Preston, B. N., *J. Polymer Sci.* **31**, 1 (1958).
55. Butler, J. A. V., Pain, R. H., Robins, A. B., and Rotblat, J., *Proc. Roy. Soc.* **B149**, 12 (1958).
56. Alexander, P., and Stacey, K. A., *Radiation Research* **9**, 85 (1958).
57. Alexander, P., Lett, J. T., Moroson, H., and Stacey, K. A., *Intern. J. Radiation Biol., Suppl.* **1**, 47 (1960).
57a. Alexander, P., and Lett, J. T., *Nature* **187**, 933 (1960).
58. Ebert, M., and Alper, T., *Nature,* **173**, 987 (1954).
59. Alper, T., and Ebert, M., *Science* **120**, 608 (1954).
60. Alper, T., *J. Gen. Microbiol.* **11**, 313 (1954).
61. Bachofer, C. S., and Pottinger, M. A., *Science* **119**, 378 (1954).
62. Miletić, B., and Alper, T., unpublished work.
63. Feingold, M. L., and Plough, H. H., *Radiation Research* **9**, 113 (1958).
64. Bachofer, C. S., and Pottinger, M. A., *J. Gen. Physiol.* **40**, 289 (1956).
65. Latarjet, R., *in* "Ionizing Radiations and Cell Metabolism" (G. E. W. Wolstenholme and C. M. O'Connor, eds.), p. 275. Churchill, London, 1956.
66. Alper, T., *Radiation Research* **2**, 119 (1955).
67. Maxwell, D., *Compt. rend.* **243**, 717 (1956).

68. Watson, J. D., *J. Bacteriol.* **63**, 473 (1952).
69. Forssberg, A., *Acta Radiol. Suppl.* **49**, (1943).
69a. Forssberg, A., and Novak, R., *Radiation Research* **9**, 115 (1958).
70. Lea, D. E., Haines, R. B., and Coulson, C. A., *Proc. Roy. Soc.* **B123**, 1 (1937).
71. Rubin, B. A., *J. Bacteriol.* **67**, 361 (1954).
72. Spoerl, E., Loveless, L. E., Weisman, T. H., and Balske, R. J., *J. Bacteriol.* **67**, 394 (1954).
73. Henshaw, P. S., and Turkowitz, H., *Am. J. Roentgenol. Radium Therapy* **43**, 93 (1940).
74. Henshaw, P. S., *Am. J. Roentgenol. Radium Therapy* **43**, 899 (1940).
75. Alper, T., *in* "Advances in Radiobiology" (G. C. de Hevesy, A. G. Forssberg, and J. D. Abbatt, eds.), p. 90. Oliver & Boyd, Edinburgh, 1957.
76. Laser, H., and Thornley, M. J., *J. Gen. Microbiol.* **17**, viii (1957).
77. Burns, V. W., *Radiation Research* **4**, 394 (1956).
78. Kimball, R. F., *Ann. Rev. Microbiol.* **11**, 199 (1957).
79. Evans, H. J., Neary, G. J., and Tonkinson, S. M., *Nature* **181**, 1083 (1958).
80. Powers, E. L., *Ann. N. Y. Acad. Sci.* **59**, 619 (1955).
81. Daniels, E. W., *J. Exptl. Zool.* **127**, 427 (1954).
82. Daniels, E. W., *J. Exptl. Zool.* **130**, 183 (1955).
83. Ducoff, H. S., *Radiation Research* **1**, 492 (1954).
84. Latarjet, R., *J. Gen. Physiol.* **31**, 529 (1948).
85. Tobin, J. O'H, *Brit. J. Exptl. Pathol.* **34**, 635 (1953).
86. Pollard, E., Adams, W. R., and Robbins, S., *Radiation Research* **1**, 514 (1954).
87. Davis, M., and Pollard, E., *Radiation Research* **2**, 47 (1955).
88. Fluke, D. J., and Brustad, T., *Radiation Research* **9**, 115 (1958).
89. Lwoff, A., Siminovitch, L., and Kjelgaard, N., *Ann. inst. Pasteur* **79**, 815 (1950).
90. Latarjet, R., *Ann. inst. Pasteur* **81**, 1 (1951).
91. Marcovich, H., *Ann. inst. Pasteur* **90**, 458 (1956).
92. Marcovich, H., personal communication.
93. Zelle, M. R., and Hollaender, A., *in* "Radiation Biology" (A. Hollaender, ed.), Vol. II, Chapter 10. McGraw-Hill, New York, 1955.
94. Crabtree, H. G., and Cramer, W., 11th Scientific Report, Imperial Cancer Research Fund, pp. 89, 103 (1934).
95. Mottram, J. C., *Brit. J. Radiol.* **8**, 32 (1935).
96. Anderson, R. S., and Turkowitz, H., *Am. J. Roentgenol. Radium Therapy* **46**, 537 (1941).
97. Giles, N. H., and Beatty, A. V., *Science* **112**, 643 (1950).
98. Patt, H. M., *Physiol. Revs.* **33**, 35 (1953).
99. Gray, L. H., Conger, A. D., Ebert, M., Hornsey, S., and Scott, O. C. A., *Brit. J. Radiol.* **26**, 638 (1953).
100. Alper, T., and Howard-Flanders, P., *Nature* **178**, 978 (1956).
101. Deschner, E., and Gray, L. H., *Radiation Research*, **11**, 115 (1959).
102. Kihlman, B. A., *Exptl. Cell Research* **14**, 639 (1958).
103. Kihlman, B. A., *Nature* **182**, 730 (1958).
104. Stapleton, G. E., and Hollaender, A., *J. Cellular Comp. Physiol.* **39**, *Suppl.* **1**, 101 (1952).
105. Tallentire, A., *Nature* **182**, 1024 (1958).
106. Powers, E. L., Webb, R. B., and Kaleta, B. F., *Proc. Natl. Acad. Sci. U.S.* **46**, 984 (1960).
107. Anderson, E. H., *Proc. Natl. Acad. Sci. U. S.*, **37**, 340 (1951).

108. Kimball, R. F., and Gaither, N., *Proc. Soc. Exptl. Biol. Med.* **82,** 471 (1953).
109. Whiting, A. R., *Genetics* **39,** 851 (1954).
110. Howard-Flanders, P., and Moore, D., *Radiation Research* **9,** 422 (1958).
110a. Caldecott, R. S., Johnson, E. B., North, D. T., and Konzak, C. F., *Proc. Natl. Acad. Sci. U.S.* **43,** 975 (1957).
111. Alper, T., *Radiation Research* **5,** 573 (1956).
111a. Gordy, W., Ard, W. B., and Shields, H., *Proc. Natl. Acad. Sci. U.S.* **41,** 983 (1955).
112. Read, J., *Brit. J. Radiol.* **25,** 651 (1952).
113. Alper, T., and Gillies, N. E., *Nature* **181,** 961 (1958).
113a. Hornsey, S., Howard-Flanders, P., and Moore, D., *Intern. J. Radiation Biol.* **2,** 37 (1960).
113b. Hornsey, S., and Silini, G., *Intern. J. Radiation Biol.*, in press (1961).
114. Howard-Flanders, P., *Nature* **180,** 1191 (1957).
115. Gray, L. H., Green, F. O., and Hawes, C. A., *Nature* **182,** 952 (1958).
115a. Sparrman, B., Ehrenberg, L., and Ehrenberg, A., *Acta Chem. Scand.* **13,** 199 (1959).
116. Hollaender, A., *in* "Symposium on Radiobiology" (J. J. Nickson, ed.), p. 285. Wiley, New York, 1952.
117. Ebert, M., Hornsey, S., and Howard, A., *Nature* **181,** 613 (1958).
118. Goucher, O. R., Kamei, I., and Kocholaty, W., *Arch. Biochem. Biophys.* **65,** 522 (1956).
119. Gray, L. H., *in* "Progress in Radiobiology" (J. S. Mitchell, B. E. Holmes, and C. L. Smith, eds.), p. 267. Oliver & Boyd, Edinburgh, 1956.
120. Patt, H. M., *in* "Radiobiology Symposium 1954" (Z. M. Bacq and P. Alexander, eds.), p. 105. Academic Press, New York, 1955.
121. Marcovich, H., *Ann. inst. Pasteur* **93,** 456 (1957).
122. Hollaender, A., and Stapleton, G. E., *in* Proc. *1st. Intern. Conf. Peaceful Uses Atomic Energy, Geneva, 1955* **11,** 311 (1956).
123. Stapleton, G. E., and Edington, C. W., *Radiation Research* **5,** 39 (1956).
124. Marcovich, H., *in* "Organic Peroxides in Radiobiology" (R. Latarjet and M. Haïssinsky, eds.), p. 117. Pergamon, London, 1958.
124a. Dewey, D. L., *Nature* **187,** 1008 (1960).
125. Wood, T. H., *Arch. Biochem. Biophys.* **52,** 157 (1954).
126. Houtermans, T., *Z. Naturforsch.* **11b,** 636 (1956).
127. Webb, R., Ehret, C. F., and Powers, E. L., *Radiation Research* **12,** 171 (1960).
128. Houtermans, T., *Z. Naturforsch.* **9b,** 600 (1954).
129. Wood, T. H., and Taylor, A. L., *Radiation Research* **6,** 611 (1957).
130. Wood, T. H., and Taylor, A. L., *Radiation Research* **7,** 99 (1957).
131. Webb, R., Ehret, C. F., and Powers, E. L., *Experientia* **14,** 324 (1958).
132. Fabergé, A. C., *Radiation Research* **1,** 130 (1954).
133. Rugh, R., and Clugsten, H., *Proc. Soc. Exptl. Biol. Med.* **88,** 467 (1955).
134. Iwasaki, T., *Radiation Research* **9,** 133 (1958).
135. Bellamy, W. D., and Lawton, E. J., *Ann. N. Y. Acad. Sci.* **59,** 595 (1955).
136. Moos, W. S., *J. Bacteriol.* **63,** 688 (1952).
137. Puck, T. T., Marcus, P. I., and Cieciura, S. J., *J. Exptl. Med.* **103,** 273 (1956).
138. Marcus, P. I., Cieciura, S. J., and Puck, T. T., *J. Exptl. Med.* **104,** 615 (1956).
139. Puck, T. T., Morkovin, D., Marcus, P. I., and Cieciura, S. J., *J. Exptl. Med.* **106,** 485 (1957).

139a. Morkovin, D., and Feldman, A., *Brit. J. Radiol.* **32,** 282 (1959).

140. Warburg, O., Gawehn, K., and Geissler, A. W., *Z. Naturforsch.* **13b,** 61 (1958).

141. Hewitt, H. B., and Wilson, C. W., *Nature* **183,** 1060 (1959).

142. Conger, A. D., *Radiology* **66,** 63 (1956).

143. Révész, L., *in* "Advances in Radiobiology" (G. C. de Hevesy, A. G. Forssberg, and J. D. Abbatt, eds.), p. 80. Oliver & Boyd, Edinburgh, 1957.

144. Hewitt, H. B., and Wilson, C. W., *Brit. J. Cancer* **13,** 675 (1959).

145. Kaufmann, B. P., *in* "Radiation Biology" (A. Hollaender, ed.), Vol. I, Part 2, Chapter 9. McGraw-Hill, New York, 1954.

146. Read, J., *Brit. J. Radiol.* **31,** 60 (1958).

147. Revell, S. H., *Proc. Roy. Soc.* **B150,** 564 (1959).

147a. Revell, S. H., *Heredity Suppl.* **6,** 107 (1953).

148. Whiting, A. R., *Am. Naturalist* **79,** 193 (1945).

149. Kenworthy, W., *Am. Naturalist* **90,** 119 (1956).

150. Mortimer, R. K., *Radiation Research* **9,** 312 (1958).

151. Lucke, W. H., and Sarachek, A., *Nature* **171,** 1014 (1953).

152. Magni, G. E., *Radiation Research Suppl.* **1,** 347 (1959).

153. Elkind, M. M., and Beam, C. A., *Radiation Research* **3,** 88 (1955).

154. Alper, T., *Intern. J. Radiation Biol.* **1,** 414 (1959).

155. Birge, A. C., and Tobias, C. A., *Arch. Biochem. Biophys.* **52,** 388 (1954).

156. Beam, C. A., *Proc. Natl. Acad. Sci. U. S.* **41,** 857 (1955).

157. Alper, T., *Brit. J. Radiol.* **31,** 714 (1958).

158. Laser, H., *Ciba Foundation Symposium, Ionizing Radiations and Cell Metabolism* 106 (1956). Churchill, London, 1956.

159. Stapleton, G. E., *Ann. N. Y. Acad. Sci.* **59,** 604 (1955).

160. Houtermans, T., *Strahlentherapie* **93,** 130 (1954).

161. Meynell, G. G., *J. Gen. Microbiol.* **19,** 380 (1958).

162. Stuy, J. H., *Biochim. et Biophys. Acta* **22,** 241 (1956).

163. Donnellan, J. E., and Morowitz, H. J., *Radiation Research* **7,** 71 (1957).

164. Powers, E. L., Webb, R. B., and Ehret, C. F., *in Progr. in Nuclear Energy,* series VI **2,** 189 (1959).

165. Barner, H. D., and Cohen, S. S., *J. Bacteriol.* **71,** 149 (1956).

166. Moustacchi, E., *Ann. inst. Pasteur* **94,** 89 (1958).

167. Cook, E. V., *Radiology* **32,** 289 (1939).

168. Latarjet, R., *Compt. rend.* **217,** 186 (1943).

169. Schrek, R., *J. Cellular Comp. Physiol.* **28,** 277 (1946).

170. Stapleton, G. E., Billen, D., and Hollaender, A., *J. Cellular Comp. Physiol.* **41,** 345 (1953).

171. Anderson, E. H., and Billen, D., *J. Bacteriol.* **70,** 35 (1955).

172. Stapleton, G. E., Sbarra, A. J., and Hollaender, A., *J. Bacteriol.* **70,** 7 (1955).

173. Wainwright, S. D., and Nevill, A., *J. Bacteriol.* **70,** 547 (1955).

174. Kimball, R. F., Gaither, N., and Wilson, S. M., *Genetics* **42,** 661 (1957).

175. Kimball, R. F., *Radiation Research* **9,** 138 (1958).

176. Pahl, G. and Bachofer, C. S., *Biol. Bull.* **112,** 383 (1957).

177. Gillies, N. E., and Alper, T., *Nature* **181,** 961 (1959).

178. Pahl, G., *Radiation Research* **9,** 164 (1958).

179. Gillies, N. E., *Intern. J. Radiation Biol.*, in press (1961).

180. Davydoff, S., *Compt. rend.* **243,** 1683 (1956).

181. Roberts, R. B., and Aldous, E., *J. Bacteriol.* **57,** 363 (1949).

182. Alper, T., *Intern. J. Radiation Biol.*, in press (1961).

183. Latarjet, R., and Gray, L. H., *Acta Radiol.* **41,** 61 (1954).
184. Engelhard, H., and Houtermans, T., *Z. Naturforsch.* **5b,** 264 (1950).
185. Latarjet, R., *in* "Symposium on Radiobiology" (J. J. Nickson, ed.), p. 241. Wiley, New York, 1952.
186. Gray, L. H., *Brit. J. Radiol.* **26,** 609 (1953).
187. Gray, L. H., *Ciba Foundation Symposium, Ionizing Radiations and Cell Metabolism* 255 (1956).
188. Ord, M. G., and Danielli, J. F., *Quart. J. Microscop. Sci.* **97,** 29 (1956).
189. Guild, W. R., *Radiation Research* **11,** 38 (1959).
190. Howard-Flanders, P., *Nature* **186,** 485 (1960).
191. Sarachek, A., *Exptl. Cell Research* **6,** 45 (1954).
192. Harold, F. M., and Ziporin, Z. Z., *Biochim. et Biophys. Acta* **28,** 482 (1958).
192a. Gillies, N. E., and Alper, T., *Biochim. et Biophys. Acta* **43,** 182 (1960).
193. Zirkle, R. E., and Tobias, C. A., *Arch. Biochem. Biophys.* **47,** 282 (1953).
194. Dainton, F. S., *in* "Progress in Radiobiology" (J. S. Mitchell, B. E. Holmes, and C. L. Smith, eds.), p. xix. Oliver & Boyd, Edinburgh, 1956.
195. Alexander, P., *Radiation Research* **6,** 653 (1957).
196. Shalek, R. J., and Gillespie, T. L., *Radiation Research* **9,** 180 (1958).
197. Zimmer, K. G., Ehrenberg, L., and Ehrenberg, A., *Strahlentherapie* **103,** 3 (1957).
198. Lea, D. E., Haines, R. B., and Bretscher, E., *J. Hyg.* **41,** 1 (1941).
199. Alper, T., *Ann. Rev. Nuclear Sci.* **10,** 489 (1960).

CHAPTER 6

Radiation Genetics

SHELDON WOLFF

Biology Division, Oak Ridge National Laboratory, Oak Ridge, Tennessee

CONTENTS

I. Introduction

In 1927 H. J. Muller (1) first demonstrated that the administration of X-rays to the sperm of the fruit fly *Drosophila melanogaster* can induce "gene mutations." Shortly thereafter (1928) Stadler (2) independently reported similar effects in barley. In the intervening years radiation studies

419

have grown to become one of the most important aspects of modern genetics. By its very nature, radiation genetics has come to include not only the simple production of mutants but also studies on the fundamentals of genetic mechanisms.

Comprehensive reviews of the field have been written by Muller (3) and Catcheside (4). This chapter, however, will not try to cover the whole field as comprehensively as a review but instead will concentrate on establishing a background of the basic principles, facts, and theories in radiation genetics. Many important aspects of the field such as the radiation genetics of microorganisms, mammals, human populations, and considerations of plant breeding and human hazards, although properly a part of radiation genetics, are covered in detail in other chapters of this book and will not be included here.

II. Types of Genetic Effects

The genetic effects of radiation may be broadly classified into the intragenic effects or true gene mutations and the intergenic effects or chromosomal aberrations. Since (Chapters 1 and 2) the ionizations produced by radiation have sufficient energy to break chemical bonds, it is obvious that the molecular structure of the gene can be rearranged following exposure to radiation. This would result in true gene mutations. It is also possible for the energetic radiation to break the chromosome threads. These breaks and their fates determine the production of intergenic effects.

A. Intragenic Effects

In the following discussion of gene mutations, it will be assumed that the phenomena discussed are all intragenic alterations. However, since many of the phenotypic effects of a true gene mutation are identical to effects produced by intergenic change, this assumption is an oversimplification that will be considered after the discussion of intergenic changes.

1. Methods of Observing

Before a mutation can be studied, it must become manifest. In haploid organisms, all mutations readily appear because there are usually no dominant alleles present to mask the expression of the mutant. To work with mutations in bacteria therefore, all that is necessary is to irradiate the bacteria and then plate them out onto appropriate selective media. Thus if a strain of bacteria (auxotroph) cannot grow on minimal media because of a gene controlled block in the formation of a required metabolite within the organism, it will be able to grow on minimal media after the gene has mutated to a state whereby the metabolite is formed. Similarly, if one began with a strain (prototroph) that would grow on minimal media, after irradiation some bacteria would not be able to grow because of mutations causing the loss of biosynthetic capacity. The various mutants are detected by the addition of different substances to the medium; i.e., if a cell could not grow on a minimal medium because it lacked the ability to synthesize adenine, after the addition of adenine to the medium the cell would grow (5).

Similarly, methods have been developed to detect mutations in various fungi (6), phage (7), and protozoa (8).

In diploid organisms, however, the problem becomes more complicated, since any given mutant gene may have its normal allele present in the homologous chromosome. If the induced mutation is dominant, it will be observed rapidly. However, most mutations, both spontaneous and induced, are recessive. Therefore detection depends upon their becoming homozygous. In most cases this requires the growing of at least two generations of the organism. In plants, which are self-fertile, the techniques are not too laborious and induced recessive mutants may be detected with a fairly high frequency (Chapter 7). In animals, which cannot be self-fertilized, however, the problem is technically more difficult. Yet in the fruit fly *Drosophila*, the development of special genetic stocks to allow the detection of mutants has been so successful that it is from *Drosophila* that much of our information on radiation-induced mutations has come.

If the males of *Drosophila* are irradiated and then mated to nonirradiated females, the progeny will inherit one-half of their chromosomes from the irradiated father. A certain proportion of the zygotes will contain a paternally inherited dominant lethal change and will not hatch (9–11). There is good evidence that many of the dominant lethals are intergenic changes (chromosome breaks and rearrangements), and so further discussion of them will be deferred until later.

If a dominant visible mutation has been induced in the sperm, it will be detected immediately in the F_1. But this class forms a very small proportion of the mutations observed. Ordinarily in *Drosophila*, the female has two X chromosomes each derived from one of the parents, whereas the male has one X and one Y. The X is inherited from the female parent and the Y from the male. There are, however, attached X stocks of flies in which the two X chromosomes in the female are connected to one another. This then means that the two X chromosomes from the mother are passed down as a unit to her daughters. It also means that the X chromosome from the father is passed to his sons rather than his daughters as is the usual case (Fig. 1). Thus when males are mated to attached X females, the recessive mutations induced in the X chromosome of the male become hemizygous in his sons. If these are visible mutations, they will be observed by checking the F_1 males in culture. Since only a small proportion of the gametes in the

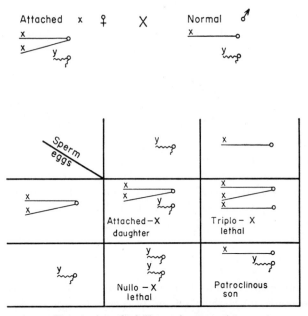

Fig. 1. Attached X test for mutations

irradiated male will contain a mutation on the X chromosome, only a very low percentage of the sons from a given male will be mutants. Because it is easy to overlook a single mutant fly among many normal ones and also because the mutants often have low viability, the attached X method usually gives a lower estimation of the mutation rate than other methods to be described.

Muller devised a more sensitive method called the ClB technique. The females of this stock have one normal X chromosome and one X chromosome (ClB) with a large inversion (C) that will reduce recombination, a recessive lethal gene (l) that will kill flies homozygous or hemizygous for it, and the dominant marker Bar eye (B). After irradiated males are crossed to ClB females, the sons in the F_1 generation must all have a normal X chromosome from the mother, since the ClB chromosome is inviable when hemizygous. One-half the daughters will have an irradiated X chromosome from the father and a ClB chromosome from the mother. These Bar-eyed females are then mated individually to any normal male, and the males from this cross are checked. The only surviving sons are those that receive the irradiated X chromosome derived from their grandfather. If a visible mutation has been induced in this X chromosome, all the males in a given culture will carry the same mutation and will be easily observed (Fig. 2). Ordinarily one expects two females for every male from the last cross in the ClB technique, because one-half of the males will receive the ClB chromosome from their mother and die. Of course, if a recessive lethal has been induced in the other X chromosome, no males will be produced by this cross, and if a semilethal is induced the frequency of males will become less than the expected one-third.

Another method that is used extensively to detect visible mutations is the specific locus method. In this test irradiated organisms that are homozygous for several dominant genes at selected loci are mated to organisms that are homozygous recessives at these same loci. The offspring are then checked for the appearance of the recessive characteristics controlled by these loci. If the recessive characteristic appears, it indicates that the irradiated gene has mutated (or been lost).

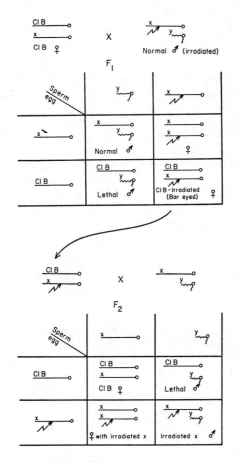

FIG. 2. ClB test for mutations

2. LETHALS

If we remember that during the course of evolution natural selection fixed those gene mutations that gave the organism an adaptive advantage, it becomes obvious that all living organisms are rather well adapted for their particular niche in life. Any mutation induced in the genes, therefore, will have a high probability of upsetting the finely determined balance established by years of evolution and thus of being detrimental. Studies on mutations that arose spontaneously in *Drosophila* (12) have shown that indeed this is the case.

In *Drosophila* a lethal mutation has been defined as one in which the given type of individual never reaches maturity, a semilethal is one in which 0 to 10 % of the flies expressing the character will survive, and a detrimental is a mutant that gives more than 10 % but less than 100 % survival. The radiation-induced mutations seem to show a similar pattern to the spontaneous ones (13), with lethal mutations (those that result in the death of the individual before maturity) outnumbering visible mutations (those that although viable result in some observable abnormality) by about 7 to 1. Detrimentals (14) occur at a rate three to five times as high as do lethals and semilethals.

3. DOSE-ACTION CURVES AND EXPLANATIONS

In Fig. 3 may be seen a dose action curve resulting from plots of the numbers of visible mutations in *Drosophila* against the dose of radiation. Within the dose range utilized the mutations produced increase linearly with the dose. The same phenomenon has been observed in barley (15), snapdragons (16), liverworts (17), and fungi (18). This simply means that

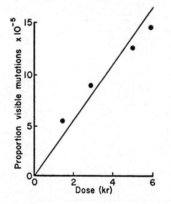

FIG. 3. Linear relation of visible mutations to dose (data of Timoféef-Ressovsky and Delbrück (14a).

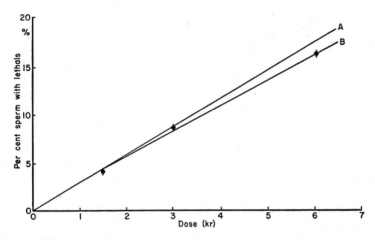

FIG. 4. Percentage of sperm with sex-linked recessive lethals versus dose of X rays (data of Timoféef-Ressovsky, 18a). Curve A, linear curve; curve B, plot of equation $1 - e^{-kd}$.

mutations will be induced with a certain probability that is directly proportional to dose. It also means that there is no interaction of the various ionizations or clusters of ionizations in inducing mutations but that each mutant is produced by an individual ionizing particle or "hit." If an interaction of hits were necessary for the formation of a mutant, then the yield would increase at a rate greater than the first power of the dose. For example, if two hits were necessary then the probability of getting both hits would be the product of the probabilities of getting each alone, $p \times p$ or (p^2), which of course would increase as the square of the dose.

The percentage of sperm containing sex-linked recessive lethals is presented in Fig. 4. This class of mutations too increases linearly with the dose, and the linearity has been found to extend down to doses as low as 25 r (19). However, it has been noted (20) that the method of detecting sex-linked recessive lethals does not distinguish between sperm carrying one lethal and those that carry more than one. Lea (20) has postulated that the curve for these mutations should form a plateau at the higher doses, since a yield of more than 100 % cannot be attained. Indeed the chi-square test shows that the data fit better the equation: Yield $= 1 - e^{-kD}$, where D is the dose and k is the initial slope of the curve of yield against dose. The proportions of cells having zero, one, two, three, etc., lethals will be distributed according to the formula for the Poisson distribution: $e^{-m} \cdot m^r/r!$ where m is equal to the mean number of lethals (or hits) at a given dose and r is the number of lethals in a cell. In Table I it may be seen that the proportion of cells not having a lethal is e^{-m}, and it follows that the propor-

TABLE I

PROPORTION OF CELLS WITH 0, 1, 2, 3, ETC., LETHALS (HITS) IF LETHALS
ARE DISTRIBUTED AS THE POISSON FORMULA $e^{-m} \cdot m^r / r!$

Number (r) of lethals (hits) in a cell	0	1	2	3	4
Proportion of cells with r lethals (from $e^{-m} \cdot m^r / r!$)	e^{-m}	$e^{-m} \cdot m$	$e^{-m} \cdot m^2/2$	$e^{-m} \cdot m^3/6$	$e^{-m} \cdot m^4/24$

tion of cells having one or more lethals is one minus the proportion having
no lethals $(1 - e^{-m})$. This, according to Lea, is the quantity being measured
by the recessive lethal experiment.

4. PHYSICAL BASES OF MUTATION PROCESS

Further evidence that mutations are the result of single ionizations or
of the clusters of ionizations from a single particle comes from dose intensity
and dose fractionation experiments. If interaction between independent
(groups of) ionizations were necessary, then it would be expected that
when the radiation was given at low intensities, a decay or repair of the
effects of some of the earlier ionizations could occur before the total number
of ionizations was completed. Thus there would be a decrease in the number
of mutations formed for a given dose when the intensity of the radiation
decreased. The same reasoning applies to the fractionation effect. In this
type of experiment, however, the dose is administered at a constant intensity but is divided into at least two parts with rest periods in between.
During the rest periods the effects of the ionizations again would decay or
be repaired so that a decrease in mutation rate would occur.

The experimental results for sex-linked recessive lethals in *Drosophila*
sperm show *no* such decrease at low intensities or after fractionation. If the
experimental results of several workers (19, 21–25) are pooled, it is found
that if the intensity of the dose is varied over the range of 0.001 r/min to
2700 r/min (almost a three million-fold variation in intensity) there is no
significant change in mutation yield. Similarly Timoféeff-Ressovsky and
Zimmer (25) found the same frequency of sex-linked lethals when the dose
was fractionated with intervals of weeks as with a continuous dose.

It has been shown by Russell *et al.* (25a) that for the mouse a similar
lack of intensity effect is obtained for visible mutations induced in sperm.
For mutations induced in spermatagonial stages, however, fewer are recovered following low-intensity irradiation than high. Russell believes that,
although the initial induction of mutations may be independent of intensity,
there may be a proportion of mutations that are repaired in the metabolically active spermatagonia. This repair then decreases the observable
mutations if the radiation is administered at low intensities.

Another argument for the "one-hit" nature of induced mutations comes from the work in which the wavelength or ion density of the radiation was varied (25–33). Wavelengths from those of γ-rays and β-rays on up to 2 A (10 kv) have shown no difference in yield of mutations per unit dose. It is true that occasionally at the longest wavelength there is a decrease in yield; however, this is probably caused by the lack of penetrance of the softer X-rays and the concurrent decrease in dose. Since the ion density is greater at the longer wavelengths, the yields should have been higher here than at shorter wavelengths if the mutations were induced by the interactions of ionizations. This, however, would only be true up to a point of greatest efficiency. After this particular ion density was reached, any increase would waste ionizations in the sense that more would be present within a certain volume than is necessary to induce mutation. From this point on, higher ion densities would be less efficient.

This argument would only hold for those mutations that increase linearly with dose, i.e., are one hit. The class of mutations known as recessive lethals, however, is not homogeneous. In fact it consists of at least three different types of effects: (1) the true point mutations that increase linearly with dose, (2) small deletions (a form of intergenic alteration) that increase linearly with dose at low doses but have a large two-hit component at high doses, and (3) other types of two-hit intergenic changes (3). The latter two classes depend upon chromosome breakage, a phenomenon that occurs with greater efficiency as the ion density of the radiation increases (see section on neutrons). Consequently, it might be expected that the lack of wavelength effect for true point mutations would be masked by those recessive lethals that are intergenic effects.

The work of Edington and Randolph (34, 35) on the relative biological effectiveness of different radiations on the production of sex-linked recessive lethals in *Drosophila* has indicated that the more densely ionizing radiations are more efficient in producing mutations. As the energy average LET (linear energy transfer) value increased, the number of mutations increased from γ-rays, to X-rays, to fast neutrons. The increase in effectiveness, however, was much greater for dominant lethals that were considered to be mainly intergenic changes than it was for recessive lethals that have a large component consisting of point mutations. This is taken as an indication that the point mutations do not exhibit a wavelength effect. This indication in addition to the above-cited lack of a wavelength effect in the X-ray region supports the idea derived from the linear dose-effect curve and the time intensity or fractionation experiments that a single ionization or cluster of ionizations in the tail of a single electron path can cause a mutation.

That such mutations are the result of a physical (i.e., not a chemical) process such as ionization within or near the gene itself is supported by the independence of induced mutations of the temperature at the time of irradiation (36, 37).

B. Intergenic Effects

According to the theory most generally accepted (38), radiation breaks chromosomes, and these breaks can then either remain open or rejoin in one of several ways. The types of changes induced can be grouped broadly into those that are the result of one break or one hit and those that require two breaks. This does not preclude the formation of aberrations that are the result of more than two breaks, but since this class is such a small proportion of the total number of intergenic changes produced it may be ignored in any discussion dealing with the principles and quantitative relations of aberration formation.

1. ONE-BREAK EFFECTS

a. Terminal Deletions. The easiest type of change to visualize is the simple terminal deletion. If a chromosome is broken into a piece containing a centromere and an acentric fragment and the break does not restitute (rejoin in the original configuration), a terminal deletion is obtained. The fragment not having a centromere is unable to move towards the poles during mitosis, and the genes in the fragment are consequently not included in the daughter nucleus (Fig. 5). The genetic effects of such gene loss will be dependent upon the number and importance of the genes that are lost. If the piece is small perhaps a visible mutation will result, if it is larger the effect may be a recessive lethal, whereas even larger deficiencies will be dominant lethals. In maize gametophyte and endosperm it has been shown (40) that after a terminal break has been induced in a chromosome the ends of the sister strands can rejoin with one another to form an iso-chromatid that will give a bridge in the succeeding anaphase. Such bridges break and the sister ends again fuse giving rise to a bridge-breakage-fusion cycle (Fig. 6). The position of the break determines the genic constitution

Interphase   Metaphase   Anaphase

Fig. 5. Schematic representation of terminal deletions

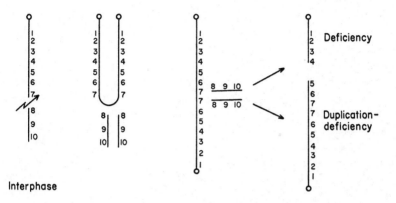

Interphase

FIG. 6. Schematic representation of bridge-breakage-fusion cycle

of the daughter cells. Some cells will have certain genes in duplicate whereas others will be deficient. In the endosperm of maize, which is triploid, the resulting deficiencies are viable because they are covered by the genes in the normal homologous chromosomes. In *Drosophila* it has been found that the bridge itself may be lethal, since the addition of a normal chromosome to cover the deficiency does not increase viability (9). The mechanism of such death is as yet undetermined. It has also been shown (38) that in *Tradescantia* microspores there is no union of sister chromatids if the breakage of the chromosome occurs before the chromosome has split. Thoday (41) has found in root tip cells of *Vicia faba* (the broad bean) that sister union occurs only in breaks induced after the cell has completed its phase of nucleic acid synthesis. In these systems therefore one would not expect the bridge-breakage-fusion cycle to operate.

2. TWO-BREAK EFFECTS

The two-break effects can be classified into interstitial deletions, duplications, inversions, and translocations.

a. Interstitial Deletions. The interstitial deletions are formed when the chromosome is broken in two different places and then rejoins with the interstititial piece missing. Such chromosomes are deficient for the genes within the piece. All that has been said in regard to terminal deletions applies to the interstitial deficiencies too, the one exception being that no bridge-breakage-fusion cycles result after the induction of an interstitial deletion. Although these intergenic changes are two-break alterations, they may be either one hit or two hit as seen in Fig. 7.

b. Inversions. If the two breaks are in the same chromosome, occasionally the interstitial piece instead of being deleted is inverted and reinserted into the chromosome. If the two breaks are in the same arm of the chromosome,

a paracentric inversion results. If they are on opposite sides of the centromere, i.e., in different arms of the chromosome, then a pericentric inversion
results. The genetic effects of inversions are usually of two types: (1) a
position effect, and (2) an effect of reduced fertility. The position effect
comes about from a change in gene action when a gene is removed from
its usual position in a chromosome and placed in a different neighborhood.
In *Drosophila*, many of the position effects are similar to the effects of true
gene mutation, with the exception that when the gene is returned to its
original physical position it reverts to its original type in regard to gene
action. Many other types of position effects have been noted in *Drosophila*
(42) in which a euchromatic segment of chromosome is shifted to a position
close to the heterochromatin. In many of these cases the gene expresses
itself in a variegated manner. In Fig. 8 it may be seen that a paracentric
inversion pairs as a loop with its normal homolog. A crossover within the
loop of an inversion results in the formation of a dicentric bridge. Such
bridges lead to lethality in zygotes formed from the gametes containing
the abnormal chromosomes and a concurrent decrease in fertility of inversion heterozygotes. This is not the case in *Drosophila*, however, for this
organism is peculiar in the respect that there is no crossing over in the male,
and that in the female the bridge formed after a single crossover within
the loop of an inversion is not included in the egg nucleus during meiosis
(43). Only one of the noncrossover chromosomes enters the egg; the homologous chromosomes enter the polar nuclei.

If the inversion is pericentric, then a crossover within the loop would
result in a duplication deficiency product and again lead to some sterility.

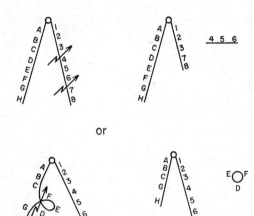

FIG. 7. Schematic representation of interstitial deletions

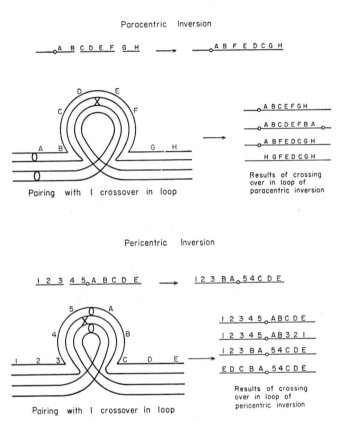

Fig. 8. Schematic representation of inversions

It should be noted that if the inverted segment is very small then the frequency of crossing over within the inverted region will be very slight and the resultant sterility will consequently not be very high. As in the case of interstitial deletions, the inversion, although two break, can be either one or two hit.

c. *Duplications.* Occasionally a segment of chromosome with its genes may act as a free chromosome or may be added onto another either homologous or nonhomologous chromosome so that following segregation the cells now can contain a duplication for certain genes. Duplications are usually more viable than are deficiencies.

d. *Translocations.* If the two breaks are in two different chromosomes, the segments instead of restituting may on occasion rejoin symmetrically with one another to give two compound chromosomes (Fig. 9). It has been observed that translocations lead to a reduced fertility of the organism, since only those gametes that contain a normal complement of genes can form a viable zygote. This can occur if either two normal chromosomes or two translocated chromosomes are included in the gametes. If a normal chromosome and a translocated chromosome are in the same gamete, it will have a duplication for some genes and a deficiency for others. The resultant zygote will therefore usually be inviable. Translocations by their very nature also lead to altered linkage relations and position effects.

In *Drosophila* the intergenic effects studied are necessarily restricted to those combinations of the above types of effects that are viable, since an inviable effect will never reach the adult stage or even the larval stage where it may be observed cytologically in the salivary gland chromosomes. Consequently, many of the experiments designed to observe quantitative effects of radiation on intergenic changes have been performed in material in which the large class of inviable changes may be observed. Plants possessing large chromosomes that are easily observed in cytological preparations have been an excellent tool for this type of research. The usual procedure is to irradiate either mitotically dividing cells (root tips, seeds, or microspores) or meiotically dividing cells (pollen mother cells, etc.) and then to observe the chromosomes at the first metaphase after irradiation. This

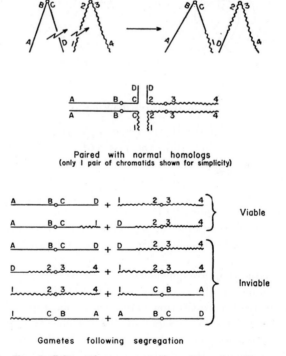

Paired with normal homologs
(only 1 pair of chromatids shown for simplicity)

Gametes following segregation

Fig. 9. Schematic representation of translocations

ABERRATIONS

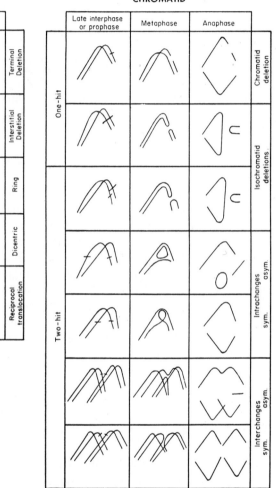

FIG. 10. Chart of the various types of chromosome and chromatid aberrations. From Sax (48), Swanson's modification (87).

technique allows the easy detection of many types of chromosomal aberration that would be inviable or eliminated by cell death if the organism were allowed to grow beyond one or two cycles of cell division. The aberrations observed are in most cases special classes of the various possible types of intergenic alterations. However, since the breakage and rejoining of chromosomes following radiation generally is a random process, these types of aberrations (inviables) bear a simple, direct relation to the larger class from which they are derived.

Figure 10 is a schematic representation of the various types of chromosome aberrations observed in the cytological studies. The chromosomes in the figure are represented by lines bent at the centromeres, and the aberrations are separated (*a*) into those induced before the chromosome has effectively divided (chromosomal aberrations) and those induced after the chromosome has effectively divided (chromatid aberrations), and (*b*) into one-hit and two-hit aberrations.

3. TYPES OF ABERRATIONS

Cells that are irradiated at interphase show the chromosome type of aberrations as follows:

Chromosome terminal deletions. If the radiation produces a single break in an unsplit chromosome, the chromosome will be divided into a centric and into an acentric fragment which, barring restitution, will give rise to a terminal deletion including all the genes in the acentric fragment. At metaphase the shortened centric fragment and the acentric piece will be readily observed. At anaphase the acentric portions will not proceed to the poles and can usually be seen between the two groups of chromosomes.

Chromosome interstitial deletions. Sometimes a single ionizing particle will break a chromosome in two places by passing through a gyre of the spiraled chromonema. The interstitial piece may then be deleted. Such deletions are in all probability in the shape of small rings; however, at metaphase and at anaphase the chromosomes may be so completely contracted as to obliterate the hole in the ring. In these cases, the interstitial deletion will appear as acentric dots which of course will not move to the poles. These dots can also be formed after the passage of two independent ionizing particles each of which produces only one of the breaks contributing to the deletion.

Chromosome exchanges. When two independent breaks are induced in the same chromosome or in different chromosomes, the breaks often, instead of restituting, rejoin illegitimately with other ends. If the breaks are in different arms of the same chromosome, a centric ring and acentric fragment are formed. At anaphase the rings can proceed to the poles leaving the fragment behind. However, sometimes the rings become interlocked when the chromosome doubles and thus form a bridge at anaphase. When the breaks are in different chromosomes, interchanges can occur. These may be classified as symmetrical translocations and dicentrics (asymmetrical translocations). The translocations which have already been discussed are viable and will be passed through many cell divisions. However, this class of aberration is cytologically observable in a mitotic cell division only if the exchange is grossly asymmetrical in regard to the size of pieces exchanged so as to form one chromosome with an extremely long arm and one with a very short arm. It therefore cannot be scored quantitatively and is ignored in scoring aberrations. The asymmetrical exchange, however, forms a dicentric chromosome and an accompanying acentric fragment. These may be scored more objectively. At anaphase, the dicentric in those cases in which the two centromeres on the same chromatid do not go to the same pole will give a double bridge.

When the radiation is administered after the chromosomes are effectively doubled, i.e., late interphase and prophase, the chromatid type of aberration is induced.

Chromatid deletions. A single break in one of the two chromatids present will form a chromatid deletion. At metaphase this type of deletion will appear as an interruption in one of the chromatids. The fragment will not be found lying free in the cytoplasm but will be fairly close to its usual position because of sister-strand attraction. At anaphase, however, the fragment will fall free and not proceed to the pole.

Isochromatid deletions. Occasionally a single ionizing particle will pass through both chromatids at a given level. The resultant break in the two chromatids may then fuse with one another to form an isochromatid aberration and its fragment. If there is fusion in both the acentric portion and the centric portion, this is known as sister union (SU) and is represented in the figure. At anaphase, when the centromeres go to opposite poles, a bridge will result if sister union has occurred. Occasionally, the unions may be incomplete in the distal portion so as to form an isochromatid and two acentric fragments. This is called nonunion distal or NUd. Similarly nonunion may occur proximally. This is known as NUp. Nonunion may also occur both proximally and distally, NUpd. Isochromatid deletions or what appear to be isochromatid deletions can also be formed when both breaks are produced by independent particles.

Intrachanges. When two breaks are produced in different arms of the same chromosome pair, chromatid intrachanges occur. These may be classified as symmetrical and asymmetrical intrachanges. The asymmetrical intrachange gives rise to a chromatid ring and a fragment. The chromatid symmetrical intrachange is observed at metaphase as a loop in one of the chromatids. However, at anaphase this is indistinguishable from normal chromatids.

Interchanges. If the two chromatid breaks occur in different chromosomes, symmetrical or asymmetrical interchanges can be formed. The asymmetrical interchange is observed as a chromatid dicentric at metaphase and at anaphase. The symmetrical chromatid interchange may be observed at metaphase by the pairing relations of the chromatids. However, at anaphase this type of aberration will appear normal.

4. DOSE-RESPONSE CURVES

According to the theory described by Sax (38), the radiation first breaks the chromosomes. These breaks can then either remain open to give one-hit aberrations or may rejoin in one of two different ways. They may restitute (rejoin in the original condition and not produce an aberration) or they may reunite illegitimately with other broken ends and form a two-break aberration.

a. Linear and Dose-Square Curves. The dose-response curve for one-break aberrations is linear (Fig. 11) and independent of the intensity of the radiation (Fig. 12) which indicates that these breaks are produced by the passage of a single ionizing particle, i.e., are one hit. Mathematically this simply means that there is a probability, p, that radiation will break a chromosome and that p is directly proportional to the dose. When p is less than one, it also means that aberrations that are the result of two independent breaks are formed with a probability of $p \times p$, or p^2, which is proportional to the square of the dose. In Figs. 11 and 13, it may be seen that for two-break aberrations in *Tradescantia* this is indeed the case.

b. Intensity or Fractionation Effect. As Sax early recognized, in order for two breaks to rejoin with one another and form a two-hit aberration, they

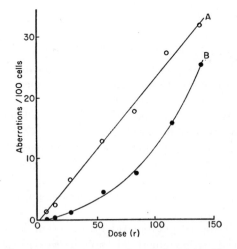

FIG. 11. Dose-effect curves for aberrations induced by X-rays. Curve A, one-break aberrations, linear curve; curve B, two-break aberrations, dose-square curve. Data from Sax (48).

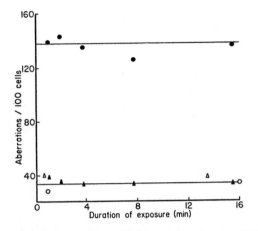

FIG. 12. Independence of aberration yield from intensity of radiation. ● Chromtid breaks, 150 r of X-rays (Catcheside *et al.*, 45); ▲ isochromatid breaks, 150 r of X-rays (Catcheside *et al.*, 45); △ isochromatid breaks, 130 r of X-rays (Giles, 45a); isochromatid breaks, ○ 10 n of fast neutrons (Giles, 45a).

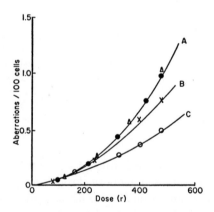

FIG. 13. Dependence of two-break aberrations on intensity of radiation. Data from Sax (45b). Curve *A*, 160 r/min; curve *B*, 20 r/min; curve *C*, 2.7 r/min.

must be close to one another both in time and in space. The time limitation is observed in intensity or dose fractionation experiments in which the aberration yield decreases as the intensity of the radiation decreases (Fig. 14). The rationale behind this dose intensity or dose fractionation experiment is schematically represented in Fig. 15. There it is seen that, if only part of the radiation is given, one of the chromosomes may be broken. In a rest period or during the time before more of the radiation is given, this first break may restitute. When other radiation is administered, the second

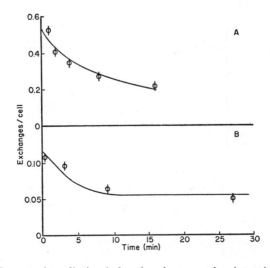

FIG. 14. Decrease in radiation-induced exchanges at low intensities of radiation. Curve A, 320 r, chromosome exchange; curve B, 150 r, chromatid exchanges. Data from Sax, (48, 52).

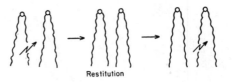

FIG. 15. Schematic representation of dose intensity or dose fractionation effect on two-hit aberrations.

chromosome may be broken, and, although a total dose has now been given which has been capable of breaking both chromosomes, because both breaks were not open at the same time, a two-hit aberration cannot result. The length of time over which there is no decrease in aberration yield when an intensity or fractionation experiment is given is a measure of the time which breaks stay open (44). It may be noticed in Fig. 13 that at low enough intensities the aberration yield for two-hit aberrations increases linearly with the dose of radiation. Observations of this kind have led Catcheside *et al.* (45) to postulate that some two-break aberrations are produced by single ionizing particles and that the true shape of the curve would best be expressed by the equation $y = aD + bD^2$, where a is the probability of getting the two breaks that participate in the rearrangement with a single ionizing particle and b is the probability of getting a single one of the breaks with an ionizing particle. At high intensities the term bD^2 contributes by far the most to the aberration yield, whereas at low intensities this term becomes less and less important and the curve approaches the values represented by the term aD.

In *Tradescantia*, because of the intensity effect, unless the dose is given within a very short time, the dose-square relationship is usually not achieved.

In *Drosophila* (22), it has long been known that the translocations induced in irradiated sperm increase only as the 1.5 of the dose. This is true even though intensity experiments have shown that the breaks induced in sperm stay open until the time of fertilization of the egg even if this may be months. That is, there is no decrease in aberrations at low-intensity radiation or with fractionated doses of radiation. The usual explanation for this effect is that, although the total number of aberrations produced increases as the square of the dose, in *Drosophila* only those aberrations that are viable can be scored, e.g., reciprocal translocations. It is suspected that at high doses proportionately more inviable aberrations are produced than viable ones, and thus the biological sieve which operates in *Drosophila* selectively decreases the aberration yield that can be scored.

Another possible explanation for the lack of the theoretically expected dose-square relation in plants has been advanced by Thoday (46). The argument given is that, although aberrations are induced as the square of the dose, breaks are induced between the two centromeres of a dicentric in proportion to the dose. These breaks will disrupt the dicentrics. At high doses, this complication could decrease significantly the number of two-hit aberrations. It has been found that the numbers of breaks per cell follow the Poisson distribution $e^{-kD} \cdot kD^n/n!$, where k is the probability of getting a break with a given ionizing particle, D is the dose, and n is the number of aberrations per cell (20). This, then, means that the proportion of cells having no breaks will be e^{-kD}, where kD is equal to the mean number of breaks observed at that dose. Similarly $e^{-k_2 D}$ will be equal to the number of dicentrics containing no breaks between the two centromeres, and one minus this quantity will be the probability of getting at least one single break between the two centromeres of a dicentric. Therefore, the curve for aberration yield will take the form $y = \alpha D + \beta D^2 - \beta D^2 (1 - e^{-k_2 D})$ (K. C. Atwood, personal communication). At high doses the final term will become large enough to cause the curves to deviate significantly from a dose-square relation.

5. NEUTRON DOSE CURVES

With neutron irradiation, Giles (47) has clearly shown that the two-break aberration yield increases in direct proportion to the dose (Fig. 16). This has been interpreted as meaning that with the densely ionizing neu-

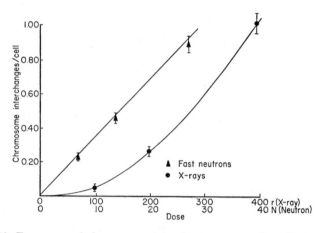

Fıɢ. 16. Frequency of chromosome interchanges versus dose. Data from Giles (129).

trons both breaks are always produced by a single ionizing particle. It has further been shown that neutrons are much more efficient at producing chromosome breaks than are X-rays (20). This has been interpreted (39) as indicating that more than one ionization is necessary to break a chromosome, for if only one ionization were necessary it would be expected that, with more densely ionizing radiation, ionizations would be wasted and these radiations would be less efficient. By utilizing calculations based on the relative efficiencies of different types of radiations, Lea (20) has arrived at the conclusion that 15 to 20 ionizations are necessary for a break. However, it is yet unknown why such apparently large amounts of energy are needed for chromosome breakage. Muller (3) has argued that the spatial relations of the chromosomes and also the stresses and strains imposed upon chromosomes by their pairing and coiling might influence the relative efficiency of different radiations and, consequently, only one ionization may be all that is needed to break the chromosome.

Calculations by Atwood and Wolff (unpublished) of the numbers of primary breaks that have to be put into the cell to get a given yield of visible aberrations have indicated that, although neutrons are much more efficient than X-rays at producing visible aberrations, they are not much (if any) more efficient at inducing the primary breakage. The reasons for this are that the spatial relations of the breaks are important in the production of visible aberrations (see below) and that if the breaks cannot rejoin to form a visible aberration they will restitute and so not be seen. Again, therefore, it seems that only one (or perhaps a few) ionizations may be all that is needed to break a chromosome.

6. SPATIAL RELATIONS

In addition to the time relations which have been observed, there are spatial limitations on the production of two-hit aberrations. Such limitations were first demonstrated by Sax in studies on the relative numbers of ring chromosomes to dicentric chromosomes produced in *Tradescantia* (48). *Tradescantia* microspores have six pairs of chromosomes with median centromeres so that there are twelve chromosome arms. If there is a given break in one arm of a chromosome, it is expected that a dicentric would be formed ten times as frequently as would a ring. This expectation arises because there are ten arms on other chromosomes which can be broken and rejoined with the first break formed, whereas there is only one other arm on the same chromosome that will give a ring. However, instead of observing the 10-to-1 ratio, Sax observed a 2-to-1 ratio of dicentrics to rings, suggesting that breaks in the same chromosome, because of spatial proximity, are more likely to rejoin with one another than are those in different chromosomes.

The straight line observed for aberration yield against neutron dose is also an indication of spatial limitations on rejoining. If the neutron breaks could rejoin at the same relative frequency with breaks produced any place in the nucleus, a two-hit curve would be expected. In other words, a break would be able to rejoin with other breaks produced by independent particles just as frequently as it could rejoin with a break produced by the same particle. However, almost all neutron aberrations are produced by breaks induced by the same particle and therefore close to one another. In *Drosophila* one also finds evidence for such a spatial limitation. If only two breaks take part in an exchange, there is only one type of viable exchange that can occur. With three breaks taking part in a cyclical exchange, again there is only one type of viable exchange that can occur. However, with four breaks, a cyclic exchange of all four of the breaks or two separate two-break exchanges may result. On the assumption of random reunion, the number of the different types of exchanges to be observed in *Drosophila* may be calculated. However, the experimental data (49) show that there are far too few cyclical exchanges and far too many exchanges of the two-by-two type, indicating that the reunions are not random and that the two-by-two exchanges are preferred.

This lack of randomness in the rejoining of breaks is also evident in the work on chromosome dicentrics and rings, where it is found that the numbers of cells having 0, 1, 2, 3, etc., exchanges do not fit the Poisson distribution (50). This is contrary to the evidence for all other types of aberrations (Table II), where it is seen that all simple chromosome breaks and chromatid aberrations fit the Poisson distribution and thus are formed randomly. The evidence that chromosome exchanges do not fit this distribution are presented in Table III. This lack of randomness has been explained (51) as being due to a limited number of sites within the nucleus where the chromosomes approach one another close enough to form an exchange.

Lea (20) has calculated the distance, h, over which an exchange can take place. The chief calculation was based on the fact that in *Tradescantia* with 50 rep the X-ray curve increases as the square of the dose indicating that

TABLE II

NUMBERS OF CELLS CONTAINING 0, 1, 2, 3, ETC., ABERRATIONS

Material	Aberration		Aberrations per cell					χ^2 test	Ref.
			0	1	2	3	4		
Chortophaga neuro- blasts, 62.5r X- rays	Chroma- tid + isochro- matid breaks	Observed[a] Expected[b]	174 178.4	112 104.2	28 30.5	5 5.9	1 1.0	$\chi^2 = 1.0$ $n = 3$ $p = 0.8$	(50a
Tradescantia micro- spores, 46.6 rep neutrons	Chromatid breaks	Observed Expected	408 425.7	263 233.1	56 63.8	8 11.6	1 1.8	$\chi^2 = 6.9$ $n = 3$ $P = 0.08$	Thoday in (20)
	Isochroma- tid breaks	Observed Expected	483 480.4	204 205.0	38 43.7	10 6.2	1 0.7	$\chi^2 = 3.4$ $n = 3$ $P = 0.3$	
	Chromatid ex- changes	Observed Expected	478 475.8	202 207.5	49 45.3	7 6.6	0 0.8	$\chi^2 = 1.4$ $n = 3$ $P = 0.7$	
Tradescantia micro- spores, 400 r X-rays	Chromo- some in- terstitial deletions	Observed Expected	614 619.6	219 209.6	33 35.5	3 4.3		$\chi^2 = 1.0$ $n = 2$ $P = 0.6$	(50b)
Tradescantia micro- spores, 150 r X-rays	Chromatid inter- changes	Observed Expected	2278 2280.2	273 269.2	15 15.9	0 0.7		$\chi^2 = 0.8$ $n = 2$ $P = 0.7$	(45)

[a]Observed is the experimentally observed number of cells with the stated number of aberrations.

[b] Expected is the number expected on the Poisson distribution.

TABLE III
NUMBER OF CELLS CONTAINING 0, 1, 2, OR 3 CHROMOSOME DICENTRICS AND RINGS
(Data from K. C. Atwood and S. Wolff)

Material		Aberrations per cell				χ^2 test
		0	1	2	3	
Tradescantia, 300 r	Observed[a]	153	131	16		$\chi^2 = 24.1$
	Expected[b]	174.3	94.5	31.2		$n = 2$
						$P < 0.001$
Tradescantia, 300 r	Observed	155	127	18		$\chi^2 = 19.8$
	Expected	174.3	94.5	31.2		$n = 2$
						$P < 0.001$
Tradescantia, 300 r	Observed	162	120	17	1	$\chi^2 = 9.17$
	Expected	178.5	93	24.3	4.8	$n = 3$
						$P < 0.02$
Vicia seed, 700 r	Observed	314	89	1		$\chi^2 = 12.17$
	Expected	342	73.5	8.5		$n = 2$
						$P < 0.01$
Vicia seed, 70 rep neu-trons	Observed	411	134	5		$\chi^2 = 13.51$
	Expected	423	110.4	11.6		$n = 2$
						P ca. 0.001
Barley seed, 30 krγ-rays	Observed	399	98	3		$\chi^2 = 6.21$
	Expected	407	84.6	8.9		$n = 2$
						$P < 0.05$

[a] Observed is the experimentally observed number of cells with the stated number of aberrations.
[b] Expected is the number expected on the Poisson distribution.

the exchanges are produced by two independent particles, whereas the neutron curve increases linearly indicating that the aberrations are produced by single particles. At 50 r, there are 303 electrons being projected within the nucleus of Tradescantia by X-rays. Lea divided the volume of the nucleus by 303 and arrived at the conclusion that the two independent breaks which must be at least 1/303 of the volume apart in order to give two-hit kinetics were at least 0.9 micron apart. In the case of neutrons, 50 rep projects 23 protons in the nucleus. Since one-hit kinetics results, the two breaks must be within 1/23 of the cross-sectional area of the nucleus or within 1.3 microns. With these figures as upper and lower limits, the conclusion was reached that the two breaks usually are within 1.0

micron of one another when an exchange is formed. However, this point of view has been challenged by Wolff and Atwood (51) on the basis that any dose could have been used and that the volume or the cross-sectional area of the nucleus could have been divided by any number of electrons or protons to arrive at any distance h. Calculations by Atwood based upon the additivity of the two-break aberration yields induced by X-rays and neutrons have led to the conclusion that the distance h must be of the order of 0.1 micron (50, 51).

As was pointed out earlier, the intensity effect on two-hit aberrations led Sax (52) to postulate that many of the primary breaks induced by radiation restitute and do not appear as aberrations. Lea (20) has made several different calculations in an attempt to indicate the proportion of breaks that restitute in *Tradescantia*. The methods he used are based on (1) a comparison of the frequencies of complete (SU) versus incomplete (NUp, NUd, NUpd) union of chromatid breaks; (2) the departure at high doses from the dose-square relation in X-ray-induced exchanges; (3) a comparison of the expected and observed aberration yield with neutrons; (4) the relative frequency of chromatid and isochromatid breaks; and (5) a comparison of the number of chromatid-isochromatid breaks.

Calculations by all five methods substantially agreed with one another and indicated that for X-rays and neutrons approximately 10 % of the breaks were not joinable. The other 90 % of the primary breaks induced restitute or rejoin. With α-particles only 50 % of the breaks restitute; the others either rejoin illegitimately or are unjoinable. Similar results have been obtained by Fabergé (52a).

The relations described in the preceding sections seem to hold only for aberrations observed at metaphase where all the chromosomes can be seen and scored accurately. Different relations are observed at anaphase (52b). If the centromeres of a dicentric segregate randomly, one-half of the di-centrics will form an anaphase bridge, and these should show the same shape of dose curves as do the dicentrics. However, it has been observed by Wolff and Luippold (53) that, although the dicentrics increase as the square of the dose, the anaphase bridges increase linearly with dose. This indicates that there is no direct correlation between anaphase observations and the true amount of radiation effect that can be measured at metaphase. This anomaly has been explained by Conger (54), who noticed that at very early anaphase when the chromosomes of *Tradescantia* microspores are still completely separate from one another, the bridges are equal to one-half the dicentrics and they increase as the same power of the dose. However, at later anaphase, when the chromosomes are clumped at the poles, making observation of the individual chromosomes difficult, many of the bridges have broken reducing the number of abnormal cells scored. Conger believes that the regions between the centromeres of bridges have weak spots caused by restituted breaks. At higher doses these are more numerous and more bridges break than at lower doses. It is concluded that the number of anaphase bridges observed is not an adequate measure of the amount of nuclear damage (53, 54).

III. The Effect of Slow Neutrons

The neutron experiments discussed heretofore have all been performed with fast neutrons whose principal reaction is the ejection of recoil protons from hydrogen atoms. However, thermal neutrons which are produced when the fast neutrons are slowed down to thermal energies by elastic collisions with graphite or heavy water also enter into capture reactions with the various elements in the biological material irradiated. The main elements that capture thermal neutrons are hydrogen, boron, and nitrogen. The nuclei formed after capture are unstable and break down by emitting either a γ-ray in the hydrogen case, an α-particle in the boron case, or a proton and β-ray in the nitrogen case. It is these internally produced radiations that bring about the biological damage.

Conger and Giles (55) studied the aberration induction in *Tradescantia* by slow neutrons. They found that the chromosome exchanges increased linearly with the dose of thermal neutrons, indicating that most of the biologically effective dose came from the capture reactions of boron and nitrogen which produce heavy-particle radiation rather than from the hydrogen capture reactions that emit γ-rays and that might be expected to produce aberrations as the square of the dose. They also calculated that heavy-particle radiations arising internally from capture reactions are more efficient at producing genetic damage than are the same radiations produced outside the cell. One possible explanation for this observation is that the elements boron and nitrogen, whose emissions are responsible for much of the genetic damage, are not distributed at random throughout the cell but are preferentially located in the chromosomes.

IV. Induction of Mutations by Cosmic and Other Natural Radiations

Since the earth is constantly being bombarded by cosmic rays and also since biological systems on earth are being irradiated by natural radioactive substances both without and within the organism, the question has come up whether or not these radiations can account for the spontaneous mutation rate (see ref. 3). However, calculations on the amount of radiation received from these sources in short-lived organisms such as *Drosophila* have indicated that only a negligible proportion of the spontaneous mutations could be attributed to this radiation. In the case of long-lived organisms such as man, calculations have indicated that only up to a fourth of the spontaneous mutation rate could be the result of cosmic rays and natural radiation. Even when long-lived organisms live at high altitude where the intensity of cosmic radiation is increased, it seems unlikely that the spontaneous mutation rate can be wholly accounted for by natural radiation.

V. Gene Size from Target Theory

Shortly after it was found that mutations could be caused by single or single clusters of ionizations, several workers attempted to calculate a target size for gene mutations. To be effective, the ionizations had to be within the target. They assumed that the target whose size was found was the actual gene. In recent years, however, a more cautious attitude has been taken by the people who utilize this type of approach, and they now only refer to the sensitive volume of the gene.

The basic assumption in these target volume calculations is that there is a probability, i, that a given individual atom within the gene will be ionized with a given dose of radiation. If there are a atoms within that region of the gene, and if the ionizations are randomly distributed, then the chance, m, of a mutation being produced in that gene by the given dose of radiation will be equal to ai. From the equation $m = ai$, one can calculate the number, a, of atoms within the gene. The value of i is obtained from tables of physical data, and the value of m comes from the genetic data. The number of atoms, a, within the sensitive volume can be converted into a volume after considering the approximate density of the material irradiated. By such methods, values for this size of the gene ranging from a 1-mμ sphere up to a 9-mμ sphere have been obtained by various authors (56, 57). These values for the volume of a gene are about one-thousandth of the maximum gene size which was calculated by Muller (58).

As Muller has pointed out, however, (3, p. 525) calculations of gene size by target theory methods are extremely sensitive to error. The main sources of error are that the target hypothesis supposes the mutation is only caused when the ionization falls within the gene, that there is a unit probability that an ionization within the gene will cause a mutation, that only ionizations and not excitation of molecules will cause mutations, and that all mutations are detectable. Since there is evidence that none of these four conditions is met completely (3), it must be assumed that the volume of the gene arrived at by target considerations is only an approximation at best.

VI. Dominant Lethals

It has long been known that after the irradiation of sperm some of the fertilized eggs will not give rise to an adult organism but will die. In these cases, usually not enough radiation has been administered to the sperm to cause an effect on the sperm cytoplasm. It is suspected that these embryo deaths are caused by dominant lethal mutations. Muller (22) cited the evidence for *Drosophila* that the effect was mainly genetic rather than physiological. The evidence is that the sperm consists almost entirely of chromatin and that the action of radiation on sperm could not readily be an action on cytoplasm. Secondly, after fertilization by irradiated sperm, fewer females hatch from the fertilized eggs than do males. This is taken as an indication that the X-bearing sperm are more sensitive than those sperm containing a Y chromosome. In view of the fact that the Y chromosome is almost genetically inert, it seems probable that the effect of irradiation is on the chromosomes. Another point in favor of this interpretation is that the sex ratio is reduced more when the X-bearing sperm contains an X ring chromosome instead of the normal rod type of chromosome (59). The reason advanced for this is that many of the breaks in a ring chromosome will restitute in a crisscross fashion (torsional restititution) to give a double-sized ring at anaphase with a consequent loss of the chromosome.

A very striking indication that dominant lethals are genetic in nature comes from A. R. Whiting's work (60) with the parasitic wasp *Habrobracon*. In *Habrobracon*, fertilized eggs normally develop into diploid females whereas unfertilized eggs develop into haploid males. When one irradiates the eggs and then fertilizes, there is a decrease in hatchability (increase in dominant lethality) with increasing doses of radiation. This continues until the entire female chromosome complement in the egg is held together by chromosome bridges resulting from the radiation. At this point there is a sudden increase in viability as the dose increases. The eggs that hatch at this point are all haploid males that instead of having the female chromosomes are androgenetic males containing the chromosomes from the sperm. This indicates that when dominant lethals are induced in eggs the diploid embryo will die. It is only after the irradiated female chromosomes are inactivated that haploid males with the new chromosomes from the unirradiated sperm arise. It further indicates that at extremely high doses of radiation (ca. 60 kr) the cytoplasm is still capable of supporting the nucleus incorporated from the sperm and of giving a viable zygote, and that the dominant lethal effect at doses below 60 kr is not due to the irradiation of the cytoplasm.

It has further been shown in *Habrobracon*, where the egg nucleus is close to the dorsal side of the egg, that irradiation of the nuclear side with radiations of low penetrability such as ultraviolet (61) or α-rays (62) induces much more death than does irradiation of the cytoplasmic side of the egg. This phenomenon again indicates that the lethality is nuclear in origin.

It should be noted, however, that Atwood *et al.* (63) have shown in *Habrobracon*, at least, that the dominant lethality can be divided into three types distinguished by the time of death. Von Borstel (64) has evidence indicating that two of the types are caused by chromosome imbalance phenomena and that the other, and most prominent, type is caused by permanent inhibition of mitosis unrelated to formation of chromosome breaks.

It has also been shown in *Drosophila* that those eggs that do not hatch have many abnormal mitotic divisions (65) with clumped and broken chromosomes and chromosomal bridges. As was pointed out earlier, it is expected that any large interstitial deletion with consequent loss of important genes or any dicentric interchange will be cell lethal and give rise to a dominant lethal mutation. However, these types of chromosomal changes are two hit and increase as the square of the dose. If the survival curves for *Drosophila* eggs fertilized by irradiated sperm are plotted semilogarithmetically, they are linear in the beginning portions (10). This suggests that a single ionizing particle causes the effect and that at low doses dominant lethals are the result of a one-hit event. At higher doses the two-break aberrations which increase more rapidly than the first power of the dose play a predominantly larger part in the production of dominant lethals and thus account for the shape of the curve. It has been proposed (22) that the one-hit mechanism involved in the linear portion of the dominant lethality curve is the formation of a terminal deletion with the consequent bridge-breakage-fusion cycle of the centric portion. Because the effects of the resultant duplication deficiencies cannot be canceled by the addition of an extra normal chromosome, it has been concluded (22) that the bridge and not necessarily the loss itself results in the death of the embryo. It has also been suggested (11) that the death occurs following the formation of polyploid cells which result from a single restitution nucleus being formed when a bridge prevents the complete separation of the daughter nuclei. Another finding which is consistent with the notion that the dominant lethals are the result of chromosomal changes is the fact that irradiation with neutrons is more efficient in the production of dominant lethals than is X-ray irradiation (35).

Lea and Catcheside (57) have developed a mathematical expression for the yield of dominant lethals. Their expression is based on the concept that unrejoined breaks and asymmetrical exchanges result in dominant lethals. Essentially, they have taken the fact that the proportion of cells with various numbers of breaks in them will be distributed according to the Poisson formula, and then calculated the probabilities that each of the terms of the Poisson would have an unrestituted break or at least one dicentric. The sum of these probabilities is the chance that a dominant lethal will be induced in the sperm.

It is probable that several different effects other than bridge formation contribute to dominant lethality, such as gross deletions, formation of translocation aneuploidy during meiosis itself, and mitotic cessation (64). Since it is implicit in the induction of dominant lethality that the organism die, much ingenuity is required to sort out the different causes from the dominant lethal complex.

VII. The Genetic Effects of Ultraviolet Radiation

Following the discovery that ionizing radiation would induce mutations, attempts were made to find the effect of the nonionizing radiations such as ultraviolet light on the production of mutations in *Drosophila* (66). The first experiments were performed on *Drosophila* sperm to pick up sex-linked recessive lethals. Since ultraviolet radiation does not penetrate very deeply into tissues, these experiments were performed on adult males which had their abdomena compressed between quartz plates. In order to decrease the problem of low penetrability of the radiation, later experiments (67, 68) were performed by irradiating the superficial polar cap cells (primordial germ cells) of the *Drosophila* egg. Many of the problems of low penetrability do not exist if the pollen of higher plants such as maize (69) or the spores of fungi such as *Trichophyton* (70) are treated.

The mutations induced by ultraviolet radiation in *Drosophila* and in maize seem to be very similar to those which occur spontaneously inasmuch as there is usually no sterility connected with the observed mutations. This is contrary to what has been found in many cases with X-rays where a large proportion of the observable mutants are caused by chromosome aberrations. Stadler has maintained that X-ray-induced mutations almost always are changes to the amorphic form of the gene in which the gene seems to lose all activity. Because of this, and because maize pollen is always affected deleteriously by X-rays, showing a lowered viability and growth, he believed that X-ray mutations are almost always chromosome deletions. This is in contrast to ultraviolet-induced and spontaneous mutations. Muller has argued that this is not the case in all organisms and that true mutations may be induced by X-rays in addition to those mutations which result from deletions. He cites evidence for the occurrence of back mutation of X-radiation-induced mutants in *Drosophila*. In order for a back mutation to occur, it is obvious that the gene could not be lost. Similarly, Giles (71), working with *Neurospora*, has observed reversions for several X-ray-induced inositol mutants, and de Serres (72) with the same material has found several radiation-induced reversions of adenine mutants which were originally produced by radiation.

In spite of the observation that many of the mutants induced by ultraviolet were not the result of chromosome deletions, it has long been known that ultraviolet can break chromosomes in *Drosophila* (73). Stadler and

SHELDON WOLFF

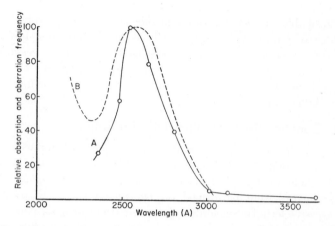

Fig. 17. Action spectrum for ultraviolet-induced chromosome aberrations and nucleic acid absorption spectrum. Curve A, action spectrum for ultraviolet-induced isochromatid aberrations; curve B, absorption spectrum for nucleic acid. Data from Kirby-Smith and Craig (77).

Uber (74) irradiated pollen of maize and then fertilized nonirradiated plants with this pollen. They checked cases of endosperm deficiencies produced in the irradiated pollen. These deficiencies affected only about one-half of the endosperm, suggesting to Stadler and Uber that the chromosomes in the sperm nuclei were already divided into two chromatids at the time of irradiation and that the ultraviolet radiation was capable only of breaking a single chromatid.

Swanson (75) irradiated the pollen tubes of *Tradescantia* and checked the chromosomes there. He found, too, that only simple chromatid breaks were produced in abundance by ultraviolet radiation, and he postulated that the radiation can break a chromosome only where the energy is absorbed and cannot spread across to a sister chromatid. Swanson also believed that breaks induced by ultraviolet radiation could not rejoin with other breaks. Nevertheless, Fabergé (76) by checking the effects in endosperm fertilized with irradiated maize pollen has found dicentric translocations, inversions, and rings to be produced by ultraviolet radiation; and Kirby-Smith and Craig (77) find that in *Tradescantia* pollen tubes they, too, are able to observe all types of aberrations including those produced following reunion of breaks. However, they point out that the simple chromatid break is by far the most frequent aberration observed and that the isochromatid aberrations and the translocations form only a very small percentage of those aberrations induced by the ultraviolet radiation.

When the relative efficiency of various wavelengths of ultraviolet radiation in producing mutation in fungi was checked (78), it was found that the curves of genetic effect per unit energy were very similar to the absorption spectrum curves for nucleic acids. This was later confirmed in *Zea mays* (74) and *Tradescantia* (77). Such curves showed a peak of energy absorption at 2650 A. Since the chromosome consists of nucleic acid and protein, it is not surprising that the curves for mutability or aberration production (Fig. 17) should be similar to that for nucleic acid absorption.

In spite of the fact that the greatest efficiency for the induction of mutations occurs at 2650 A, and irradiation of polar cap cells in *Drosophila* showed 2537 A to be ten times as efficient as 3130 A, much of the work in *Drosophila* has been done at the longer wavelength. This is because the *Drosophila* seem to tolerate greater doses at this wavelength than at the shorter wavelengths, and also absorption by the body wall is less, so that relatively more of the incident light will reach the testes of the organism. Similarly, greater sensitivity to 2650 A has been observed by Kirby-Smith and Craig (77) and Lovelace (79) in *Tradescantia* pollen tubes. If they used the lower wavelength, they found that the chromosomes instead of exhibiting simple breaks and aberrations frequently were completely shattered and unanalyzable.

Swanson (Fig. 18) has observed that the ultraviolet dose curve for simple chromatid aberrations is a straight line (79a). This is consistent with the concept that these breaks are caused by a single photon or hit. The dose curves for the induction of mutations with ultraviolet radiation (78, 80) indicate that the mutants increase more than the first power of the dose at low doses, reach a peak, and then decrease (Fig. 19). Since this surprising decrease in the numbers of mutants with increasing dose occurs at levels where only about 1% of the irradiated organisms survive, it has been postulated that the decrease is caused by selection of nonmutated spores by the radiation. The reasoning behind this is that at these dose levels almost all spores will have mutations and the mutant organisms will be

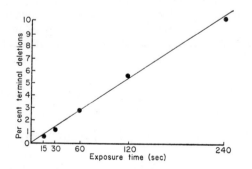

FIG. 18. The relation of chromatid terminal deletions to dosage of ultraviolet light. Data from Swanson (79a).

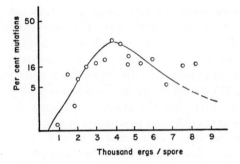

Fig. 19. Percentage of mutations versus ultraviolet dose. Data from Hollaender and Emmons (78).

less fit and therefore sensitive to further irradiation. Thus, at the high doses, the mutants will be selectively killed.

Novick and Szilard (81), working on *E. coli*, found that exposures to visible light after ultraviolet light reactivated the genetic damage induced by the ultraviolet. It was found that the photoreactivating light given after ultraviolet effectively decreased the dose of ultraviolet radiation. Thus, Newcombe and McGregor (82) showed that at low doses where the number of mutations increased with dose a postirradiation treatment with visible light decreased the mutation yield, whereas at high doses where the number of mutations were decreased this same treatment increased the mutation yield.

The fact that at low doses the curve shows that mutations increase more than the first power of the dose has been explained in one of two different ways, the first being that more than one photon is required for a mutation to occur. However, since the curve for chromosome aberrations is linear with dose, it seems unlikely that, whereas only one photon would be necessary for breakage, more than one would be necessary for the production of an intragenic change. The second explanation advanced by Stadler and Uber (74) is based on the fact that the nucleus does not lie in the exact center of the cytoplasm but lies eccentrically in the mass of protoplasm. All pollen grains then will not receive uniform doses of radiation because of absorption of the radiation in the cytoplasm before it reaches the nucleus. Their calculations have indicated that this factor could change the shape of the curve in the direction observed.

VIII. Modification of X-Ray-Induced Mutagenesis

Over the years many experiments have been performed in attempts to modify the yield of gene mutations induced by radiation. This has been done not only for the practical reasons of being able to induce more mutations for work in breeding programs, or to kill cells more efficiently, but also in the hope of getting some theoretical insight into the nature and mechanisms of gene mutations. Many of the experiments have tested theories about genes and chromosomes and have led to confirmation of some of the preconceived ideas. Other experiments, on the contrary, have led to the revamping of ideas that we have had about the chemical nature of the chromosomes and genes.

Since most of the intergenic and perhaps some of the intragenic mutations are the result of two independent processes, breakage of the chromosomes and the subsequent rejoining of these breaks, most attempts to modify the numbers of mutations and aberrations have tried to modify either of these processes. It is extremely difficult to classify the types of treatments that have been utilized by various researchers, for even supposedly simple physical treatments can have profound chemical effects as in the case of changing the temperature which, although being a physical agent, can change the amount of oxygen present in the cell and also change the rate of chemical reactions. We shall, however, classify these modifying treatments in respect to the primary nature of the material being tested. Using this criterion, we may divide the conditions that alter the genetic response to radiation into those that are determined biologically, physically, and chemically.

A. STAGE SENSITIVITY

It had been observed in the early days of radiation studies that tissues with high rates of mitotic activity were more easily damaged by radiation than other tissues (3), and in 1938 Knapp (83) found that meiotic divisions of *Sphaerocarpus* were more susceptible to the induction of mutations than were mitotic divisions. Sax and Swanson (84) found that in *Tradescantia* the sensitivity of cells to radiation during mitosis as measured by chromosome aberrations increased as the cell left interphase and proceeded through prophase to metaphase. Similar effects were found for the stages of meiosis in *Trillium* by Sparrow (85). It has also been observed that *Drosophila* spermatozoa in various stages of maturity have different sensitivity to chromosome breakage (86) with the spermatid stage being more sensitive to the effects of X-rays than the later spermatozoon stage.

The explanations usually advanced (87) for this stage sensitivity is that the rejoining of broken ends is decreased by the movement of the chromosomes as the cell proceeds through the various stages of cell division. This movement prevents many of the chromosome ends from finding one another and restituting, and thus the aberration yield is increased. To this must be added the movement of spiralization of the chromosomes. It has not yet been determined (87) if differences in coiling, DNA content, and water

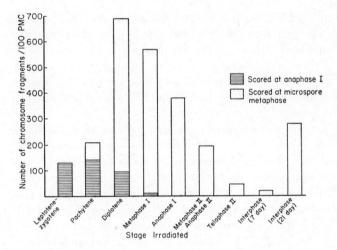

Stage Irradiated

FIG. 20. Numbers of chromosome fragments induced at various stages of meiosis in *Trillium*. From Sparrow *et al.* (88a).

content, or perhaps even other factors, contribute to this sensitivity of the different stages of cell division. It has, however, been shown for *Drosophila* (88) that a part of the stage sensitivity during spermatogenesis can be attributed to the amount of oxygen present in the cells at various times (see Oxygen Effect below). Thus the resistant spermatozoa seem to be more anoxic than the relatively more sensitive spermatids.

In Fig. 20 (88a), it may be seen in meiosis of *Trillium* that the very late prophase stages are the most sensitive to radiation. However, the figure also shows that many of the aberrations induced at metaphase when there is a considerable amount of matrix on the chromosomes are not visible until the cell proceeds through an intervening interphase. It is suspected that this masking of the aberration yield during the first division is caused by the matrix holding the broken pieces of chromosome in place.

Since most aberrations come from breaks that rejoin abnormally rather than restituting, it is also apparent that much of the increase in sensitivity in the various stages of cell division is really a reflection of the spatial relations of the chromonemata of the different stages. For instance, it has been found that there are a limited number of places within the nucleus where the chromosome is by chance within the rejoining distance h of one another; breaks not in these places would restitute. After chromosome duplication, however, a sister chromatid is closely associated with the whole length of the original chromatid, and thus breaks that ordinarily would restitute now can rejoin with another strand to give rise to isochromatid aberrations. On this basis it can be seen that a stage difference of sensitivity to radiation in the production of aberrations does not necessarily indicate that the nucleoprotein strand, that is, the chromosome, changes in its sensitivity at the molecular level.

B. Intensity and Dose Fractionation

If the prevention of restitution by chromosome movement would increase the radiation damage induced in the cell, then it might be expected that the enhancement of restitution would decrease the genetic damage. Such is the case as we have already seen when the radiation is either fractionated or given at low intensities so that there will be fewer open breaks available for rejoining with one another to form two-hit aberrations.

C. Centrifugation

Physical methods have been used to prevent the restitution that occurs and is demonstrated in the course of an intensity or dose fractionation study. Thus, if the material is centrifuged either during (89) or after (90) radiation, the chromosome ends can be forced apart, decreasing restitution and thus increasing the aberration yield. Similarly, exposing the material to ultrasonic vibrations (91) can accomplish the same end. On the other hand, preirradiation centrifugation which might be expected to pack down the chromosomes and so prevent movement decreases the amount of genetic damage (90) by a factor of 2 to 3.

D. The Effect of Ultraviolet

Another factor that modifies the response of chromosomes to X-rays is ultraviolet radiation. When the pollen tubes of *Tradescantia* are treated with ultraviolet rays either before or after exposure to X-rays (92), it is found that the amount of chromosomal aberrations observed is less than the additive amount of damage. In other words, the ultraviolet radiation decreases the numbers of X-ray-induced chromosome aberrations. A similar effect has been observed in *Drosophila* salivary glands (93). It is believed (94) that the effect of ultraviolet is again an effect on the rejoining of chromosome breaks. Swanson and Stadler have postulated that the ultraviolet radiation coagulates the matrices of the chromosomes and in this manner inhibits the realization of both simple breaks and chromosome exchanges.

These observations are complicated by opposite results obtained by Nicoletti and Kirby-Smith (personal communication) who treated pollen grains, not tubes, of *Tradescantia*, with X-rays and ultraviolet radiation. They found that the X-radiation and ultraviolet were highly synergistic in the production of visible aberrations. Such results are explainable in terms of inactivation by ultraviolet of the "rejoining system" postulated by Wolff (see p. 466). With rejoining inhibited, restitution would not occur and many more of the primary breaks induced by the X-radiation would appear as visible aberrations at metaphase. In a wet growing system, it appears as though the rejoining mechanism is not sensitive to ultraviolet radiation and the synergism disappears.

E. The Effect of Infrared

In 1946 Kaufmann et al. (95) observed that when they treated *Drosophila* sperm with infrared radiation between two doses of X-rays an increased frequency of chromosome translocations but not of dominant lethals or of recessive lethals resulted. They further observed that the infrared treatment to be effective had to be given previous to the X-rays. Posttreatment had no effect. Further experiments by Kaufmann and his co-workers established that if post X-ray infrared treatment were given at the time of fertilization when chromosome breaks induced in the sperm are supposed to rejoin then the frequency of translocations increased. Kaufmann argues that these data show the effect of infrared to be an effect on the processes involved in translocation formation, i.e., an increase in breaks that are capable of rejoining. Since infrared alone has no effect, he favors the interpretation that the combined treatment of infrared X-rays increases recombination of broken ends.

Swanson and Hollaender (96) soon confirmed the general effect of combined infrared X-ray effects on chromatid aberrations induced in *Tradescantia* microspores. Although infrared itself would not break the chromosomes, if the inflorescences were treated with infrared light of 600- to 1150-mμ wavelength either before or after X-ray exposure, an increased aberration yield resulted. Even though all types of aberrations were increased, chromatid interchanges showed the greatest increase as may have been expected from the *Drosophila* experiments.

Swanson and Yost (97) have observed that a heat shock between the two doses will remove the infrared effect.

In order to explain the postirradiation effect, the preirradiation effect, as well as the dissipation of the infrared effect following heat shock, McElroy and Swanson (98) have postulated that both X-rays and infrared are capable of raising the chromosomes to a metastable state that can be reduced by heat treatments. Further irradiation of the opposite type is then capable of producing breaks at these metastable positions. This hypothesis is diametrically opposed to the rejoining hypothesis inasmuch as it postulates that the effect of infrared is one of increasing breakage rather than being due to recombination.

Experiments by Moh and Withrow (98a) have shown that the effective wavelengths for this potentiation of X-ray-induced aberrations are in the region from 7100 to 8200 A. Technically speaking, this is the far red rather than the infrared. They also noted that the far red effect can be reversed by exposure to red light with wavelengths shorter than 7000 A. They have postulated that the far red effect is mainly caused by an inhibition of restitution as was observed by Wolff *et al.* (see section IX) following treatment with metabolic inhibitors.

Among the difficulties of the two theories that have been advanced is that the rejoining concept does not fit all the observations made in *Tradescantia*, whereas the "metastable state" concept of breakage does not explain why the final rupture of a metastable locus on the chromosome can only be brought about by the opposite type of radiation. A priori, it might be expected that two doses of X-rays or of infrared could induce some breaks with two-hit kinetics by first inducing a metastable state and then cleaving the chromosome at this place.

Both theories imply that the effect is only on chromosome aberrations and not on true genic mutations. Support for this concept comes from the experiments of Hollaender and Swanson on the fungus *Aspergillus* (100) in which they found that the pretreatment with infrared would increase the rate of morphological mutants produced by X-rays but would not affect those mutations which were induced by ultraviolet and which are thought to be true point mutations.

Wolff and Luippold (100a) have found in lateral roots of *Vicia faba* that the far-red treatment simply slows cell division. This, then, allows at any given time after X-irradiation, selection of cells that were closer to metaphase at the time of irradiation. Under these circumstances the far-red effect is a reflection not of differences in breakage or rejoining but of the stage sensitivity phenomenon.

F. The Effect of Temperature

It has been observed many times in *Tradescantia* microspores (45, 101, 102) that lowering the temperature will increase the numbers of chromatid aberrations induced by X-rays. Sax and Enzmann (101) have postulated that the observed increase by low temperatures during and after radiation is caused by an effect on restitution of the breaks. At the lower temperatures, chemical reactions would be slowed down and less restitution would occur. A similar effect of low temperature on X-ray-induced translocations was observed by Mickey (103) in *Drosophila*. Baker and Sgourakis (104) found that the recessive lethals induced in *Drosophila* were decreased by low temperature only when the material was irradiated in air and not in nitrogen. They postulated that the effect then was due to the oxygen in solution and was on the breakage of the chromosomes. At low temperatures there would be more oxygen in solution and, consequently, more of the damaging radicals produced by the irradiation of oxygenated water would be formed with a subsequent increase in aberration yield. However, in 1950 Giles and Riley (105) found that in the case of *Tradescantia* they could not account completely for the increased aberration yield at low temperatures by the amount of oxygen in solution at the time of radiation. They feel that this particular factor is only one of many which can contribute to the aberration yield. In support of this contention, it has been found that postirradiation treatment at 0°C will prevent restitution from occurring, ostensibly by inhibiting enzyme activity and preventing respiration and the formation of ATP which is the source of energy for the biosyntheses taking place when ends restitute (106). When, however, the temperature is lowered even farther than normal physiological ranges, it is found (107) that a temperature of minus 192°C causes a decrease and not an increase in the numbers of aberrations induced by X-rays. Fabergé (107) has pointed out that his curve for aberrations induced at various temperatures is similar to the curve obtained by Bonet-Maury and LeFort (108) for hydrogen peroxide formation at various temperatures in irradiated water. This latter observation of Fabergé's strengthens the concept of an indirect effect produced by the products of irradiated water as postulated by Baker.

It seems likely that the possible complex effects of an agent like temperature change can affect both breakage and rejoining; breakage by affecting the amount of oxygen in solution and the amounts of damaging radicals formed and their rates of diffusion; reunion by slowing down those chemical reactions necessary for the formation of bonds produced when a break rejoins.

G. Spindle Poisons

As was seen in the section on stage sensitivity, the movement of chromosomes has a profound effect upon the aberration yield finally realized in irradiated cells. Consequently, Brumfield (109) placed onion root tips in colchicine solutions in an attempt to destroy the spindle and thus affect chromosome movements. The irradiated roots remained in colchicine for a short time before irradiation and for 48 hours afterwards, at which time squash preparations were made and the cells scored. He observed a decrease in chromatid aberrations whereas the chromosome aberrations were the same in the treated material as in the controls. The usual interpretation of these observations is that, with the spindle destroyed, the movement of those chromosomes in prophase at the time of radiation is inhibited, and thus the broken ends stay closer to one another and the probability of restitution is increased. Conversely, the movement of chromosomes that were in interphase at the time of irradiation would be unaffected by spindle poisons, and therefore the aberration yield would not change after the application of such substances.

If, however, the material remained in colchicine for long periods before irradiation then many cells would accumulate in metaphase, one of the more sensitive stages to radiation. In this case the opposite effect of more chromosome damage following colchicine treatment was reported (110). It should be realized that under these circumstances the movement of spiralization would not be inhibited and this would be another factor that could tend to increase the damage by decreasing restitution.

H. WATER CONTENT

It has been found that the water content of the irradiated cells greatly determines the amount of genetic change induced by the radiation. Thus, in 1937 Gustafsson observed that chromosome aberrations were induced at a higher rate in soaked barley seeds than in dry (111). Similar results have been noted by many others working with a multitude of materials. The explanations advanced at the time were that water started the germinative processes in the seeds treated and that the cells then advanced to those stages of mitosis that were more sensitive to the radiation. In recent years the discovery of the indirect effects of radiation caused by the products of irradiated water have added the possibility that in the presence of irradiated water more active radicals are formed than in the dry condition. That this phenomenon is more complex than these simple explanations indicate is illustrated by the experiments of Ehrenberg and Nybom (112) and of Caldecott (113) indicating that there is not a simple relation between water content and radiation damage. In both these cases, when the water content of the barley seed was reduced below that found in normally dry seeds, the mutation rate went up. This shows that changing the water content in either direction from an optimal one will change the mutation yield. Caldecott et al. have postulated that the change in sensitivity between desiccated and normal seeds is correlated with the availability of oxygen following irradiation (114).

I. CHEMICAL TREATMENTS

Various chemical treatments have been applied to cells in conjunction with radiation in an attempt to elucidate the nature of radiation-induced mutagenesis. Some of these have led to new concepts regarding chromosomal structure. An example of this may be seen in Steffensen's work in which he found that calcium-deficient plants showed increased chromosomal aberrations following X-irradiation (115). This result led him to postulate that the chromosome consists of many nucleoprotein units that are bound together by ionic links of calcium or magnesium. However, it should be pointed out that many of the chemical treatments utilized are nonspecific and have far-ranging effects; thus, the removal of calcium may be expected not only to affect those ionic links in the chromosome but also to affect the permeability of membranes and the activation of many enzymes. Similarly, the effect noted by Marshak (116) that treatment with NH_4OH during irradiation will decrease the frequency of aberrations in root tip mitoses is difficult to characterize because changes in pH can be expected to have far-reaching effects within the cytoplasm. It is not clear whether or not the differences brought about by those treatments that change the pH in the cell are the result of decreased breakage of the chromosomes or increased rejoining. However, Kaplan (117), who observed similar effects of ammonium hydroxide when barley seeds were presoaked with this compound, favors the latter process of increased rejoining as being the cause of the reduced mutation frequency.

In other cases it is easier to distinguish the reason for the changed aberration yield; thus, Stadler (15) found a significant increase in point mutation rate induced by X-rays in barley seeds when these seeds had been impregnated with salts of lead, uranium, or barium. The increased mutations in this case were caused by the increased absorption of the radiation energy by the heavy metal ions incorporated into the cell.

Other chemical compounds such as cyanide in barley seeds (118) or carbon monoxide in *Tradescantia* (119) have been found to increase the radiation-induced mutagenesis. It is thought that these compounds increase the amount of direct damage and chromosome breakage brought about by the radiation because they will block the cytochrome system in the respiratory cycle of the cell. This would be expected a) to increase the amount of intracellular oxygen, since that oxygen in solution in the cell will not be reduced to water if the electron transport system is inoperative, and b) to increase the hydrogen peroxide present in the cell, since blockage of the cytochrome system, especially by carbon monoxide, will increase the activity of the flavoprotein pathway of oxygen reduction. It should be pointed out, however, that experiments (107) have shown that the rejoining of chromosome breaks is dependent upon cellular metabolism and the production of ATP. In those cells that have been treated with cyanide or with carbon monoxide in the dark, chromosome breaks cannot rejoin. This latter effect can also be partly responsible for the effects of carbon monoxide and cyanide in increasing the amount of genetic damage.

Shortly after various chemicals were found to offer successful protection against radiation-induced death in bacteria and in mice, these chemicals were tried on plant chromosomes. Mikaelson (120) found that pretreatment with glutathione could cause a significant decrease in chromosome aberrations induced in *Tradescantia* root tips. Similar effects were also found with other chemicals such as cysteine and sodium hydrosulfite (121). A marked protection against two-hit aberrations in *Vicia* seed was noted by Wolff who pretreated with British antilewisite (BAL) and also with sodium hydrosulfite (122). It was further noticed that neither of these chemicals decreased the aberration yield beyond that induced following simple oxygen removal. Riley (123, 124) made extensive studies on the optimum concentrations of both BAL and sodium hydrosulfite in onion roots. This concentration was found to be about $2 \times 10^{-3} M$. Because all of these compounds can act as reducing agents, it is thought that their main activity is to remove the intracellular oxygen and thus bring about an oxygen effect. Whether the oxygen effect is induced by decreased breakage under anoxic conditions or by increased restitution will be covered in the discussion of the oxygen effect in the following section. It might be pointed out that these compounds in addition to removing oxygen might also either cover sensitive sites within the cell and so protect them or act as traps for the radicals produced by radiation. In either case one would expect less damage to be induced by the radiation.

IX. Oxygen Effect

In 1947 Thoday and Read (125) discovered that if the root tips of *Vicia faba* were irradiated with X-rays in the presence of oxygen more chromosomal aberrations were formed than if the irradiation was carried out anoxically. Later (126) it was found that if the irradiation was performed with densely ionizing α-rays an oxygen effect did not exist. These studies gave great impetus to further experiments designed to yield information on the physical-chemical nature of radiation-induced genetic damage. The experiments of Thoday and Read (125, 126) were explained on the basis that irradiation produces a damaging compound such as hydrogen peroxide in the water of the cell. The reactions by which this substance is formed have been presented in the chapter on radiochemical effects. It is thought that upon irradiation the water forms the active radicals H and OH. If oxygen is present in the water, then the H radicals will react with this to form HO_2 and H_2O_2 which are highly reactive oxidizing compounds. When α-rays are used, because of their dense pattern of ionization, radicals are produced so close together that two OH radicals have as great a probability of forming H_2O_2 in the presence of oxygen as in its absence. Thus no oxygen effect occurs with α-irradiation. This explanation of the oxygen effect is consistent with the observations made on the irradiation of water (108, 127, 128). Muller has argued against the rigorousness of this argument in reference to α-rays (3). He points out that if α-particles break chromosomes with a probability close to 1 under anoxic conditions then any increase in damage brought about by the presence of oxygen in the system will be superfluous and an oxygen effect will not be observed. However, he does agree that the experiments with X-rays do show that when the irradiation is performed with oxygen something is produced that is not produced under anoxic conditions.

Most workers have taken the explanation of Thoday and Read as a working hypothesis and then proceeded with experiments to elucidate the nature of this oxygen effect. Thus, in a series of experiments, Giles and co-workers (see review by Giles, 129) discovered in the microspores of *Trades-cantia* that the oxygen had to be present during irradiation to be effective. Anoxia before or after irradiation had no effect whatsoever on the aberration yield. Furthermore, they observed that the oxygen effect was only operative between 0 and 21 % oxygen. As soon as 21 % oxygen was reached, (129a), the addition of more oxygen had very little effect on increasing radiation damage (Fig. 21). Kihlman (129b) has found that the actual intracellular oxygen concentration under these conditions is much lower than 0.2 atm and that the saturation really occurs at very low oxygen tensions.

As might be expected from the α-radiation work, Giles also found that if the radiation was performed with fast neutrons that had an ion density and LET value between X-rays and α-particles then an intermediate oxygen effect would be found, i.e., less of an oxygen effect with neutrons than X-rays but more than with α-particles. This latter experiment whereby a different effect is observed with different radiations has led to the rejection of the idea that the oxygen effect is really a reflection of a physiological change brought about in the cell by the radiation, i.e., that the rate of mitosis was being affected and that after treatment with oxygen cells that were in a more sensitive stage at the time of the radiation were being sampled. It would be expected that if this were the case the oxygen effect would be similar with all radiations.

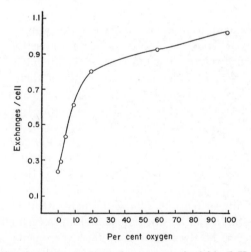

FIG. 21. Relation between amount of oxygen and yield of X-ray-induced exchanges. Data from Giles and Beatty, (129a).

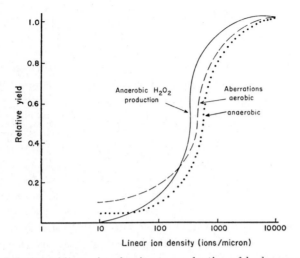

FIG. 22. Relation of linear ion density to production of hydrogen peroxide and chromosome aberrations. From Gray (129c).

The LET experiments have indicated (Fig. 22) that the amount of chromosomal damage induced by radiations of various ion densities closely follows the curve observed for peroxide production in water irradiated with various radiations (129c). This supports the concept that the products formed in water are the damaging compounds.

Since the genetic effects (aberrations) observed are the result of chromosome breaks, it is obvious that the increased damage in the presence of oxygen could be a reflection either of more breakage produced when the cell is irradiated with oxygen in the system, or of less rejoining of an equal number of breaks induced. Because of the lack of a postirradiation effect of anoxia in *Tradescantia* and also because a similar rejoining pattern occurred after irradiation in the presence of air or helium, Giles and coworkers have rejected the concept that the effect is due to a differential rejoining of the chromosome breaks and advocate that the oxygen effect really is caused by more primary breakage.

This latter conclusion, however, has been disputed by Schwartz (130) and by Baker (131), who believe the oxygen effect is caused by a differential reunion of the breaks induced by the radiation. Schwartz's experiments were performed on endosperm characters in maize. He found a difference in the ratios of two types of aberrations after the X-irradiation of pollen in oxygen or nitrogen. The mosiacs formed, which were assumed to be the result of the breakage of chromosomes with the resultant breakage-fusion-bridge cycle, showed a greater effect of oxygen than did the whole losses of characters which were assumed to be caused by two-break interstitial deletions. The argument utilized here is that rejoining occurs anyway both in oxygen and in nitrogen for the class of whole losses (interstitial deletions), and so any effect noted in this class of aberrations really is a reflection of the amount of breakage. Since only a small difference in oxygen versus nitrogen occurs for whole losses, it is assumed that the breakage was the same in both gases. Muller has pointed out that the actual chromosomal nature of the observed endosperm characteristics is not well known and that it seems premature to allow these experiments to cast doubt upon those performed by other workers who observed the chromosomes by direct cytological observation (3).

A series of papers by Baker and co-workers (104, 132, 133) on dominant lethals induced in *Drosophila* sperm demonstrates the complexity of determining between the two alternatives for the cause of the oxygen effect. These experiments can be explained on either hypothesis and do not help resolve the issue, nor do experiments performed on ring chromosomes in *Drosophila* in which it was found that the loss of the ring chromosome which supposedly always rejoins after breakage was not affected by radiation in oxygen as contrasted to nitrogen (131). The argument utilized for these experiments was similar to that used by Schwartz; i.e., since the breaks always rejoined in either gas and there was no oxygen effect it indicated that the same amount of breaks were induced in air as in nitrogen. From this the conclusion was drawn that in any system where the oxygen effect is observed it must be produced by differential rejoining. However, later experiments (134) have shown that a similar lack of oxygen effect occurs in the rod chromosome controls for these ring chromosome studies. This seems to weaken the force of the earlier argument, but Baker believes his data are still consistent with it.

In *Tradescantia* it has been reported that the oxygen effect is greater for two-hit phenomena than for one-hit phenomena. Those aberrations that are produced by single breaks show an air-to-nitrogen ratio of about 1.4 whereas the two-hit aberrations, which increase as the square of the dose, show a greater air-to-nitrogen ratio of 2.5. This would be expected on either hypothesis, since in both cases the number of effective breaks is increased. It has further been observed that the method of producing anoxia is immaterial, since anoxia produced by nitrogen is as effective as that produced by helium or vacuum (122, 129). Contrasted to this, however, is the work of Ebert et al. (135) showing that when gases are applied under high pressures those gases that are more fat soluble enter the cell more readily and are more protective than others. This has led them to postulate that within the cell there are particular sites at which the presence of oxygen confers radiation sensitivity. In order for a gas to be protective it must displace the oxygen from that site.

Since 100% protection is never observed in the absence of oxygen,

Giles and co-workers have postulated that the effects of radiation on chromosomes may be divided into those that are the direct effects and those that are indirect. The direct effects are caused by ionization within the chromosome itself, whereas the indirect effects are produced by the highly reactive substances which are formed in the immediate vicinity of the chromosomes and then diffuse to them. Operationally this enlarges the sensitive volume of the target to include not only its actual volume but also the surrounding area through which the products of irradiated water may diffuse to reach the chromosome.

It has been thought that the protection afforded by oxygen removal affected only the indirect effect (105, 122). This idea, however, may now have to be modified in light of the oxygen effect observed by Alexander (136) upon the irradiation of dry polymer films and by Caldecott (113) on the irradiation of dry barley seed. In either case the production or diffusion of the products of irradiated water would not be expected. These authors favor an interpretation whereby oxygen reacts with the activated sites within the molecules irradiated, much as the mechanism proposed by Alper to explain the oxygen effect observed when bacteria are irradiated (137).

Although the oxygen effect has been noticed in many materials and for mutations as well as for aberrations, i.e., in *Paramecium aurelia* (138), in *Aspergillus* (139), in *Drosophila* (132), and in barley (140), it is not always found. Thus Russell *et al.* (141) found that reducing the oxygen pressure failed to decrease the frequency of dominant lethals induced in the spermatozoa of mice. This, however, was taken as an indication that the spermatozoa of mice are already relatively anoxic.

Most workers have assumed that hydrogen peroxide is the damaging substance produced by irradiation of the cell in the presence of oxygen; however, this has been disputed by Kimball *et al.* (142), who found that they could not affect the mutations produced in *Paramecium aurelia* by adding high concentrations of peroxide to the media containing the animals. This has strengthened the conviction of some that HO_2 rather than H_2O_2 is the actual damaging radical. However, the experiments of King *et al.* (119) in which they found that carbon monoxide under pressure increased the aberrations induced in *Tradescantia* microspores have been interpreted as indicating that monoxide will block the cytochrome oxidase system in the microspores and thus increase the production of hydrogen peroxide within the cell by means of the flavoprotein pathway, and that this hy- . drogen peroxide is the actual damaging compound. Sobels (143, 144) has found that treatment of *Drosophila* males with the catalase inhibitors azide and cyanide before and after radiation increases the number of mutations and translocations. He therefore favors the concept that organic peroxides formed by the radiation are responsible for the damage.

In a later series of experiments in which it has been possible to separate the effects of radiation on breakage and rejoining, Wolff and co-workers (44, 145) have discovered that irradiation in the presence of anoxia affects both the *amount* of breaks induced and the *time* over which restitution occurs. If the seed of *Vicia faba* (146) or the microspores of *Tradescantia* (147) are irradiated under anoxic conditions, a double oxygen effect of less damage is noted. This is reflected both in fewer breaks being produced, and in those formed rejoining faster than if the irradiation were performed in air. It has further been shown that the rejoining of the breaks is dependent upon cellular metabolism and the production of ATP. Thus, if the irradiation of the seed of *Vicia faba* is fractionated into two doses such that complete rejoining of the breaks induced by the first dose takes place before the second irradiation, then one observes, in accordance with the fractionation effect, the sum of the aberrations produced by the two doses. However, if after the first dose one treats the material with various metabolic inhibitors such as low temperature, potassium cyanide, carbon monoxide in the dark, but not in the light, or with dinitrophenol, then the breaks from the first dose will not rejoin but will remain open and capable of forming exchanges with breaks induced by the second dose (106). The quantitative results from such experiments indicate that the application of metabolic inhibitors between two doses will give the same result as though the dose were not fractionated at all. This type of experiment has now been performed not only on *Vicia* (106), *Tradescantia* (147), *Allium* (148), and *Drosophila* (149) but also on *Chlamydomonas* (150). To explain these phenomena, Wolff and Luippold (146, 147) have postulated a "rejoining system" which is damaged by irradiation. When the irradiation is performed in the absence of oxygen, a typical oxygen effect of less damage occurs. This is reflected both in fewer breaks being induced and also, because of less damage to the "rejoining system," in those breaks rejoining faster. If, however, oxygen is removed after the irradiation or if cellular metabolism and the production of ATP are halted, then a converse effect is noted: no recovery to the damage primarily induced by the radiation can occur and the breaks remain open for longer periods of time. Only when the "rejoining system" is operative do chromosome breaks rejoin.

It has also been demonstrated that the numbers of two-hit aberrations can be decreased by the addition of ATP which accelerates the restitution of breaks (146). In this case a postirradiation treatment can cause a recovery of some of the radiation-induced genetic damage. It is still not clear whether or not the energy is utilized for the syntheses that rejoin the ends or for the recovery of the rejoining system. The results of these studies have confirmed Giles' hypothesis that the largest effect of oxygen is on the initial breakage of the chromosomes (145, 147). Actually these experiments have shown that the effect of anoxia on the rejoining of the breaks is in the opposite direction than that of the usual oxygen effect. In other words, the breaks are kept open by postirradiation anoxia, and an increase in damage rather than a decrease in results.

The breaks observed in most of these split-dose experiments remain open for long periods of time ranging from 4 minutes for *Tradescantia* chromatid breaks (20) to several hours for chromosome breaks in seed (44, 148), to several days in *Drosophila* sperm (151). They then require energy before they can rejoin. Because of these two observations it has been postulated that they are breaks of covalent bonds (106, 152). These are the breaks that have been affected by metabolic inhibitors. There is another class of breaks that closes faster than the above type (148, 152, 153). It has been proposed that these might be breaks of ionic bonds. In *Allium* it has been found that these fast-closing breaks may be kept open by post-irradiation treatments of carbon monoxide in the dark similarly to those breaks that are believed to occur in covalent bonds (148). This finding seems inconsistent with the concept that these are breaks of ionic bonds.

Split dose experiments on *Vicia faba* in which Wolff (50) used chloramphenicol and other protein synthesis inhibitors showed that protein synthesis was necessary for the rejoining of breaks of the nucleoprotein chromosomes. It was further shown (153a) that the inhibitors affected only protein synthesis and not nucleic acid synthesis in these beans. Consequently, Wolff has argued that the breaks induced by X-rays are probably breaks of protein bonds and that the "rejoining system" might be protein synthesis. This hypothesis is also consistent with the fact that rejoining, like protein synthesis but unlike DNA synthesis, can occur at any stage of the cell cycle.

It is usually assumed that the breaks induced by the radiation are formed immediately. Thoday (154) and Swanson (155) have maintained nevertheless that there is another type of break produced, a latent break that is not manifested until long after completion of the radiation. Swanson and Luning (156) believe that in the absence of oxygen this type of break is repaired and that in this manner postirradiation anoxia can induce a change in the amount of actual breakage. Conversely, Alper (137) has suggested that the latent breaks are not repaired by anoxia but rather are transformed into a real break by the oxygen. As yet, however, this concept of latent breaks may only be considered a working hypothesis.

X. The Effects of Polyploidy on Radiation-Induced Mutagenesis

A. In Higher Organisms

In 1929 Stadler (157) noticed that polyploid plants were seemingly more resistant to the induction of recessive mutations by X-rays than were diploids. He irradiated seeds of polyploid series of wheat and oats to induce mutations. After self-fertilization the plants grown from these seeds were checked in the next generation for seedling mutations. If a dominant gene was homozygous in diploid seeds, after the gene mutated to a recessive form in a given primordial cell, the head of seeds derived from that primordium would be heterozygous

$$\frac{A}{A} \rightarrow \frac{A}{a}.$$

Following self-fertilization the genes would be expected to segregate randomly and yield a 3:1 ratio of dominant to recessive plants, i.e.,

$$1\frac{A}{A} : 2\frac{A}{a} : 1\frac{a}{a}.$$

Thus, one-fourth of the offspring should show the mutant character. However, if the plant was tetraploid and possessed the genes in duplicate, then after mutation to a recessive form, the genotype of the mutated plants should be

$$\frac{A_1 A_2}{A_1 a_2}.$$

In the F_2 generation, although one-fourth of the offspring would be

$$\frac{A_1 a_2}{A_1 a_2},$$

the mutation would not be expressed in the phenotype because of the presence of the dominant A_1 genes. Thus it is seen that the expression of recessive mutations induced in polyploids would be masked. Stadler's results show just such an effect with hexaploid oats yielding no recessive mutations in the second generation whereas diploid oats showed many. Similarly, in wheat the hexaploid plants showed no mutations, the tetraploids showed but a few, and the diploids showed many.

It should be emphasized that this is an effect on the expression of recessive mutations rather than an effect on their induction. The sensitivity of individual chromosomes to radiation does not change in polyploids. Conger and Johnston (158) have found that diploid microspores of *Tradescantia*, with twice the chromosome number (i.e. twice the target size), have twice the chromosome aberration frequency as do haploid cells. These aberrations are immediately apparent in polyploids whereas recessive mutations are not. Thus, although irradiated polyploid seeds show fewer mutations than do diploid seeds, the polyploids show higher frequencies of chromosome aberrations (159, 160).

The apparent difficulties in obtaining plants showing the radiation-induced mutant characters has in the main discouraged the use of mutation breeding in polyploid crop plants. However, McKey (161) has shown that certain types of mutations can be observed with a much higher frequency in polyploids than in diploids. Checking in future generations mutations that were induced in hexaploid and diploid wheats, McKey found that there were many more mutations, a large proportion of which were dominant, in the polyploid species. He believes that the mutations he is observing are caused by chromosome exchanges, which, although lethal following segregation in the diploid, do get through the polyploid. The rationale here is that the extra sets of chromosomes will buffer an unbalanced chromosome exchange so that it will not be lethal to the gametophytic generation of the plant. These effects, rather than being caused by true gene mutations, are intergenic effects that become apparent only after segregation.

B. Experiments on the Radiation-Induced Inactivation of Haploid and Diploid Microorganisms

Latarjet and Ephrussi (162) and Zirkle and Tobias (163) have shown that the inactivation curves for haploid yeast are exponential or one hit whereas the curves for the inactivation of diploid yeast are sigmoid or multihit. The shapes of these curves led them to postulate that the inactivation was caused by recessive lethal mutations. If this were the case, the equations for the theoretical curves could be explained as follows: In the haploid organisms the inactivation of any gene presumably would cause death because the dominant form of the gene would not be present in the system to overcome the deficiency of gene product. Since the radiation hits on the genome would be distributed according to the Poisson formula $e^{-m} \cdot m^r / r!$ (see p. 426) then the proportion of cells having no hits would be e^{-kD} where m (the mean number of hits) is equal to kD (a constant $\times$ dose). This would be the proportion of survivors. One minus this ($1 - e^{-kD}$) would be the fraction receiving one or more hits and thus becoming inactivated. The curve for survival, $s = e^{-kD}$, is exponential. If the organism were diploid, then in order to inactivate the cells both genes at a given locus would have to be hit. If the organism were triploid, then all three genes would have to be hit to produce inactivation. Since the probability of hitting one of the genes at a given locus in a polyploid series is $(1 - e^{-kD})$ as explained above, then the probability of hitting two genes at this locus independently will be the product of the separate probabilities or $(1 - e^{-kD})^2$. In the case of the triploid this will be $(1 - e^{-kD})^3$. Thus the survivors of hits at a particular gene locus will be equal to $1 - (1 - e^{-kD})^n$, where n is equal to the ploidy of the organism. However, the survival of the organism as a whole not only is dependent upon survival of one locus but is subject to survival at all different loci. If the sensitivity reflected by the constant k is the same for all genes in the genome then the survival curve will be equal to $[1 - (1 - e^{-kD})^n]^x$, where x is the number of genes in the system. This simply means that the probability of simultaneous survival at all loci is equal to the product of the survivals at each locus.

Unfortunately, most survival data for diploid microorganisms have shown that although the ploidy number (n in the above equations) might be 2, the number of genes (x in the above equation) usually is 1 (164). Some experiments (165, 166) have indicated that the number x might be 12 to 30. Since this patently cannot be the number of genes in the organism, it is obvious that the interpretation that inactivation of microorganisms is based upon recessive lethal killing does not give a true explanation of the experimental data. Experiments by Mortimer (167) have shown that in the yeast case in addition to recessive lethal damage there is another type of damage characterized as dominant lethality which shows a progressive increase in radiosensitivity with increases in ploidy above the diploid. Thus, in yeast the haploids are the most sensitive to radiation, the diploids the most resistant, and the higher ploidy cells intermediate in resistance. The increased sensitivity of cells of higher ploidy than 2 is consistent with the concept that the dominant lethality is produced by chromosome aberrations. However, since the cells are so small, adequate cytology has not yet been performed to confirm this point.

In view of the fact that the value of x obtained from fitting survival curves to the above equations is too small to represent the number of genes in the organism, the equations must be interpreted in a more abstract sense. Thus it may be considered that x instead of referring to the number of genes refers only to the number of homologous sites necessary to be hit for inactivation of the organism (166, 168). A more formal definition of x must await further insight into the nature of the radiation-induced killing of microorganisms.

XI. Concluding Remarks

In this chapter an attempt has been made to give an elementary background to the problems and theories in radiation genetics. Many topics only alluded to here are treated in more detail in the various chapters of the book dealing with specific groups of organisms. Similarly many of the important questions in radiation genetics such as the effects on mammals, on populations, and genetic hazards of radiation to man will be found in other chapters.

XII. References

1. Muller, H. J., *Science* **66**, 84 (1927).
2. Stadler, L. J., *Proc. Natl. Acad. Sci. U. S.* **14**, 69 (1928).

3. Muller, H. J., in "Radiation Biology" (A. Hollaender, ed.), Vol. I, pp. 351–626. McGraw-Hill, New York, 1954.
4. Catcheside, D. G., Advances in Genet. 2, 271 (1948).
5. Zelle, M. R., in "Radiation Biology" (A. Hollaender, ed.), Vol. II, pp. 365–430 McGraw-Hill, New York, 1955.
6. Pomper, S., and Atwood, K. C., in "Radiation Biology" (A. Hollaender, ed), Vol. II, pp. 431–454. McGraw-Hill, New York, 1955.
7. Luria, S. E., in "Radiation Biology" (A. Hollaender, ed.), Vol. II, pp. 333–364. McGraw-Hill, New York, 1955.
8. Kimball, R. F., in "Radiation Biology" (A. Hollaender, ed.), Vol. II, pp. 285–332. McGraw-Hill, New York, 1955.
9. Muller, H. J., and Pontecorvo, G., Genetics 27, 157 (1941).
10. Catcheside, D. G., and Lea, D. E., J. Genet. 47, 1 (1945).
11. Demerec, M., and Fano, U., Genetics 29, 348 (1944).
12. Muller, H. J., Proc. Intern. Congr. Eugenics, and Congr., New York, 1921, pp. 7–8 (1923).
13. Timoféeff-Ressovsky, N. W., "Experimentelle Mutationsforschung in der Vererbungslehre," Steinkopf, Leipzig, 1937.
14. Timoféeff-Ressovsky, N. W., Nachr. Ges. Wiss. Göttingen Math.-Physik. Ke., Fachgruppe VI 1, 163 (1935).
14a. Timoféeff-Ressovsky, N. W., and Delbrück, M., Z. Induktive Abstammungs- u. Vererbungslehre 71, 322 (1936).
15. Stadler, L. J., Science 68, 186 (1928).
16. Noethling, W., and Stubbe, H., Verhandl. Intern. Kongr. Lichtforsch, 3rd Kongr , Wiesbaden 1, 238 (1936).
17. Knapp, E., Z. Induktive Abstammungs- u. Vererbungslehre 70, 309 (1934).
18. Sansome, E. R., Demerec, M., and Hollaender, A., Am. J. Botany 32, 218 (1945)
18a. Timoféef-Ressovsky, N. W., Chromosoma 1, 310 (1939).
19. Uphoff, D. E., and Stern, C., Science 109, 709 (1949).
20. Lea, D. E., "Actions of Radiations on Living Cells." Cambridge Univ. Press, London, 1946.
21. Patterson, J. T., Biol. Bull. 61, 133 (1931).
22. Muller, H. J., J. Genet. 40, 1 (1940).
23. Ray-Chauduri, S. P., Proc. Intern. Congr. Genet. 7th Congr., p. 246 (1941).
24. Ray-Chauduri, S. P., Proc. Roy. Soc. Edinburgh B62, 66 (1944).
25. Timoféeff-Ressovsky, N. W., and Zimmer, K. G., Strahlentherapie 53, 322 (1935).
25a. Russell, W. L., Russell, L. B., and Kelly, E. M., Science 128, 1546 (1958).
26. Hanson, F. B., Am. Naturalist 60, 201 (1929).
27. Schechtmann, J., J. Exptl. Biol. U.S.S.R. 6, 271 (1930).
28. Efroimson, W. P., Biol. Zentr. 51, 491 (1931).
29. Pickhan, A., Strahlentherapie 52, 369 (1934).
30. Zimmer, K. G., Griffith, H. D., and Timoféeff-Ressovsky, N. W., Strahlentherapie 59, 130 (1937).
31. Wilhelmy, E., Timoféeff-Ressovsky, N. W., and Zimmer, K. G., Strahlentherapie 57, 521 (1936).
32. Fricke, H., and Demerec, M., Proc. Natl. Acad. Sci. U. S. 23, 320 (1937).
33. Stubbe, H., Z. Induktive Abstammungs- u. Vererbungslehre 64, 181 (1933).
34. Edington, C. W., Genetics 41, 814 (1956).
35. Edington, C. W., and Randolph, M. L., Genetics 43, 715 (1958).
36. Timoféeff-Ressovsky, N. W., and Zimmer, K. G., Biol. Zentr. 59, 358 (1939)
37. Timoféeff-Ressovsky, N. W., and Zimmer, K. G., Naturwiss. 26, 108 (1938).

38. Sax, K., *Genetics* **23**, 494 (1938).
39. Lea, D. E., and Catcheside, D. G., *J. Genet.* **44**, 216 (1942).
40. McClintock, B., *Genetics* **26**, 542 (1941).
41. Thoday, J. M., *New Phytologist* **53**, 511 (1954).
42. Muller, H. J., *XV Intern. Physiol. Congr.* (*Leningrad-Moscow*) 286 (1935).
43. Sturtevant, A. H., and Beadle, G. W., *Genetics* **21**, 554 (1936).
44. Wolff, S., *Nature* **173**, 501 (1954).
45. Catcheside, D. G., Lea, D. E., and Thoday, J. M., *J. Genet.* **47**, 137 (1946).
45a. Giles, N. H., *Genetics* **28**, 398 (1943).
45b. Sax, K., *Cold Spring Harbor Symposia Quant. Biol.* **9**, 93 (1941).
46. Thoday, J. M., *Nature* **181**, 932 (1958).
47. Giles, N. H., *Proc. Natl. Acad. Sci. U. S.* **26**, 567 (1940).
48. Sax, K., *Genetics* **25**, 41 (1940).
49. Bauer, H., Demerec, M., and Kaufmann, B. P., *Genetics* **23**, 610 (1938).
50. Wolff, S., *Radiation Research Suppl.* **No. 1**, 453 (1959).
50a. Carlson, J. G., *Proc. Natl. Acad. Sci. U. S.* **27**, 42 (1941).
50b. Rick, C. M., *Genetics* **25**, 467 (1940).
51. Wolff, S., Atwood, K. C., Randolph, M. L., and Luippold, H. E., *J. Biophys. Biochem. Cytol.* **4**, 365 (1958).
52. Sax, K., *Proc. Natl. Acad. Sci. U. S.* **25**, 225 (1939).
52a. Fabergé, A. C., *Z. Induktive Abstammungs- u. Vererbungslehre* **87**, 392 (1956).
52b. Caldecott, R. S., Beard, B. H., and Gardner, G. O., *Genetics* **53**, 240 (1954).
53. Wolff, S., and Luippold, H. E., *Nature* **179**, 208 (1957).
54. Conger, A. D., *Proc. 10th Intern. Congr. Genet.* VII 57 (1958).
55. Conger, A. D., and Giles, N. H., *Genetics* **35**, 397 (1950).
56. Timoféeff-Ressovsky, N. W., Zimmer, K. G., and Delbrück, M., *Nachr. Ges. Wiss. Göttingen Math.-physik. Kl. Fachgruppe VI* **1**, 163 (1935).
57. Lea, D. E., and Catcheside, D. G., *J. Genet.* **47**, 41 (1945).
58. Muller, H. J., *Am. Naturalist* **59**, 405 (1935).
59. Bauer, H., *Naturwiss.* **27**, 821 (1939).
60. Whiting, A. R., *Radiation Research* **2**, 71 (1955).
61. von Borstel, R. C., and Wolff, S., *Proc. Natl. Acad. Sci. U. S.* **40**, 1138 (1955).
62. Rogers, R. W., and von Borstel, R. C., *Radiation Research* **7**, 484 (1958).
63. Atwood, K. C., von Borstel, R. C., and Whiting, A. R., *Genetics* **41**, 804 (1956).
64. von Borstel, R. C., *Proc. 10th Intern. Congr. Genet.* VII 303 (1958).
65. Sonnenblick, B. P., *Proc. Natl. Acad. Sci. U. S.* **26**, 373 (1940).
66. Altenburg, E., *Anat. Record* **47**, 383 (1930).
67. Altenburg, E., *Science* **78**, 587 (1933).
68. Altenburg, E., *Am. Naturalist* **68**, 491 (1934).
69. Stadler, L. J., and Sprague, G. F., *Proc. Natl Acad. Sci. U. S.* **22**, 572 (1936).
70. Hollaender, A., *Proc. 7th Intern. Congr. Genet.* (J. Genet. Suppl. 1941) **128**, 153 (1939).
71. Giles, N. H., *Cold Spring Harbor Symposia Quant. Biol.* **16**, 283 (1951).
72. de Serres, F. J., *Genetics* **43**, 187 (1958).
73. Demerec, M., Hollaender, A., Houlahan, M. B., and Bishop, M., *Genetics* **27**, 139 (1942).
74. Stadler, L. J., and Uber, F. M., *Genetics* **27**, 84 (1942).
75. Swanson, C. P., *J. Gen. Physiol.* **26**, 485 (1943).
76. Fabergé, A. C., *Genetics* **36**, 549 (1951).
77. Kirby-Smith, J. S., and Craig, D. L., *Genetics* **42**, 176 (1957).

78. Hollaender, A., and Emmons, E. W., *Cold Spring Harbor Symposia Quant. Biol.* **9**, 179 (1941).
79. Lovelace, R., *Proc. Natl. Acad. Sci. U. S.* **40**, 1129 (1954).
79a. Swanson, C. P., *Genetics* **27**, 491 (1942).
80. Swanson, C. P., *J. Cellular Comp. Physiol. Suppl.* **1**, 27 (1952).
81. Novick, A., and Szilard, L., *Proc. Natl. Acad. Sci. U. S.* **35**, 591 (1949).
82. Newcombe, H. B., and McGregor, J. F., *Genetics* **39**, 619 (1954).
83. Knapp, E., *Z. Induktive Abstammungs- u. Vererbungslehre* **74**, 54 (1938).
84. Sax, K., and Swanson, C. P., *Am. J. Botany* **28**, 52 (1941).
85. Sparrow, A. H., *Ann. N. Y. Acad. Sci.* **51**, 1508 (1951).
86. Luning, K. G., *Hereditas* **38**, 91 (1952).
87. Swanson, C. P., "Cytology and Cytogenetics." Prentice-Hall, Englewood Cliffs, New Jersey, 1957.
88. Oster, I. I., *in* "Advances in Radiobiology" (G. C. de Hevesy, A. G. Forssberg, and J. D. Abbatt, eds.), pp. 475–479. Oliver & Boyd, Edinburgh, 1957.
88a. Sparrow, A. H., Moses, M. J., and Steele, R., *Brit. J. Radiol.* **25**, 182 (1952).
89. Sax, K., *Proc. Natl. Acad. Sci. U. S.* **29**, 18 (1943).
90. Wolff, S., and von Borstel, R. C., *Proc. Natl. Acad. Sci. U. S.* **40**, 187 (1954).
91. Conger, A. D., *Proc. Natl. Acad. Sci. U. S.* **34**, 470 (1948).
92. Swanson, C. P., *Genetics* **29**, 61 (1944).
93. Kaufmann, B. P., and Hollaender, A., *Genetics* **31**, 368 (1946).
94. Swanson, C. P., and Stadler, L. J., *in* "Radiation Biology" (A. Hollaender, ed.), Vol. II, pp. 249–284. McGraw-Hill, New York, 1955.
95. Kaufmann, B. P., Hollaender, A., and Gay, H., *Genetics* **31**, 349 (1946).
96. Swanson, C. P., and Hollaender, A., *Proc. Natl. Acad. Sci. U. S.* **32**, 295 (1946).
97. Swanson, C. P., and Yost, H. T., *Proc. Natl. Acad. Sci. U. S.* **37**, 796 (1951).
98. McElroy, W. D., and Swanson, C. P., *Quart. Rev. Biol.* **26**, 328 (1951).
98a. Moh, C. C., and Withrow, A. B., *Radiation Research* **10**, 13 (1954).
99. Yost, H. T., *Genetics* **36**, 176 (1951).
100. Hollaender, A., and Swanson, C. P., *Genetics* **32**, 90 (1947).
100a. Wolff, S., and Luippold, H. E., *in* "The Finsen Memorial Congress, Proceedings Third International Congress of Photobiology." Elsevier, Amsterdam, 1961.
101. Sax, K., and Enzmann, E. V., *Proc. Natl. Acad. Sci. U. S.* **25**, 317 (1939).
102. Fabergé, A. C., *J. Genet.* **39**, 229 (1940).
103. Mickey, G. H., *Genetica* **21**, 386 (1939).
104. Baker, W. K., and Sgourakis, E., *Proc. Natl. Acad. Sci. U. S.* **36**, 176 (1950).
105. Giles, N. H., and Riley, H. P., *Proc. Natl. Acad. Sci. U. S.* **36**, 337 (1950).
106. Wolff, S., and Luippold, H. E., *Science* **122**, 231 (1955).
107. Fabergé, A. C., *Genetics* **33**, 609 (1948).
108. Bonet-Maury, P., and LeFort, M., *Nature* **162**, 381 (1948).
109. Brumfield, R. T., *Proc. Natl. Acad. Sci. U. S.* **29**, 190 (1943).
110. Davidson, D., *Ann. Botany* **22**, 183 (1958).
111. Gustafsson, A., *Hereditas* **22**, 281 (1937).
112. Ehrenberg, L., and Nybom, N., *Acta Agr. Scand. IV* **3**, 396 (1952).
113. Caldecott, R. S., *Radiation Research* **3**, 316 (1955).
114. Caldecott, R. S., Johnson, E. B., North, D. T., and Konzak, C. F., *Proc. Natl. Acad. Sci. U. S.* **43**, 975 (1957).
115. Steffensen, D., *Proc. Natl. Acad. Sci. U. S.* **41**, 155 (1955).
116. Marshak, A., *Proc. Soc. Exptl. Biol. Med.* **38**, 705 (1938).

117. Kaplan, A. W., *Naturwiss.* **37**, 546 (1950).
118. D'Amato, F., and Gustafsson, A., *Hereditas* **34**, 181 (1948).
119. King, E. D., Schneiderman, H., and Sax, K., *Proc. Natl. Acad. Sci. U. S.* **38**, 34 (1952).
120. Mikaelson, K., *Science* **116**, 172 (1952).
121. Mikaelson, K., *Proc. Natl. Acad. Sci. U. S.* **40**, 171 (1954).
122. Wolff, S., *Genetics* **39**, 356 (1954).
123. Riley, H. P., *Genetics* **37**, 618 (1952).
124. Riley, H. P., *Am. J. Botany* **42**, 765 (1955).
125. Thoday, J. M., and Read, J., *Nature* **160**, 608 (1947).
126. Thoday, J. M., and Read, J., *Nature* **163**, 133 (1949).
127. Weiss, J., *Nature* **153**, 577 (1944).
128. Allen, A. O., *J. Phys. & Colloid Chem.* **52**, 479 (1948).
129. Giles, N. H., *in* "Radiation Biology" (A. Hollaender, ed.), Vol. I, pp. 713–761. McGraw-Hill, New York, 1954.
129a. Giles, N. H., and Beatty, A. V., *Science* **112**, 643 (1950).
129b. Kihlman, B. A., *Nature* **182**, 730 (1958).
129c. Gray, L. H., *Brit. Jour. Radiol.* **26**, 609 (1953).
130. Schwartz, D., *Proc. Natl. Acad. Sci. U. S.* **38**, 490 (1952).
131. Baker, W. K., *Brookhaven Symposia in Biol.* **No. 8**, 191 (1955).
132. Baker, W. K., and Edington, C. W., *Genetics* **37**, 665 (1952).
133. Baker, W. K., and Von Halle, E. S., *Proc. Natl. Acad. Sci. U. S.* **39**, 152 (1953).
134. Baker, W. K., *Genetics* **42**, 735 (1957).
135. Ebert, M., Hornsey, S., and Howard, A., *Nature* **181**, 613 (1958).
136. Alexander, P., *in* "Advances in Radiobiology" (G. C. de Hevesy, A. G. Forssberg, and J. D. Abbatt, eds.), pp. 8–13. Oliver & Boyd, Edinburgh, 1957.
137. Alper, T., *Radiation Research* **5**, 573 (1956).
138. Kimball, R. F., and Gaither, N. T., *Genetics* **36**, 558 (1951).
139. Stapleton, G. E., and Hollaender, A., *J. Cellular Comp. Physiol.* **39**, Suppl. III (1952).
140. Hayden, B., and Smith, L., *Genetics* **34**, 26 (1949).
141. Russell, W. L., Kile, J. C., and Russell, L. B., *Genetics* **36**, 574 (1951).
142. Kimball, R. F., Hearon, J. Z., and Gaither, N. T., *Radiation Research* **3**, 435 (1955).
143. Sobels, F. H., *Z. Induktive Abstammungs- u. Vererbungslehre* **86**, 399 (1955).
144. Sobels, F. H., *in* "Advances in Radiobiology" (G. C. de Hevesy, A. G. Forssberg, and J. D. Abbatt, eds.), pp. 449–456. Oliver & Boyd, Edinburgh, 1957.
145. Wolff, S., and Atwood, K. C., *Proc. Natl. Acad. Sci. U. S.* **40**, 187 (1954).
146. Wolff, S., and Luippold, H. E., *in* "Progress in radiobiology" (J. S. Mitchell, B. E. Holmes, and C. L. Smith, eds.), pp. 217–222. Oliver & Boyd, Edinburgh, 1956.
147. Wolff, S., and Luippold, H. E., *Genetics* **43**, 493 (1958).
148. Cohn, N., *Genetics* **43**, 362 (1958).
149. Abrahamson, S., *Genetics* **44**, 173 (1959).
150. Jacobson, B., *Radiation Research* **7**, 394 (1957).
151. Kaufmann, B. P., *Cold Spring Harbor Symposia Quant. Biol.* **9**, 82 (1941).
152. Wolff, S., *in* "Advances in Radiobiology" (G. C. de Hevesy, A. G. Forssberg, and J. D. Abbatt, eds.), pp. 463–474. Oliver & Boyd, Edinburgh, 1957.
153. Wolff, S., and Luippold, H. E., *Proc. Natl. Acad. Sci. U. S.* **42**, 510 (1956).
153a. Wolff, S., *Am. Naturalist* **94**, 85 (1960).
154. Thoday, J. M., *Heredity* **6** *Suppl.* 299 (1953).

155. Swanson, C. P., *in* "Radiobiology Symposium, 1954" (Z. M. Bacq and P. Alexander, eds.), p. 254. Academic Press, New York, 1955.
156. Swanson, C. P., and Luning, K. G., *in* "Radiobiology Symposium, 1954" (Z. M. Bacq and P. Alexander, eds.), pp. 260. Academic Press, New York, 1955.
157. Stadler, L. J., *Proc. Natl. Acad. Sci. U. S.* **15**, 876 (1929).
158. Conger, A. D., and Johnston, A. H., *Nature* **178**, 271 (1956).
159. Fröier, K., Gelin, O., and Gustafsson, A., *Botan. Notiser* p. 199 (1941).
160. Smith, L., *J. Agr. Research* **73**, 137 (1946).
161. MacKey, J., *Acta Agr. Scand.* **4**, 549 (1954).
162. Latarjet, R., and Ephrussi, B., *Compt. rend. acad. sci.* **229**, 306 (1942).
163. Zirkle, R. E., and Tobias, C. A., *Arch. Biochem. Biophys.* **47**, 282 (1953).
164. Lucke, W. H., and Sarachek, A., *Nature* **171**, 1014 (1953).
165. Zelle, M., and Ogg, J., *J. Bacteriol.* **74**, 485 (1957).
166. Uretz, N., *Radiation Research* **2**, 240 (1955).
167. Mortimer, R., *Radiation Research* **9**, 312 (1958).
168. Atwood, K. C., and Norman, A., *Proc. Natl. Acad. Sci. U. S.* **35**, 696 (1949).

CHAPTER 7

The Induction of Mutations as a Method in Plant Breeding

ÅKE GUSTAFSSON

Genetics Department, Forest Research Institute, Stockholm, Sweden

CONTENTS

I. Historical Background

In his famous "Mutationstheorie" (1901) de Vries declared that a knowledge of the laws of mutation will probably lead to the production of mutations artificially and deliberately and in this way to new properties in plants and animals. Possibly, through our command of mutations, we shall be able to raise better species of crop plants and animals (1). In 1904 he then proposed that "the rays of Röntgen and Curie, which are able to penetrate into the interior of living cells, be used in an attempt to alter the hereditary particles in the germ cells" (2). The production of useful mutations was inaugurated in an *empirical* sense, however, by Muller's discovery that X-irradiation induces mutations in *Drosophila*. In fact, he concluded that "similarly for the practical breeder, it is hoped that the method will prove useful" (3). Stadler, in his contemporary work on mutations in higher plants, was more negative in his attitude. He considered

477

the induced ones as largely valueless for practical purposes, possibly with the exception of fruit tree improvement (4).

Contrary to this view, positive results were obtained in crop plants by Soviet scientists, notably Delaunay and Sapehin (5), in the early thirties. Simultaneously a series of German workers, around Baur and Stubbe, reached similar conclusions (6). Evidence in favor of their attitude was gained by Freisleben and Lein (7), who worked out practical means for the production and isolation of induced mutations in barley. In later years a great number of important data have been gathered by Stubbe and his co-workers at Gatersleben (8).

The first productive mutants tested on a large scale seem to have been raised by Tollenaar in Indonesia (9) and by Nilsson-Ehle and Gustafsson in Sweden (10), starting their work with induced mutations soon after Muller's discovery. Gustafsson concludes that "by appropriate methods we may induce hereditary changes causing an increase in grain yield, or in yield of vegetative matter, or in both of these properties. Moreover, we can alter the ecological requirements entirely, and in this way create new ecotypes—with the same, an abbreviated, or a prolonged life cycle. Even conspicuous changes may reach a remarkable level of productivity. Finally, chromosome breakage and rearrangement do not prevent a complete or even raised production."

The isolation of new market varieties in crop plants is, of course, a complicated task, owing to the long time needed for large-scale testing (in Swedish cereals 5 to 10 years). X-Ray products released into the market are the Svalöf Primex white mustard (11) and the Weibull variety "Strål" (Ray) pea (12). Approved also are the Svalöf Pallas barley (13) and Mari barley (cf. ref. 85). In tobacco a chlorophyll mutant was cultivated on a large scale in the thirties owing to its high quality (9, 13).

In recent years workers all over the world, especially in the United States, India, and Japan, have devoted much interest to the production of useful mutants in crop plants. Of special importance is the utilization of chronic and acute γ-irradiation (14). Another method, that of "chromosome engineering" (15, 16), has recently attracted wide interest. The expression implies that genes and chromosome segments can be transferred from one species to another by means of chromosome breakage and translocation.

According to Dubinin (17) the Soviet scientists Nadson and Filipof, even in 1925, were able to show that X-irradiation influences the sexual processes in lower fungi and induces mutations, said to produce improvements from a practical point of view. Thanks to the work of Hollaender and co-workers, it was then really proved that induced mutants can be selected and utilized for practical purposes in lower organisms, e.g., *Peni-*

cillium and *Aspergillus* (18). The early achievements with regard to penicillin-producing mutants can be summarized in the following manner (19):

Stock No. NRRL 1951. *Penicillium chrysogenum,* isolated from a moldy cantaloupe, producing 100 units of penicillin per milliliter in submerged culture.

Stock No. 1951. B 25. A natural variant producing up to 250 units of penicillin per milliliter.

Stock X-1612. *An X-ray mutant,* producing more than 500 units of penicillin per milliliter.

Stock Wis. Q-176. *An ultraviolet mutant,* producing more than 900 units of penicillin per milliliter.

Stock Wis. 49-2105. *Reapplication of ultraviolet and nitrogen mustard* gave rise to this variant—a mixture of culture types—producing more than 1500 units of penicillin per milliliter.

In this way, by the repeated application of mutagenic agents (X-rays, ultraviolet, nitrogen mustard), mutants increasing penicillin yield were isolated. In a similar fashion "blockade" mutants leading to the accumulation of different metabolic products, organic acids, vitamins, etc., have been produced—for fungi, illustrated by the increased production of ithaconic acid (20). Such mutants have also been detected in crop plants, for instance with regard to the formation of anthranilic acid in maize (21).

These examples suffice to illustrate the general correctness of the suggestions originally put forward by de Vries, as well as the validity of Muller's findings, for crop plants and microorganisms. In some animals induced translocations can be utilized, too (17). Results obtained with chemical mutagens add conclusive evidence to the view that artificial mutagenesis may imply a supplementary, for some species even a better, method of improvement than the traditional ones of mere selection and recombination.

II. Spontaneous Mutability

The organism generally functions as a balanced whole. This implies that the various structures and enzyme systems work together in carrying out a series of vital functions. When differentiation of a multicellular plant organism proceeds, however, individual tissues and organs may take in distinct functions and become specialized. The genetic material will change according to the demands put on the tissue or organ in question. The tissue may acquire polyploidy of various levels and of various kinds, as known for many normal and abnormal tissues in plants and animals (22).

In addition, single chromosomes or chromosome pairs, or whole bunches of chromosomes, can be lost or gained in specialized tissues. Even a far-reaching breakdown of the chromosome material may take place so that, finally, just the centromere regions remain of the full chromosome complement (23). To what extent a *genic* differentiation takes place inside an organism is not known. The frequent occurrence of chimeras in nature, especially in vegetatively propagating organisms like potato and fruit trees (24), indicates that somatic mutations are not rare and that such mutations may accumulate and even be of importance for the harmonious functioning of the organism. Moreover, mutation is known to take different courses in different tissues (25).

Natural radiation is not responsible for more than a small part of an organism's mutability, say less than 10 %. In addition, spontaneous mutation may be caused by the formation of intracellular (or even intranuclear) mutagens like formaldehyde, peroxides, and various epoxides (26) or simply by the upset of cell balance, for instance by the breakdown or nonformation of antimutagens (e.g., catalase), or by a loss of Ca^{++} and Mg^{++} ions inside the chromosomes. Such may be the cause of the increased mutation rates after aging of seeds and pollen (27).

Moreover, we must take into account that the individual gene molecule is not a rigid entity but will become more or less stable with changes in the remaining genotype. As shown by studies in maize (28) individual genes drastically or slightly influence the mutability of other genes. The "activator-dissociation" complex of maize should here be considered, too, although we do not yet know how far its principles of heterochromatic influence are valid for other crop plants, especially those lacking in visible heterochromatin. But also a condition of general heterozygosity may lead to enormously high mutation rates, as shown for the speltoid locus of chromosome IX in hexaploid wheat, higher than ever obtained with X-irradiation or neutron irradiation (29). Wheat is a regularly self-fertilizing species. Conversely, inbred lines of some cross-fertilizing organisms, like rye, maize, or *Nicotiana*, may show a rapid transformation into heterozygosity (30). This is another indication that an unusual (unadapted) state of the organism, via unknown changes in metabolism, may raise mutability.

Finally, temperature and intramolecular agitation will influence mutation rate, as outlined by Timoféeff-Ressovsky and co-workers in their classical studies (31).

Summarizing, we conclude that a plant breeder cannot ignore spontaneous mutations. Many commercial varieties, said to be the outcome of gene recombination, no doubt go back to spontaneous mutation, appearing independent of or in connection with heterozygosity. In other instances the isolation of spontaneous mutations has been skillfully applied. Such is the case with regard to the isolation of alkaloid-free varieties in lupine breeding and the subsequent improvement of the original variants by means of mutation (32). In *Avena* a mutant resistant to Victoria blight (the American mid-south oat variety C.I. 6977), was isolated by the help of a special infection technique and then released into the market (33). In sugar beet, monogerm mutants indicate a definite progress, compared to the multigerm materials generally cultivated (34). Similarly in vegetatively propagating organisms, like potato and fruit trees, sports have given rise to commercial varieties. Such a sport is "Giant Bintje potato VK," which is cultivated in some areas of Sweden (35). Various sports in apples, peaches, and plums (36) form other examples. In any crop plant where the breeder can elaborate precise screening techniques for selection (like the precipitation method of alkaloids devised for lupines) he will be able to select favorable mutations, whether these have arisen spontaneously under normal conditions, or whether they depend on rare biochemical events within the organism, on heterozygosity, or on artificial influences, enumerated on the following pages.

III. Mutagenic Agents and the Process of Mutation

In this section some rules will be presented with regard to the artificial production of useful mutations, comparing different types of *radiation* with one another as well as with *chemical mutagens*.

A. IONIZING RADIATIONS

The most commonly used mutagenic agent in higher plants is irradiation from the X-ray tube. X-Rays are easy to apply and to measure. For the first stage of planned mutation production and analysis X-irradiation forms a most valuable tool. In recent times X-rays have been replaced or supplemented by γ-rays, chiefly from the radioactive isotopes Co^{60} and Cs^{137}, or by neutrons produced in cyclotrons or reactors.

By the use of different isotopes as well as radiations from cyclotrons and synchrotrons a wide range in linear energy transfer (ionization density) (37) can easily be obtained in mutation work.

In 1948 it was shown for barley that X-rays, on the one hand, and neutrons, on the other, do not work alike genetically. It was possible by means of neutron treatment to decrease the fertility of the first-generation (X_1) plants, resulting from irradiated seeds, below the level generally obtained with X-irradiation (38). Later on, numerous workers have shown that the physiological state of the irradiated seeds exerts a much greater influence in the case of X-rays than of neutrons. Water content, oxygen *contra* nitrogen atmosphere, and type of storage after irradiation are examples of such physiological factors (39). Also with regard to chromosomal effects the two types of radiation are dissimilar. Chromosome breakage is relatively much more frequent with neutrons than with X-rays. The dose curve of induced translocations is a two-hit event with X-rays, but it often approaches a one-hit event with neutrons (40). Similarly, the types of mutation and the mutation spectra are not identical (39).

In a publication dealing with the so-called erectoides mutations in barley it was shown that the two types of ionizing agent do not act identically with regard to specific gene loci (41). Sixty-nine erectoides mutations, induced by different kinds of sparsely ionizing agents as well as by neutrons and α-rays (from radon), implied changes in twenty-two different loci. Locus *a* never mutated with neutrons, although mutations were common with X- and γ-rays, whereas, with regard to loci *c*, *m*, *d*, and *g*, neutrons were highly effective in producing mutations. Changes in locus *c* were frequently connected with chromosome breakage at the erectoides locus itself. This never happened in the case of locus *a* and only once with regard to other loci (one case in locus *d*). The results indicate how significant is an analysis applying different kinds of ionizing radiations, and that a conclusion drawn from the behavior of one or a few loci can be applied to that of other loci only with some caution. This is verified by the erectoides loci *a*, *b*, *c*, *m*, and *r*, which all have definite properties or mechanisms of mutation. Consequently different types of ionizing radiation really lead to different results, also in a strict genetic sense.

On the other hand, γ-irradiation can be given in extremely high dosages within a short time, to large objects like potato tubers, fruit and forest trees, or parts of such, with a Co^{60} or Cs^{137} source of reasonable strength. Moreover, it is easily arranged by such means to irradiate distinct phases of development, characterized by a variation in cell and tissue sensitivity or, possibly, a variable gene stability (14, 42).

With these considerations taken into account, it is advisable when beginning mutation research on a large scale to apply at least three different types of ionizing radiation: the sparsely ionizing γ- and X-rays and the densely ionizing neutrons, especially those of the thermal type. A carefully worked out dosimetry shows that for a corresponding dose neutrons are twenty to thirty times as effective on seed materials of higher plants as are γ- and X-rays (43, 44).

B. Ultraviolet Radiation

This type of radiation excites the molecules but does not cause ionization. The pioneer work of Stadler and co-workers (45) indicates that wavelengths of 2600 Å are especially effective in pollen grains of *Zea mays*, i.e., wavelengths corresponding to the absorption spectrum of nucleic acids. In *Drosophila* sperm monochromatic wavelengths of 2537 Å are about ten times as effective as wavelengths between 2900 and 3200 Å (46). Ultraviolet radiation affords a differentiation between chromosome rearrangements, on the one hand, and gene mutations or deficiencies, on the other.

With ionizing radiations there arises in general a mixture of rearrangements and intragenic changes, capable or not capable of reverse mutation. In fact, it has been suggested that X-ray-induced mutations in locus A of maize (gene for anthocyanin formation) do not revert to the original state, either by means of repeated irradiation, or when influenced by another gene Dt (dotted aleuron) which makes the spontaneous recessive gene easily revert; nor can spontaneous recessives be brought to back-mutate under the action of X-irradiation (47). This result cannot be generalized (48). Appropriate tests in *Neurospora* show that back mutations occur both with ionizing radiations and with chemical mutagens, although variable in frequency for individual loci (49).

In a crop plant like barley the difference in action between X-radiations and ultraviolet has been found to be distinct, too (U. Lundqvist, unpublished observations). Here pollen material can easily be irradiated. To a high percentage, plants resulting from egg cells fertilized by X-irradiated pollen will be heterozygous for induced chromosomal translocations as shown by a striking degree of X_1 sterility. In progeny from ultraviolet-treated pollen such translocation sterility is rare, even when the rates of chlorophyll mutation are fairly high.

Barley (as well as maize) is a diploid organism. Steinitz-Sears and Sears (50) have shown that in a polyploid organism like hexaploid wheat the results are in a certain sense different. Both ultraviolet and X-ray-treated pollen gave rise to reciprocal translocations. In twenty-two aberrant ultraviolet-treated plants nineteen translocations were discovered; the corresponding number for X-rays was ninety translocations in ninety-two aberrant plants. More of the ultraviolet translocations were deficient for a terminal segment, however. This can be considered evidence for less re-union and more healing of broken chromosomes after ultraviolet treatment. The virtual absence of translocations in previous ultraviolet experiments is attributed to the strong tendency of ultraviolet-induced translocations to involve deficiencies. In diploid species like maize (*cf.* 50a) such deficiencies often cause inviability. Whatever explanation is correct, there apparently is some difference in reaction between barley and corn, on the one hand, and hexaploid wheat, on the other.

For organisms like fungi or bacteria ultraviolet treatment is just as simple a means of inducing mutations as are X-rays.

C. CHEMICAL MUTAGENS

Without going into detail with regard to the mode of action of chemical mutagens we may divide the compounds tested in higher plants (aside from some mentioned in Stubbe's review paper of 1937, ref. 51) into alkylating and oxidizing agents, in addition to compounds, like purines, which interfere with the normal formation and functions of nucleic acids (52). Some compounds used in crop plants, in addition to the mustards and urethans (53), are illustrated in Fig. 1.

Among the alkylating agents with high effects in phanerogam species the two compounds ethylene oxide (I) and ethylenimine (III) are especially noticeable. Highly effective also are epichlorohydrin (IV) and glycidol (V). Diepoxybutane (II), which in *Neurospora* is a most effective compound for reverse mutation in the *adenine-less* locus but little effective with regard to the *inositol-less* locus, is also greatly mutagenic in barley (54). Owing to its high toxicity, however, it is less useful in mutation work with cereal materials than the simple epoxide (or epimine).

In appropriate experiments ethylene oxide gives maximum rates of mutation on a level corresponding to that ever reached with any kind of ionizing radiation (54). Probably it acts via a chemical reaction with the phosphate groups of DNA. This being true, a positive ion possessing a basic structure similar to that of ethylene oxide should be even more reactive with the negatively charged phosphate groups. Such a compound is ethylen-

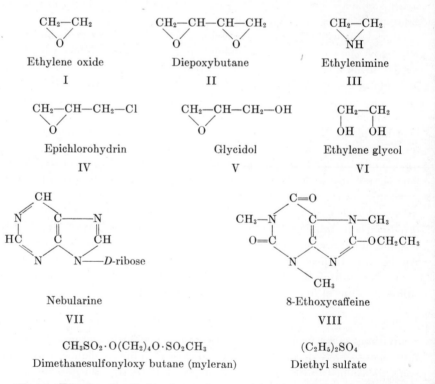

FIG. 1. Effective chemical mutagens in crop plants (mustards and urethans not considered).

imine. This compound, administered in an adequate way, accordingly gives mutation rates in barley far above those ever found with ionizing radiations or ethylene oxide; in fact the maximum rates lie several times as high (55). This holds true not only for lethal or semilethal chlorophyll mutations and dwarfs but also for viable and high-productive mutants. The second generation (X_2) after ethylenimine treatment of barley seeds almost simulates a segregating F_2 progeny.

In Table I some data are gathered with regard to X-ray, neutron, ethylene oxide, and ethylenimine effects. The basis for the comparison is founded on the maximum rates of viable and high-productive mutations.

The maximum rates of viable mutation in the four types of mutagens are in the ratio of 1:1.6:2.6:6.9. With regard to chlorophyll mutations the corresponding rates run in the proportion of 1:1.1:0.9:4.3, whereas the maximum rates of translocation sterility are on the same general top level (40%). In simple ethylene epoxide and epimine we consequently possess agents which, relative to chromosome translocation, are much more effective in producing viable mutants and, with regard to epimine, also more effective in raising the rate of chlorophyll mutations. The field analysis indicates that numerous ethylenimine mutants in barley are of practical interest

TABLE I

RATES OF LETHAL CHLOROPHYLL MUTATION AND TRANSLOCATION STERILITY IN
RELATION TO MAXIMUM RATES OF VIABLE MUTATION IN OFFSPRING OF
TREATED BARLEY SEEDS (DATA OF 1958; CF. REFERENCE 84)

Treatment	Maximum rates of viable mutation[a] (per spike progeny)	Corresponding rates (per spike progeny) of:	
		Chlorophyll mutation[b]	Translocation sterility[a]
Neutrons			
400 rep	3.6%	6.3%	38.4%
240 rep	2.4%	3.4%	24.9%
X-rays			
8000 r	5.4%	6.8%	38.9%
4000 r	4.2%	3.4%	25.5%
Ethylene oxide			
Dry seeds, 0.2%	9.0%	5.4%	27.0%
Dry seeds, 0.3%	7.7%	5.8%	40.6%
Ethylenimine			
Soaked seeds, 0.25%	25.0%	6.9%	25.0%
Soaked seeds, 0.2%	18.4%	9.8%	39.5%
Dry seeds, 0.04%	12.7%	27.0%	38.8%
Dry seeds, 0.07%	11.9%	23.4%	40.5%

[a] Field tests.
[b] Laboratory tests.

(erectoides, straw-stiff, early mutants), and rare morphological and physiological mutants are relatively common.

Of considerable interest is the action of some purine derivatives. The pure purine, in the form of its D-riboside (VII), does not produce chromosome translocation (X_1 sterility) but enhances the rate of chlorophyll mutations of a special type (*"viridis,"* ref. 52). Possibly the compound enters the nucleic acid molecule as a "wrong" purine constituent. On the other hand, 8-ethoxycaffeine (VIII) is known strikingly to break chromosomes in plant roots, its action being coupled to oxidative phosphorylation (56). It has been found to cause a pronounced translocation sterility in barley without noticeably increasing visible mutation (52). In *Neurospora* it is ineffective with regard to reverse gene mutation (57). This contrast in behavior between the two purines indicates that the statement that "probably all mutagens which induce point-mutations also break chromosomes" (see ref. 57, p. 232) may not be true. Consequently, in an organism like barley it should be possible, by the use of special mutagens, to separate chromosome breakage and gene mutation. In barley, ethylene glycol (VI) appears to behave like 8-ethoxycaffeine (L. Ehrenberg, Å. Gustafsson, and U. Lundqvist, unpublished observations).

Moreover, 8-ethoxycaffeine breaks the chromosomes of barley in quite a distinct manner. Especially apt to breakage, relatively seen, are the two satellite chromosomes 6 and 7 (58). Here the breaks concentrate in the regions around the centromeres, the satellite necks, and the tertiary constrictions. In the horse bean, *Vicia faba*, which, in contrast to barley, is rich in heterochromatin, the breaks also cluster in the heterochromatin. With X-irradiation chromosome breakage is at random.

Another compound, dimethanesulfonyloxybutane (IX), or myleran, has a similar chromosome-breaking effect, but in contrast to 8-ethoxycaffeine chromosome rearrangements do not arise—as evidenced by the absence of "bridges" at mitotic metaphase and anaphase (59). There is a tendency for a diminution of chromosome size during ontogenesis, indicating a successive shortening of genome length by means of deficiencies. Chromosome breakage is concentrated in distinct regions: heterochromatin, centromere regions, secondary and tertiary constrictions. Here it may be added that ethylmethane sulfonate, which is half a molecule of myleran, perhaps is the most mutagenic chemical found in barley so far (59a, 84). It primarily works on the genic material. Its effects on chromosome breakage and gross rearrangements are almost negligible.

Findings of the last few years with regard to chemical mutagenesis have thus opened new facilities for plant genetics and plant breeding. A planned use of various types of ionizing radiations and of chemical mutagens will certainly in the future give a most diversified and far-reaching instrument for the intentional reconstruction and improvement of all sorts of crop plants. For each organism the appropriate mutagens and treatments have to be determined and chosen.

In addition, there exist wide possibilities in detecting new chemical mutagens or improving old ones by combining them with other mutagenic agents or antimutagens or, finally, in altering the organism's response to irradiation or chemical mutagenesis by changes in the physiological state of the organism itself or parts of it.

Especially promising is the fact that different mutagens show different modes of action and mutation spectra (6, 26, 60), not only with regard to chromosome breakage and gene mutation but also with regard to the mutation of individual loci. Even mutations of the productive type are now, in principle, open for an experimental attack (41, 61, 84).

IV. Mutations and Viability

Common yield trials determine in an adequate manner the productivity or viability of a mutation, in homozygous condition, in populations as heterozygote or homozygote, or in mixed culture together with biotypes of the same or of other species. In addition, they tell how the mutation performs, relatively seen, in the "normal type of environment," with changes in irrigation and manuring, or in entirely new types of environment often not suited to the mother variety but suitable for the mutant.

Most mutations, spontaneous or induced, are lethal, semilethal, or viability-decreasing in the homozygous state. A few, although deleterious homozygously, increase vigor when heterozygous. One or two per thousand homozygous mutations are equal or superior to the mother variety in "normal environments." The less deviating a mutant in morphological and physiological respects, the more normal or seminormal is its productivity. To judge from all experience in wild and cultivated organisms, the mutants of a modifying type, rather than drastic ones, are the commonest. With regard to dominance relationships in diploid species most mutations are recessive or semirecessive. Some are dominant in part characters, recessive in others (25). Mutations in some loci, like the erectoides locus r of barley (41), behave like complete dominants. In polyploid species, for instance common wheat, dominant or semidominant mutations seem to be more frequent (29). Environment and genotypic milieu are effective in changing the dominance reaction of new mutations (25).

A. POPULATION STRUCTURE, MUTATION VIABILITY, AND NEW CROP VARIETIES

In the following discussion some data will be given with regard to species of different population structure:

1. *Drosophila melanogaster*, as a model of cross-fertilizing diploid species.

2. The self-fertilizing diploid *Hordeum vulgare* convar. *distichon*, two-rowed barley.

3. The self-fertilizing hexaploid *Triticum aestivum*, common bread wheat.

4. The vegetatively propagated but diploid and sexual *Ribes nigrum*, black currant.

5. The parthenogenetic asexual and polyploid *Poa pratensis*, blue grass.

1. *Drosophila melanogaster*, as a model of cross-fertilizing diploid species.

After a sperm irradiation with 6000 r of X-rays, about two or three per thousand tested mutations increase viability (62). A greatly widened variability is realized, most mutations being of the defective type.

If phenotypic effects are considered, about 3 % of all spontaneous mutations studied imply "conspicuous" changes. The remainder, or 97 %, belong to the "inconspicuous" or modifying group (63). Conspicuous mutations with full viability are realized to a frequency of about two per thousand; inconspicuous mutations with full viability are ten times as frequent, or two per hundred.

Of importance for the extraction of high-productive populations in plants is the finding that the continued selection with regard to quantitative characters corresponding to an increase in oil or protein content, seed size, yielding ability, etc., in plants) will be more easily realized when X-irradiation is carried out repeatedly in successive generations (64).

That the results indicated hold true also with regard to cross-fertilizing crop plants is shown by the successful extraction of a new trade variety in white mustard, the so-called Primex white mustard, which produces more seed per hectare than the original mother strain and, in addition, a higher oil content of the seed. By repeated selection within the irradiated population, oil yield per hectare has been successively increased up to 10 or 12 % above that of the mother variety. The original X-irradiation caused a widely increased heterozygosity, indicated by the occurrence of homozygous segregates of the lethal, semilethal, and indifferent types (6, 11).

2. *Hordeum vulgare convar. distichon, Two-Rowed Barley*

A treatment of dormant seeds with a dose of 10,000 r produces a detected total mutation rate of 45 to 50 %, translocations included and calculated per spike progeny. Taking into account also "small, modifying" mutations, with normal, seminormal, or slightly decreased viability, we may conclude that every spike progeny contains a mutation (6). In the case of maximal mutation rates, induced by ethylenimine or ethylmethane sulfonate, the corresponding figure probably rises to four, five, or more mutations per spike progeny. Circa two per thousand of all X-ray mutations have a productivity raised or normal also under conditions optimal to the mother variety.

Eight or ten per thousand X-ray-induced changes involve morphological mutations of a more or less drastic type; slightly less than half consist of so-called erectoides mutations. About one-tenth of these (or less than one per thousand mutations) have a full viability. The erectoides mutations often raise the lodging resistance and are favored, relatively seen, by an increase in manuring. In consequence some of them are performing well in advanced agriculture. One, erectoides 32, Pallas barley, is approved as an original Svalöf variety (13). Other drastic changes, among them a mutant with a profoundly increased earliness (Svalöf 04080, early 8), are now tested on a large scale. In fact, early 8 was recently declared an original variety under the name of Mari (cf. 85).

In barley drastic changes may help to reconstruct and modernize the crop plant morphologically and physiologically (6). In other diploid species, like *Pisum* or leguminous species in general, such drastic changes are often completely sterile and useless in breeding work (65). Here mutations with small affects are the ones of special interest.

3. *Triticum aestivum*, Bread Wheat

In this species the mutation spectrum is strikingly different from that of diploid barley or wheat. Lethal chlorophyll mutations, for instance, are extremely rare. On the contrary, lax-eared, speltoid, short-awned, and dense-eared mutants are common, implying mixtures of point mutations, deficiencies, translocations, defiency duplications, and aneuploids. Calculated per plant progeny, a dose of 10,000 r of X-rays induces about 50 % of mutations easily detected in the second generation. Owing to the high tolerance to chromosomal rearrangements an induced mutation often gives rise to secondary products of deviating appearance in later generations. For this reason the polyploid wheat species will show even higher total mutation rates than related diploid species (29).

Of thirty-four X-ray mutants in winter wheat, so good as to be included in yield tests, approximately one-third showed full productivity (95 to 105 % of the yield of the mother strain) (66). One or two mutants appeared to be superior. A spontaneous bearded mutant (locus B_1) was consistently higher in yield than its mother line. Of nine bearded mutants out of a spring variety seven were on the same productivity level as or above the mother strain.

4. *Ribes nigrum*, Black Currant

Cut shoots with a length of 15 cm were irradiated with an X-ray dose of 3000 r (just below the lethal point) (67). The rate of vegetative mutations, selected in a 5-year period from irradiated cuttings or their descendants, approached 100 %; i.e. on an average every irradiated cutting gave rise to an artificial sport. The proportion of small and large mutations is as follows:

Small mutations (originally denoted as "uncertain")	20%
Small mutations (originally denoted as "certain")	64%
Large ± drastic mutations	16%
Sum of all mutants	324

Large mutations are generally worthless in breeding work. Small mutations, especially those denoted as "uncertain," often imply partial improvements. Artificial sports in which only positive properties are combined are rare; they form approximately 1 %. This value is still twice the rate of the outstanding selections obtained from seedlings in normal hybridization work, however.

5. *Poa pratensis, Blue Grass*

Irradiation of seeds with an X-ray dose of 20,000 to 25,000 r gives a rate of 14 % aberrants calculated on surviving X_1 plants (68). After vegetative propagation 286 seemingly aberrant plants were studied in clone trials. Of these one-quarter (26 %) could no longer be distinguished from the mother clone, and 13 % looked similar. Of the propagated clearly deviating X_1 plants (62 %), the majority were inferior, often highly so. The vigorous plant propagations amounted to 7 % of all clearly deviating plants, and one-third of these showed a pronounced increase in stem height.

The used mother strain (Fylking, with $2n = \pm72$ chromosomes) is almost fully apomictic. The irradiation led to a breakdown of the parthenogenetic mechanism, so that numerous X_1 plants became sexual or semisexual. Sexuality results both when the X_1 plants are clearly distinguished morphologically from the mother strain and when they look almost identical. Consequently, a mutagenic breakdown of apomixis appears, also when no morphological changes are found.

	Apomixis still present	Partial sexuality	Complete sexuality	Number of X_1 plants
X_1 plants similar to mother strain	74%	20%	6%	110
X_1 plants distinctly deviating	47%	35%	18%	176

The aberrants obtained after X-irradiation are in general weaker than the mother strain, but now and then, to a few per cent, induced aberrants show increased vigor. Probably new apomictic strains can be isolated, directly valuable from a practical point of view. In addition, a relatively large number of sexual or semisexual plants is produced, by the help of which a systematic cross-breeding can be carried out also in apomictic varieties.

B. GENE MUTATIONS AND CHROMOSOME BREAKAGE

The above-mentioned analysis indicates that by means of irradiation (or the use of other mutagens) new populations having a wider variability can be produced, thus allowing a selection for higher yield or an improvement of other quantitative properties. In cross-fertilizing species new harmonious equilibria can be achieved in a short time. Similarly in self-fertilizing species mutants can be isolated directly, implying improvements and forming new trade varieties. Almost any property can be improved by using a single or a repeated irradiation (or chemical treatment). With adequate selection methods also disease resistance of various kinds can be obtained by gene mutation. This is indicated by results in barley, wheat, oats, peanut, etc. (13, 15, and literature cited there).

Chromosome breakage with consequent translocation or duplication can be utilized in many ways. Elegant is the inclusion of species-foreign genes, as illustrated by the transposition of genes from *Aegilops* or *Agropyron* to the chromosomes of hexaploid wheat (15, 16). On the other hand, chromosome translocations often produce homozygous strains which are highly productive. On an average, X-ray- or neutron-induced lines in barley are almost as high-yielding as the mother variety, also when this lies on the top level of productivity (69). No position effect or influence of the translocations was in most cases detectable, possibly because of the lack of heterochromatin in the barley chromosomes. This was so even when chromosome structure was profoundly altered, for instance in karyotypes having chromosomes with two satellites (a translocation between the satellite chromosomes 6 and 7) (25, 70). Some lines were, however, distinctly inferior in viability. On the contrary, a few apparently indicated new harmonious genotypes, even increasing production capacity. In this way, the karyotype can be successively altered and modernized in the same degree as recombination and mutation work proceeds and specialization goes on. With the combination of ionizing agents and chemical treatments a skillful replanning of the karyotype is open for attack, combining euchromatin and heterochromatin (where such occurs) or its counterparts: segments around the centromeres and constrictions in a manner previously not achieved.

C. MUTATIONS AND RECOMBINATION

In all instances enumerated above, mutations of direct importance to plant breeding have been considered. Possibly, however, their widest use will be in recombination work (71). Mutations possessing some valuable feature, but negative or indifferent in other respects, may combine this valuable feature with other positive features after hybridization and re-combination. Also seemingly negative mutations may in this way be useful in breeding work. Some examples will illustrate this point. One is the successful transmission of lodging resistance from a spontaneous mutant of barley (possibly of the erectoides type), otherwise valueless, into a wide-spread high-yielding but lodging German variety (72). After recombination the cross gave rise to a high-yielding and lodging-resistant market strain (Bethge XIII), cultivated on a large scale. Similarly the bean variety "Sanilac" is a segregate of a cross between a strain resistant to *Colleto-trichum lindemuthianum* and a defective bushlike mutant out of an ir-radiated variety (73). The mutant *"eramosa"* of *Antirrhinum*, after crossing with other varieties, gave rise to a vigorous, one-stalked new garden variety (73a). Finally, a most remarkable breeding work has gone on for more than three decades in sweet lupines utilizing spontaneous mutations and successively combining them (32).

D. GENETIC COOPERATION

Extremely important in the future will be studies on the cooperation of individual biotypes within species or between species (mixed crops). High-yielding homozygous strains may yield even better when mixed with other strains, also mutants, either in heterozygous or homozygous condition (74). Often such a mixture of genotypes makes the crop plant more plastic to different environments. In certain types of soil and climate the use of mixed crops (different species) provides a distinct advantage. In its extreme this cooperation is illustrated by the phenomena of symbiosis, for example in leguminous species between the bacteria of the root nodules and their host plants, or in conifers between fungi and host tissue in mycorrhiza. Of great interest in this connection is a report of induced mutations in *Rhizobium*, the legume root nodule bacteria (75). Some mutants induced by X-irradiation showed a greater nitrogen-fixing efficiency than the parent strain after two passages through tissues of its host (*Medicago sativa*, Grimm lucerne). The mutual adaptation of host and bacterium by means of muta-tion has so far been neglected in agriculture but may certainly lead to valuable results when adequately analyzed. In a recent paper (86) Gelin was indeed able to show that the yielding ability of field peas increases line-arly with the amount of root nodules formed. Induced mutations have been useful in such a plant breeding program involving symbiotic cooperation. Also in nature, in symbiosis with *Alnus*, *Myrica*, and other genera or, possibly, as free soil inhabitants, a breeding program of nitrogen-fixing bacteria may lead to improved strains (76). A widening of the host range to cover economically more important hardwoods and, possibly, conifers may be included in future experimental possibilities and would be enormously valuable in nitrogen-poor soils.

E. Other Uses of Induced Mutations in Practice

There are other possibilities involved in planned mutation work. By irradiation at the time of fertilization, reduced egg cells may develop into embryos, and the resulting haploids can be utilized for the acquirement of a complete and rapid homozygotization of cross-fertilizing biotypes, facilitating a secondary improvement by cross-breeding (F₁ heterosis) (77). On the other hand, mutagenic agents may give rise to mutations in alleles governing self-incompatibility and so make self-fertilization possible (78), or lead to F_1 hybrids in the case of incompatible crosses (79). This would certainly imply an advantage in the breeding program of fruit and forest trees, as well as many perennial crop plants. Since, furthermore, irradiation causes a breakdown of the parthenogenetic mechanism, at least in *Poa pratensis*, sexual processes will be induced in otherwise rigid apomicts by this method. In numerous sexual species it would be feasible to induce apomixis by means of experimental mutation, since apomixis is genetically conditioned by special genes or systems of genes. This is a goal far away, however, although biotechnosis, called vivipary in maize and in a sense implying a step toward apomixis, has been induced by X-rays (80).

Gene mutations and translocations are skillfully used as markers in linkage tests of many organisms, especially in maize and barley (81). Similarly, genotypes possessing valuable properties can be selected out of segregating progenies, as evidenced for instance in *Matthiola* by the use of chlorophyll mutation (82) or in silkworm by means of translocations (17). Numerous other problems can be tackled with their help, in genetics, physiology, or even pathology (83).

V. Summary and Conclusions

Spontaneous mutation no doubt plays an important role in everyday plant breeding, although not always manifest to the breeder. In organisms, like lupines, beets, and fruit trees, clear cases are on record. The sweet lupines bear evidence of its significance for the modernization of crop plants. In recent years induced mutations have been utilized in practice, too, either in direct form (tobacco, white mustard, peas, barley, peanuts) or after crossing and recombination (beans). Mutations of practical value are of the modifying as well as the drastic type (85). In fact, the rapid transformation of agronomic properties by means of drastic mutation has been achieved in barley.

The plant breeder has to study his crop plant carefully and learn to know its genes and linkage conditions, as well as its mutation spectrum, both under spontaneous conditions and after the application of different radiations and chemical mutagens. Radiations of special significance include ultraviolet for pollen treatment, γ-rays and X-rays for chronic or acute treatments of whole plants or parts of them, and neutrons for acute irradiations, especially of seeds. By the help of these radiations the plant breeder can select among different genotypic changes, choosing chromosome translocations or gene mutations or both, and also bring different gene loci to mutate, depending on the ion density of the radiation he applies.

Some chemical mutagens cause enormously high mutation rates, higher than the rates ever obtained with ionizing radiations. Such compounds, for instance, are ethylenimine and ethylmethane sulfonate. Chromosome breakage and gene mutation can now in principle be separated from one another. Moreover, chromosome breaks can be concentrated in definite regions or segments of a chromosome. By the simultaneous application of ionizing radiations and chemical mutagens, for instance 8-ethoxycaffeine, heterochromatic and euchromatic parts of a chromosome may reunite in a manner scarcely visualized before. Karyotypes of barley have been realized, which up to now have not been found in nature.

Experiments in different crop plants prove, we consider, that mutations of the high-productive type can be induced covering almost any property of agronomic importance, including disease resistance. The application of chemical mutagens signifies important progress in the breeding work, probably even more so than the introduction of ionizing radiations thirty years ago.

VI. References

1. de Vries, H., *Die Mutationstheorie I*, p. V. Veit & Co., Leipzig, 1901.
2. Cf. Blakeslee, A. F., *Brooklyn Botan. Garden Mem.* **4**, 29 (1936).
3. Muller, H. J., *Science* **66**, 84 (1927).
4. Stadler, L. J., *J. Heredity* **21**, 3 (1930).
5. Cf. Gustafsson, Å., *Hereditas* **33**, 1 (1947).
6. Cf. von Wettstein, D., Gustafsson, Å., and Ehrenberg, L., *Arbeitsgemeinsch. f. Forsch. Nordrhein-Westfalen, Sitzung 2. Oktober* **1957** (1959).
7. Freisleben, R., and Lein, A., *Z. Pflanzenzücht.* **25**, 235 (1943); *Kühn-Arch.* **60**, 211 (1943); *Züchter* **16**, 49 (1944).
8. Cf. Stubbe, H., *Die Kulturpflanze*, Vols. II–VI. Akademie Verlag, Berlin, 1954–1958.
9. Tollenaar, D., *Genetica* **20**, 285 (1938); Cf. ref. 13.
10. Gustafsson, Å., *Acta Agr. Scand.* **4**, 361 (1954); Gustafsson, Å., and Tedin, O., *ibid.* **4**, 633 (1954).
11. Andersson, G., and Olsson, G., *Acta Agr. Scand.* **4**, 574 (1954).
12. Gelin, O., *Agr. Hort. Genet.* **13**, 183 (1955).
13. Borg, G., Fröier, K., and Gustafsson, Å., *Second U. N. Intern. Conf. Peaceful Uses Atomic Energy* A/Conf. 15/P/2468.
14. Sparrow, A. H., and Singleton, W. R., *Am. Naturalist* **87**, 29 (1953); cf. Ehrenberg, L., *Svensk Naturvetenskap* (Research Council Natural Sciences, Sweden) (1956).

15. *Brookhaven Symposia in Biol.* **No. 9** *Genetics in plant breeding* (1956).
16. Sears, E. R., *Agr. Abstr., Ann. Meetings, Davis,* **55** (1955); Chu, E. H., *Genetica* **40,** 567 (1955); Elliott, F. C., *J. Heredity* **48,** 77 (1957).
17. Dubinin, N. P., *Botan. J.* (Leningrad-Moskwa) **13,** 3 (1957).
18. Hollaender, A., *Ann. Missouri Botan. Garden* **32,** 165 (1945).
19. Backus, M. P., and Stauffer, J. F., *Mycologia* **47,** 429 (1955); Raper, K. B., *ibid.* **44,** 1 (1952).
20. Lockwood, L. B., Raper, K. B., Moyer, A. J., and Coghill, R. D., *Am. J. Botany* **32,** 214 (1945).
21. Teas, H. J., and Anderson, E. G., *Proc. Natl. Acad. Sci. U. S.* **37,** 645 (1951).
22. Levan, A., *Exptl. Cell Research* **11,** 613 (1956); Geitler, L., *Österr. Botan. Z.* **95,** 277 (1948).
23. Levan, A., and Lotfy, T., *Hereditas* **36,** 470 (1950).
24. Cramer, P. J. S., *Bibliographia genet.* **16,** 193 (1954); Breider, H., and Reichardt, A., *Strahlentherapie* **97,** 149 (1955); Bergann, F., *Wiss. Z. Pädag. Hochschule Potsdam* **3,** 105 (1957); Heiken, A., *Acta Agr. Scand.* **8,** 319 (1958).
25. Cf. Gustafsson, Å, and von Wettstein, D., "Handbuch der Pflanzenzüchtung," 2nd ed., Vol. 1, pp. 644–648, Parey, Berlin, 1958.
26. Westergaard, M., *Experientia* **13,** 224 (1957); Ehrenberg, L., Gustafsson, Å., and Lundqvist, U., *Hereditas* **45,** 351 (1959).
27. Nilan, R. A., and Gunthardt, H. M., *Caryologia* **8,** 316 (1956).
28. Stadler, L. J., *Am. Naturalist* **83,** 5 (1949), Rhoades, M. M., *Cold Spring Harbor Symposia Quant. Biol.* **9,** 138 (1943); McClintock, B., *Brookhaven Symposia in Biol.* **No. 8,** 58 (1955).
29. MacKey, J., *Hereditas* **40,** 65 (1954).
30. East, E. M., *Genetics* **20,** 443 (1935); Lamm, R., *Hereditas* **22,** 217 (1936); Schuler, J. F., *Genetics* **39,** 908 (1954).
31. Timoféeff-Ressovsky, N. W., Zimmer, K. G., and Delbrück, M., *Nachr. Ges. Wiss. Göttingen* [N. F.] **1,** 189 (1935).
32. von Sengbusch, R., *Landwirtsch. Jahrb. Schweiz* **91,** 719 (1942); Troll, H. J., *Züchter* **28,** 25 (1958).
33. Ivanoff, S. S., *J. Heredity* **48,** 101 (1957).
34. Savitsky, V. F., *Z. Pflanzenzücht.* **40,** 1 (1958).
35. *Svensk Sortlista för Potatis 1958* Stockholm, p. 8; cf. also Heiken, A., *Acta Agr. Scand.* **8,** 352 (1958).
36. Granhall, I., *Acta Agr. Scand.* **4,** 595 (1954); Brown, A. Gavin, *The Fruit Year Book,* p. 38. *Royal Horticulture Society,* 1956.
37. Ehrenberg, L., *Acta Agr. Scand.* **4,** 365 (1954).
38. Gustafsson, A., and MacKey, J., *Hereditas* **34,** 371 (1948); MacKey, J., *ibid.* **37,** 421 (1951).
39. Ehrenberg, L., and Nybom, N., *Acta Agr. Scand.* **4,** 396 (1954); Caldecott, R. S., *Radiation Research* **3,** 316 (1955); Caldecott, R. S., Johnson, E. B., North, D. T., and Konzak, C. F., *Proc. Natl. Acad. Sci. U. S.* **43,** 975 (1957); Ehrenberg, L., and Lundqvist, U., *Hereditas* **43,** 390 (1957).
40. Sax, K., *Quart. Rev. Biol.* **32,** 15 (1957).
41. Hagberg, A., Gustafsson, Å., and Ehrenberg, L., *Hereditas* **44,** 523 (1958).
42. Singleton, W. R., Konzak, C. F., Shapiro, S., and Sparrow, A. H. *Proc. 1st. Intern Conf. Peaceful Uses Atomic Energy, Geneva, 1955* **12,** 25 (1955); Sparrow, A. H., and Christensen, E., *Nucleonics* **12,** No. 8, 16 (1954); *Conference on Biol. Phys.* Industrial Aspects of Potato Irradiation Brookhaven National Laboratory, May 25, 1955.

43. Ehrenberg, L., Gustafsson, Å., and Nybom, N., *Arkiv. Botanik* [2] **1**, No. 17 (1952).
44. Ehrenberg, L., Gustafsson, Å., and Lundqvist, U., *Hereditas* **45**, 351 (1959).
45. Stadler, L. J., *Cold Spring Harbor Symposia Quant. Biol.* **9**, 168 (1941); Stadler, L. J., and Uber, F. M., *Genetics* **27**, 84 (1942).
46. Muller, H. J., *in* "Radiation Biology" (A. Hollaender, ed.), Vol. 1, Chapter 8, p. 540. McGraw-Hill, New York, 1953.
47. Stadler, L. J., and Roman, H., *Genetics* **33**, 273 (1948).
48. de Serres, F., *Genetics* **43**, 187 (1958).
49. Giles, N. H., *Cold Spring Harbor Symposia Quant. Biol.* **16**, 283 (1951); Jensen, K. A., Kirk, I., Kölmark, G., and Westergaard, M., *ibid.* **16**, 245 (1951); Kölmark G., *Compt. rend. trav. lab. Carlsberg, Sér. physiol.* **26**, 204 (1956).
50. Steinitz-Sears, L. M., and Sears, E. R., *Genetics* **42**, 623 (1957).
50a. Emmerling, M. H., *Genetics* **40**, 697 (1955).
51. Stubbe, H., *Angew. Chem.* **50**, 241 (1937).
52. Ehrenberg, L., Gustafsson, Å., and Lundqvist, U., *Acta Chem. Scand.* **10**, 492 (1956); Ehrenberg, L., Gustafsson, Å., and von Wettstein, D., Conference on Chromosomes (Wageningen), Lecture **5**, (1956).
53. Auerbach, C., *Biol. Revs. Cambridge Phil. Soc.* **24**, 355 (1949); Oehlkers, F., *Sitzber. Heidelberg. Akad. Wiss. Math.-naturw. Kl. Abhandl.* 9 (1949).
54. Ehrenberg, L., and Gustafsson, Å., *Hereditas* **43**, 595 (1957).
55. Ehrenberg, L., Lundqvist, U., and Ström, G., *Hereditas* **44**, 330 (1958); Ehrenberg, L., Gustafsson, Å., and Lundqvist, U., *ibid* **45**, 351 (1959).
56. Kihlman, B., *Exptl. Cell Research* **8**, 404 (1955).
57. Westergaard, M., *Experientia* **13**, 228 (1957).
58. Moutschen, J., and Moutschen-Dahmen, M., *Hereditas* **44**, 18 (1958).
59. Moutschen, J., and Moutschen-Dahmen, M., *Hereditas* **44**, 415 (1958).
59a. Heslot, H., Ferrary, R., Lévy, R., and Monard, C., *Compt. rend.* **248**, 729 (1959).
60. Auerbach, C., *Cold Spring Harbor Symposia Quant. Biol.* **16**, 199 (1951); Fahmy, O. G., and Fahmy, M. J., *in* "Advances in Radiobiology" (G. C. Hevesy, A. G. Forssberg, and J. D. Abbott, eds.), p. 437. Oliver & Boyd, Edinburgh, 1957.
61. Scheibe, A., and Hülsmann, G., *Naturwiss.* **44**, 17 (1957).
62. Timoféeff-Ressovsky, N. W., *Nachr. Ges. Wiss. Göttingen, Math.-physik. Kl., Fachgruppen VI* [N. F.] **1**, No. 11 (1935).
63. Timoféeff-Ressovsky, N. W., "Handbuch Erbbiol. des Mensch.," Vol. 1, p. 32. Springer, Berlin, 1940; cf. Gustafsson, Å., *Cold Spring Harbor Symposia Quant. Biol.* **16**, 277 (1951).
64. Buzzati-Traverso, A. A., *Proc. 9th Intern. Congr. Genet. Bellagio Italy, 1953, Caryologia* **4** *Suppl.* 450 (1954).
65. Lamprecht, H., *Agr. Hort. Genet* **16**, 145 (1958).
66. MacKey, J., *Acta Agr. Scand.* **4** 549 (1954); also unpublished data.
67. Bauer, R., *Hereditas* **43**, 323 (1957).
68. Julén, G., *Acta Agr. Scand.* **4**, 585 (1954); Julén, G., *Züchter* **28**, 37 (1958).
69. Nybom, N., *Acta Agr. Scand.* **4**, 507 (1954).
70. Hagberg, A., *Züchter* **28**, 32 (1958); cf. also ref. 25, p. 687.
71. Gustafsson, Å., and Tedin, O., *Acta Agr. Scand.* **4**, 633 (1954).
72. Schiemann, E., *Ber. deut. botan. Ges.* **48**, 477 (1930).
73. Down, E. E., and Andersen, A. L., *Science* **124**, 223 (1956).
73a. Stubbe, H., *Proc. 10th Intern. Congr. Genetics, Montreal* **1**, 247 (1959).
74. Gustafsson, Å., *Hereditas* **39**, 1 (1953); Gustafsson, A., *Acta Agr. Scand.* **4**, 609 (1954).
75. Jordan, D. C., *Can. J. Botany* **30**, 125 (1952).

76. Cf. experiments in *Azotobacter*: Karlsson, J. L., and Baker, H. A., *J. Bacteriol* **56**, 671 (1948); Lindstrom, E. S., *Bacteriol. Proc. Soc. Am. Bacteriologist.* 3 (1948); Wyss, O., and M. G., *J. Bacteriol.* **59**, 287 (1950).
77. Gerassimova, H., *Cytologia* **6**, 431 (1935); Ehrensberger, A. *Biol. Zentr.* **67**, 537 (1948); Swaminathan, M. S., and Singh, M. P., *Current Sci. (India)* **27**, 63 (1958).
78. Lewis, D., *Nature* **153**, 576 (1944).
79. Nishiyama, I., and Iizuka, M., *Bull. Research Inst. Food Sci. Kyoto Univ.* **No. 8**, 81 (1952).
80. Robertson, D. S., *Genetics* **40**, 745 (1955).
81. Anderson, E. G., *Brookhaven Symposia in Biol.* **No. 9**, 23 (1956); Burnham, C. R., and Hagberg, A., *Hereditas* **42**, 467 (1956); cf. also ref. 74.
82. Kappert, H., *Die vererbungswissenschaftlichen Grundlagen der Pflanzenzüchtung.* Parey, Berlin, 1948.
83. Keitt, G. W., and Boone, D. M., *Brookhaven Symposia in Biol.* **No. 9**, 209 (1956).
84. Ehrenberg, L., Gustafsson, Å., and Lundqvist, U., *Hereditas* **47**, in press (1961).
85. Gustafsson, Å., Hagberg, A., and Lundqvist, U., *Hereditas* **46**, (1960).
86. Gelin, O., *Agr. Hort. Genet.* **18**, 214 (1960).

Author Index

Numbers in parentheses are reference numbers and are included to assist in locating the reference where the authors' names are not mentioned in the text. Numbers in italics refer to the page on which the reference is listed.

A

Abrahamson, S., 466 (149), *474*
Abramova, L. V., 233 (337), *256*
Abrams, R., 290 (213), *327*
Adams, G. E., 147 (134, 139), *251*
Adams, W. R., 376 (86), 377 (86), *414*
Adamson, D. M., 335 (6), 337 (18), *351*
Adler, H. I., 362 (31), *413*
Ageno, M., 97 (6), *247*
Ahlström, L., 299 (258, 261), *329*
Albaum, H. G., 285 (172), *326*
Aldous, E., 402 (181), *416*
Aldous, J. G., 355 (4), *412*
Aldridge, W. G., 319 (326), *330*
Aleksandrov, S. N., 291 (216), *327*
Alexander, P., 86, 89 (45, 49), 90 (55), *91, 92*, 97, 163 (194), *248, 252*, 261 (4), 262 (4), 271 (4), *322*, 334 (3), 339 (33), *351*, 366 (52), 367 (56, 57, 57a), 368 (56), 410 (195), *413, 417*, 465 (136), *474*
Alexander, W. A., 245 (365), *257*
Alfert, M., 307 (297), *330*
Allard, J. G., 159 (192), *252*
Allen, A. O., 39 (99), *69*, 91 (11), 146 (127), 151 (127), 178 (225), 182 (241, 242), 191 (242, 249), 197 (259), 198 (249, 259), 203 (274, 281), 205 (288), 215 (313), 217 (316), *248, 251, 253, 254, 255*, 461 (128), *474*
Allfrey, V. G., 270 (66), 283 (155), 304 (283), 309 (155), 311 (283), 314 (155), 321 (155), *323, 326, 329*
Allison, S. K., 2 (10), 8, *67*
Allsopp, C. B., 243 (356), 244 (356), *256*
Almand, J. R., 280 (135), *325*
Almeida, A. B., 283 (160), 287 (160), *326*
Alper, C., 267 (39), 271 (39), *323*
Alper, T., 23 (54), *68*, 357 (16), 358 (18), 359 (20, 21, 21a), 360 (23), 361 (18), 364 (45), 368 (23), 369 (23, 58, 59, 60, 62), 370 (18, 23, 58, 60), 371 (23, 66), 373 (75), 374 (45, 75), 377 (18, 60), 378 (62), 379 (20, 100), 380 (20), 381 (21), 382 (20, 111,

113), 383 (20, 111), 394 (154, 157), 396 (16), 397 (20, 21, 45), 398 (21, 45), 399 (21, 45), 400 (16, 177), 401 (16, 21), 402 (45, 182), 404 (111), 405 (16, 21, 45, 113, 182), 406 (21, 75), 409 (154, 192a), 411 (20, 199), *412, 413, 414, 415, 416, 417*, 465 (137), 467 (137), *474*
Altenburg, E., 449 (66, 67, 68), *472*
Altman, K. I., 269 (60, 61), 270 (61), 271 (72), 277 (121, 122, 125), 280 (137), 288 (137), 290 (208), *323, 325, 327*
Anderegg, J. W., 319 (346), *331*
Andersen, A. L., 492 (73), *496*
Anderson, D. R., 277 (126, 127), 278 (127), *325*
Anderson, E. G., 479 (21), 493 (81), *495, 497*
Anderson, E. H., 381 (107), 399 (171), *414, 416*
Anderson, E. P., 319 (334), *330*
Anderson, N. G., 306 (287), *329*
Anderson, R. C., 174 (219), *253*
Anderson, R. S., 355 (7), 376 (7), 379 (96), *412, 414*
Andersson, G., 478 (11), 488 (11), *494*
Anger, H. O., 33 (87a, 88), *69*
Anger, R., 289 (203), *327*
Appelmans, F., 269 (56), *323*
Applegate, R. L., 319 (347), *331*
Appleyard, R. K., 13 (36), *67*, 89 (43), *92*
Arai, S., 146 (129), *251*
Ard, W. B., 89 (54), *92*, 382 (111a), 411 (111a), *415*
Arient, M., 320 (358), *331*
Armstrong, D., 188 (245), *253*
Armstrong, W. D., 277 (124), 294 (227), 313 (124, 305, 308), 315 (124), *325, 328, 330*
Aron, W. A., 17 (44), *67*
Aronson, D. M., 84 (18), *91*, 267 (37), 268 (37), *323*
Ashkin, J., 2 (6), 7 (6), 11, 17 (6), 18, 20, *66*
Ashwell, G., 265 (24), 266 (24, 31, 32),

499

Subject Index

A

Absorption coefficients, of various elements, 45
Absorption spectrometry, use in radiation chemistry, 121
Acetaldehyde, radiolysis of, 235
Acetic acid, radiolysis of, 147, 155, 161, 163, 224, 239–241
Acetone, radiolysis of, 147
Acetylcholinesterase, radiation sensitivity of, 88, 268–269
Acetylene,
  from benzene radiolysis, 153
  radiolysis of, 141, 143
  stopping power of, 13
Acrosomes, radiosensitivity of, 345–349
Adenine, uptake by DNA, radiosensitivity of, 304–305
Adenosine diphosphate, radiosensitivity of, 284
Adenosine triphosphatase, radiosensitivity of, 264–267, 316
Adenosine triphosphate,
  intranuclear generation of, radiosensitivity in, 304
  in radiation mutagenesis, 466
  radiosensitivity of, 263, 281–285
Adrenal glands, irradiation of, 278
Adrenocorticotropic hormone, M.W. by radiosensitivity, 84
Air,
  energy loss of electrons in, 11
  energy per ion pair in, radiations and, 30
  ionization energy of, 26
  radiation length of, 16
  radiation losses in, 15
Alanine, radiolysis of, 242
Albumin, serum, radiosensitivity of, 289
Alcohols,
  protective action of, 385
  radiolysis of, 154, 231–233
Aldehydes, radiolysis of, 234–235
Allium, radiation mutagenesis in, 466
Alpha particle(s),
  absorption of, rate, 116
  from radioisotopes, 62
Aluminum,

Bragg curve for deuterons in, 33
electron range-energy relation of, 21–23
radiation length of, 16
stopping power of, 8
Amines, radiolysis of, 240–241
Amino acid(s),
  pool, radiation effect on, 277
  protective action of, 262
  radiolysis of, 89, 163–164, 241–244
  urinary, radiation effects on, 276
D-Amino acid oxidase, radiosensitivity of, 263
Amino aciduria, radiation-induced, 276
3-Amino-1,2,4-triazole, effect on radiosensitivity, 267
Ammonia, irradiation of, 212–213
Ammonium hydroxide, effect on radiation mutagenesis, 460
Amoeba, radiosensitivity of, 375
Animal, whole, irradiation of, 292–300
Animal cells, radiosensitivity of, 411
Anions, radiation chemistry of, 213–223
Anthracene, radiolysis of, 159, 160
Appendix, nucleic acid, postirradiation, 295, 296, 307
Arbacia egg, radiosensitivity of, 373–374
Arginine decarboxylase, radiosensitivity of, 88
Argon,
  ionization energy of, 26
  radiation length of, 16
Aromatic hydrocarbons, radiolysis of, 151–154
Arsenite ion, radiolysis of, 221–223
Ascaris eggs, postirradiation culture of, 399
Ascites tumor cells, radiobiology of, 298–299, 391, 392
Ascorbic acid, effect on radiosensitivity, 369
Aspergillus terreus, spores, radiosensitivity of, 381, 411
Atom ejection, from irradiation, 104
Auger effect, 29, 103–105, 116, 120, 171–172

B

Bacillus cereus, spores, radiosensitivity of, 397

521